ENVIRONMENT AND ITS GLOBAL IMPLICATIONS

Global Economy and its Impact—Vol. II

ENVIRONMENT AND ITS GLOBAL IMPLICATIONS

Global Economy and its Impact—Vol. II

Editor
GOPAL BHARGAVA

KALPAZ PUBLICATIONS
DELHI–110052

Environment and its Global Implications
Rs. 1800 (Set)

ISBN : 81-7835-113-3 (Set)

ISBN: 81-7835-131-5 Vol. 2

Published in 2002 in India by
Kalpaz Publications
C-30, Satyawati Nagar
New Delhi - 110052

Lassertypesetting at: A.A. Computer
Printed at: Chawla Offset Press, New Delhi

Contents

Preface

Imprints of humanity on earth could be described as unmistakable, had these not often mistaken for work of nature or natural phenomena for human impacts. Yet, if it is no strictly unmistakable, the imprints are most of the time are sufficiently clear. Difficulties of environment today symbolise the same imprints. Growing global warming, rising sea level and depleting ozone layer, of course the undoubted results of human action.

The fears of disasters are a result of human atrocities on environment—not known as environment change in the academic and scientific community have given birth to global efforts to counts the ill-effects. A number of conventions, treaties and agreements are the clear evidence of these efforts. In this scenario, one also find individual initiatives at international level. Policies of various continents, subcontinents developed and developing nations now target expected disaster of environmental change. This volume, i.e., Vol. II of the series is an attempt in this regard. In this volume, the have documented general protections about environment and environmental change at global level and, at the same time, it presents views/opinions stands of individual nations including India.

While Volume II has been divided into seven sections and 18 chapters.

Section I presents a general picture of global perspective towards environmental change and gives information about mathematical models for global cycle.

Section II divided in three chapters is about scientific, economic and political aspects of global environment. It reviews scientific evidence on the expected greenhouse warming, examines application of political and economic stands in the post-Kyoto period and then analyses carbon abatement policy.

Section III discloses before us the perspective of European Union, Asian Continent and thereof developing countries in this regard, the three different chapters.

Section IV discusses the global perspective of developed countries. There are America, Russia and China.

Section V discussed the global perspective of few other countries which Austia, Malaysia and New Zealand.

Section VI gives description of domestic efforts and global perspective of Indian subcontinent on the issue of environmental change with special focus on energy and economy of India.

Section VII, that is, the last section is concluding part of the volume.

The book is of special interests to environmentalists and social workers and at the same time will prove highly useful to academicians, researchers and policy makers.

Editor

Introduction

For the past several years, scientists have issued number of warnings about the future of global environment. Predictions of dramatic global change arising from the regular dumping of industrial by products into the atmosphere and forest loss of massive scale can no longer be ignored. Foreign scientific evidence strongly suggests that world climatic patterns, previously called 'reliably stable' could be pushed into a state of turmoil. Emissions of natural and synthetic gases are enhancing the heat absorbing capacity of the atmosphere through a phenomena called the greenhouse effect. Consequences of this world level climate, disruptions generate number of environmental problems of the past. Global alerts could have catastrophic results for the habitation and productivity of whole planet. The associated strain and upheaval on the international scenario could have, in turn, serious, foreign policy consequence for all nations.

Significant scientific agreements and treaties exist on underlying theory of environmental change, while the nature and magnitude of the future impact from greenhouse warming as predicted by computer models remain under debate. Some among these, e.g., rise in the sea level have been established with higher certainty than others.

Anyway, the range of consequences is sufficiently clear and the magnitude of resources at stake so enormous that policy action at regional as well as global level is required sooner rather than later. After a crisis has appeared, it will be too late to act.

Machining for international legal and political system is ill-equipped to offer an alternative that will assure the integrity of earthly climate while the concept of global warming have been accepted in principle for about a century, policy makers have very recently became a ware of its significance or global environment. International community is not in a position to afford continuing delay in elevating the results of greenhouse issue to the apex of foreign policy agenda and a reformation of energy and development preferences in virtually all nations of the world.

Further, acting upon this agenda should be a global multilateral agreement that sets strict binding standards for domestic emissions of greenhouse gases.

In the aftermath of industrial revolution, human activities have dramatically altered the composition of world atmosphere. Various gases emitted in small but significant amounts, absorb infrared radiation reflected from the surface of the earth. With the centralisation of these heat-consuming gases go up, average global temperature will increase.

CO_2 emissions are the sole biggest cause of elevated terrestrial temperatures from the greenhouse effect accounting for approximately fifty per cent of the problem, since the middle of 19th century atmospheric CO_2 levels, have gone up by around 1/4 and are continuing to increase by around four per cent per year. Elevated CO_2 concentration result mainly intensified burning of fassil fuels like coal, oil and natural gas that releases the chemical in fluctuating amounts. Coal burning releases the maximum carbon dioxide. It is said that forest areas in the world are the storehouse for carbon. Global level loss of forest cover, by releasing this huge stock of carbon into the atmosphere as CO_2 multiplies the greenhouse problem.

Deforestation in the third world is specifically fast and also severe with the destruction of tropical forests in the developing nations, e.g., Brazil and Indonesia with annual cutting down of trees as high as 27 million acres through activities like burning, logging and conversion of agricultural to pasture lands. As a fact, release of carban dioxide into the atmosphere as a result of deforestation goes to 2 -10 billion tons per year.

Next important greenhouse gas, i.e., nitrous oxide (N_2O) concentrations is also on increase possibly due to heavier fossil fuel use, greater agricultural activity and many more ecological disturbances. Bath CO_2 and N_2O are unlike some other conventional pollutants are, quite stable compounds. CO_2 can be found in the upper atmosphere even ten years after its release and N_2O for considerably even more than one hundred years. As a result, in the absence of major reductions in emissions of these gases, than too with long atmospheric durations, these concentrations will continue to increase.

Family of volatile chemicals called chlorofluoro carbon, i.e., CFCs is understand to be presently responsible for 15-20% of the global warming trend. These chemicals are also strictly synthetic and not known to the nature. Main component of natural gas, i.e., methane is another prominent climate modifying chemical, which has atmospheric durations of about eleven years. Besides, low level ozone is one more greenhouse gas and is the major component for photochemical smog polluting at earth's surface.

About the affects of greenhouse warming, international scientific consensus now supports the view that accumulation of the above gases the the atmosphere could have disastrous results for our climate. But the most negative effect, can be and have to be reversed. Though it is true that all countries are likely to be losers in the global climate gamble, some countries are more at stake than others. American sub-continent has particularly large investment in the status quo. Impact of greenhouse gas emissions threatens the overall health of health economy in this process and could also necessitate a large diversion of resources to non-productive adaptive activities.

The basics of greenhouse phenomenon are now well understand and the need for quick policy response firmly established. While these responses are being executed, the development and dissemination of technologies to combat climate disturbance. More and more basic research at international level to resolve uncertainties regarding the magnitude, rate and effects of greenhouse warming should also be undertaken.

Role of developing countries in the regard holds special significance. An equitable reply to the special needs of developing nations is crucial to removing greenhouse threats to the global climate despite the fact that developing world has caused little of the problem and industrialised nations must bear the bulk of the blame. This is so because due to ignorance or sense of irresponsibility or insensitively of so called big powers, the threats of environmental changes cannot be discounted and then neglected. Otherwise they can have disastrous results for all irrespective of their developed or developing status. The consequences of the greenhouse effect strongly advise that it is in the interest of third world countries themselves to re-examine expeditiously their energy preferences. These countries, with less resource availability to adapt to environmental disturbances, stand to suffer badly from a quick climate change. To exemplify this, the productivity of common rice types falls off enormously at temperatures just a few degrees more than those presently prevailing in rice-growing areas.

Furthermore, efficiency investments represent a great opportunity for donors like US and the World Bank to assist third world nations in managing energy choices that exclude both mistakes made previously in the developed countries and cut down threats to the whole planet from global warming. As it is evident to all, World Bank is one of the principal donors aiding power generation projects in the third world.

But as we have already said, efforts are needed on the part of all developing as well as developed countries since all of them are going to be the recipients to consequences of environmental disturbances. There is an urgent need for coordinating policies on the international level to fight greenhouse warming and maximise the benefits of policies about environments. Unilateral decreases in releases of greenhouse gases by big emitters like US and Russia will go a long way towards catching hold global environmental disruptions.

Along with this, a multilateral consensus strategy will push the crucial goals of creating incentives for universal participation and establishing an equitable balancing of responsibility for problems solving. Any multilateral agreement/treaty formulated to arrest global environmental change should satisfy several basic requirements. First of all, it must necessitate reductions in releases of greenhouse gases of a magnitude and speed enough to stabilise the climate of earth. Next, the accountability for making reductions must be distributed without bias to all in an equitable manner. Last, but not the least, a treaty should also require a commitment flow the richer nations for more and better research into non CO_2 energy supply technologies and advancement assistance to support poorer countries meet the responsibility of roles imposed on theme by the so- called international (in fact mutual) agreement.

In this context, Volume I of the series i.e., Environmental change: Theory and practice concentrates on various international attempts at global as well as regional level to set the things right regarding environmental disturbances. The present volume throws light on unilateral effects of individual nations both developed and underdeveloped to fight the consequences resulting from environmental changes. It is especially of great use to the environmentalists, academicians and social workers and goes a long way in helping them to work out the solution by providing literature available on the subjects and documentation of measures adapted in this regard.

1

Global Research and Political Response

In this chapter, we are concentrating upon—how the research scientists have addressed the question of global environmental change and offered answers to it with special reference to Framework Convention on Climate Change (FCCC). Research in the natural sciences related to climate, energy and ecology are all regarded as parts of the same enterprise because they rely on the same global data sets and modelling capacities and are well-organised internationally (Boehmer-Christiansen, 1994a). Did this enterprise by the scientific community (as it prefers to describe itself) effectively influence international policy on global environmental change, as is widely assumed and even predicated (Haas, P., 1990)? Or did it primarily act to create both future markets for its products and new findings using fresh space and information technologies? Another way of posing the question is to enquire to what extent international agreements commit governments to do more than engage in further research and data collection, particularly more than they would have done anyway. If it is likely that they did not do so, then doubts may be raised both about the benign role of epistemic communities and about the impact and function of international environmental regimes (Young, 1989). Attention is attracted to wider problems which may arise for environmental policy and society if purely science-based international environmental agreements are adopted. A tacit alliance between scientific institutions, intergovernmental functionaries Northern environmentalists and assorted commercial interests took the issue of global warming to the Rio Earth Summit in 1992, but apart from issuing many exhortations, it could convince governments to do little more than make commitments to further research and data collection in order to leatn more about global environmental change (Boehmer-Christiansen, 1994a,b). This served the interests of the research enterprise, and it may well be logical international politics were it not for its impacts on national research priorities (Boehmer-Christiansen, 1995). Scientific institutions as one home of the 'epistemic community' are widely seen as a benign impact on environmental regimes and policy formulation. However, as the scientific community and its allies in international bureaucracies are primarily concerned with the solution of scientific and technological problems as defined by themselves, third suggestion cannot but reflect there priorities which, once turned into policy advice, tend to be impossible to implement because of their narrow perspectives, narrow knowledge base and simplistic theories of government and human behaviour. Once researchable uncertainties become objectives of international treaties, existing problems, including environmental ones, may be overlooked and power differentials widened further as global information is collected, stored and made accessible to only a very few countries. Even worse, if non-environmental problems (such as poverty or absence of 'development') are disguised as environmental issues, then the failure of science to provide 'proof', so easily achieved at the frontiers of knowledge, may undermine worthwhile responses. It is therefore argued that in the present world political context, the global research enterprise has not only become a significant political actor, promoting the globalization of information collection and 'business-as-usual' research, but has also done so with reference to specific global environmental concerns that were pulled on (not necessarily by all scientists but certainly by many users of their ambiguous scientific advice) for this purpose. This hypothesis will be developed with relation to the Intergovernmental Panel on Climate Change (IPCC), the scientific body formally appointed by a small number of countries at the advice of the World Meteorological Organisation (WMO) in the year 1988.

Looking for Markets for Energy and Information

Numerous attempts of the International Panel on Climate Change and its predecessors in shaping climate policy need to be analysed, and to do this, the role of these panels not only as providers of knowledge but also as political actors with deliberate policy objectives—including the advancement of research agendas—needs to be considered. Such strategic behaviour on the part of these panels is necessary because knowledge is now a commodity which must be marketed to users and must draw public funding in highly competitive conditions.

The IPCC reflects this requirement by primarily serving two global programmes, the 'private' International Geosphere Biosphere Programme (IGBP),[1] coordinated by the International Council of Scientific Unions (ICSU) set up at Sweden, and the 'public' World Climate Research Programme (WCRP), coordinated by the WMO and the United Nations Environment Programme (UNEP) but largely implemented by the research wings of national meteorological offices.

In the end, of course, most of this research is paid for by taxes. In 1994/5, the USA alone will spend $ 1.6 billion on global change, and Europe possibly more (see Fig. 1.1). The 'mission' of these research programmes is the full understanding already dreamt of by American scientists in the 1950s—of the physical systems of the planet Earth (including their complete visibility via difficult sensing by satellites) as increasingly affected by the human species. To the scientific uncertainties which so clearly afflict the human understanding of the natural system (in spite of growing attention to 'biotic feedbacks' and growth in modelling capacity), additional 'socioeconomic' uncertainties are added.

The global-warming threat was, in fact, produced by a combination of these two sets of factors: changes in the energy balance discovered by past changes in the chemical composition of the atmosphere (which have prejudiced very little warming), and rapid increases in future emissions based on socioeconomic opinions and predicted, by mathematical models, to lead to rapid warming in the next century. Behind this mission are though a small number of governments but with strong atmospheric-science/climatology research capacities and space lobbies: the USA, the UK, Sweden, Canada, Japan, Germany and Australia, all major actors in the IPCC process.[2] This Panel and its forefather, the Advisory Group on Green-house Gases (AGGG), stressed the need for more knowledge, and advocated changes in energy use and technology requiring vast investments. This created a major debate of which demands for more science were the main outcome.

Once the scientists and scientific institutions involved had begun to disseminate their message findings both to the general public and to industries and governments, world-wide political processes were set in motion—and were also studied, in as far as they impinged upon energy-policy debates. Scientific advice did indeed become an independent policy influence, but it did so via its interpretation and use by other major stakeholders: the scientific institutions themselves withdrew into neutrality. The Panel's motivation, fate and impacts were examined with the help of internal files, official reports, a questionnaire schedule returned

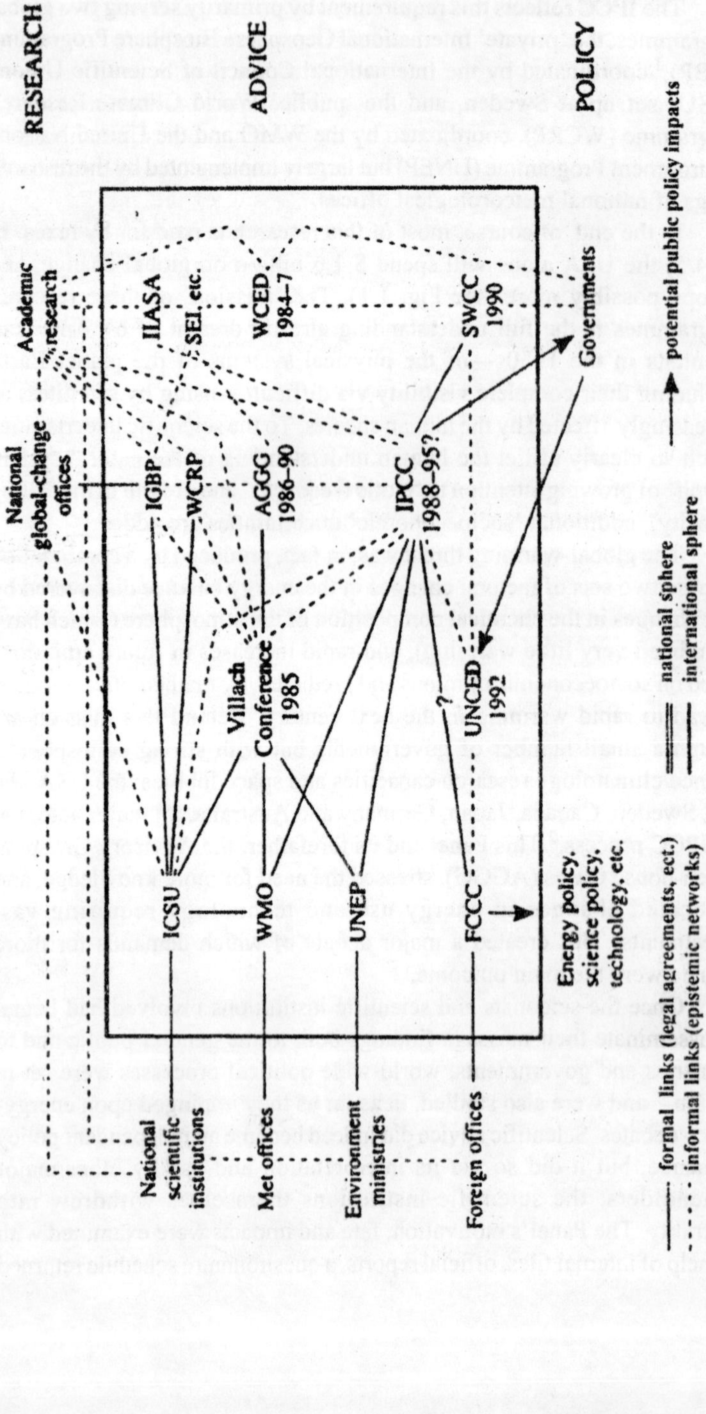

Fig 1.1. The international research enterprise: institutions and for them functional relationships.

by over 100 IPCC participants and more than sixty interviews with scientists, users and observers. To contextualise the argument, a brief explanation is needed of why the 'Rio' alliance failed to achieve its visible 1990 global goal of initiating the rapid reduction of carbon-dioxide emissions (Boehmer-Christiansen, 1994c; Boehmer-Christiansen and Skea, 1991). The analysis of this material from national, global scientific—as well as business—sources allowed some testing of the anti-Realist vision of international relations so fashionable in the study of environmental issues, and especially as felt by supporters both of the concept of 'epistemic communities' (Haas, P., 1990, 1993) and of the view that changing knowledge leads to a redefinition of interest (Haas, E.B., 1990).

Both approaches tend to view the international political process as involving 'social learning', and both exercise models of international relations which assume a shared interest among all nations in keeping 'the environment' in a scientifically defined condition of 'health'[3]. The action of such communities, defined as involving functional scientific knowledge or transactional networks of specialists, is seen to lead to managed interdependence 'where new threats or problems are identified and collective understanding develops and is mobilised to respond to and collectively manage the newly apparent risks' (Haas, P., 1993: 1). While rightly emphasising that knowledge and ideas play an innovative role here by shaping perceptions and expectations, and thus contribute to definitions of 'preferences' or interest, the research reported also suggests that the epistemic approach tends seriously to exaggerate the independence of expert communities from the political process. Indeed, such communities in fact came up as interested parties in the regime-building process in a quite unexpected manner.

However, overconfident of their influence, epistemic communities may actually be able to achieve little more than a protection of their own interests in the true belief that 'more knowledge' will automatically benefit all mankind. Indeed, it is argued that the creation of consensual, problem-solving knowledge is alien to science and tends to be a strategy which does not fulfil the interests of research communities. Scientific consensus, as marketed by epistemic communities, may well be fundamentally unreliable for policy purposes. Rather than knowledge redefining interest and power, it is recommended that power and interest select areas of new knowledge—that is, define research agendas in collaboration with 'apolitical' epistemic communities, in other words, with areas of expertise which do not challenge but confirm existing patterns of power.

The epistemic approach is this way questionable in that it is likely both to raise unrealistic expectations and to undervalue the role of informed politicians and administrators; and it is also dangerously elitist. The innovative capacity in the context of international organisations as transnational actors may suffer from the same fault: rather than being able to create consensual, cooperative, problem-solving environmental 'regimes', epistemic communities may instead seize these regimes and use them to serve the research enterprise. The exaggeration of the benign role of both expert networks and certain intergovernmental organisations may in turn mislead other inter-governmental organisations who may be convinced by theory to allocate their own scarce political resources to the least effectual level of governance and innovative action. While empirical research does not question the claim that international negotiations may be an effective process for slowing uncertainty (Winham, 1977), the very definition of epistemic communities 'as networks of knowledge-based communities with an authoritative claim to policy-relevant knowledge puts questions, if the implication is that experts are, or should be, above politics. Research networks, or rather the global-knowledge-producing enterprise itself, may have been given dangerous advice by the epistemic model.

The very persistence of their influence at the domestic level, believed by Peter Haas to be due to their capture of important bureaucratic positions (and hence of future funding), is 'subject to their ability to avoid large internal disagreement' (Haas, P., 1993: 9). (See Fig. 1.2 for international research enterprise list of acronyms.) The political forces at work behind the scenes and, de facto, acting as implicit allies of research can be identified recognised from responses to the FCCC. Fossil-fuel interests are fairly content with the treaty, while recognising that the battle is not yet won. Bureaucracies are also satisfied as they are extremely busy drafting reports to international bodies and preparing, *inter alia,* national emission plans, while also engaging in interdepartmental battles over new competencies. Major interventions in national energy and land-use policies remain a probability but little has as yet happened, as more scientific verdicts are awaited. The implementation of global research programmes linked to the IPCC, on the other hand, is growing well (Royal Swedish Academy of Sciences 1994: IGBP newsletters).

Coordinated by the WMO, UNEP and the ICSU, these programmes completed their planning stage during the mind-1980s (ICSU/IGBP 1992). They are the major market for data collected from remote sensing, that is, for the increasingly privatised earth-observation industry, an industry characterised by rapid innovation and confined competition but in need of

1.	AGGG	Advisory Group on Greenhouse Gases
2.	BAHC	Biosphere Aspects of the Hydrological Cycle
3.	CCCO	Committee on Climate Changes and the Ocean (SCOR/IOC)
4.	CMP	Climate Modelling Project (WMO)
5.	CSIRO	Commonwealth Scientific and Industrial Research Organisation.
6.	EDF	Environmental Defence Fund (US)
7.	FCCC	Framework Convention on Climate Change
8.	GAIM	IGBP Task Force on Global Analysis, Interpretation and Modelling
9.	GARP	Global Atmospheric Research Programme (WMO/ICSU)
10.	GCTE	Global Change and Terrestrial Ecosystems (IGBP)
11.	GEMS	Global Environmental Monitoring System (UNEP)
12.	GEWEX	Global Energy and Water Cycle Experiment
13.	HDP	Human Dimension on Global Environmental Change Programme
14.	ICSU	International Council of Scientific Unions
15.	IGAC	International Global Atmospheric Chemistry Programme (MIT/ICSU)
16.	IGBP	International Geosphere Biosphere Programme
17.	IGOSS	Intergrated Global Ocean Services System (WMO/IOC)
18.	IHP	International Hydrological Program (UNESCO)
19.	IIASA	International Institute for Applied Systems Analysis
20.	INC	International Negotiating Committee
21.	IOC	Intergovernmental Oceanographic Commission (of UNESCO)
22.	IPCC	Intergovernmental Panel on Climate Change
23.	ISCCP	International Satellite Cloud Climatology Project
24.	ISLSCP	International Satellite Land Surface Climatology Project
25.	JGOFS	Joint Global Ocean Flux Study
26.	LOICZ	Land-Ocean Interactions in the Coastal Zone
27.	MAB	Man and Biosphere Programme
28.	MIT	Massachusetts Institute of Technology
29.	NASA	National Aeronautics and Space Administration
30.	NCAR	National Corporation for Atmospheric Research
31.	NERC	National Environment Research Council
32.	OECD	Organisation for Economic Cooperation and Development
33.	PAGES	Past Global Changes (IGBP)
34.	SCAR	Scientific Committee on Antarctic Research (ICSU)
35.	SCOPE	Scientific Committee on Problems of the Environment
36.	SCOR	Scientific Committee on Oceanic Research (ICSU)
37.	SEI	Stockholm Environment Institute
38.	SPARC	Stratospheric Processes and their Role in Climate (WMO)
39.	START	System for Analysis, Research and Training
40.	TOGA	Tropical Ocean and Global Atmosphere Programme
41.	UN	United Nations
42.	UNCED	United Nations Conference on Environment and Development
43.	UNEP	United Nations Environment Programme
44.	UNESCO	United Nations Educational, Scientific and Cultural Organisation
45.	UNGA	United Nations General Assembly
46.	USDOE	United States Department of the Environment
47.	WCED	World Commission on Environment and Development
48.	WCP	World Climate Programme
49.	WCRP	World Climate Research Programme (WMO)

(*Contd.*)

50. WG	Working Group (IPCC)
51. WMO	World Meteorological Organisation
52. WOCE	World Ocean Circulation Experiment (WMO)
53. WRI	World Resources Institute (US)

Fig. 1.2. The international research enterprise: list of acronyms.

public subsidies (Mansell and Paltridge, 1993). Less directly, but more significantly, the energy industries, also, were deeply involved—though not united. While the FCCC, as at last negotiated, made no commitments against coal and cheap energy, these two areas of industry felt most threatened, for much was made in the late 1980s of the alleged IPCC advice that a 60 per cent reduction in carbon dioxide emissions was required soon in order to prevent catastrophe. Official responses by believers were strong: as recently as 1988, a division of the UK Department of the Environment (DoE) believed that a chain hierarchy of energy-policy responses (including increasing the price of coal, expanding nuclear energy, improving energy efficiency and eventually removing carbon dioxide from flue gases) could not be defined in accordance with the timetable of expected findings from grovernment-aided research over the next five to twenty-five years (a timetable which also made use of reliable regional predictions). Energy-policy goals would be defined by scientific progress, and research would directly serve policy.

Other governments found much less able to transform their energy economies (Grubb, 1991), and were relieved when the FCCC remained as vague as the USA (with UK Treasury support) wanted. The US and UK governments were by far the best informed on the state of climate science, a subject that they were and still are funding generously. In its 1990 report and advice, the IPCC had indeed confirmed the concern of 'independent' scientists. After the assumption had been evolved of a doubling of carbon dioxide (CO_2) concentrations in the atmosphere at certain prescribed dates early next country, energy-policy scenarios, at the request of the USA and the Netherlands, were adjusted to suit these dates and then pushed into equilibrium models which, as expected, predicted rapid and disturbing increases in the average global temperature. This emission-scenario methodology and type of model have since been improved upon, and a larger range of scenarios has now been produced.

These are highly speculative experiments and even their creators still consider them to be improper policy tools. However, the assumptions built into the 1990 climate models—and thus their predictions also—were not widely debated at the time. This was intentional. The 'climate community' had also advocated, from the very beginning, technical solutions directed against the burning of coal, a very expensive fuel in Europe (but not elsewhere). Ways out would divide the believers, however, between support for nuclear expansion and a switch to natural gas, on the one hand, and the advocacy of 'soft' energies (wind, waves, solar) and energy saving on the contrary. As most of these solutions were a long way off commercially or less attractive to governments since fossil-fuel prices were going down (oil prices collapsed in 1986 and have recovered but little), government subsidisation was called for in the name of preventing global warming. The 'new' technologies that had been developed in response to the oil-price shocks of the 1970s therefore in need of markets.

Not only the market but also the oil companies (as the owners) were ready for one change only, and had been waiting for it for some time: the use of gas as a replacement for coal or uranium—or both—in electricity generation. Both the UK and US plans for stabilising emissions under the FCCC depend on fuel-switching from coal to oil, something which would have happened and way in the UK if only for reasons of competition. Not all countries could or would avail themselves of this advantageous occasion, but it Europe, Siberian and Norwegian gas was beckoning, and the nuclear industry remained hopeful for a while. The inability of the global—as distinct from European—energy system to stabilise emissions was well-known. The International Energy Agency (IEA) alerted in 1990 that for the whole world economy, stabilisation, let alone a 60 per cent reduction, within two decades would require impossible efforts.

The World Bank argued in 1992 that global energy use and production could only be altered at the margin over the next thirty years because of weak administrative and institutional structures (WEC, 1993:20). In 1993, the governmental Negotiating Committee known as could not agree on the proposed joint implementation strategy which would allow companies to reduce CO_2 anywhere in the world because it would mean outflows of investments and loss of jobs.

The European Community's attempts to introduce a European carbon/energy tax will almost certainly experience the same fate. Coal, the world's cheapest, most widely distributed and most labour-intensive fuel, will not be wiped out at world level, though this was the British Government's aim quite irrespective of global warming—an issue which merely served to green-wash its unpopular policy. Coal's competitors, however, after Chernobyl and the collapse of oil prices, had advocated the perception of a strong warming threat. When Bolin (the IPCC's Chairman) and Houghton (the Chairman of the IPCC's Working Group I (WG I) addressed the World Energy Congress in 1993, both spoke to the World Energy Council, an NGO a major funder of environmental-energy research, in support of higher energy prices, energy efficiency and renewables (World Energy Council 1993). Bolin has been a vocal supporter of changes in energy-policy technologies for over a decade (Bolin, 1977).

Quick Background of Scientific Advice on Climate Change

Fears of global warming was constructed in research institutions a decade or so ago and widely disseminated with the help of environmentalists and international bureaucracies. It gained world political salience in the second half of the 1980s shortly after scientific institutions started to seek active involvement in policy-making. This development is attributed less to the influence of new knowledge than to the combination of a powerful threat image and the open advocacy of anti-fossil-fuel policies at a time when this was accepted by a number of energy interests. The dissemination of the threat was achieved most effectively by the UN system with the assistance of Northern environmental networks, each soon to use the IPCC as a mouthpiece for diverging policy objectives.

The intellectual debate on which subsequent politics was based, and which resulted in the FCCC, can be traced back much before. In 1827 Fourier raised the global-warming issue on the basis of a number of calculations, in 1896 Arrhenius predicted an increase in air temperature of between 4 °C and 6 °C on the ground of laboratory tests, and in 1938 a British steam technologist, Callendar, also calculated that the planet was getting warmer because of carbon dioxide emissions. The later added, however, that there was no need for concern as this meant that another ice age would be avoided. Forecasting weather and climatology remained little-respected sciences for several more decades as the splitting of the nucleus and nuclear technology rather than the complexity of nature occupied the fertile minds (Weart, 1992).

The climate-change research debate began in earnest in the last 1950s with reference to weather modification, with the USA, Germany and Sweden most deeply involved. In 1957 two American scientists mentioned that human being were carrying out a large-scale geophysical experiment which might yield far-reaching insights into the processes determining weather and climate. In 1961, Charles Keeling proved the granth in carbon dioxide concentration in the atmosphere to light by measurement, and warnings in the media began shorly afterwards. The study of man's potential influence on the climate then advanced rapidly during the 1970s as research institutions learned to link their search for knowledge to human concerns like the fears associated both with the limits-to-growth debate and with the idea of a 'nuclear winter' (Hart and Victor, 1993). Climate modelling was now making rapid progress, and the American President's Science Advisory Council argued in 1965 that supercomputers would allow useful predictions, down to the regional level, to be made within two or three years.

Almost thirty years later, no such detail is possible, and there is some doubt that it ever will be (McCracken, 1992: 13). In 1970, the Massachusetts Institute of Technology, always at the forefront of research, held a 'Study of Critical Environmental Problems' which concluded that global warming was a serious possibility. It advocated the aggressive expansion of climate research, combined with population check and protection of the food system—science was ready to solve a new problem with the help of the pill and the Green Revolution. The 1972 Stockholm Conference recommended more climate-change research, as recommended by the First International Conference on Environmental Futures. This had proposed a UN institute for planetary survival, and in a keynote paper on 'Climatic modification by air pollution', the American climatologist Bryson discussed the matter of aerosols and the ozone layer.

Atmospheric particles was feared to be the causal agent, though Bryson, in discussion, admitted to a 'sneaking' suspicion that the demands for more monitoring were 'mostly for the care and feeding of big computers' rather than for the welfare of humanity (Bryson, 1972). Others argued that the development of numerical general-circulation models which successfully simulate both the present climate and the behaviour of the atmosphere in long time runs was the first step in efforts to predict what happens to the atmosphere as a result of man's activities, then considered to be the ultimate goal of the Global Atmospheric Research Programme (GARP), the project organised by Bert Bolin when he was a young man (Polunin, 1972: 168). GARP is the predecessor to IGBP, and was never fully completed. The executive of the WMO began to include climate change into its research portfolio, and the environmental lobby, increasing in strength, would be on the look-out for new problems. By the end of the 1970s, UNEP, still a rather weak intergovernmental body in search of a function, had made climate both a research and a development subject sharing the former interest with the WMO.

UNEP's Executive Director had mentioned both energy and the

need for better climate forecasting in 1974 without any mention of global warming, but when addressing the First World Climate Conference in 1979, he referred to climate change as the process of carrying out an uncontrolled experiment on the earth's atmosphere, and convinced his audience that UNEP was ready to assess the environmental impacts of increased levels of carbon dioxide (Tolba, 1982). The worlds of politics and energy remained unimpressed. Energy-demand forecasters, on the other hand, became interested in the matter as American, German, Canadian, Swedish and British research groups began collaborating on integrating energy forecasting and environmental futures.

The nuclear lobby in particular was attracted to the subject. The more specific fear of global warming was now firmly tied to an advocacy of new energy technologies and to the frightening 'predictions' of energy-demand forecasters. The estimated temperature changes put forward in the late 1970s in relation to the doubling of carbon dioxide concentration differed surprisingly little from those put forward a decade after by the IPCC (Kellogg and Schware, 1981).[4] The numbers of academic books on the subject soared, but the global political system still took no notice.

The energy industries, still either largely in public hands or well supported by public R&D expenditure—or both—provided for the growth and use of technologies and fuels which were generating, or promised to generate, less rather than more carbon dioxide. Climatic variability as a cause of damage to food production became the main which justified the World Climate Research Programme (WCRP) which the WMO initiated in 1979 at the First World Climate Conference, but which remained poorly funded. The Paris-based International Council of Scientific Unions (ICSU), with in them its Scientific Committee on Problems of the Environment (SCOPE), had already shown a growing interest in environmental subjects and global atmospheric modelling (ICSU/IGBP 1992). SCOPE had been established in 1970 to assess environmental problems, and in the early 1980s contributed to the study of nuclear winter. The ICSU and UNEP were as concerned as the WMO about the growing inability of developing countries to contribute to data gathering and monitoring. They eventually pooled their efforts and organised the 1985 Villach Conference, the second conference on the subject of the carbon cycle and climatic change, held in Austrian nation.

Emergence of the IPCC through the Advisory Group

One tiny section of environmental scientists and research managers working on energy and the climate was set up in 1985 at a UNEP/WMO/

ICSU-sponsored meeting with an agenda revealingly mentioned as 'the second joint UNEP/ICSU/WMO international assessment of the role of carbon dioxide and other greenhouse gases in climate variations and associated impacts'. This group called itself the Advisory Group on Greenhouse Gases (AGGG), and convened its first, meeting in 1986. It was to become astonishingly active and influential until 1990. As an advisor to governments, it was replaced by the IPCC. The Villach Conference was jointly organised both by the Swedish International Meteorological Institute (IMI) (the home of Bert Bolin) and by the Beijer Institute (now the Stockholm Environment Institute—SEI) which has close research relations with British institutions.

The conference concluded that 'it is now believed that in the first half of the next century a rise of global mean temperature could occur which is greater than any in man's history', and recommended that science-based emission or concentration targets should be fixed to limit the rate of change in the global mean temperature to a maximum of 0.1°C (WMO 1986). The meeting was attended mainly by non-governmental researchers, including three scientists from the Climate Research Unit at the University of East Anglia, one from the UK Meteorological Office (UKMO), and one scientist from the US Department of Energy's Carbon Dioxide Research Division.

The proceedings were dominated by members of Harvard University and the Vienna International Institute for System Analysis (IIASA), who already saw the responses to the climate threat as part of 'sustainable development'. The Villach meeting was more bothered about science than the IPCC appeared to be in 1990. Another ten-to-twenty years of observaticn would be needed before the detection of global warming was likely, and the ecologist William Clark from Harvard stated that uncertainties dominated the greenhouse-gas issue question, from emission rates through environmental consequences to socioeconomic impacts (WMO 1986: 24).

The Conference felt that refining estimates was 'a matter of urgency', and recommended a list of actions which remained unclear with respect to policy but were very specific for research. The analysis of decision-making rules under specific kinds of risks, the determination of damage costs resulting from greenhouse warming and the evaluation of the behaviour of policy-makers were all to be researched—an agenda for rational, technocratic decision-making. The Conference went beyond advocating more research but suggested that a small task force should be formed jointly by the ICSU, UNEP and the WMO to ensure that periodic assessments both of the current state of scientific understanding and of its practical applications would be undertaken.

A global convention was to be considered, and a small group of advisors was to be set up that would suggest what required to be done at the national and international levels. The small group, in fact, already existed—it had organised the Conference and provided the backbone of the AGGG. There was no need for consensus-generating procedures as only those in agreement with the goals of the group had been asked to join in the first place. The Conference largely approved the broader, political brief urged by Tolba for UNEP under an 'agenda of action'. A non-governmental International Greenhouse-Gas Coordinating Committee (IGCC) was to:

(a) promote and coordinate research, monitoring and assessment programme.
(b) promote the exchange of information related to the issue of climate warming;
(c) prepare and disseminate educational material; and
(d) approve the possible advantages of an intergovernmental agreement on global convention.

At the time while the AGGG succeeded in taking the policy debate into the world of politics, its institutional base proved too poor to keep the issue out of the hands of big, responsible institutions, governments and the WMO, which all had the ability to fund the global-change experiment. Its documentation, all the same, would be more influential. The scientific papers read at Villach and commissioned and peer-reviewed by its organisers were published jointly by the WMO/ICSU and UNEP (Bolin *et al.,* 1988). In a 1992 interview, one British coordinator of the IPCC WG I called this Scope 29 report 'the IPCC bible'. AGGG members subsequently organised the 1988 Toronto NGO Conference on the Changing Atmosphere Implications for Global Security which demanded a 20 per cent reduction in CO_2 emissions and caused considerable unease among governments, industry and government scientists. They also organised the Second World Climate Conference in 1990.

This Conference failed to consent on CO_2 reduction targets, but its results were disseminated nonetheless (Jager and Ferguson, 1991: 473). The AGGG had drafted a recommendation which not only reflected a degree of policy ambition which was subsequently disputed but also increased the pressures for the setting-up of an intergovernmental group. The AGGG also prepared the Meeting of Legal and Policy Experts held in February 1989 in Ottawa which recommended an 'umbrella' consortium, to save the atmosphere, which was to be implemented through subsequent protocols. And it further proposed both a World Atmosphere Trust Fund and a Convention that should be served by a panel of independent experts (Churchill and Freestone, 1992:375).

There was thus considerable bitterness when the AGGG was replaced by the IPCC under pressure from the US State Department exerted through the Executive Committee of the WMO. The IPCC was also advocated by many developing countries who felt excluded from the whole process. The US State Department, presumably with the support of the US Department of Energy (a major sponsor of carbon dioxide research), wanted the scientific assessment to remain in governmental hands, not in those 'of free-wheeling academics' (a WMO source). By the year 1985, therefore, a community of scientists had formed which included people deeply involved in energy and policy research and was determined to initiate a dialogue with 'policy-makers', a chosen few of whom they invited to a1986 meeting. The IPCC is best understood as a response both to this initiative and to the policy advocacy which emerged from Villach.

Governmental scientific interests closer to meteorological marking offices and the hearts of governments would take over the research agenda. By the absorption and rejection of groups and individuals, was caused in 1988, to a gathering of individuals that would form the IPCC. The overlap of individuals and institutions attending the Villach Conference and later supporting the IPCC and IGBP is considerable, and provides evidence for the ability of the research enterprise to draw attention to its programmes by making its problems those of mankind (Boehmer-Christiansen, 1993, 1994c).

The links between the IPCC and IGBP are strong. The US Committee on Global Change and also the US National Committee for the IGBP of the Commission on Geosciences, Environment and Resources of the National Research Council have stated that the IGBP was developed as a step in the evolving process of defining the scientific requirements involved in understanding those changes in the global environment which are of great concern. One chapter out of nine in this report deals with humanity (US National Research Council 1990), and a small section of the Global Change research agenda is also today devoted to the human dimension, primarily because of the impacts of land-use changes on physical variables (Price, 1992). This, too, primarily reflects US research needs.[5]

The significance of 'Global Change' to the US research community is enormous, as is the need to ensure policy relevance. Neither science nor vested energy interests had much to gain from a global advisory body that would hurry along the policy process by recommending action, instead of further decades of research. IGBP representatives addressed the eighth plenary session of the IPCC in connection with the IGBP's START (System of Analysis, Research and Training) programme, which functions closely with the International Group of Funding Agencies for Global Change Research (IGBP 1994). START aims to strengthen the scientific capacity of developing countries (an interest it shares with the IPCC), and it is already being aided by the Global Environment Facility.[6] START's secretariat is in Washington, and is guided by the IGBP Standing Committee—at which the WCRP is also represented. The November-1992 START workshop in Niger was attended by the head of the 1985 Villach Conference who now chairs the new IPCC WG III. Space science and technology are deeply involved in all these bodies.[7]

Character of IPCC in the Collective Context

When the WMO and UNEP had been invited by the General Assembly (UNGA) in 1988 to jointly prepare a Framework Convention on Climate Change which was to contain commitments for actions, to combat climate change, 'taking into account the latest sound scientific knowledge and any existing uncertainties' (Churchill and Freestone, 1992: 249), the IPCC had already been setup. The sound knowledge (what is unsound knowledge?) and uncertainties in question were both to be supplied by a section of research managers, science-policy leaders and government officials that had formally been set up a few months earlier in response to statements and claims, about the approaching risk of global warming, made by 'independent' scientists under the umbrella of the ICSU, the WMO and UNEP. Such claims had been made for decades, but had been rejected by the WMO as too speculative until 1986 when the task of scientific assessment passed into the more efficient hands (with deeper pockets) of government laboratories and meteorological offices in the UK, the USA, Canada and Australia. The independent research sector was not excluded, but it would now work as funded and directed. The IGBP, in preparation since the early 1980s was also adopted by the ICSU in 1986.

The way it had happened for the protection of the ozone layer, UNEP expected the climate convention to be negotiated under its own auspices, but in late 1990 UNGA decided otherwise. Too many agendas fears and doubts had by then attached themselves to the climate fear for the issue to be left to environmental scientists alone. Negotiations would be undertaken not by the IPCC but by the International Negotiating Committee (INC). Politicians took the task away from the research enterprise, but had during this time become dependent on it for authority.

Science is an unreliable ally. By 1992, with funding ensured, researchers wanted not to give 'new' advice but instead to be left alone to get on with data collection and the testing of global models in order to evaluate and reduce a growing number of uncertainties. There was not much that was 'new' anyway. The scientific perspective is not that of the policy-makers; rather, 'it is important that we are able to predict the results of global environmental changes on the long-term climate, but our present understanding of the problem is far from complete and our ocean-climate models are not sophisticated enough, nor is current computing power sufficient' (Smithon, 1994:9). The IPCC consists of a small secretariat and bureau of about thirty people, the former based in Geneva inside the WMO's headquarters. Its financial estimate in 1992/3 was under 2 million French francs. Biannual plenary sessions bring together leading government scientists and research managers, plus mainly junior government officials in charge of designing national level climate policy or preparing international negotiations—or both. While formal decisions are taken at these plenaries, most of the real work of the Panel—collecting and assessing scientific evidence and theories—happening in Working Groups whose subdivisions act as writing teams for individual chapters.

The structure of these chapters has been decided both by small groups of lead authors and by the WG (Working Group) Chairman, who together also condense the observations of these chapters into 'policy-makers' summaries' for general consumption. Each Working Group represents a more or less stable research network which operates in a symbiotic relationship with the writing teams. The networks present data and ideas for the authors, and the IPCC management structure brings research results and needs to the attention of governments and other interested parties, including UN agencies. The IPCC Bureau and also the bureaux of its WGs are able to function as the decision-makers, selecting authors and reviewers for reports (in consultation with governments), negotiating consensus and transmitting research needs to governments. Three WGs were established to deal with knowledge issues.

The most coherent and basic WG dealt with scientific assessment (WG I, Science), and is coordinated from the Hadley Centre of Climate Prediction and Research in the UK Meteorological Office (UKMO). It has had a great impact on UK research policy and environmental diplomacy. WG I as a whole reflects the existing research interests of the WMO, coordinated as the WCRP, while WG II, dealing with climate-change impacts, reflects those of UNEP. As part of the WRCP, research programme of also complements the more ambitious IGBP (ICSU/IGBP 1992). WG III attracted most countries, but was attended by government officials and NGO lobbyists rather than scientists. The purpose of WG III was to define 'realistic' answer strategies, but it was also, de facto, the meeting place for those people with whom scientists did not want to mix.[8] From both IPCC reports and especially their more disputed policy-makers' summaries, actors in the world of politics and commerce would develop threat images, select options and define positions based on particular interests. Bureaucratic empire-builders, NGOs driving for new members and party-political and commercial competitors all fast took up 'global warming' prevention as a goal to suit themselves. The main achievement of the IPCC so far has been its reports, which are addressed both to policy-makers and to the UN. Very first science assessment was published in 1990 (Houghton *et al.,* 1990) and updated for UNCED in 1992.

A Second Assessment is under way for 1995, but will not become available in time to help in the preparations of the first meeting of the parties of the FCCC, as scientists refuse to be hurried by political timetables (Pearce, 1994: 5). These same scientists had, however, helped to define these timetables by promises made when the research programmes were marketed as strategic knowledge wanted for policy-makers. The WG structure, as it turned out, proved highly unsuitable for policy-making, as the producers and users of knowledge had hardly ever met. It reflected a highly linear conception of policy-making in which scientists think and recommend, while politicians merely add values and execute (Bolin, 1994; Boehmer-Christiansen, 1994b).

The Art of Vogueness or IPCC Advice

It first met in the Autumn of 1988. By 1990 the first stage of funding for global systems research had been achieved, and experts began to talk (as those opposed to rapid-abatement action had already done for some time) more about those uncertainties that needed studying instead of confirming the predicted warming range (namely, a rate of increase in the global mean temperature, during the next century, of about 0.3 °C per decade, with an uncertainty range to between 0.2 and 0.5). Environmentalists responded with that particular version of the precautionary principle which proved attractive to those in favour both of higher energy prices and of regulation for non-environmental reasons.

Like all lobbies, the research lobby makes with more than one voice. For example, two climatologists who had attended the 1985 Villach Conference and contributed to the work of the IPCC (and therefore added their voice to what appeared to many to be calls for quick action) argued shortly afterwards, when addressing the science-policy community, that the range of scientific uncertainty was still so large that neither the 'do nothing' option nor the 'stop emissions' option could be excluded from consideration (Warrick and Jones, 1988: 48-62).

Full support for a research effort which would narrow the range of scientific uncertainty, and which would indicate how socioeconomic and environmental (but not political) systems were likely to be affected, was needed. The IPCC follows this example. While a lot has been made of its scientific consensus, especially in the UK, this consensus includes clear statements on uncertainty, and, if read closely, remains highly ambiguous, especially as far as the Executive Summaries matter (Houghton, Jenkins and Ephraums, 1990: xi-xxiii). Instead of using the terms 'model' and 'prediction' (as injected into the 1990 policy debate), scientists might have used more neutral terms such as 'numerical experimentation' and 'scenario-building'. Vagueness and its political utility are readily documented. In 1990, IPCC lead authors had agreed that they could calculate with confidence—not measure—average global temperature increases from models which a few pages later were found to be 'comparatively crude', and from which two important greenhouse gases, water vapour and ozone, as well as aerosols and processes involving the biosphere, had been omitted.[9]

The Executive Summary combined both the phrase 'will result' with the phrase 'a likely increase'—a grammatical device to create both certainty and uncertainty simultaneously. It was not stated that the predicted rate of temperature increase was likely only in association with specific emission picture. Given these assumptions, the prediction was

> "a rate of increase of global mean temperature during the next century of about 0.3 degree C per decade (with an uncertainty of 0.2 to 0.5 degree C per decade) . . . . (T) his will result in a likely increase in global mean temperature of about 1 degree C above the present value by 2025 and 3 degrees C before the end of next century."
>
> (Houghton, Jenkins and Ephraums, 1990: xi)

This vogueness range is huge, and ensured that most researchers, but not all, could support the consensus. The real source of friction, as already mentioned, was the prescribed emission scenarios. The IPCC has always admitted in its fuller reports that its understanding of the connections between greenhouse-gas concentrations and 'climate sensitivity', involving a consideration of the actual changes produced by their accumulation and interaction in the air, remained poor. While some may well decide that more greenhouse-gas consecrations provide sufficient reason for mitigation and adaptation strategies, the IPCC has never explicitly said so. To have decided this would have been against the interests of research.

Both environmentalists, a previous director of UK Friends of the Earth could claim that 'the consensus view of the IPCC' was that a 60 per cent reduction in CO_2 is needed to stabilise the climate at an acceptable temperature (Gee 1994: 17), and Greenpeace continues to campaign in the impression that the climate is 'in danger of catastrophic destabilisation' (Greenpeace, undated). The UK Treasury, also bowing to the 'authoritative IPCC assessment by several hundred scientists', stressed 'huge uncertainties' instead, and concluded that another decade of research would be needed before any policy could be made in response to man-made changes, adding that there should not be excessive costs for the world economy (Her Majesty's Treasurry, 1992), an opinion privately supported by some IPCC leaders. The IPCC had wisely 'calculated with confidence' that an immediate 60 per cent reduction in emissions would have to take place if the stabilisation of current concentrations were to be the aim but this was not advocated, and the difficulties of linking calculated temperature rises with real temperatures were pointed out.

When addressing the World Energy Council, Houghton discarded the idea of certainty altogether, describing that 'IPCC publications explain the degree of scientific uncertainty regarding future climate change .... Research therefore needs urgently to be undertaken in order to reduce scientific uncertainty' (WEC 1993: 47). And Bolin, in turn, advocated the statement that 'as long as we do not know the natural carbon cycle adequately the prediction of atmospheric concentrations due to future emissions remains uncertain' (*ibid.*: 43). The uncertainty of uncertainties is threatening scientists.

Few groups in government and a growing number of scientific 'sceptics' have rejected not the idea of *some* level of warming but the idea of a *dangerous* level of warming, and hence have challenged not so much science but more some of the policy responses it has given birth rise to (Lindzen, 1992; Michaels, 1992).

The debate clearly continues, and it is my judgement that the uncertainty involved will increase for quite some time yet. The coal industry is now supporting research into global greening (carbon dioxide stimulates plant growth), thus recalling Russian claims made during the 1970s that global warming should be encouraged.[10] Little significant consensus was reached on this subject in the other, subsidiary WGs. And to the extent that the observations of these WGs would depend on WG I, their results must remain irrelevant to policy as long as WG I is largely reporting research needs—as is now admitted by the academic group making assessments using emission scenarios. If it had not been for opposition on the part of US and UK policy advisors fully aware of the scientific base, an international climate regime reflecting the demands of environmentalists and European energy interests might have committed other nations to considerable policy changes and possibly created disaster for the poorest and most dependent on cheap energy. The political pressures to reduce fossil-fuel use in favour of more expensive options may yet become unstoppable unless 'science' is used to reverse these pressures. Having said this, however, scientific messages can themselves be reversed, science being by nature self-correcting.

Research Coordination and Science-Policy Advising of WMO

Final decision to establish a panel on climate change was made at the WMO's 1987 Congress where, after extensive briefing by the Secretary of the Brundtland Commission, the WMO also made a strong bid for a consideration of the socio-economic implications of climate change, as suggested by the AGGG. The WMO had become bothered that UNEP might 'run with' the global-warming issue without proper scientific advice (WMO interview 1992). The WMO invited governments to join the IPCC by appointing their WMO representatives. About thirty countries did so and that way gave their blessing to what can be called the largest international exercise of scientific-advice-giving.[11] The panel, as envisaged in 1987, was 'to provide the international assessment that would enable the Directors of National Meteorological Services to decide their governments on the evidence for and nature of the climate threat and what they might do about it' (McTegart and Zillman 1990: 10). It was to be small, involving experts from no more than fifteen to twenty-nine countries active in climate-change study and including both a few other nations and those main scientific bodies responsible for international leadership in climate research. The IPCC was established jointly with UNEP, but with the WMO very much in control. And the political response to the WMO's proposal surprised the research community not involved in the AGGG, for

> "almost overnight, greenhouse-induced climate change moved from being the business of specialised bodies . . . to become the centrepiece of a major political happening . . . an impressive array of world leaders, mostly unaware of what had been going on in national scientific laboratories and the UN system over the preceding decades, immediately seized on the need for drastic action."
>
> (McTegar and Zillman, 1990: 8)[12]

In the year, 1988, the WMO Executive Council agreed the brief of the IPCC after considerable debate. It was agreed that uncertainties and gaps in present knowledge with regard to climate change and its potential impacts needed to be identified. And links both with existing research programmes and with the IGBP were also emphasised. The choice of the WMO by the global research enterprise as the organisation most fitted for the task of promoting global research and advice-giving has surely been wise. The WMO is by far the most efficient organisation for advancing the interests of interdisciplinary research. With a world-wide network of meteorological offices and a senior scientific elite deeply involved in atmospheric and oceanographic research, it has provided the necessary national-international linkage for effective policy-making and research implementation. These WMO links were particularly important for the IPCC because they brought informal contacts not only with the ICSU and national research agencies but also with national meteorological offices and government departments. Since 1987 the research agenda underlying the IPCC has grown enormously, and the WMO appears to be laying claim to it (WMO 1992).

Negotiation for the Framework Treaty on Climate Change

Talks of a treaty (albeit an ambiguous one) on climate change had become unstoppable by the end of the 1980s. In 1992, the treaty emerged rich in exhortations and good advice, but opposite on commitments on the energy-policy side. Rather, it codifies enormous data-collection needs and research commitments, serving both the natural sciences, the earth-observation industry and mixed bureaucracies.

Tough international policy decisions dealing with immediate problems were postponed, or left to the national level to be decided on the basis of sovereignty. The process of scientific advice-giving can here thus, in retrospect, be analysed as a dimension of 'power' politics, power referring both to energy and to the capacity of nations, official stakeholders and other interests to decode outcomes. The negotiations were formally based on scientific evidence and its interpretation, and for this reason, very few countries could genuinely participate, though efforts were made to involve delegates from other countries as learners. Less openly, the Convention also reflected expectations about future energy demands, fuel choice and energy technologies, as well as creating new markets for the earth-observation industry and that may space agencies and their suppliers.

·Most importantly from the perspective adopted here, the climate treaty provided the rapidly expanding and encroaching field of environmental science with an almost regular research agenda at the very heart of the IGBP and WCRP, with a small human dimensions component more recently added by the International Social Science Council (Boehmer-Christiansen, 1994a, b; Price, 1992). The data needs are enormous. The very purpose of the FCCC depends on further scientific evidence. The objective of the treaty is the

> "stabilisation of greenhouse gas concentrations... at a level that would prevent dangerous anthropogenic interference with the climate system. Such a level should be achieved within a time frame sufficient to allow ecosystems to adapt naturally to climate change, to ensure that food supply is not threatened and to enable economic development to proceed in a sustainable manner."
>
> (IUCC (undated) *UNFCCC*)

A tall order in fact. How and by whom will 'dangerous' be defined? The IPCC has already claimed that defining this objective should be its task. Two 'subsidiary bodies' are to be set up by the Parties of the Convention in order to provide 'scientific-technical' information. The accurate link between the IPCC and these bodies is not yet clear. Information will be needed on four subjects:

(a) the stabilisation of concentrations,
(b) emission permanence,
(c) the ecological limits or levels of patiene,
(d) emission inventories and reduction programmes.

The emission-reduction commitments that governments have approved so far, apart from being very easy ones (the EU as a whole has already stabilised its carbon dioxide emissions), consist of major data-collection and planning efforts. This obligation, too, is very research-intensive and needs much national expertise. Governments are required to make national inventories of all their greenhouse gas emissions (other than CFCs controlled under the Montreal Protocol) using comparable research methodologies. (The methodologies in question have been defined by the IPCC with the help from the

OECD/IEA.) This information concerning implementation must then be communicated to the Conference of the Parties. Countries also have to—

> "fomulate, implement, publish and regularly update national and, where appropriate, regional programmes containing measures to mitigate climate change by addressing anthropogenic emissions by sources and removals by sinks of all greenhouse gases not controlled by the Montreal Protocol, and measures to facilitate adequate adaptation to climate change; and promote and cooperate in the development, application and diffusion, including transfer, of technologies, practices and processes that control, reduce or prevent anthropogenic emissions."
>
> (IUCC (undated) *UNFCCC*, p. 8, para. 2)

The concerned sectors specifically referred to are energy, transport, industry, agriculture, forestry and waste management. Other paragraphs of the same article mention sustainable management and coastal zone management, water resources and agriculture, impact evaluation and research collaboration, and even training and education. Remote sensing will be essential, and the global-change research enterprise will provide the major market for this heavily subsidised activity (Mansell and Paltridge 1993). If knowledge is a common public good, then the public should be involved in deciding what knowledge, and technologies, it wants to finance, raising another hornets' nest of issues. The Convention goes to considerable lengths to make sure that the parties will be provided with abundant technical advice.

Two subsidiary bodies will be set up, one to give 'scientific and technological advice' and the other to assist the Parties with the implementation of the Convention. This former would offer the kind of knowledge that the IPCC's WGs have been gathering and assessing since 1988. Its functions and terms of reference may be further elaborated in future, but the range of expertise is generally defined as 'scientific'. Its liabilities remain firmly linked to the natural and technical sciences, but will also include the identification of innovative and efficient technologies. The implementation experts of the second subsidiary body will not, it seems, be asked to guide on implementation as such, but rather on its measurement. A main task of this body will be to help countries with their inventories of emissions and sinks—a rather fundamental inquiry, in the nature of economic activities within national jurisdictions, which is already under way. This knowledge will become widely available. The Earth's surface has been made transparent.

Final Findings

The well said climate-change threat rose to the top of the agenda in international political and diplomatic debates not so much because science meekly responded to public concern but more because a global network of national organisations, devoted to research into atmospheric sciences, climate predictions, ecosystems, energy-demand forecasting and new energy and information-gathering technologies, actively helped to create and disseminate concern. Basic environmental research serves to diagnose problems, but once action is appeared, other forms of knowledge are needed.

The research enterprise must therefore continuously invent new problems which it can then credibly claim to solve. To acquire policy relevance for climate-change research, ambiguity, a shaking consensus and scientific controversy were as much an expression of real issues as they were a form of strategic behaviour. Once funded, scientific institutions demand freedom and prefer to withdraw from advocacy to stress on uncertainty, ignorance and even indeterminacy. They seek to become neutral and value free. Such scientific advice has one advantage over most other tools of politics: it can legitimate U-turns on the grounds of new evidence or persisting uncertainty. Science does not, therefore, make a reliable ally for environmentalists, and any international policy which defines itself in relation to 'rational and optimal' knowledge is pursuing a moving target that cannot be executed.

Scientific uncertainties invite delay not action. To the extent that science is always uncertain, it is useful to states that want to protect their sovereignty. International regimes are therefore particularly attractive to the research enterprise.[13] Here, action-oriented agreements are highly easily resisted, while commitments to more research (or learning), via lowest-denominator agreements, are most attractive. This makes the research enterprise a potential ally for the growth of regimes that remain very open to future politics, and allow for the growth and exchange of information, but avoid genuine global regulations. The consensual knowledge that academic policy advisors seek will rarely if ever be available in the complex sector of global environmental impacts (Wynne, 1992). It would be against the interest of research if it were. Many governments are now considered their replay without additional scientific guidance. They would probably agree to do more research and collect more data. Responses beyond this are likely to be defined in a purely national context. Energy, information and the climate are far too important to be overlooked for long in international relations, and the IPCC had successfully brought them to the attention of most governments.

It allowed natural-science research and branches of economics both to define the global-change problem as a research issue and to suggest solutions, most of which would need further massive research (or subsidisation) efforts. The main allies at this early stage of problem definition have comprised the Northern environmental lobbies, some commercial interests and several international bureaucracies with bold research interests. Opponents have comprised a small number of scientists who did not want to be part of a 'government science' programme with strong energy-policy implications as well as fossil-fuel and cheap-energy interests as promised to defeat 'new' fuels and technologies when an era of expensive energy ended in 1986. The oil companies, as the owners of gas, have emerged as the major winners —but this is different story.

Global warming provided the justification for intervention on the side of potential losers, but the costs of this intervention have proved unpalatable to most governments.

At last, the concept of the atmosphere as a global common·needing joint protection proved of little help in analysing and explaining observed behaviour. No common interest could be identified beyond that which institutions could create within themselves. Research bodies and the global knowledge claims they make are self-serving and are best constrained, like other political actors, by open politics and the free flow of information. The climate-change story is therefore a hopeful one, because at the relatively anarchical international level, interests and values are expressed openly and the role of science in international relations is revealed more readily, perhaps, than it is at many national levels. It must remain the task of politics to transform present knowledge into policy in the context of many other ingredients.

The question remains of whether the global epistemic community and the international environmental regimes it has created are indeed benign phenomena. Instead of being potectors of an accepted common property or resource, they may be just another manifestation of dominance and power politics—this at least is how they appear to be perceived at the global grass roots.

The findings of the IPCC reported here suggests that for complex environmental issues there can be no common policy enterprise for mankind, only attempts to generate such an enterprise by certain actors with reference to global threats that cannot be proven. Such threats nevertheless carry considerable political and technical innovative potential. The assumption that leading members of the climate-change community subscribe 'to holistic ecological beliefs about the necessity for policy coordination subject to ecosystemic laws' (Hass, P., 1993: 9) is not justified in this case and would even be dangerous. Indeed, climate scientists have disagreed as much as anybody else about what to do. Humanity would be ill-advised to accept any coherent plans put forward by climate-change specialists for the management of entire ecosystems, or, in this case, of the entire atmosphere, biosphere, hydrosphere . . . indeed of virtually everything and everybody.

References

1. The IGBP was planned during the early 1980s by US research institutions and then disseminated globally for approval and implementation by the ICSU in response to the concern about climate change which had meanwhile been generated. In 1984, Roy Rapley, Head of Remote Sensing and Associate Director of the Department of Space and Climate Physics at the ULC's Mullard Space Laboratory, became its Executive Director.
2. About half of the lead authors in the IPCC science reports (WG I) came from the UK and USA; contributing authors and reviewers were selected by them. Policy-makers summaries were drafted by very small groups of senior science managers close to the UK government. Hartmut Grassl, Vice-Chairman of WG I from the Max Planck Institute for Meteorology, is the new Director of the WCRP at the invitation of the WMO, the ICSU and the Intergovernmental Oceanic Commission.
3. Apart from the critique presented here, there is a more fundamental objection. Pure environmental regimes, usually assumed by theorists, do not exist because of the many and varied impacts on costs of production, trade and competition. Trade or financial interests may therefore drive environmental 'regimes'.
4. This book is based on Aspen Institute workshops held in the USA and West Germany. Major participants were the US National Corporation for Atmospheric Physics (NCAR) based in Boulder and the Austrian International Institute for Applied Systems Analysis, where the climate threat was explored by two Germans, H. Flohn (climatologist, WMO) and W. Hafele (inventor of the breeder reactor) during the 1970s.
5. Opposition by social scientists in the EC Commission was overruled (CEC interview).

6. Organisations attending included the Joint Research Centre of the CEC, UNEP, the UNDP, the US Committee on Earth and Environmental Sciences and the Consortium for the International Earth Science Networks.
7. A 1992 German IGBP newsletter (*Global Change Prisma*) lists fifty-six satellite and four space-shuttle launches between 1992 and 1998 for remote sensing. The countries involved are the USA (NASA and NOAA), Japan, Russia, Germany, India and UK and France—the major global-change research nations.
8. WGs II and III were merged in 1993 and a third group on cross-cutting (natural/socioeconomic) issues set up. This time, natural scientists have already planned joint meetings between WG I and the new WG III, thus by-passing governments.
9. It had previously been thought that aerosols would lead to another ice age. Luckily, the recent major volcanic eruption in the Philippines could be used to explain the less-than-predicated level of warming in 1992. The role of water vapour is not well understood, but would be affected by the unknown impacts of actual warming—as distinct from radiative forcing.
10. The Russians were quickly thrown out of WG I.
11. The Group of Experts on the Scientific Aspects of Marine Pollution (GESAMP) is much older and has over fifteen working groups. It has never attracted the same attention, but may have been more effective as a low-profile organisation.
12. W.J. McTegart was the Australian Vice-Chair of IPCC WG II until 1993, and I am most grateful for his assistance over several years. W.J. Zillman is Director of the Commonwealth Bureau of Meteorology. Both are thanked for their help.
13. Others that may be considered for comparison are the acid-rain regime under the Geneva Convention and the control of marine pollution under the Law of the Sea Convention. Ozone is a different matter in that its agreement was one which advanced the interests of two chemical companies. Biodiversity also deserves to be studied.

2

Cycles of Global Environmental Change

When we talk of attempts towards redressing the environmental problems, the first thing that are needs to start with understanding the basics about global environment change, i.e., how it takes place. In the present chapter, therefore, we are concentrating on the cycles of change. Humans have forever been worried over their environment as they seek out a better standard of living. Land has been cleared for agriculture or commerce, and animal populations have been exploited by human beings. What is different about the situation that we find ourselves in today is the magnitude of our impacts. We are more numerous: 5.7 billion people on earth seek out an existence, and are multiplying. Every six months, there is another contingent of people equal in population to the country of France, almost 50 million. Imagine, every six months another France for whom to provide food, housing, shelter, and jobs.

Every ten years, there is another population nearly the size of China. And coupled with population is the problem of an ever-increasing per capita consumption among developed countries, especially. We are powerful. Twin juggernauts—burgeoning population and per capita consumption—are leading global change. In this chapter, we will see how mathematical models can help us examine where we are going from where we have been with respect to our global environs. Environmental modelling should aid us in decision-making about our collective future, as dynamics of our environmental and social systems become e.:tremely complex. A projection of global population from 1750 to 2100 is shown in Fig. 2.1.[1] Following the industrial revolution, population in developed countries increased rapidly from 1850 to 1950. But in recent past developing countries in Asia, Africa, and South America have increased population as the industrializing countries did 100 years ago.

Global population is projected to rise rapidly until the end of the 21st century and then stabilize at 10-11 billion. Increase in population is the first driving force of global change. The second driving force of global change is per capita consumption. It has grown as fast or faster than

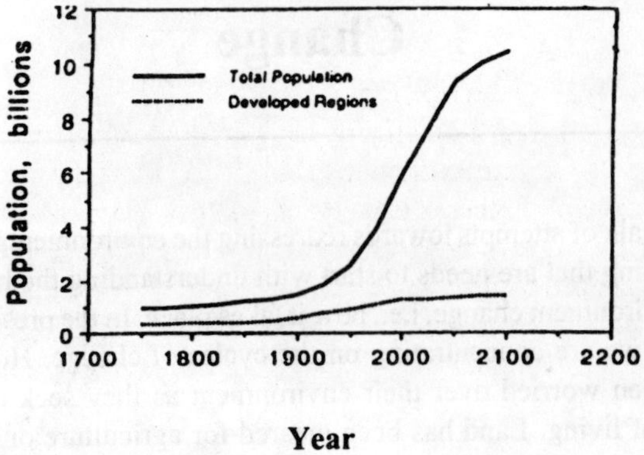

Fig. 2.1. Past and Projected World Population.

population. From 1950 to1986, the population doubled from 2.5 billion to 5.0 billion, a rate of two per cent per year. But during that same period the annual growth in global primary energy consumption was four per cent per year, about double that of population. The example reveals that per capita consumption, especially among developed countries, has contributed significantly to our energy and pollution (emission) problems. (Fig. 2.2).

Comparatively, atmosphere is a small compartment in the earth's movement of environmental pollutants. It contains a mass of 5×10^{18} kg of air that is dwarfed by the ocean (1.4×10^{21} kg for 3800-m deep ocean). Furthermore, residence times of pollutants in the atmosphere are short compared to the ocean. It is relatively easy to pollute the atmosphere. It responds quickly to global emissions, but it also cleanses itself quickly when emissions are abated. Greenhouse gases are increasing in the

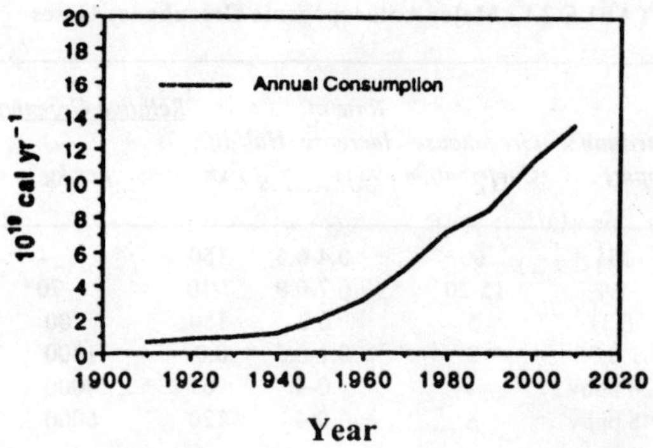

Fig. 2.2. Past and Projected Global Energy Consumption.

atmosphere. Carbon dioxide from fossil fuel emissions is increasing at 0.4-0.5% per year (Fig. 2.3). Slightly half of the anthropogenic greenhouse gas effect is due to carbon dioxide (Table 2.1)[2]. Methane concentrations in the atmosphere, another potent greenhouse gas, are increasing at ~0.7% per year, mainly due to flooded agriculture (rice production) and animal husbandry needed to feed an expanding population (Fig. 2.4).[3] But the *rate of increase* in methane concentrations is beginning to decline; perhaps because leaks at natural gas pipelines have been brought under control.

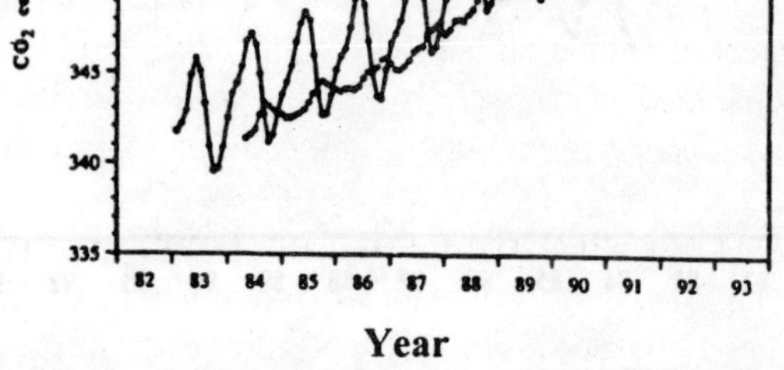

Fig. 2.3. Trend of Carbon Dioxide Concentration at two Stations: in the Northern hemisphere. Mauna Loa, Hawaii, and the southern hemisphere at Cape Grim, showing the exponential increase in CO_2 at 0.5% per year.[3]

TABLE 2.1. Major Anthropogenic Greenhouse Gases

Gas	*Concentration, ppmv*	*Greenhouse Contribution*	*Rate of Increase % yr⁻¹*	*Half-life, yr*	*Relative Greenhouse Effect*	
					per kg	*per mol*
CO_2	355	60	0.4-0.5	150	1	1
CH_4	1.7	15-20	0.7-0.9	7-10	70	25
N_2O	0.31	5	0.2	150	200	200
O_3	0.01 0.05	8	0.1-0.5	0.01	1800	2000
$CFCl_3$	0.28 ppbv	4	0-4	65	4000	12,000
CF_2Cl_2	0.48 ppbv	8	0-4	120	6000	15,000

Concentrations are on a volumetric basis (mixing ratios)
Source: Modified from Rodhe.[2]

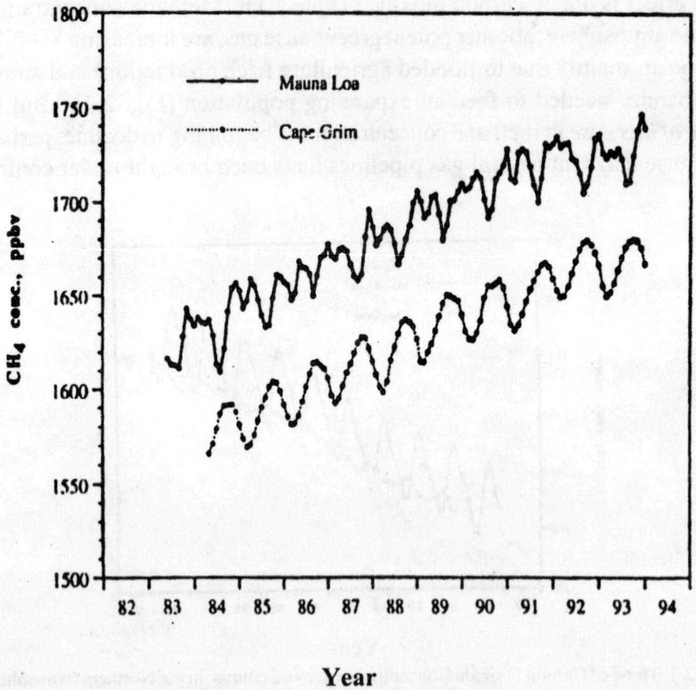

Fig. 2.4. Trend of Methane Concentrations at two Stations, in the Northern Hemisphere, Mauna Loa, Hawaii, and Southern Hemisphere at Cape Grim, showing the Exponential increase of Methane at 0.9% per year but Concentrations Appear to be Leveling off.[1]

Nitrous oxide (N_2O) is produced by increasing fossil fuel emissions, biomass burning, and nitrogen fertilizer applications worldwide. As ammonia-nitrogen is oxidized in the soil and nitrate is denitrified, nitrous oxide presents itself an intermediate oxidation state, which is volatilized to the atmosphere. Fig. 2.5 shows that N_2O is increasing rapidly in the atmosphere and, even though it is only ~5% of the anthropogenic greenhouse gas effect, it is quite difficult to control. Fertilizer applications of ammonia, ammonium nitrate, and ammonium sulphate are likely to increase worldwide. Chlorofluorocarbon (CFC) concentrations are also increasing, and they have a long half-life in the atmosphere (Table 2.1.)[3] They are used as refrigerants, blowing agents, and cleaning chemicals in the microelectronics industry. Two of the most widely used are CFC-11 ($CFCl_3$, trichlorofluoromethane) and CFC-12 (CF_2Cl_2, dichloro-difluoromethane). Owing to a slow reaction rate with hydroxyl radical, OH, in the lower atmosphere, they are transported into the stratosphere (upper atmosphere), where they deplete the ozone layer that protects the earth from harmful ultraviolet radiation. The Montreal Protocol of 1987and later

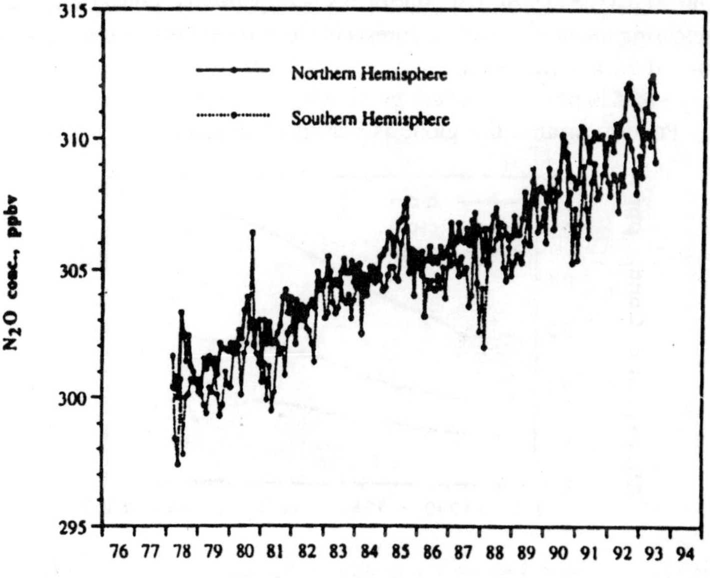

Fig. 2.5. Trend of Nitrous Oxide Concentrations at two Stations in the Northen and the Southern Hemispheres, Depicting the Exponential Increase of N_2O at 0.2% per year.[1]

amendments (London, 1990; Copenhagen, 1992) have banned the production of CFCs by the year 2000. Starting from conception of the problem by Mario Molina and Sherwood Rowland[4] in 1974, down to measurement of the Antarctic ozone hole in 1985, and acceptance by industry and the scientific community in 1987, the control of CFC chemicals is among the major success stories of international environmental agreements.[5,6] Methylchloroform, a potent ozone-destroying chemical, is now becoming in the atmosphere[6] as a result of the Montreal Protocol (Fig. 2.6). Other CFC chemicals will do likewise within the next decade or so. For their vision, Molina and Rowland were awarded the Nobel Prize in Chemistry for 1995.

Still, due to long half-lives of the chemicals, ozone depletion will continue for some years. In addition, CFC chemicals account for a significant fraction of the anthropogenic greenhouse gas effect. Globally, the clearing of land for agriculture and commerce amounts to ~50,000 mi^2 per year or roughly the area of the State of Iowa. It results in destruction of habitats for plant, animal, and microbial species. Nearly 100,000 species are thought to become extinct per year, from a total of perhaps 4 40 million species.[7] Fifty per cent of the biodiversity is in the tropics and developing countries, so the elearing of rain forests is of particular concern. Nations are clearing about 0.5% of the forests each year, and if this causes a loss of half of the natural species present, then the rate of extinction would be nearly ~0.25% per year, a very grave long-term problem indeed.

Poverty around the globe is perhaps the greatest environmental

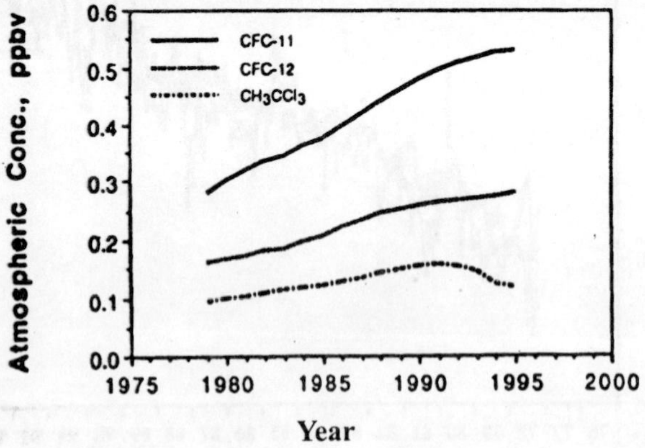

Fig. 2.6. Chlorofluorocarbon (CFC) and methyl chloroform (CH_3CCl_3) concentrations (mixing ratios in ppb by volume) in the atmosphere.

problem of all. 1.3 billion people lack safe drinking water; 2.3 billion lack access to sanitation facilities; 1.5 billion do not have enough firewood or fuel for cooking and heating; and 13 million children die from diarrhea, and hunger each year.[8] Till such time the developed world finds its way clear to invest in developing countries, it will not be easy to make collaborative progress on forest preservation, biodiversity, and CO_2 emissions. Developed countries need to restrain their own per capita consumption (a major part of the problem) while helping other countries with their development. Much of the global atmospheric problems were created by emissions from the developed world, and they are most responsible for controlling them. One responsibility is to analyze global problems rationally using environmental models and by engineers contributing to international policy formulation.

An Example on the Earth's Compartment

What is the mass of the atmosphere in comparison to that of the oceans and "living soil" (pedosphere)?

Solution: The column of air above earth exerts an atmospheric pressure that is a measure of the integrated mass. We can use pressure to estimate the mass of the atmosphere.

P_A = Atmospheric pressure = 101 kPa = 101 kN m^2

S_E = Surface area of earth = 5.1×10^{14} m^2

M_A = Mass of atmosphere = $(P_A/g)\ S_E$
= (101,000 N m^2 / 9.807 m s^{-2}) / (5.1×10^{14} m^2)
= 5.25×10^{18} kg

Earth's lower atmosphere (~10 km elevation) is called the troposphere. The barometric pressure at that elevation is 220 millibars or 22 kPa. Thus, the troposphere contains 78% of the mass of the total atmosphere. The earth's upper atmosphere or stratosphere (10-100 km elevation) contains the rest.

Mass (%) in troposphere = (101-22) kPa / 101kPa
= 78%

The mass of the oceans is extremely large. Assuming a density of

1.03 g cm^{-3}, a depth of 3800 m, and a surface area of 70 % of the earth's surface, the following calculations apply:

$$\text{Ocean mass} = S_o\, d\rho = (0.7 \times 5.1 \times 10^{14}\ \text{m}^2)\ (3800\ \text{m})\ (1.03\text{g cm}^{-3}) = 1.40 \times 10^{21}\ \text{kg}$$

The mass of living soil is very less conparatively. Assuming a depth of 2 m, a bulk density of 1.5 kg L ^{1}, and a surface area of 25.5% of the earth's surface area, the mass of the soil is much smaller than the oceans and one order-of-magnitude smaller than the atmosphere.

$$\text{Soil mass} = S_s\, d\rho_b = (0.255 \times 5.1\times 10^{14}\ \text{m}^2)\ (2\ \text{m})\ (1.5\ \text{kg L}^1) = 3.9 \times 10^{17}\ \text{kg}$$

Huge mass of the oceans suggests that residence times of pollutants could be very long compared to the atmosphere and soil. Later in the chapter, we will make estimates of atmospheric residence times.

Climate Change and Some General Circulation Models

Greenhouse Gases and Climate

Rise in "greenhouse gases" in the atmosphere has caused a concern regarding the potential for global warming and climate change. While it is certain that greenhouse gases absorbing long-wave radiation are increasing (Table 2.1), it is not certain whether climate has been affected. The natural structure (temperature and pressure) of the earth's atmosphere is shown by Fig. 2.7.[9] Divisions of troposphere, stratosphere, mesosphere, and thermosphere are dependent on temperature variations. Figure 2.8 is a schematic of the energy budget for the earth and its atmosphere.[10] Of the incoming short-wave solar radiation, only about 51 % eventually strikes the earth and is absorbed. Twenty-six per cent of the incoming solar radiation is reflected by clouds, dust and haze.

Once radiant energy strikes the earth and gets absorbed, warming occurs and energy is emitted back to the atmosphere according to the Stefan-Boltzmann law of blackbody radiation. 70% of all short-wave solar energy that is received by the earth's atmosphere is radiated back in the shape of long-wave radiation. But water vapour, clouds, CO_2, and other greenhouse gases absorb back-radiation and cause the "greenhouse" effect. The vast majority (about 98%) of the greenhouse effect is natural, caused by water vapour, preindustrial CO_2, and clouds. Without these gases, the earth would be so cold as to be uninhabitable, 33 °C cooler than what it is now. The annual global mean surface temperature of the earth is 15°C, and the global temperature in the absence of natural greenhouse gases would be 18°C. The "greenhouse effect" is natural and it is beneficial to life on earth.[10] Concern arises because of the increase of anthropogenic greenhouse gases including excess, CO_2, CH_4, CFCs, and N_2O (Table 2.1). They are rising at a rapid rate, and they have the potential to change climate if left unchecked. Molecules with more than two atoms absorb long-wave radiation, and when they do, they increase their vibrational and rotational energies. There is a "window" in the absorption wavelength spectrum of the atmosphere that is particularly important to the planetary radiation budget, 8-20-μ.m wavelength, where H_2O, CO_2, O_3, N_2O, CH_4, $CFCl_3$, and CF_2Cl_2 are efficient absorbers. The relative effectiveness of each of the gases is not equal. Table 2.1 shows that

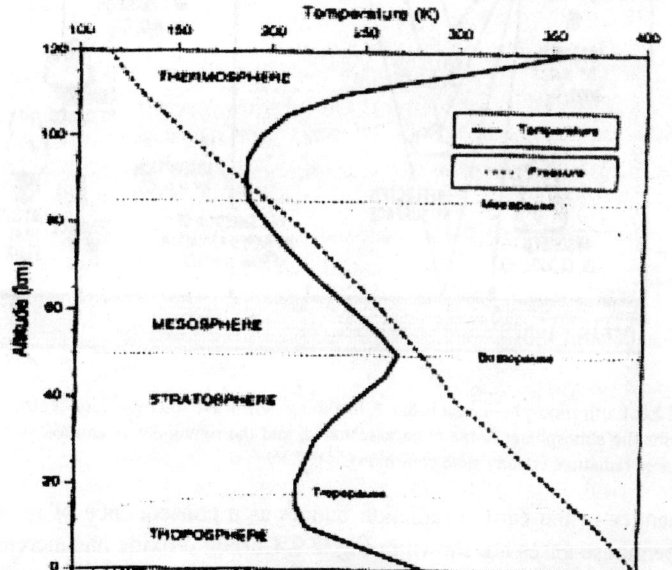

Pressure (mbar)

Fig. 2.7. Typical vertical themal and pressure structure of earth's atmosphere. From the U.S. Standard Atmosphere[9]

$CFCl_3$ (CFC-11) and CF_2C1_2 (CFC-12) are 12,000 and 15,000 times more effective, rcspectively, at absorbing long-wave radiation in comparison to carbon dioxide on a molar basis.

Projections Concerning Climate

Information on greenhouse gases can be included in a model for planetary heat, mass, and momentum transfer. Global models of coupled atmospheric, terrestrial, and ocean processes have been summarized by the Intergovernmental Panel on Climate Change (IPCC).[11,12]

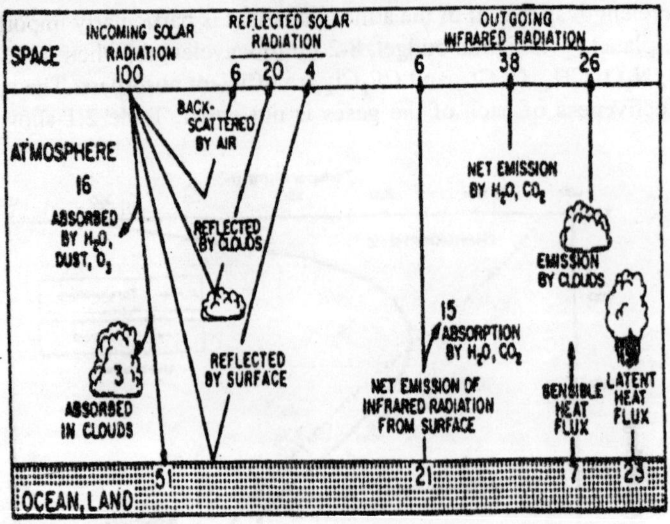

Fig. 2.8. Earth atmospheric heat balance. Incoming short wave solar radiation is absorbed and warms the atmosphere. Some is back-scattered, and the remainder is emitted as outgoing infrared radiation. (steady state condition).[13]

Changes in the earth's radiation budget as a consequence of increasing greenhouse gases are shown in Fig. 2.9. Carbon dioxide has increased 27 per cent from 280 ppm in 1765 to 355 ppm in 1990. A total change of 2.5 watts m^2 is attributed to anthropogenic greenhouse gases. To put it into perspective, a standard Christmas tree light bulb puts out ~4 watts of energy, so if there was one additional light bulb of this kind shining continually on every square meter of the earth's surface, it would cause a climate forcing of 4 W m^2. Nevertheless, the climate forcing is small relative to the total input of energy from the sun (the solar irradiance or solar constant) of 1372 W m^{2}.[10] The solar constant is not constant—it changes with sunspot activities and other factors (±0.1%)—and it may have increased a little in recent time (Fig. 2.9). Also, humans have put more sulphur dioxide into the atmosphere (from coal combustion), which causes the formation of sulphate aerosols and brighter clouds (albedo increases) that causes "global cooling" (Fig. 2.9).[11,12] This cooling effect is on the same order of magnitude, but somewhat less than the estimated warming effect due to greenhouse gases.

There is considerable uncertainty in all of these effects. They are estimated by use of global dynamic models, General Circulation Models or GCMs. One of the "feedback effects" of greenhouse gases in GCMs in the potential for a slight surface warming to be amplified by clouds and water vapour. As the earth's surface becomes warmer, evaporation rises. As evaporation increases, water vapour increases and clouds are formed, which are potent greenhouse gases. This climate feedback can multiply the effect of CO_2 by four times in GCMs. We do not know how many new clouds would form or where they would be located in the atmosphere. Thus, it is not easy to parameterize the models to determine the exact feedback effect. For now, one can only parameterize models in

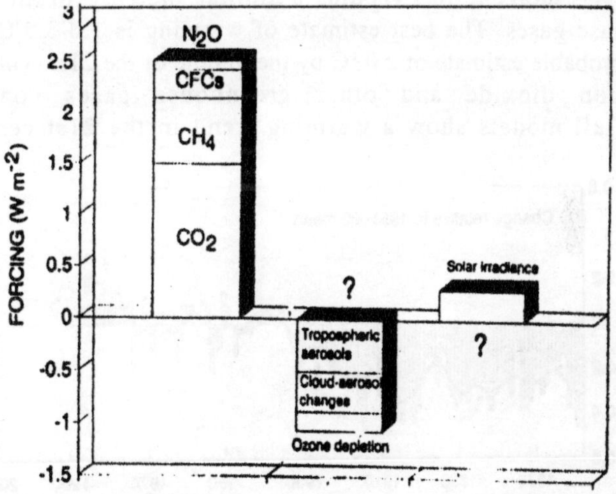

Fig. 2.9. Changes in contributions (in Wm^2) to global warming of various gases and processes between 1765 and 1990 (IPCC). [11, 12]

logical ways and compare the results of future scenarios and simulations from different models. At issue is the extent of warming, not the presence of warming. The relative degree of warming will be strongly affected by cloud and water vapour feedback mechanisms. We are currently in a relatively warm climate pattern (Fig. 11.10).[11, 12] The global average surface temperature of the earth is ~0.5°C warmer that the earliest period of record, 1860.

But this temperature change is still within the interannual variability of temperature (± 0.7°C) owing to large-scale circulation patterns (El Nino Southern Oscillation events, etc.) that we do not fully understand. Seven out of eight of the warmest years on record have occurred since 1980 (1980-1995) in a 130-year period. The year 1995 was the warmest on record and 1990 was the second warmest year. The year 1992 and 1993 were relatively cool as SO_2 and ash particles were blown high into the atmosphere (> 35, 000 ft) by the eruption of Mt. Pinatubo volcano.

Potential Global Warming

General circulation models are driven by an assumed 1% yr^{-1} increase in CO_2 concentrations. This is done to mimic the ~0.5% yr^{-1} increase in CO_2 plus a similar increase in all other greenhouse gases. The best estimate of warming is 1.0-3.5°C with a most probable estimate of 2.0 °C by the middle of the 21st century.[12] If carbon dioxide and other greenhouse gases continue to rise, all models show a warming trend in the 21st century.

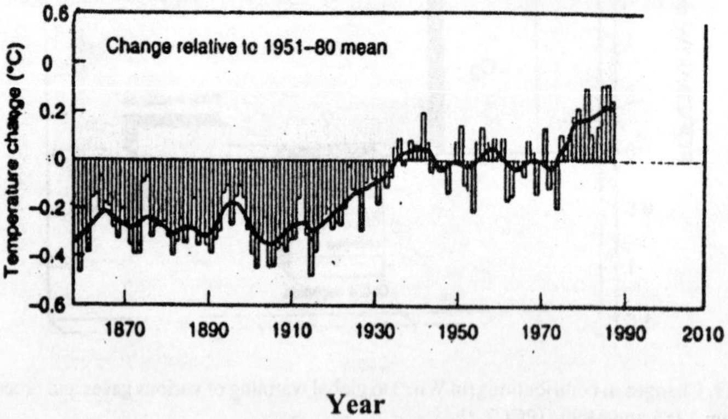

Fig. 2.10. Annual deviation of the global mean (land and sea) temperature change over the past century compared the average for 1951-1980. The curve reveals the results of a smoothing filter applied to the annual values.[11]

Global average surface air temperatures are currently about 0.5 °C higher than average temperatures of the 19th century. However, this change cannot as yet be unambiguously attributed to an increased concentration of greenhouse gases. GCMs have hind-casted a larger change during the past 130 years than has been observed, and this is perhaps owing to the cooling effects of anthropogenic aerosols.[13] GCMs predict global precipitation to increase in the 21st century under a scenario of one per cent yr^{-1} increasing greenhouse gases, but the geographic distribution is uncertain.

The global scale of GCMs does not lend itself very well to mesoscale (regional) predictions, and the different models differ on the locations where precipitation will change the most.[13] Northern hemisphere sea-ice will be reduced by warming in the 21st century according to GCMs. The models suggest polar amplification of global warming, and Arctic land areas will come across winter time warming. Mean sea level is projected to rise at an increasing rate in the 21st century, at first due to thermal expansion of the ocean as its surface warms, and then owing to the melting of polar ice and the breaking off and melting of the Ross ice shelf in Antarctica.

The sea level has risen 3.9 ± 0.8 mm yr^{-1} in 1993 and 1994.[14] Most models estimate the rate of sea level increase as 15-95 cm by the year 2100.[12] With predictions of such significance for humans everywhere, we might ask ourselves how these models are formulated and how great is their uncertainty.

General Circulation Models (GCMs)

More than 30 General Circulation Models (GCMs) are in use today for analyzing climate change, and five of the original models were evaluated by the IPCC (1990).[11] These include models such as the Geophysical Fluids Dynamics Laboratory (GFDL) model of the National Oceanic and Atmospheric Administration,[15] the Goddard Institute for Space Studies (GISS) model of the National Atmospheric and Space Administration,[16] the National Center for Atmospheric Research (NCAR) model,[17] the Oregon State University (OSU) model,[18] and the United Kingdom Meteorological Office (UKMO) model.[19] The models are run in a steady-state mode with a doubling of CO_2 and also in a transient mode in which the concentration of CO_2 is increased in a time-variable fashion (~1% per year). Some of the GCMs are directly coupled to the oceans with a full, dynamical treatment of ocean mixing and dynamics, but in early simulations the oceans were just a constant temperature heat sink for atmospheric warming. Each model divides the atmosphere into various layers and the earth into a grid along the lines of latitude and longitude. The grid cells are as large as 4.5 degrees latitude × 7.5 degrees longitude (450×750 km^2) or as small as 1° × 3°. Mesoscale (regional) models are sometimes embedded within the GCM for smaller scale model testing with resolutions as fine as 10×10 km^2 to 50×50 km^2. Atmospheric layers often number between 10 and 30, and they rise at least 30 km into the stratosphere. The time step in most GCMs is ~30 minutes and the number of equations is on the order of 150,000, so the computing power of a supercomputer is needed. A 100-year simulation of the NCAR ocean-coupled model requires 1000 processor hours on a Cray Y-MP supercomputer. However, coarse grids and uncoupled ocean models can be run on a workstation.

A detailed description of GCMs is beyond the scope of this text, and the reader is referred to the book *Climate System Modeling* by K.E. Trenberth.[20] GCMs depend on first principles to simulate atmospheric and oceanic large-scale circulation and heat content. This amounts to the principle of continuity for heat, momentum, and mass transfer. The basic equations are reached at following Newton's laws: the second law of motion (momentum transport); conservation of mass; conservation of energy (the first law of thermodynamics); an equation of state concerning pressure, density, and temperature; and an equation of state that relates temperature, density, and salinity of the oceans.[21]

The change in heat content of a layer of atmosphere is equal to the change in internal energy and the pessure-volume work that it does to the surrroundings (the first law of thermodynamics for an ideal gas in a closed system).

$$dq = du + dw = du + P\,dV \qquad \text{. . . (i)}$$

where dq is the change in heat, du is the change in internal energy, dw is the change in work, P is the pressure, and dV is the change in volume of the parcel of air. The change in internal energy associate with the change in enthalpy minus the work performed.

$$dq = (dh - P\,dV - V\,dP) + P\,dV \qquad \text{. . . (ii)}$$

$$dq = dh - V\,dP \qquad \text{. . . (iii)}$$

$$dq = C_p\,dT - 1/\rho\,dP \qquad \text{. . . (iv)}$$

Here C_p is the heat capacity of the volume of air at constant pressure, dT is the change in absolute temperature, ρ is the density of the air, and dP is the change in pressure. Equation (iv) depicts the interplay between pressure, density, and temperature for a parcel of air. As the parcel of air rises in temperature or falls in pressure at a constant density, the heat content (dq) increases. Changes in pressure cause forces to be created that move the mass of air:

$$\Delta F = (\partial P/\partial x)\ dx\ dy\ dz \qquad \ldots \text{(v)}$$

where $\partial P/\partial x$ is the pressure gradient in the longitudinal dimension and dx, dy, dz are the incremental distances in three- dimensions. Equation (V) causes the momentum equation (due to the net pressure gradient force). It allows atmospheric circulation as air moves from areas of high pressure to areas of low pressure. Pressure gradients are developed by differential heating and cooling.

$$\Delta M_o = \{(\partial P/\partial x)\ dx\ dy\ dz\}\ \Delta t \qquad \ldots \text{(vi)}$$

$$\Delta M_o = m\ \Delta v \qquad \ldots \text{(vii)}$$

where ΔM_0 is the change in momentum of the parcel of air, Δv is the change in velocity, and Δt is the time increment. In the vertical dimension, the air is approximately adiabatic as it expands into the upper atmosphere ($dq = 0$). We can rewrite equation (iv) as

$$C_P\ dT = 1/\rho\ dP \qquad \ldots \text{(viii)}$$

Taking the derivative in the vertical direction, and substituting the hydrostatic pressure equation $dP = -\rho g\ dz$ into equation (viii), we get

$$(-dT/dz)_{\text{adia}} = g/C_p \qquad \ldots \text{(ix)}$$

where g is the gravitational constant. If the changes in g and C_p are supposed to be negligible over small vertical elevations, then the change in temperature with elevation under adiabatic conditions is a constant, independent of elevation! The following units apply in the SI system for dry air at 25 °C:

$$C_p = 1.005 \text{ kJ kg}^{-1}\ {}^{\circ}\text{C}^{-1}$$

$$g = 9.806 \text{ m s}^{-2}$$

Equation (ix) is known as the dry adiabatic lapse rate, and it is equal to – 9.8 °C km^{-1}. Air cools as it increases about 10 °C per km; this is especially applicable in the troposphere, the lower atmosphere.

However, equation (ix) does not include the effect of water vapour condensation as the parcel of air cools (latent heat). The actual standard temperature profile for air as it rises in the troposphere is –6.6 °C km^{-1} owing to water vapour condensation. Equations (i)–(ix) are simplifications of the numerical calculations in a GCM that generate atmospheric circulation and temperature change, but they do illustrate the principles. Apart from heat and momentum transfer, we have mass transfer, including effects of carbon dioxide sorption by oceans and the biosphere. In the next section, we will examine the biogeochemistry of carbon cycling.

The Carbon Box Model

Equations of the Model

As an Illustration of a global biogeochemical model, a Simple Global Carbon Model (SGCM) for carbon flows through the ocean, atmosphere, and terrestrial biosphere is shown in this section. A box model is a compartmentalized approach to solution of mass balance transport equations. Bulk dispersion and flows between boxes allow simplification of the problem and result in a numerical solution of the sets of ordinary differential equations instead of partial differential equations. A schematic of a global carbon box model is presented in Fig. 2.11, together with carbon reservoirs (numbers inside boxes) and fluxes (numbers by arrows) based on reported values.[22] Units are Gt C (gigatons carbon, 1×10^{15} g C) in reservoirs and Gt C per year in fluxes. It is composed of three large carbon pools that are the atmosphere, the terrestrial biosphere, and the ocean.

The terrestrial biosphere is compartmentalized into the land biota, soil, and detritus. The ocean is compartmentalized into the warm ocean surface water, the cold ocean surface water, the intermediate and deep waters, and two ocean biota compartments in both warm and cold surface waters. Therefore, the box model includes eight compartments and 19 fluxes, as shown in Fig. 2.11 Table 2.2 is the physical description of the eight compartments. The volume of atmosphere was calculated with the total carbon mass divided by the carbon concentration of the atmosphere, and surface areas of the land and the ocean were taken from *Medallion World Atlas*.[23] The depth of ocean surface water is generally taken to be 75-100 m, and the total average ocean depth ~3800 m.[22] Most processes are formulated with first-order kinetics except for CO_2 fertilization of terrestrial biota, which follow a Michaelis-Menton formulation.

Ninety-five percent of the land biota compartment is composed of C_3 plants, and the remainder consists of C_4 plants.[24] C_3 plants have various photosynthetic mechanisms such that photosynthesis increases with increases of atmospheric CO_2 concentration, while that of C_4 plants, mainly tropical grasses, does not rise at high CO_2 concentrations.[25] Here we suppose that all plants are C_3. Plants fix CO_2 from the atmosphere and store it as organic carbon (photosynthesis). They also release organic carbon in the form of CO_2 (respiration). Additionally organic carbon in the stems, leaves, and roots is incorporated into the soil compartment seasonally and as plants die (litterfall). The CO_2 fertilization effect is supposed to follow a Michaelis-Menton kinetic, expression similar to the hyperbolic relationship used by Raich et al.[26], and temperature feedback follows a Q_{10}-type exponential

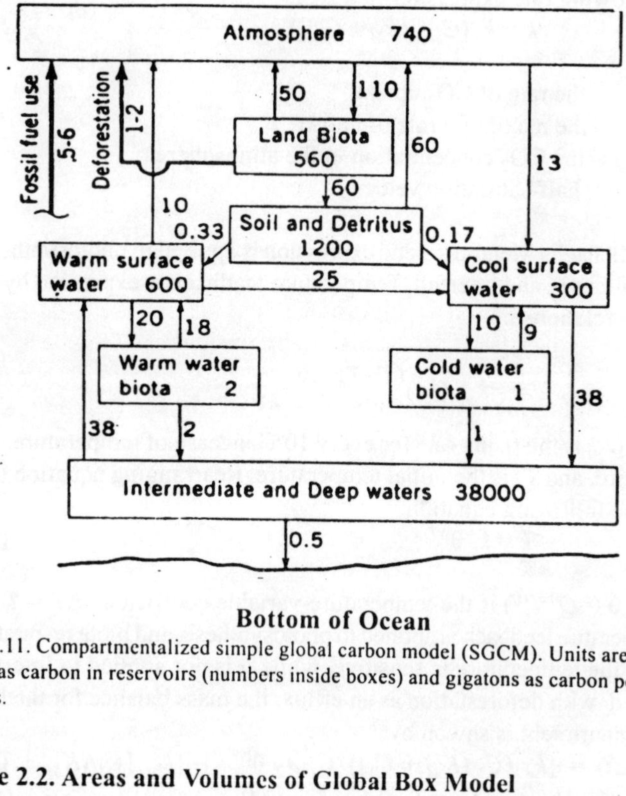

Fig. 2.11. Compartmentalized simple global carbon model (SGCM). Units are gigatons (GT) as carbon in reservoirs (numbers inside boxes) and gigatons as carbon per year in fluxes.

Table 2.2. Areas and Volumes of Global Box Model

Description	*Size*
Volume of atmosphere (V_1)	3.99×10^{18} m^3
Area of land biota (A_2)	1.33×10^{14} m^2
Volume of soil and detritus (V_3)	6.65×10^{14} m^3
Depth of ocean surface water	100 m
Depth of average ocean	3800 m
Area of warm ocean surface water (A_4)	2.42×10^{14} m^2
Volume of warm ocean surface water (V_4)	2.42×10^{16} m^3
Area of cold ocean surface (A_6)	1.21×10^{14} m^2

Volume of cold ocean surface water (V_6)	1.21×10^{16} m^3
Area of intermediate and deep waters (A_8)	3.63×10^{14} m^2
Volume of intermediate and deep waters (V_8)	1.318×10^{18} m^3

function. Thus, the CO_2 fertilization effect on the land biota is included in the following rate expression:

$$k = k_o (C_{atm} / k_M + C_{atm}) \quad \ldots (x)$$

where k = the rate of CO_2 uptake
k_o = the maximum rate of uptake
C_{atm} = the CO_2 concentration in the atmosphere
K_M = half-saturation velocity

Similar Michaelis Menton kinetic expression is applied to photosynthesis, biota respiration, and litterfall. Temperature feedback is expressed by the following relationship

$$k = k_o (Q_{10})^{(T-T_o)/10} \quad \ldots (xi)$$

in which Q_{10} is the rising rate for every 10°C incease of temperature, T is temperature, and T_o is the initial temperature. Rearranging equation (xi), we get the following equation:

$$k = k_o \, \theta^{\Delta T} \quad \ldots (xii)$$

in which θ $(=Q^{0.1/10})$ is the temperature-variable coefficient, $\Delta T = T - T_0$. The temperatue feedback is applied to photosynthesis and biota respiration to which the temperature is sensitive, while it is not applied to litterfall. Combined with deforestation as an efflux, the mass balance for the land biota compartment is shwon by[27]

$$A_2 (dC_2/dt) = \{k_p \{C_1/(K_M + C_1)\} C_2 A_2 \theta^{\Delta T/P}\} - \{k_{br} \{C_1/(K_M + C_1)\} C_2 A_2 \theta^{\Delta T/br}\} - [k_e \{C_1/(K_M + C_1)\} C_2 A_2] - D(t) \quad \ldots (xiii)$$

where A_2 = land surface area, L^2
C_1 = carbon concentration in the atmosphere, M L^{-3} (converted from ppm)
C_2 = carbon concentration in land biota, ML^{-2}
K_M = half-saturation velocity, ML^{-3}
k_p = maximum photosynthesis rate constant, T^{-1}

k_{br} = maximum land biota respiation rate constant, T^{-1}
k_e = maximum litterfall rate constant, T^{-1}
θ_p = temperature-variable coefficient of photosynthesis, dimensionless
θ_{br} = temperature-variable coefficient of land biota respiration, dimensionless
ΔT = temperature change from steady-state (preindustrial time) temperature, °C
$D(t)$ = deforestation, MT^{-1}

Most of the organic carbon exists in the upper layer of the land surface that is assumed to be 5-m depth global average. Organic carbon get smixed with the soil by litterfall, where it is decomposed by soil microbes and emitted to the atmosphere in the form of CO_2 (soil respiration). Owing to a strong influence of temperature on microbial activity, equation (12) is applied to soil respiration to account for the effect of temperature. Also, a small amount of carbon is washed out and transported to the ocean surface water (runoff). During this process, organic carbon is assumed to be entirely oxidized to inorganic carbon and contributes to the increase of total inorganic carbon of the ocean surface water. A mass balance of the soil compartment is given below.[27]

$$V_3\ (dC_3/dt) = [k_e\ \{C_1/(K_M + C_1)\}\ C_2\ A_2] - \{k_{sr}\ C_3\ V_3\ \theta^{\Delta t/sr}\} - \{k_w\ C_3\ V_3\} \qquad \ldots \text{(xiv)}$$

where, V_3 = volume of the soil compartment, L^{-3}
C_3 = carbon concentration of the soil compartment, ML^{-3}
k_{sr} = soil respiration rate constant, T^{-1}
k_w = runoff rate constant, T^{-1}
θ_{sr} = temperature-variable coefficient of soil respiration, dimensionless.

Illustrated in Fig. 2.1, is the ocean is composed of three compartments, the warm ocean surrface water, the cold ocean surface water, and the intermediate and deep waters. Carbon is internally cycled by way of ocean circulation.[28] Denser water is formed due to lower temperature and increased salinity in the cold surface water compartment. It is basically composed of water from two regions, Antarctic cold water and water near Greenland, and it sinks to the intermediate and deep water compartment (cold surface water sinking); whereas a part of the intermediate and deep water is upwelling to the warm surface water compartment, basically in the equatorial area (deep water upwelling). In order to balance the water mass, water is transported from the warm surface water compartment to the cold surface water compartment (surface water advection). In addition to ocean circulation, ocean biota, composed mainly of organic carbon, is also involved in the carbon cycle through biological, chemical, and physical processes. Biota photosynthesize and incorporate dissolved CO_2 and nutrients such as nitrogen and phosphorus (ocean biota primary production). It is often believed that primary production is not rate limited by dissolved CO_2 but by nutrients. Ocean primary production follows first-order kinetics and is linear with respect to the dissolved CO_2 concentration of the surface water. Nearly, ninety per cent of primary production is remineralized to dissolved CO_2 within the surface water (ocean biota respiration), with the remaining 10 per cent sinking to the intermediate and deep waters, where most of it is remineralized, and a small amount is buried into the ocean bottom as organic carbon (organic carbon burial).

Even though the activity of ocean biota strongly controls alkalinity and CO_2 partial pressure in the ocean, SGCM does not include diurnal and seasonal oscillations as the model deals with an annually averaged carbon cycle. Organic carbon is also transported into the ocean surface water from the soil compartment (runoff). Two-thirds of it is supposed to be transported into the warm ocean surface water and one-third of it into the cold ocean surface water. Carbon in the form of CO_2 is exchanged between the atmosphere and the ocean surface waters. The driving force of CO_2 gas exchange is the difference of CO_2 partial pressure between the atmosphere and the ocean surface water. Carbon dioxide partial pressure in the ocean is a function of alkalinity, temperature, salinity, and total inorganic carbon and is computed with the method proposed by Peng et al. [29] A mass balance of carbon of each compartment is given below.

For the warm ocean surface water,

$$V_4\,(dC_4/dt) = -\{k_o\,S_{wo}\,(P_{wo} - P_{atm})\,A_4\} - \{k_{pwo}\,C_4\,V_5\} + \{k_{rwo}\,C_5\,V_5\} + \{k_{up}\,C_8\,A_4\} - \{Q_{46}\,C_4\} + \{{}^{2/3}\,k_w\,C_3\,V_3\} \quad \ldots(xv)$$

where, V_4 = volume of warm ocean surface water, L^3

V_5 = volume of warm ocean biota, L^3

C_4 = carbon concentration of warm ocean surface water, ML^{-3}

k_o = gas transfer velocity, LT^{-1}

S_{wo} = solubility of warm ocean surface water, $ML^{-3}\,ppm^{-1}$

P_{wo} = CO_2 partial pressure of warm ocean surface water, ppm
P_{atm} = CO_2 partial pressure of the atmosphere, ppm
k_{pwo} = warm ocean biota primary production rate constant, T^{-1}
k_{pwo} = warm ocean biota respiration rate constant, T^{-1}
C_5 = carbon concentration of warm ocean biota, ML^{-3}
k_{up} = intermediate and deep waters upwelling velocity, LT^{-1}
C_8 = carbon concentration of intermediate and deep waters, ML^{-3}
A_4 = area of warm ocean surface water, L^2
Q_{46} = advection between surface waters, $L^3\ T^{-1}$

For the cold ocean surface water,

$$V_6\,(dC_6/dt) = \{k_t\, S_{co}\,(P_{atm} - P_{co})\, A_6\} - \{k_{pco}\, C_6\, V_7\} + \{k_{nco}\, C_7\, V_7) - \{k_{dc}\, C_6\, A_6\} + \{Q_6\, C_4\} + \{1\, k_w\, C_3\, V_3\} \quad \ldots \text{(xvi)}$$

where V_6 =volume of cold ocean surface water, L^{-3}
V_7 = volume of cold ocean biota, L^3
C_6 = carbon concentration of cold ocean surface water, ML^{-3}
S_{co} = solubility of cold ocean surface water, ML^{-3}/ppm
P_{co} = CO_2 partial pressure of cold ocean surface water, ppm
k_{pco} = cold ocean biota primary production rate constant, T^{-1}
k_{nco} = cold ocean biota respiration rate constant, T^{-1}
C_7 = carbon concentration of cold ocean biota, ML^{-3}
k_{dc} = cold ocean surface water sinking velocity, LT^{-1}
A_6 = area of cold ocean surface water, L_2

For the warm ocean biota,

$$V_5\,(dC_5/dt) = \{k_{pwo}\, C_4\, V_5\} - \{k_{rwo}\, C_5\, V_5\} - \{k_{swo}\, C_5\, A_4\} \ldots \text{(xvii)}$$

where, k_{swo} = warm ocean biota sinking rate constant, LT^{-1}

For the cold ocean biota,

$$V_7\,(dC_7/dt) = \{k_{pco}\, C_6\, V_7\} - \{k_{rco}\, C_7\, V_7\} - \{k_{sco}\, C_7\, A_6\} \ldots \text{(xviii)}$$

where, k_{sco} = cold ocean biota sinking rate constant, LT^{-1}

For the intermediate and deep waters,

$$V_8\,(dC_8/dt) = \{k_{dc}\,C_6\,A_6\} - \{k_{up}\,C_8\,A_4\} + \{k_{swo}\,C_5\,A_4\} + \{k_{sco}\,C_7\,A_6\} - \{k_{sed}\,C_8\,A_8\} \quad \ldots \text{(xix)}$$

where, V_8 = volume of intermediate and deep water, L^3
A_8 = area of intermediate and deep waters, L^2
k_{sed} = organic carbon burial rate constant, T^1

The carbon mass fluxes to and from the atmosphere include land biota photosynthsis, land biota respiration, soil respiration, and CO_2 gas exchange between the atmosphere and the ocean surface water. Coupled with anthropogenic emissions including fossil fuel combustion and deforestation as inputs (forcing functions in this model), a mass balance for the atmosphere compartment is

$$V_1\,(dC_1/dt) = F(t) + D\,(t) - \{k_p\,(C_1/K_M) + C_1\,C_2\,A_2\,\theta_p{}^{\Delta r}\} + \{k_{br}\,(C_1/k_M + C_1)\,C_2\,A_2\,\theta_{br}{}^{\Delta r}\} + \{k_{sr}\,C_3\,V_3\,\theta_{sr}{}^{\Delta T}\} + \{k_o\,S_{wo}\,(P_{wo} - P_{atm})\,A_4\} - \{k_0\,S_{co}\,(P_{atm} - P_{co})\,A_6\} \quad \ldots \text{(xx)}$$

where, V_1 = volume of the atmosphere, L^3
$F(t)$ = fossil fuel combustion, MT^{-1}

The eight mass balance equations from (xiii) to (xx) form a set of ordinary differential equations that were solved numerically with the time step of 1 day following a fourth-order Runge-Kutta method.[30]

Calibration of Model

SGCM was calibrated with the help of a 32-year record (1958-1989) of atmospheric CO_2 concentrations measured at Mauna Loa (Hawaii, United States),[3] which was supposed to represent the global average CO_2 concentration for the purpose of this study (it is slightly higher than the true global average. An oceanic sink constraint was set as 0.6-2.6 Gt C yr^{-1} in the 1980s. On the basis of literature values.[12,31] Yearly CO_2 emissions from fossil fuel combustion was used as input data.[3] The other input, CO_2 emissions from deforestation, was estimated at 0.4-2.6 Gt C in 1980.[32,33] Since it included a wide range of uncertainty, however, it was considered to be an adjustable parameter. For the temperature input the annual mean global surface air temperature (Fig. 2.12) was taken from observed data reported by Hansen et al.[34]

The temperature change ΔT that appears in temperature-related flux terms is a difference between the temperature at time t and the preindustrial temperature that was assumed to be –0.4 °C based on historical data.[35] Calibrated parameter values including deforestation are shown in Table 2.3. Most rate constants were derived from the carbon reservoirs and fluxes (Fig. 2.11) and adjusted. A half-saturation constant k_M of 400 ppm for C_3 plants was used.[36] Temperature-variable coefficients θ_p, θ_{br}, and θ_{sr} were arrived at following model calibrations, and their values were 1.032, 1.066, and 1.069, respectively. The conversion of those to Q_{10} results in 1.37 for photosynthesis, 1.89 for biota respiration, and 1.95 for soil respiration. These are in accordance with reported values in the literature, which range from 1.03 to 2.0 for photosynthesis,[37,38] 1.4 to 3.0 for biota respiration,[38-42] and 0.77 to 3.3 for soil respiration[38,43,47] (barring one high value of 4.3).[48] The model calibrated value[49] for deforestation was 1.21 Gt C yr^{-1} and that is within the range of 0.4-2.6 Gt C yr^{-1} reported by Moore and Bolin and by Houghton et al.[22,32] and 1.6 ± 1.0 Gt C yr^{-1} by IPCC.[11] Gas transfer velocity k_t was adopted from the study using natural and bomb-produced ^{14}C methods.[50] Ocean CO_2 partial pressures (P_{wo} and P_{co}) as well as solubilities S_{wo} and S_{co} were calculated with the method proposed by Peng. et al.[20] In order to compute them, total alkalinities (TA_{wo} and TA_{co}), salinities

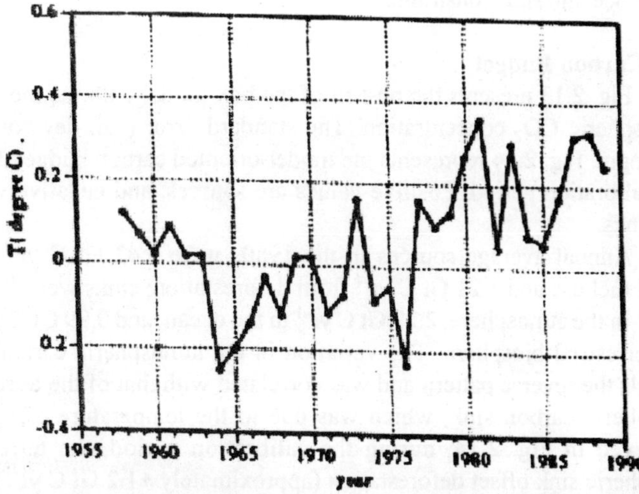

Fig. 2.12. Global annual mean surface air temperature relative to mean temperature, 1951-1980. (Data from Hansen et al.[14])

Table 2.3 Parameter Values Including Deforestation

Parameter	Value	Parameter	Value
$D(t)$	1.21 Gt C yr^{-1}	k_{nco}	9.0 yr^{-1}
k_p	0.44286 yr^{-1}	k_{swo}	100 m yr^{-1}
k_{br}	0.19232 yr^{-1}	k_{sco}	100 m yr^{-1}
k_e	0.24911 yr^{-1}	k_{sed}	0.051 m yr^{-1}
k_{sr}	0.05146 yr^{-1}	θ_p	1.032
K_w	0.00042 yr^{-1}	θ_{br}	1.066
k_M	400 ppm	θ_{sr}	1.069
k_t	1752 m yr^{-1}	T_{wo}	25 °C
k_{up}	5.55856 m yr^{-1}	T_{co}	8 °C
k_{dc}	12.4502 m yr^{-1}	SA_{wo}	35.51%
Q_{46}	1.046 x 10^{16} m^3 yr^{-1}	SA_{co}	34.17%
k_{pwo}	0.03448 yr^{-1}	TA_{wo}	2272 µmol kg^{-1}
k_{rwo}	9.0 yr^{-1}	TA_{co}	2237 µmol kg^{-1}
k_{pco}	0.03448 yr^{-1}		

(SA_{wo} and SA_{co}), and surface water temperatures (T_{wo} and T_{co}) that were assumed constant were on the basis of the Geochemical Ocean Sections Study data[51] but were slightly adjusted (within ±5%) to satisfy the needs of the oceanic sink constraint.

The Carbon Budget

Fig. 2.13 presents the best fit of the box model with the measured atmospheric CO_2 concentration. The standard error (std. dev./$\sqrt{n}$) was 0.08 ppm. Fig. 2.14 represents the model-oriented carbon budget during the calibration period. Positive values are sources, and negative values are sinks.

Annual average sources in the 1980s were 5.42 Gt C yr^{-1} from fossil fuel use and 1.21 Gt C yr^{-1} from deforestation; sinks were 3.35 Gt C yr^{-1} in the atmosphere, 2.29 Gt C yr^{-1} in the ocean, and 0.99 Gt C yr^{-1} in the terrestrial biosphere. The variation in the atmospheric carbon sink reveals the reverse pattern and was correlated with that of the terrestrial biospheric carbon sink, which was due to the temperature effect. As observed in Fig. 2.14, during the calibration period, the terrestrial biospheric sink offset deforestation (approximately ±1.2 Gt C yr^{-1}). The atmospheric sink and the oceanic sink increased with an increase of CO_2

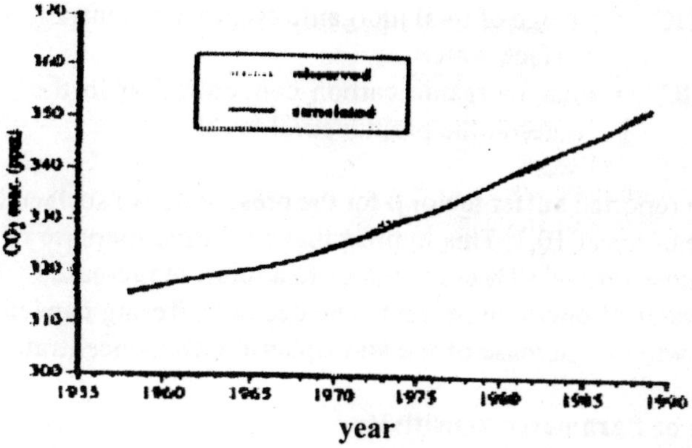

Fig. 2.13. Best fit of atmospheric CO_2 concentration, model calibration, 1957-1989.

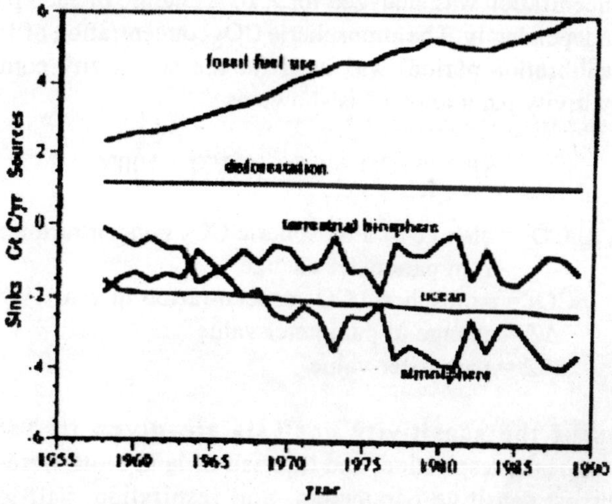

Fig. 2.14. Model results of carbon budget for sources and sinks gigatons of carbon per year.[46]

emissions from fossil fuel use. However, the atmosphere accumulated carbon faster than the ocean. This is because of the so-called "buffering capacity" of the ocean. The buffer factor (β) is written as

$$\beta = \Delta pCO_2/pCO_2/\Delta TIC/TIC \quad \ldots \text{(xxi)}$$

where, ΔpCO_2 = change of atmospheric CO_2 concentration

pCO_2 = atmospheric CO_2 concentration at preindustrial level

ΔTIC = change of total inorganic carbon concentration in the surface water

TIC = total inorganic carbon concentration in the surface water at the preindustrial level

The reported buffer factor β for the present ocean surface waters are of the order of 10.[52] This implies that a relative increase of pCO_2 in the atmosphere of 10% corresponds to a relative increase of TIC in surface water of only one percent. The ocean buffering capacity will decrease with an increase of the atmospheric CO_2 concentration.

Analysis of Parameter Sensitivity

A sensitivity analysis was carried out to understand where more research is needed (priority setting). Sensitivity of the atmospheric CO_2 concentration was analyzed for ± 10% change of each parameter value, independently. The atmospheric CO_2 concentration of 1989 (end of the calibration period) was used for the sensitivity comparison. The sensitivity parameter SP is shown as

$$SP = (\Delta pCO_2/pCO_2)/|\Delta Z/Z| \times 100\% \qquad \text{... (xxii)}$$

Where, ΔpCO_2 = change of atmospheric CO_2 concentration resulting from parameter change

pCO_2 = atmospheric CO_2 concentration in year 1989

ΔZ = change of parameter value

Z = parameter value

Results of the sensitivity analysis are given in Table 2.4. Photosynthesis, respiration, and litterfall of land biota were found to be the most sensitive parameters. Soil respiration, half-saturation velocity, and deep water upwelling and cold surface water sinking in the ocean were the next group. Others were not sensitive, as shown by $|SP| \leq 10\%$. Temperature-variable coefficients θ_{pr}, θ_{br}, and θ_{sr} were not included in the sensitivity analysis due to the difficulty of direct comparison with other parameters, but results are quite sensitive to these coefficients. Sensitivity parameter results show that terrestrial biospheric activities and carbon exchange processes between the surface water and the intermediate and deep waters are most important in controlling CO_2 concentration in the atmosphere.

Table 2.4 Sensitivity of CO_2 Concentration Due to a ± 10% Variation in Model Parameters

	Percent Change in CO_2 SP (%)			*Percent Change in CO_2 SP (%)*	
Parameter	*+ 10%*	*– 10%*	*Parameter*	*+ 10%*	*– 10%*
k_p	–516	+649	Q_{46}	–4	+5
k_{br}	+292	266	k_{pwo}	5	+5
k_e	+289	–275	k_{rwo}	+4	–5
k_{sr}	+67	–74	k_{pco}	–2	+2
k_M	+37	–46	k_{rco}	+2	–2
k_t	–2	+3	k_{swo}	–4	–4
k_{up}	+85	–99	k_{sco}	2	+2
k_{dc}	–86	+80	k_{sed}	0	0

Analysis of Model Scenario

The feedback temperature due to global warming by CO_2 was determined by model calibration before the scenario analysis. Since historical data brings out strong evidence of a linear relationship between global average surface temperature and the atmospheric CO_2 concentration,[53] the global temperature was assumed to be a linear function of the atmospheric CO_2 concentration. To approximate the feedback temperature, the global temperature at preindustrial CO_2 levels (here 280 ppm) was assumed to be –0.4 °C (relative temperature referred to in Fig. 2.12. Setting the feedback temperature as X °C ppm^{-1}, the temperature at a given atmospheric CO_2 concentration was expressed by relationship

$$\text{Temp}(t) = -0.4 + [pCO_2(t) - 280] \times X \quad \text{. . . (xxiii)}$$

in which Temp(t) is global temperature at time t and $pCO_2(t)$ is the atmospheric CO_2 concentration at time t. Test results are given in Fig. 2.15. The model with 0.01 °C ppm^{-1} of feedback temperature resulted in the best fit with the measured values (thick line). This is a reasonable result as a global average surface temperature rise of roughly 0.5-0.7 °C and an rise of 60 ppm CO_2 have been measured in the past. Scenario analysis with a selected feedback temperature (0.01 °C ppm^{-1})was performed for three CO_2 emission scenarios from fossil fuel use with a constant emission from deforestation (1.21 Gt C yr^{-1}). Case A is the 1.5% rise per year; case B, the constant emission; and case C, the recovery case, that is, fire decrease per year beginning in 1989. Figure depicts the resulting concentrations and masses of atmospheric CO_2, the land biota carbon reservoir and the soil carbon reservoir. The atmospheric CO_2

concentration doubled from preindustrial levels (280 ppm) in the year 2060 in case A; it increased but did not double within the mid-22nd century in case B; and it stabilized to 350 ppm in case C.

Land biota carbon decreased and then increased until a sudden drop occurred in case A because fertilization effects were altimately dominated by respiration effects. Concentrations of CO_2 slowly went down to a steady state in case B, but they continued to decrease in case C. Changes in the mass of carbon in land biota resulted due to the competition between allowed deforestation and land biota growth stimulated by CO_2 fertilization and temperature effects. The loss of land biota carbon mass in Fig. 2.16 (case C) is not owing to the decrease of net primary productivity NPP (photosynthesis minus respiration) but rather due to a constant rate of defroestation. Model results show that in case A, NPP increased by ~24% when the CO_2 concentration in the atmosphere was doubled. Even though an increased temperature was favourable to the biota growth, a relatively high temperature (+5.5°C and 900 ppm) resulted in a sudden drop, as shown in case A. This was so because the increased biota respiration (Q_{10} = 1.89) combined with increased litterfall exceeded the enhanced photosynthesis (Q_{10} = 1.37). The soil carbon reservoir role until a sudden drop occurred in case A; it maintained nearly constant value in case B; and decreased in case C. Change in the soil carbon reservoir occurred, mainly due to competition between carbon accumulation by litterfall that was influenced by a direct fertilization effect of CO_2, and carbon depletion by soil respiration influenced by a direct temperaure effect. High temperatures resulted in a sudden fall in the soil carbon reservoir similar to that of the land biota carbon reservoir Fig. 2.16. The high tempreature reduced the land biota rapidly and thereby decreased litterfall, and soil respiration was enhanced by high temperature, which accelerated the soil carbon depletion. Fig. 2.17 shows the scenarios of both ocean surface waters and the intermediate and deep waters. The carbon concentration time series in both surface waters showed a very similar pattern to that of the atmospheric CO_2 concentration.

The difference is that the rate of increase was slower in the surface waters than in the atmosphere; that is, the increase of buffer factor (β) occurred with the increase of the atmospheric CO_2 concentrations. Using equation (xxi) with an assumed steady-state concentration for the surface waters (1980 μmol kg^{-1} in the cold ocean surface water and 1955 μmol kg^{-1} in the warm ocean surface water) satisfied the buffer factor of

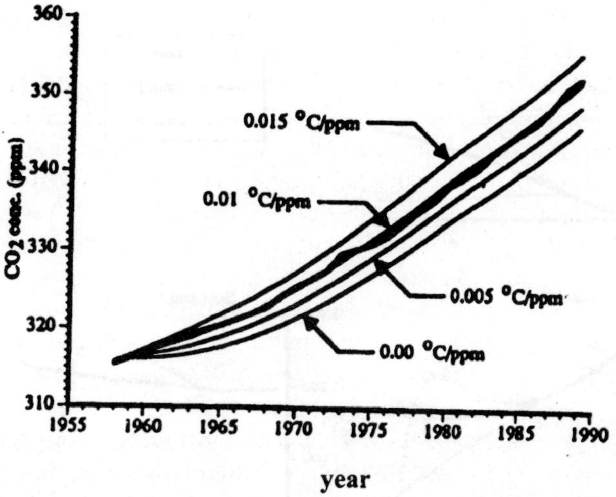

Fig. 2.15. Use of various temperature feedback parameters in model calibration to fit measured atmospheric CO_2 data.

10.0 in year 1980, but buffer factors of the warm and cold ocean surface waters increased to 16.4 and 13.9 in the year 2035 (CO_2 450 ppm), and 21.6 and 18.5 in the year 2070 (600 ppm), respectively. This causes a decreased capacity for oceans to uptake atmospheric carbon dioxide. The carbon concentration of the intermediate and deep waters increased for all three cases because of increased biota sinking to the intermediate and deep waters. Cold water sinking into intermediate and deep waters was a major flux of carbon.

Summary

Though it is a rather simple model in its spatial and temporal scale, it includes CO_2 fertilization and temperature effects for the terrestrial biosphere and inorganic chemistry that with ocean water circulation enables the calculation of time-variable oceanic carbon uptake. It shows that simple box mass balance models can yield realistic and rich dynamics of global biogeochemical cycles. Model-derived Q_{10} values for land biota photosynthesis (1.37), land biota respiration (1.89) and soil

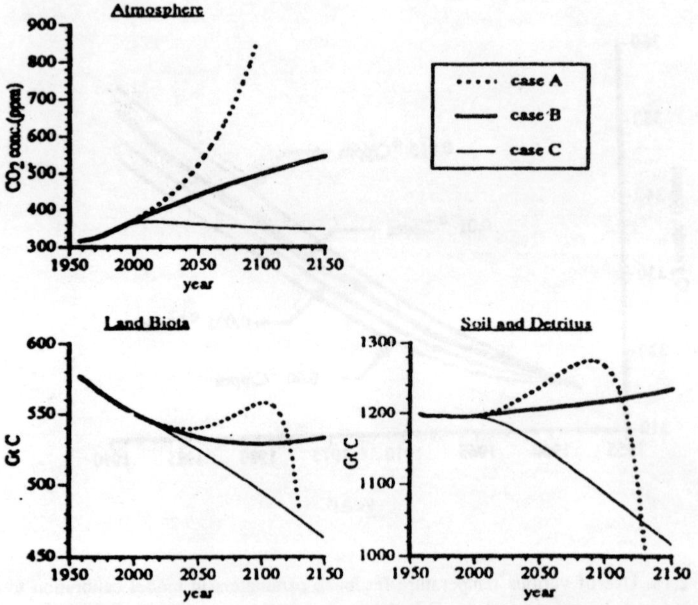

Fig 2.16. Scenarios of the atmospheric CO_2 concentration and the carbon reservoirs of terrestrial biosphere. Case A is the 1.5% increase per year, case B is the constant emission, and case C is the 5% decrease per year from year 1989.[10]

respiration (1.95) are in line with reported values. Using a model-derived feedback temperature of 0.01 °C ppm^{-1} a scenario analysis was conducted. Based on the model results, a CO_2 doubling from preindustrial level (280 ppm) will appear in the mid-21st century if CO_2 emissions from fossil fuel continue at the present increasing rate of 1.5% yr^{-1}, whereas it will not occur until the mid-22nd century if CO_2 emissions are held constant at the present level. The ocean buffering capacity to take up excess CO_2 will go down with an increase of atmospheric CO_2 concentrations. A climate feedback temperature of 0.01 °C ppm^{-1} is very sensitive to the terrestrial biospheric carbon reservoirs, suggesting an increase of land biota and a decrease of soil carbon due to the global warming. Models such as these are used for prioritizing research needs and understanding global cycles.

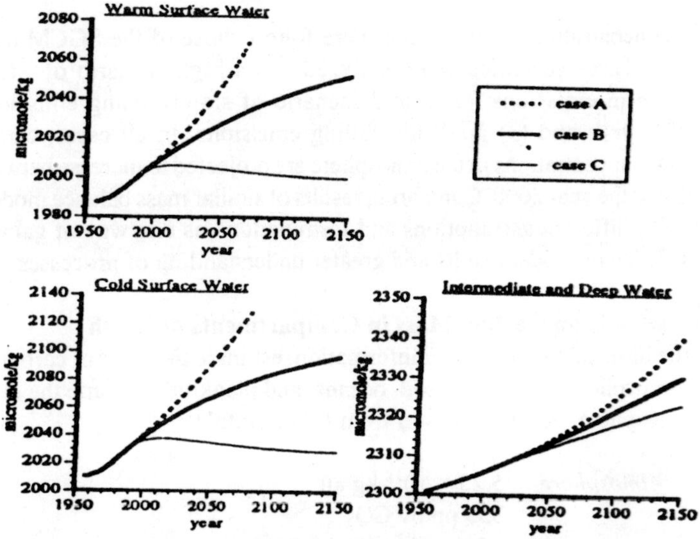

Fig. 2.17. Scenarios of the carbon concentrations of ocean compartments. Case A is the 1.5% increase per year, case B is the constant emission, and case C is the 5% decrease per year from year 1989.[10]

Table 2.5. Carbon Sources and Sinks Based on Box Model in the Year 1989

	Carbon Sources, Gt C yr^{-1}	*Carbon Sinks, Gt C yr^{-1}*	
Fossil fuel emissions	6.0	1.2	Biosphere uptake
Deforestation	1.2	2.5	Oceanic uptake
		3.5	Atmosphere accumulation
TOTAL	7.2	7.2	

Prospects for the future indicate that CO_2 concentrations in the atmosphere will continue to rise. Table 2.5 shows a global carbon budget for 1989. If fossil fuel emissions continue to increase as they are projected by the IPCC (Fig. 2.18), then the atmosphere will be the main sink for CO_2.

The Intergovernmental Panel on Climate Change examined many carbon models of the kind discussed in this section, and projections of

CO_2 concentrations in the atmosphere follow those of the SGCM quite closely. Three scenarios were analyzed: (1) a high scenario of ~1.5% yr^{-1} rise in emissions; (2) a mid-scenario of slowly rising emissions, ~0.95% yr^{-1}; and (3) gradually falling emissions. In all cases, carbon dioxide concentrations in the atmosphere are projected to increase between 1990 and the year 2000. Comparing results of similar mass balance models, but with different assumptions and formulations, is one way of gaining confidence in model results and greater understanding of processes.

An Example on Carbon Mass in Compartments of Earth

On the basis of the following information, estimate the mass of carbon in the atmosphere, land biota, soil, oceans, and plankton. Assume the mass of atmosphere, oceans, and soil from first example.

Atmosphere	5.25×10^{18} kg air
	355 ppmv CO_2
	44 g mol^{-1} MW of CO_2
	12 g mol^{-1} MW of C
	29.2 g mol^{-1} MW of air
Land biota	100 metric tons per ha dry biomass
	1.33×10^{14} m^2 land surface area
	0.4 g C per g biomass (dry)
Soil	3.9×10^{17} kg
	0.5% organic carbon (avg.)
Ocean	1.4×10^{21} kg ocean mass
	2250 μeq kg^{-1} HCO_3 alkalinity
Plankton	80 μg L^{-1} planktonic organic carbon in ocean
	3.6×10^{16} m^3 surface ocean volume

Solution: Dimensional examination allows calculation of the mass of carbon in each compartment. The answers are:

Atmosphere = 7.66×10^{17} g C (766 Gt C)
Land biota = 5.32×10^{17} g C (532 Gt C)
Soil = 1.95×10^{18} g C (1950 Gt C)
Ocean = 3.78×10^{19} g C (37,800 Gt C)
Plankton = 2.88×10^{15} g C (2.9 Gt C)

These results compare well with those estimated by Moore and Bolin and shown in Fig. 2.11.

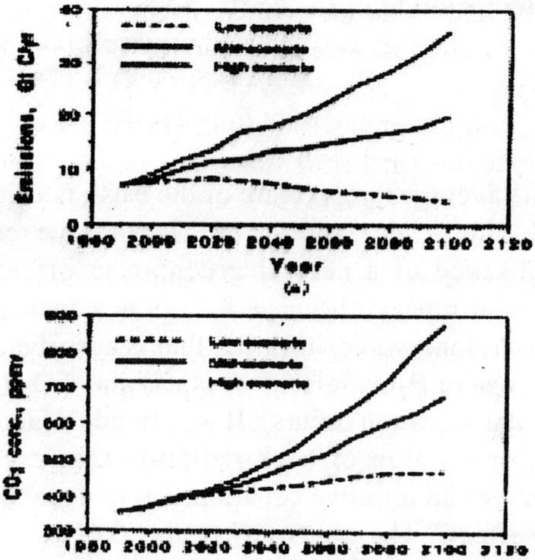

Year

(b)

Fig. 2.18. Intergovernmental Panel on Climate Change (IPCC) projections of CO_2 concentrations in the atmosphere for three scenarios. Results are best estimate from several models.[54] (a) Emissions scenarios. (b) CO_2 concentrations.

An Example on the most Simple Climate Model

In this context, Back-radiation from the Earth must be equal to solar energy inputs to the earth's surface under steady-state conditions. Guess the average temperature of the earth based on a solar constant of 1367 W m^2 and the Stefan-Boltzmann law.

Answer

Back radiation: $E_e = \sigma T_e^4 (4 \pi r^2)$ Stefan-Boltzmann law . . . (a)

where σ = Stefan-Boltzmann constant = 5.5597×10^{-8} W m^{-2} K^{-4}

T_e = earth's temperature K (kelvin units)

E_e = energy emitted, W

$4 \pi r^2$ = surface area of the earth, m^2

Energy input: $E_i = (\pi r^2) S(1 - A)$ . . . (b)

where πr^2 = circular disk (earth) getting solar energy

S = solar constant = 1367 W m^{-2}

A = albedo or reflectivity of the earth ~ 0.31

Equations (a) and (b) can be equated, and one can solve for T_e, the averagetemperature of the earth.

$$\text{Energy emitted} = \text{Energy received from sun} \quad \ldots (c)$$

$$\sigma T_e^4 = S(1 - A)/4$$

$$T_e = 255 \text{ K}$$

This way, the average temperature of the earth is calculated to be 255 K or −18 °C. This is very cold! It reflects what the temperature would be in the absence of a natural greenhouse effect. However, the calculation is at mistake because it fails to consider the fraction of back-radiation (long-wave, infrared) that is absorbed by water vapour (λ = 12 μm, where H_2O molecules rotate) and CO_2 (λ =15 μm where there molecular vibration occurs). If we include a factor for emissivity, the opacity or fraction of back-radiation that escapes the earth's atmosphere, we can improve equation (iii) to account for the "natural greenhouse effect." The emissivity (*e*) is ~0.615)

$$e\sigma T^4 = S(1 - A)/4 \quad \ldots (d)$$

$$T = 288 \text{ K}$$

Total global average surface temperature of the earth is 288 K or 15 °C, which is verified by statistics from monitoring stations throughout the world.

We can use equation (d) as a simple climate model to test the effect of increasing cloud cover (decreased emissivity by 1%) or increasing the albedo of the earth due to sulfate aerosols by 1%. In the case of decreased emissivity, the global average surface temperature increases by 0.7 °C. For raised albedo of 1%, the global average surface temperature decreases by 0.3 °C.

Cycle of Nitrogen Gas

This cycle is critical to life because it provides major nutrients for plants (NH_4^+, NO_3) and animals (protein N, amino acids) alike. In a natural ecosystem, biological N_2-fixation is the crucial mechanism that provides nutrients for photosynthesis; however, human activities of fertilizer production and fossil fuel combustion now rival natural levels of N-fixation.

Above Fig. 2.19 is a schematic of the N-cycle in a natural ecosystem. Major processes include N-fixation by legumes and bacteria on roots; N-fixation from the atmosphere by lightning to form NO; redox reactions in soils and biomass burning that form N_2O, NO_3, and NO_2; and uptake of gases like ammonium and nitrate by vegetation (Table 2.6).

The problem is that human activities are fixing amounts of nitrogen equal to those of nature, which results in disturbances to ecosystems. Human activities include fertilizer preparation of anhydrous ammonia from natural gas; NO_x production from internal combustion engines that convert N_2 o NO_x during fossil fuel burning; NO_x production from organic nitrogen in coal and other fossil fuels when they are combusted; and N_2O and other N_xO_y mixtures from biomass burning (Table 2.7). As a result of these activities, air pollution and smog are formed from NO_x, N_2O is increasing in the atmosphere, and forests are showing symptoms of nitrogen saturation and decline because of acid deposition. Natural cycles are being disrupted, the consequence of human activity, intensive agriculture, and fossil fuel combustion. Galloway et al.[55] have guessed the global nitrogen cycle in preindustrial and anthropogenic times (Fig. 2.20). The accumulation of N_2O in the atmosphere amounts to ~3.4 Tg N yr^{-1} (teragram = 1×10^{12} g). It emanates from fertilized soil and biomass burning. Fluxes of NO (and NO_x) to the atmosphere have gone up six-fold due to fossil fuel combustion and biomass burning. Nitrate deposition to terrestrial and oceanic ecosystems has gone up resulting in a fertilization effect.

Fertilization constitutes a disruption of natural cycles, and, in some instances, it has resulted in problems of eutrophication and forest decline.

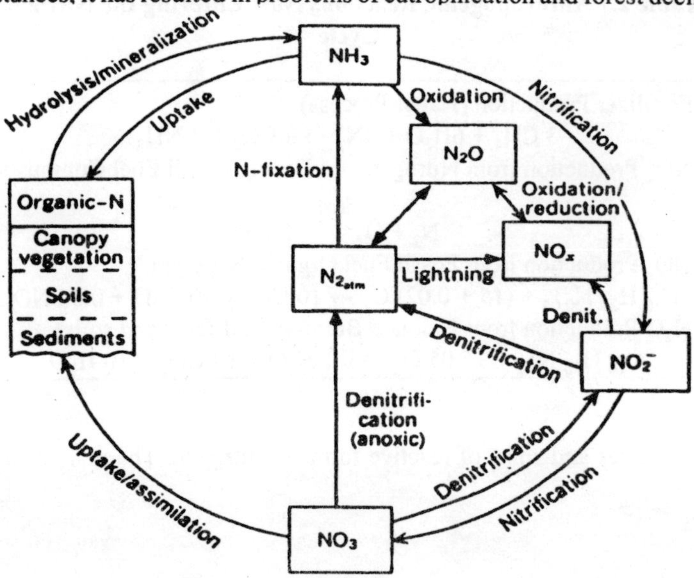

Fig. 2.19. Nitrogen cycle in a natural terrestrial ecosystem. State variables also include NH_3 ($+NH_4^+$). N_2O, NO_3, and organic-N.

Table 2.6. Some Important Significant Reactions of the Nitrogen Cycle

1. N_2-Fixation by Plants

$$N_2 + CH_2O + 2H_2O \rightarrow 2NH_3 + CO_2 + \frac{1}{2} O_2$$

2. N_2-Fixation by Lightning

$$N_2 + O_2 \rightarrow 2\,NO$$

3. Nitrification

$$NH_3 + 2\,O_2 \rightarrow NO^- + H_2O + H^+$$

4. Dentrification

$$NO_3 + 2\frac{1}{2}CH_2O + H^+ \longrightarrow \frac{1}{2}N_2 + \frac{3}{4}CO_2 + \frac{7}{4}H_2O$$

5. Biomass Synthesis:

$$106\,CO_2 + 16\,NO_3 + HPO\frac{2}{4} + 122\,H_2O + 18\,H^+ \underset{R}{\overset{P}{\rightleftharpoons}} C_{106}H_{263}O_{110}N_{16}P_1 + 138\,O_2$$

Table 2.7 Anthropogenic Reactions Now Entering the Nitrogen Cycle

1. Fertilizer Production (Haber Process)

$$3\,CH_4 + 6H_2O + 4N_2 \rightarrow 3\,CO_2 + 8\,NH_3$$

2. NO_x Production from Nitrogen Gas During Fossil Fuel Combustion

$$N_2 + O_2 \xrightarrow{2000\,^\circ F} 2\,NO$$

3. NO_x Production from Fossil Fuel Organic Nitrogen

$$C_{10}\,H_{20}\,N_{0.04} + (15 + 0.02)\,O_2 \rightarrow 10\,CO_2 + 10\,H_2O + 0.04\,NO$$

4. N_2O Production from Biomass Burning (and fertilized soils)

$$C_{10}\,H_{20}\,N_{0.2} + 15.05\,O_2 \rightarrow 0.1\,N_2O + 10\,CO_2 + 10\,H_2O$$

The sources and sinks of reactive forms of nitrogen. The main sources and sinks of reactive forms of nitrogen (NH_3, NO_x, N_2O) that are caused by human activities is given by Table 2.8.[55] Nitrogen is accumulating globally, but many of the sinks have not been measured, including the accumulation blend of nitrogen in soils, the accumulation of nitrate in groundwater, and denitrification to N_2 gas.

A large fraction of reactive nitrogen runs off to oceans as nitrate or it is deposited by atmospheric deposition as $NO_{x(g)}$ and $NO_{3(aq)}$. Fig. 2.21 shows consequences of the Geophysical Fluid Dynamics Laboratory Chemical Transport GCM for global NO_y deposition. Preindustrialized NO_y deposition was less than 10 (mmol N) m^{-2} yr^{-1}. It is apparent that a large fertilization and deposition experimentation is underway for nitrogen species to terrestrial and oceanic environments. (NO_y refers to natural plus anthropogenic sources.)

Moreover, there is a linkage between the global carbon model of Section 2.3 and the global nitrogen deposition model shown by Fig. 2.21. Nitrogen could act as the "trigger," the most important variable guiding net primary photosynthesis. If biomass production in boreal and temperate forests is increasing at 1.0 Gt C yr^{-1}, it is possible that N-fertilization, and not CO_2-fertilization, has been responsible for the increased growth rate of forests (the so-called missing carbon sink in various global carbon models).

Hudson et al.[56] estimate that anthropogenic deposition of nitrogen species has resulted in an increased biomass synthesis of 26-30 Tg N yr^{-1}. Table 2.8 includes a conservative estimate of ~20 Tg N yr^{-1} due to

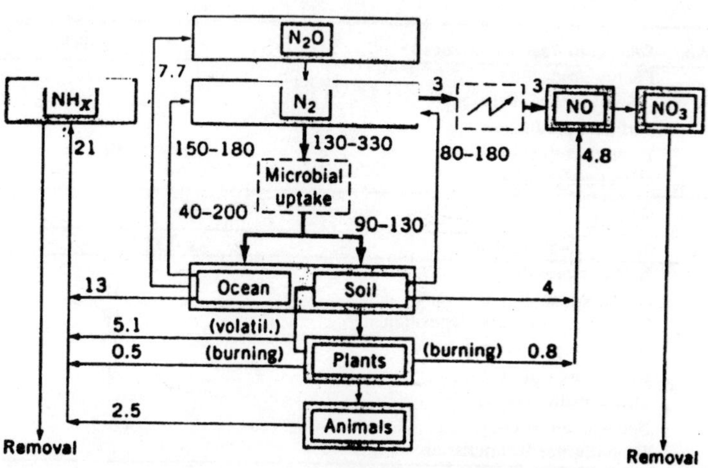

(a)

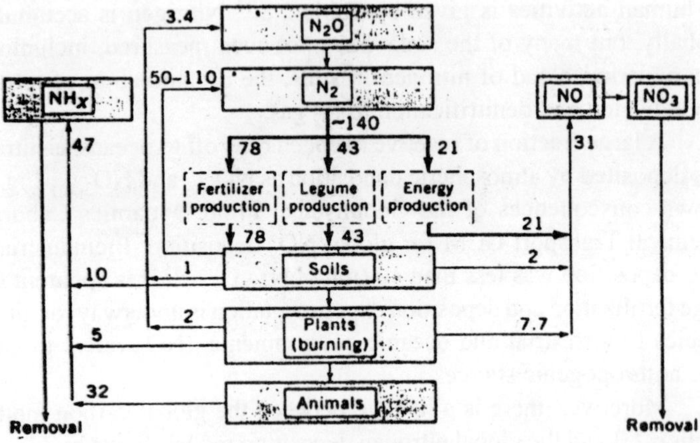

(b)

Fig. 2.20. Global nitrogen cycle (1) Biogenic or preindustrial situation where microbial uptake is the principal form of N-fixation and the fluxes to the atmosphere of NH_x and NO are relatively small (2) Additional fluxes due to the anthropogenic factors that rival or exceed natural fluxes of reactive nitrogen. (From Galloway et al.[55]) Reprinted with approval from the American Geophysical Union.

Table 2.8. Assumed Sources and Sinks of Global Reactive Nitrogen (NH_3, NO_x, N_2O) from Human Activities[55]

Sl.No.	*Sources of Reactive Nitrogen*	*Tg N yr^{-1}*
1.	Energy production (fossil fuel combustion)	20
2.	Fertilizer production	80
3.	Legume crop agriculture (land use changes)	40
	TOTAL	140
Sl.No.	*Sinks of Reactive Nitrogen*	*Tg N yr^{1}*
1.	N_2O in atmosphere	3
2.	Riverine transport to oceans	41
3.	Oceanic atmospheric deposition	18
4.	Biomass uptake (fertilization)	20
5.	Remaining sinks (?)	58
	Denitrification to N_2	
	Soil accumulation	
	Groundwater accumulation	
	TOTAL	140

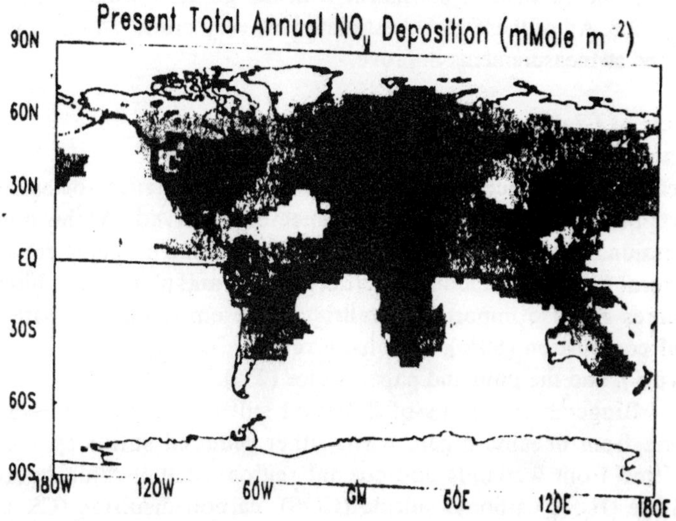

Fig. 2.21. Global atmospheric deposition of NO_y in mmol N m^{-2} yr^{-1}. With courtesy of Hiram Levy. NOAA Geophysical Fluid Dynamics Laboratory, Princeton, NJ.

boreal zones as had been clear-cut by settlers at the turn of the century and are now in a regrowth phase.

Alternatively, the fertilization of forests by HNO_3, NH_3, and excess CO_2 may have increased net primary production. In either case, the result would be an enhaned standing crop of forests and, eventually, more organic carbon stored in upper soil horizons. Reported ranges for carbon/nitrogen ratios in woody biomass range from 25:1 (C/N) to 50:1 (C/N). In soils, C/N ratios are typically 25:1. The grounds of a potential carbon sink of 1 Gt C yr^{-1} (1.0×10^{15} g C yr^{-1}), estimate a range for the nitrogen sink that would be required for incremental forest growth to explain the lost carbon sink.

Answers: Stoichiometry allows us to mix carbon uptake to nitrogen uptake in forests.

$$(1\ \text{N}/25\ \text{C}) \times (1 \times 10^{15}\ \text{g C})/\text{yr} = 4 \times 10^{13}\ \text{g N/yr} = 40\ \text{Tg N yr}^{-1}$$

$$(1\ \text{N}/50\ \text{C}) \times (1 \times 10^{15}\ \text{g C})/\text{yr} = 2 \times 10^{13}\ \text{g N/yr}^{-1} = 20\ \text{Tg N yr}^{-1}$$

The second estimate is consistent with the global nitrogen balance in Table 2.8. All of these global estimates are very crude, and they will be refined as measurements improve.

Cycle of Global Sulfur

Reactions of Species

Clearly, it is difficult to make a global mass balance for sulfur, in part, because there are so many species involved. Anthropogenic emissions of sulfur dioxide (SO_2) are greater than biogenic emissions (natural reactions including microorganisms and plants), but biogenic sources are also important. Anthropogenic emissions emanate from coal combustion (60%), petroleum refining (28%), smelting of ores (~10%), and the pulp and paper sector (2%).[57]

Biogenic emissions of dimethyl sulfide or DMS (CH_3SCH_3) come from oceanic algae, while other reduced sulfur species are emitted from wetlands and coastal regions that include hydrogen sulfide (H_2S), carbonyl sulfide (COS), carbon disulfide (CS_2), and DMS.

These decreased sulfur species are volatile, and they eventually oxidize to form $SO_{2(g)}$ and sulfate aerosols that are deposited by both wet and dry deposition. In wetlands and coastal zones, anaerobic microbial processes cause sulfate ions to be cut to hydrogen sulfide (or accurately as bisulfide anion, HS).

$$SO_4^{2-} + 2\,CH_2O \xrightarrow{\text{Desulfivibrio}} H_2S + 2\,HCO_3^-$$

CH_2O is reflective of organic carbon compounds that are present in atmosphere strate for sulfate-reducing bacteria, while sulfate ions serve as a major source. H_2S is a volatile species, but maximum of it oxidizes in aerobic water and can escape the water surface.

In soils, H_2S is reoxidized or it is predictably being emitted. Aerobic soils can actually absorb H_2S from the observed matter in swamps and coastal zones, at large scale biogenic emissions occur. Dimethyl sulfide (DMS) is produced by ocean phytoplankton when phytoplankton are grazed upon by zooplankton

$$2\,CO_2 + 2\,H_2O \xrightarrow{\text{Sun}} 2\,CH_2O + 2\,O_2$$

$$SO_4^{2-} + 2\,CH_2O + 2H^+ \xrightarrow{\text{algae}} CH_3SCH_3 + 3\,O_2$$

DMS is sufficiently volatile, and it accounts for a large fraction of biogenic sulfur emissions from oceans. Decreased forms of sulfur in the atmosphere react with hydroxyl radicals. For H_2S and DMS, the reaction is quite fast with lifetimes in the troposphere of 4.4 days and 0.6 days, respectively. A series of free radical reactions happen for H_2S.

$$OH + H_2S \rightarrow H_2O + HS\cdot$$
$$HS\cdot + HCHO \rightarrow H_2S + HCO\cdot$$

or

$$HS\cdot + O_3 \rightarrow HSO + O_2$$

Definitely, the HS radical does not build up in the atmosphere, so it is throught that formaldehyde and ozone react with HS· . Likewise, DMS undergoes a series of independent radical reactions.

$$OH + CH_3SCH_3 \rightarrow CH_3S\,(OH)CH_3$$
$$CH_3S(OH)CH_3 + O_2 \rightarrow (O_2\text{—DMS—}OH)\ \text{complex}$$
$$\text{complex} \rightarrow \underbrace{CH_3\,(SO_3)\,H}_{\text{MSA}} + CH_3\cdot$$

Methane sulfonic acid (MSA) is a main product of the reaction between hydroxyl radicals and DMS. It is a condensable product that helps to form aerosol particles in the atmosphere (cloud condensation nuclei).

James Lovelock has proposed that the formation of MSA is a negative feedback loop to global warming, consistent with his Gaia hypothesis. The hypothesis states that the earth is something akin to a huge organism able to homeostasis and feedback controlling processes. As the earth heats up under more CO_2 concentrations, algal production will increase causing DMS release and conversion to MSA, resulting in more aerosols, more clouds, and more albedo for the earth (a negative feedback effect).

A number of scientists feel that Gaia is a fascinating hypothesis and that feedback loops are, indeed, very important in earth surface processes, but that there is no need to invoke teleological reasoning or to attribute a "persona" to the earth. Still, it makes an interesting story.

Carbon disulfide (CS_2) also reacts with hydroxyl radicals in the atmosphere with a lifetime of ~12 days.[57]

$$OH + CS_2 \rightarrow SCSOH$$
$$SCSOH + O_2 \rightarrow COS + SO_2 + H$$

On the other hand, carbonyl sulfide (COS) is slow to be oxidized. Its lifetime in the atmosphere is on the order of 44 years.[57]

$$OH + COS \rightarrow CO_2 + H_2S$$

In the situation where it is impossible to estimate a residence time for a chemical in the atmosphere because of a lack of information on reservoir pools or flux rates, it is often convenient to use the concept of "lifetime." Lifetime is explained as the reciprocal of the pseudo-first-order rate constant. It is the time that it takes to reach one-third of its original concentration (0.368 C_0) in batch reactor, which is equal to $1/k^l$.

$$\text{Lifetime} = 1/k^l \qquad \text{. . . (xxiv)}$$

where k^l is the pseudo-first-order rate constant.

Kinetics of reactions of decreased sulfur species with hydroxyl radicals are not truly first order; they are generally second order, For example, the oxidation of hydrogen sulfide with ·OH is first order with respect to ·OH, first order regarding H_2S, and second order overall.

$$d[H_2S]/dt = \text{Rxn rate} = -k[\cdot OH][H_2S] \qquad \text{. . . (xxv)}$$

A pseudo-first-order reaction can be utilized if the hydroxyl concentration is approximately constant.

$$d[H_2S]/dt = -k^l\,[H_2S] \qquad \text{. . . (xxvi)}$$

where $k^l = k[\cdot OH]$, the pseudo-first-order rate constant.

Both gas and aqueous phase reactions are significant in the oxidation of sulfur dioxide in the atmosphere. Oxygen and hydroxyl radicals can oxidize SO_2 to SO_4^{2} in the gas phase, and humidity in the air (H_2O) can change SO_3 to acidic aerosol particles.

$$SO_2 + \cdot OH \rightarrow HOSO_2 \xrightarrow{O_2} SO_3 + HO_2 \text{ (superoxide)}$$
$$SO_3 + H_2O \rightarrow H_2SO_4 \text{ (aerosol)}$$

Undoubtedly, a queous phase reactions for SO_2 include reaction with O_3 and H_2O_2; both these can be significant depending on the concentrations of ozone and hydrogen peroxide in clouds.

$$SO_2 + H_2O \rightarrow SO_3^{2-} + 2H^+$$

$$SO_3^{2-} + O_{3(aq)} \rightarrow SO_4^{2-} + O_2$$

$$SO_3^{2-} + H_2O_{2(aq)} \rightarrow SO_4^{2-} + H_2O$$

Thus, Lifetimes ($1/k^1$) for the reactions in clouds are on the order of 1-50 days. Clouds process a tremendous amount of air and water vapour. They act as a concentrating vortex for particles and gases that react with SO_2. Fig. 2.22 is a schematic of the reactive sulfur species in the atmosphere, a summary of the reactions in this part. Most emissions (both biogenic and anthropogenic) are in the form of reduced sulfur species and SO_2.

Sulfur falls back to earth (continents and oceans) in the form of $SO_{2(g)}$ (dry deposition), sulfate aerosols (H_2SO_4, $MgSO_4$, $CaSO_4$ in non-wet deposition), and sulfatetions (H_2SO_4 and $CaSO_4$ in wet deposition). Sulfate aerosols and cloud condensation nucleii play an important role as a negative feedback effect to global warming by increasing the earth's albedo.

Budget for Global Level Sulfur

Leading emissions and transport mechanisms of the global sulfur cycle are shown in Fig. 2.23. Anthropogenic emissions of SO_2 on land are 93 Tg S yr^{-1} (93×10^{12} gS yr^{-1}), which are greater than emissions because of volcanoes, wind-blown dust, and biogenic sources. Most sulfur is deposited over the oceans as SO_2 (dry deposition) and sulfate (dry + wet deposition).

Emissions follow those of Schlesinger,[58] and they are estimated such that inputs are similar to outputs in the atmosphere compartment. We assume that sulfur is not accumulating in the atmosphere because removal mechanisms have such fast reaction rates.

If we sum all the inputs and outputs to the land compartment and the oceans compartment in Fig. 2.23, we find that the land is emitting slightly more sulfur than is coming-in, and the ocean is accumulating sulfur species. But the reservoirs of sulfur in the land (reduced S and sulfates) and in the ocean (sulfates) are numerous. The atmosphere is a small reservoir for sulfur species, only 4.6 Tg S, resulting in a mean residence time in the atmosphere, only 4.9 days. SO_2 travels 500-2000 km by long-range transport, but it does not go well with the atmosphere. There has been given a summary of the atmospheric global sulfur budget is Table 2.9. Estimates have a large uncertainty and each year can vary

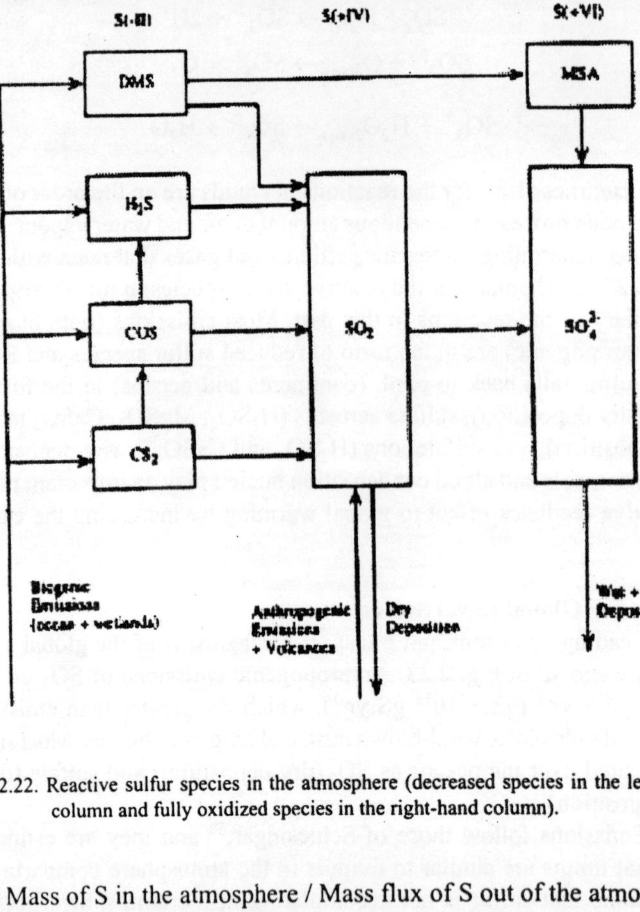

Fig. 2.22. Reactive sulfur species in the atmosphere (decreased species in the left- hand column and fully oxidized species in the right-hand column).

$$\tau_s = \text{Mass of S in the atmosphere / Mass flux of S out of the atmosphere} \quad \ldots \text{(xxvii)}$$

significantly. Volcanic activity is highly variable. There are almost 500 active volcanoes on earth, 90 of which are active in an average year. The Mt. Pinatubo eruption in 1991 was the largest in 100 years, and it emitted 15-20 Tg S, (on the same order of magnitude as US electric benefits in that year, 14 Tg S). But Mt. Pinatubo blasted SO_2 into the lower level of the stratosphere where sulfate aerosols have a longer lifetime.

The albedo effect caused global cooling (0.3-0.5°C) for two years after the event. The Kuwait oil fires following the Gulf War emitted 3-10 Tg S, but the plume went up only about 3 km into the troposphere and caused regional sulfur pollution, which did not produce a global effect.

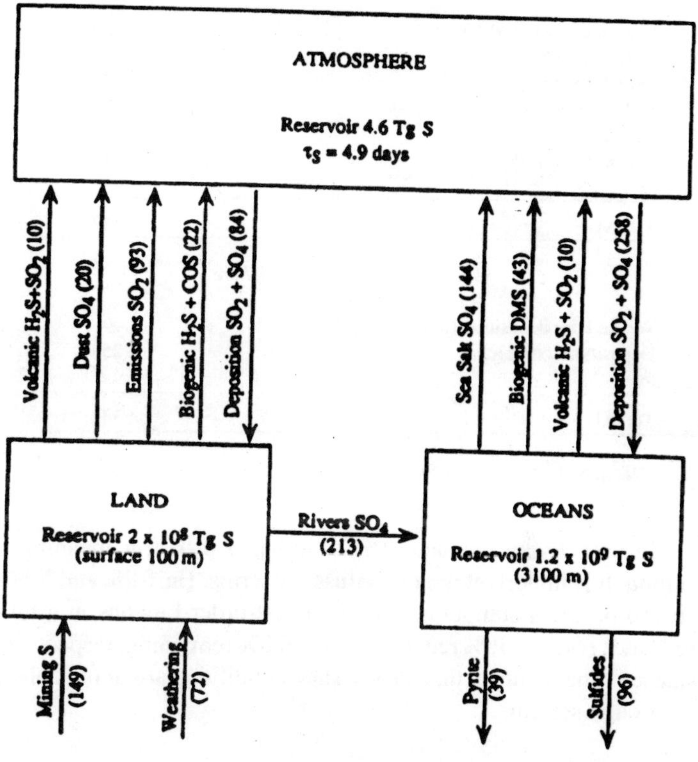

Fig. 2.23. Global sulfur cycle and budget. All numbers are fluxes expressed in Tg S yr^{-1} but the reservoir masses, which are expressed in units of Tg S. (Modified from Schlesinger[58])

Instance on Characteristic Times for SO_2 in the Atmosphere

If we calculate the half-life, lifetime, are residence time of SO_2 species in the atmosphere.

$SO_{2(g)}$ = 2 Tg S mass reservoir in the atmosphere

SO_2 deposition = 150 Tg S yr^{-1} total

$k' = 0.02\ h^{-1}$ pseudo-first-order rate consistent for oxidation reactions

Table 2.9. Global Sulfur Budget[a] to and from the Atmosphere

Sl.No.	Sources and Sinks	$Tg\text{-}S\ yr^{-1}$
	Sulfur Sources to Atmosphere	
1.	Volcanoes ($SO_2 + H_2S$)	20
2.	Dust ($CaSO_4$)	20
3.	Emissions (SO_2)	93
4.	Soil and wetlands (H_2S + COS)	22
5.	Sea salt (Na_2SO_4)	144
6.	Ocean flux (DMS)	43
	TOTAL	342
	Sulfur Sinks from the Atmosphere	
1.	Wet and dry deposition (terrestrial)	84
2.	Deposition (oceanic)	258
	TOTAL	342

[a] 10^{12} g S yr^{-1} = 1 million metric tonnes.

Answer: Every characteristic time has a different meaning and definition. It is important not to confuse the terms. Half-life and lifetime are based on the assumption of pseudo-first-order kinetics in a totally mixed batch reactor (50% remaining and 36.8% remaining, respectively). Residence time assumes that steady state conditions are applicable in a flow-through system.

Half-life:
$$C = C_o e^{-k^l t}$$
$$\tfrac{1}{2} = e^{-k^l t}$$
$$t_{1/2} = 0.693/k^l$$
$$t_{1/2} = 0.693/0.02 = 35 \text{ hours}$$

Lifetime:
$$t_{life} = 1/k^l = 50 \text{ hours}$$

Residence time:
$$\tau_3 = \text{Mass/Flux out} = 2/150 = 0.13 \text{ yr}$$
$$\tau_3 = 4.9 \text{ days}$$

Here, response time is another characteristic time in model simulations. It is based on the givenvalue of the dynamic mass balance equation, and it forecasts how quickly the environmental compartment will change after a step-function change in inputs.

Atmospheric Trace Gases

These include methane (CH_4) nitrous oxide (N_2O), methyl chloroform, and chlorofluorocarbons (CFCs). Methane and nitrous oxide are anthropogenic greenhouse gases. The global budget for N_2O is not well-known, especially regarding its sources. Sources involve industrial emissions and incomplete combustion of fossil fuels, 1 Tg N_2O yr^{-1}, and biomass burning ~1 Tg N_2O yr^{-1}. Natural ecosystems emit 3-9 Tg N_2O yr^{-1} as an intermediate oxidation state (leakage) from the nitrogen cycle.

Fertilized fields are assumed to emit up to ten times more N_2O per m^2 than without fertilizer. Deforestation and the opening of the soil nitrogen cycle after clear-cutting may account for another large source, and surface oceans waters are ~4% supersaturated with N_2O. Since N_2O is growing in the atmosphere at only 0.2% yr^{-1}, there must be a large sink in the atmosphere. Atmospheric sinks for N_2O include photolysis and a slow oxidation with monoatomic oxygen to form NO and N_2 (Table 2.11). Methane is one more trace greenhouse gas that occupies 1.7 ppm by volume in the atmosphere. Anthropogenic sources of methane rival natural sources with flooded rice agriculture and ruminant animals as the biggest sources (Table 2.10). Wetlands emit large amounts of natural methane due to methanogenesis in anaerobic sediments and soils.[59]

Methane reacts with hydroxyl radicals in the atmosphere as the principal sink. Eventually methane reacts all the way to produce CO_2, but the reactions are slow. Table 2.11 is a compilation of some trace gas reactions for carbon species in the atmosphere including methane assuming pseudo-steady state approximations. Methane reacts with · OH to cause formaldehyde, HCHO; and formaldehyde undergoes photolytic oxidation to form carbon monoxide, which eventually gives carbon dioxide. Natural emissions of non-methane hydrocarbons (NMHC) are also important means of formaldehyde and carbon monoxide to the atmosphere. They enter the photolytic cycle and participate in the formation of ozone and smog.

NMHCs are primarily C_{10} and higher alkenes that are emitted by vegetation, such as terpene and isoprene (Table 2.12). They are responsible for the haze seen in the Smokey Mountains of Appalachia. These models indicate that CH_4 is the trace gas that would be most simple to control. If we could control emissions at 1990 levels (constant anthropogenic emissions), the concentration in the atmosphere would level off at 1.85

ppmv by the year 2005.[60] This is so since methane has a relatively short residence time in the atmosphere (5-10 years). Indeed, the rate of increase of CH_4 concentrations in the atmosphere is already decreasing. Control of leaky gas pipelines may be sufficient to cause CH_4 concentrations to remain constant in the 21st century. Still, nitrous oxide concentrations are projected to increase even if we can keep emissions at a constant level. N_2O has a long residence time in the atmosphere that will cause it to increase over the next few decades, even assuming constant emission levels.

Table 2.10. Methane Balance[a] meant for the Atmosphere Adapted from Paterson[59]

Sources and Sinks	*Tg CH_4 yr^{-1}*
Sources	
(A) Anthropogenic	
1. Biomass burning	44
2. Coal extraction	37
3. Waste systems	52
4. Natural gas losses	51
5. Rice production	99
6. Ruminant animals	82
Subtotal	365
(B) Natural	
1. Biomass burning	10
2. Freshwater	5
3. Hydrates clathrates	5
4. Oceans	10
5. Termites	21
6. Wetlands	109
Subtotal	160
TOTAL	525
Sinks	
(1) Oxidation with hydroxyl radical	436
(2) Oxidation with chlorine in stratosphere	26
(3) Accumulation in atmosphere	26
(4) Oxidation by soil microorganisms	37
TOTAL	525

[a] 1 Tg CH_4 = 10^{12} g CH_4.

Table 2.11. Simplified Reactions for Selected Trace Gas Species within the Atmosphere (not Balanced)[60]

Sl. No.		*Reactions*
(1)	$CO + HO^{\cdot}$	$\rightarrow CO_2 + HO_2^{\cdot}$
(2)	$CH_4 + OH^{\cdot}$	$\rightarrow HCHO + HO_2^{\cdot} + H_2O$
(3)	$CH_4 + Cl$	$\rightarrow HCHO + HO_2^{\cdot} + HCl$
(4)	$HCHO + h\nu$	$\rightarrow H_2 + CO + 2HO_2^{\cdot}$
(5)	$HCHO + HO^{\cdot}$	$\rightarrow CO + HO_2^{\cdot} + H_2O$
(6)	$HCHO + Cl$	$\rightarrow CO + HO_2^{\cdot} + HCl$
(7)	$NMHC + HO^{\cdot}$	$\rightarrow 1.23HCHO + 1.68CO_2 + 0.09CO + H_2O$
(8)	$NMHC + NO_3$	$\rightarrow 1.23HCHO + 1.68CO_2 + 0.09CO + HNO_3$
(9)	$N_2O + h\nu$	$\rightarrow N_2 + O(^1D)$
(10)	$N_2O + O(^1D)$	$\rightarrow N_2 + O_2$
(11)	$N_2O + O(^1D)$	$\rightarrow 2\ NO$

Table 2.12. Trace Gas Emissions[a] from Anthropogenic and Natural Sources[60]

	Anthropogenic Sources	Natural Sources		
		Ocean	Continents	Total
(1) N_2O	6.5	1	6	13
(2) CH_4	274	11	109	394
(3) CO	500	71	29	600
(4) NMHC	125	90	920	1135

[a]Units: Tg C yr^{-1} for carbon species; Tg N yr^{-1} for N_2O.

Another Instance of *Mean Residence Time of N_2O in the Atmosphere*

Trace the mean residence time of N_2O in the atmosphere. Its concentration is currently 0.31 ppmv and emissions are given in Table 2.12.

Answer: The concentration in the atmosphere is 0.31 ppmv, and the sources (or sinks at slow state) are 13 Tg N yr^{-1} (20.4 Tg N_2O yr^{-1}).

$$0.31 \times 10^{-6}\ N_2O \times (44\ g\ mol^{-1}\ N_2O)/(29\ g\ mol^{-1}\ air) \times 5.25 \times 10^{18}\ kg\ air = 2.47 \times 10^{12}\ kg\ N_2O$$

$$\tau_{N_2O} = \text{Mass/Flux out} = 2470\ Tg\ N_2O/20.4\ Tg\ N_2O\ yr^{-1} = 121\ yr$$

Clearly, the residence time of N_2O is quite long, indicating that the concentration in the atmosphere is likely to continue to increase for several decades even if emissions are controlled at constant levels.

In this example, we have assumed steady state, which is not the case for N_2O. It is likely that the "Flux out" must be higher to achieve steady state.

As is evident by now, stratospheric ozone depletion is caused primarily by CFC chemicals and methyl chloroform. These chemicals react with hydroxyl radicals in the troposphere before they are transported by vertical adding to the stratosphere, but the rate of reaction is slow compared to transport times.

Thus, they accumulate in the stratosphere, where they react with ozone and this may, deplete the ozone layer. Hydrochlorofluorocarbon (HCFC) and hydrofluorocarbon (HFC) chemicals have been mandated to replace CFCs. These substitutes have shorter lifetimes ($1/k^1$) in the troposphere (Table 2.13). The rate of reaction is second order:

$$dC/dt = \text{Rxn rate} = k[\cdot OH][C] \quad \ldots \text{(xxviii)}$$

$2O_3$

where k is the second-order reaction rate constants.

After examing Table 2.13, it is easy to see that the CFC substitutes are much more rapidly degraded than CFC-12, but they are still likely to accumulate in the stratosphere similar to that of methyl chloroform (CH_3CCl_3). The happy news in that methyl chloroform has a short enough lifetime that it is now decreasing in the atmosphere as a result of the Montreal Protocol and subsequent amendments. Eventually, there will be a necessity to phase-out of HCFC and HFC chemicals as well.

There is an additional concern regarding HFC-134a, HCFC-123, and HCFC-124. Their reaction products include trifluoroacetic acid (CF_3COOH), which is quite persistent and toxic in aquatic and terrestrial ecological systems.

Lifetime and the Reaction Level of HCFC-22

Guess the reaction rate and the lifetime of HCFC-22 from the following information. Assume standard temperature and pressure.

$[\cdot OH] = 5 \times 10^5$ molecules cm^{-3} (average tropospheric concentration)
$[CHF_2Cl] = 0.1$ ppbv (average tropospheric concentration)
$k = 1.44 \times 10^{-11}$ cm^3 $molecule^{-1}$ h^{-1} (second-order rate constant)

Answer: Use a second-order kinetic expression to calculate the reaction rate. The lifetime is defined as the reciprocal of the pseudo-first-order reaction rate constant.

Table 2.13. Atmospheric Lifetime of CFCs, HCFCs, and HFCs for the Reaction with Tropospheric Hydroxyl Radical

Sl. No.	*HCFC or HFC*	*Total Lifetime, yr*
(1)	CFC-11 ($CFCl_3$)	22.8
(2)	CFC-12 (CF_2Cl_2)	114
(3)	CFC-14 (CF_3Cl)	680
(4)	CH_3CCl_4 (methyl chloroform)	2.9
(5)	HFC-32 (CH_2F_2)	6.7
(6)	HCFC-22 (CHF_2Cl)	15.8
(7)	HFC-152a (CH_3CHF_2)	1.6
(8)	HFC-134a (CH_2FCF_3)	14.3
(9)	HFC-125 (CHF_2CF_3)	30
(10)	HCFC-141b (CH_3CFCl_2)	10.8
(11)	HCFC-142b (CH_3CF_2Cl)	22.4
(12)	HCFC-123 ($CHCl_2CF_3$)	1.7
(13)	HCFC-124 ($CHFClCF_3$)	6.9
(14)	HCFC-225ca ($CHCl_2CF_2CF_3$)	2.8
(15)	HCFC-225cb ($CHClFCF_2CClF_2$)	8.0

Source: David.[61]

$$dC/dt = -k[\cdot \text{OH}]\,[\text{C}] = -1.44 \times 10^{-11}\,(5 \times 10^5)(\text{C})$$

$$C = (0.1 \times 10^{-9}\ \text{mol/mol})\ |(6.02 \times 10^{23}\ \text{molecules/mol})\ |(\text{mol}/22.4\ \text{L})\ |(\text{L}/1000\ \text{cm}^3)$$

$$= 2.69 \times 10^9\ \text{molecules/cm}^3$$

$$-\,dC/dt = +\,1.94 \times 10^4\ \text{molecules/cm}^3\ \text{h}$$

$$1/k^l = 1/k[\cdot\text{OH}] = 15.8\ \text{yr lifetime}$$

The solution is equal to the estimate of David[61] in Table 2.13.

Instance of Concentration of Products in Global Rainwater: HCFC-141b

Find the concentration of HF and HCl in global rainwater as a consequence of HCFC -141b reaction with hydroxyl radicals in the troposphere. Global annual rainfall is 4.8×10^{17} L yr^{-1}, and the future annual production of HCFC-141b is estimated as 527,000 metric tons of $CF_2Cl_2CH_3$. (This example is drawn from David.[61])

Answer: Use stoichiometry to calculate the yield of HF and HCl.

$$CFCl_2CH_3 + 2\,O_2 \rightarrow HF + 2\,HCl + 2\,CO_2$$

$$\text{M W HCFC-141b} = 116.9 \text{ g mol}^{-1}$$

$$\therefore \quad \text{Production of HCFC-141b} \cong 5 \times 10^9 \text{ mol yr}^{-1}$$

Therefore, there are 2 moles of HCl and 1 mole of HF formed for every mole of HCFC-141b reacted. Assuming steady state, global annual rainfall would carry the total annual production.

HF: 5×10^9 (20 g mol^{-1}) = 1×10^{11} g
(1×10^{11} g)/(4.8×10^{17} L) = 2.1×10^{-7} g L^{-1}
= 0.21 μg L^{-1}

HCl: (10×10^9) (36.5 g mol^{-1}) = 3.7×10^{11} g
(3.7×10^{11} g)/(4.8×10^{17} L) = 7.6×10^{-7} g L^{-1}
= 0.76 μg L^{-1}

Once CFC, HCFC, and HFC chemicals approach the stratosphere they react in free radical reactions to yield free chlorine. It is the free chlorine in the stratosphere that reacts with ozone. Ozone is continuously formed in the stratosphere by a photodissociation of molecular oxygen and revnion to form O_3, but it is also decomposed by the back-reaction[10]:

$$CFCl_3 + O_2 \xrightarrow{hv} CO_2 + F + 3Cl$$

$$2\,O_3 \xrightarrow{hv} 3\,O_2$$

In this process, joins with ozone to form chlorine monoxide radicals. ClO reaches a peak concentration over Antarctica during the months of October and November when there is early spring sunlight, stable vortex conditions, and extremely cold air with polar stratospheric clouds for heterogeneous reactions that catalyze the below givens reactions:

$$Cl + O_3 \rightarrow ClO + O_2$$
$$O_3 + h\nu \rightarrow O + O_2$$
$$\underline{ClO + O \rightarrow Cl + O_2}$$
$$\text{Net: } 2\,O_3 + h\nu \rightarrow 3\,O_2$$

It is important that Cl is a catalyst in the reaction that is regenerated. One chlorine atom can recycle ~20,000 times before it is terminated in the series of free radical reactions, destroying considerable O_3 molecules.

Certain chlorine atoms would reach the stratosphere naturally, ~0.6 ppbv, by volcanic eruptions and the transport of methyl chloride (CH_3Cl) from seaweed. But the current concentration due to CFC chemicals is five times greater than background, and it is responsible for destruction of ozone in the stratosphere. Mathematical models of global cycles and trace gas constituents can be used to understand global change, to set research priorities, and to predict the results of policy decisions. In this chapter, we have analysed the role that greenhouse gases (CO_2, CH_4, N_2O) play in global warming. Major nutrient cycles of sulfur and nitrogen are coupled to the carbon cycle through common sources of emissions and fertilization effects on biota.

CFCs will came down in concentration in the atmosphere as emissions are curtailed, but long lifetimes of the chemicals and some of their substitutes will remain a concern for stratospheric ozone depletion for years. Because reaction times are slow in the atmosphere, certain trace gases are accumulating, and their long-term effects are not fully known. It will be difficult to curtail emissions of CO_2, SO_x , and NO_x because of the twin driving forces: burgeoning population and increasing per capita use of energy and mineral resources. Sustainable development will require increased use of renewable resources, pollution prevention, recycling, reuse, energy efficiency, and a stable human habitats.

References

1. Soule, M.E., *Science,* 253, 744 (1991).
2. Rodhe, H., *Science,* 248, 1217 (1990).
3. Boden, T.A., Kanciruk, P., and Farrel, M.P., *Trends' 90: A Compendium of Data on Global Change,* Oak Ridge National Laboratory, U.S. Department of Energy, Oak Ridge, TN (1990).
4. Molina, M.J., and Rowland, F.S., *Nature,* 249, 810 (1974).
5. World Meteorological Organization (WMO), Scientific Assessment of Ozone Depletion: 1991, Report No. 25, Geneva, Switzerland (1992).

6. Ravishankara, A.R., and Albritton, D.L., *Science,* 269, 183 (1995).
7. Mann, C.C., *Science,* 253, 736 (1991).
8. United Nations Development Report, New York (1992).
9. Brasseur, G., and Solomon, S., *Aeronomy of the Middle Atmosphere,* Reidel Publishers, New York (1986).
10. Graedel, T.E., and Crutzen, P.J., *Atmospheric Change—An Earth System Perspective,* W.H. Freeman and Company, New York (1993).
11. Intergovernmental Panel on Climate Change (IPCC), *Climate Change, The IPCC Scientific Assessment WMO/UNEP,* Cambridge University Press, Cambridge, United Kingdom (1990).
12. Intergovernmental Panel on Climate Change (IPCC), *Climate Change, The Second IPCC Scientific Assessment WMO/UNEP,* Cambridge University Press, Cambridge, United Kingdom (1996).
13. Barron, E.J., *EOS Trans. Am. Geophys. Union,* 76, 185 (1995).
14. Nerem, R.S., *Science,* 268, 667 (1995).
15. Manabe, S., and Wetherald, R.T., *J.Atmos. Sci.,* 32, 3 (1985).
16. Hansen, J., Lacis, A., Rind, D., Russell, G., Stone, P., Fung, I., Ruedy, R., and Lerner, J., in *Climate Processes and Climate Sensitivity,* J.E. Hansen and T. Takahashi, Eds., Maurice Ewing Series Vol. 5, p. 130 (1985).
17. Washington, W.M., and Meehl, G.A., *J. Geophys. Res.,* 89, 9475 (1984).
18. Schlesinger, M.E., and Jiang, X., *Climate Dynamics,* 3,1 (1988).
19. Wilson, C.A., and Mitchell, J.F.B., *J. Geophys. Res.,* 92, 13315 (1987).
20. Trenberth, K.E., Ed., *Climate System Modeling,* Cambridge University Press, Cambridge, United Kingdom (1992).
21. Perry, T.S., *IEEE Spectrum,* 30: 7, 33 (1993).
22. Moore, B. III, and Bolin, B., *Oceanus*, 29, 16-29 (1986/87).
23. Hammond, *Medallion World Atlas,* Hammond Incorporated, Maplewood, NJ (1985).
24. Warrick, R., Gifford, R., and Parry, M., in *The Greenhouse Effect, Climate Change, and Ecosystems, SCOPE 29,* B. Bolin et al., Eds., Wiley, New York, pp. 393-473 (1986).
25. Acock, B., in *Impact of Carbon Dioxide, Trace Gases, and Climate Change on Global Agriculture, ASA Spec. Publ. 53,*pp. 45-60, (1990).
26. Raich, J.W., Rastetter, E.B., Melillo, J.M., Kicklighter, D.W., Steudler, P.A., Peterson, B.J., Grace, A.L., Moore, B. III, and Vörösmarty, C.J., *Ecol. Appl.,* 1, 399-429 (1991).
27. Kwon, O. Yul, Ph.D. Dissertation, The University of Iows, Iowa City (1994).
28. Murray, J.W., in *Global Biogeochemical Cycles,* S.S. Butcher, R.J. Charlson, G.H. Orians, and G.V. Wolfe, Eds., Academic Press, San Diego, CA, pp. 175-211, (1992).

29. Peng, T.H., Takahashi, T., Broecker, W.S., and Olafsson, J., *Tellus Ser. B,* 39B, 439-458 (1987).
30. Griffiths, D.V., and Smith, I.M., Eds., *Numerical Methods for Engineers,* CRC Press, Boca Raton, FL (1991).
31. Quay, P.D., Tilbrook, B., and Wong, C.S., *Science,*256, 74-79 (1992).
32. Houghton, R., et al., *Tellus Ser. B,* 39B, 122-139 (1987).
33. Detwiler, R.P., and Hall, C.A.S., *Science,* 239, 42-50 (1988).
34. Hansen, J., Lacis, A., Ruedy, R., and Sato, M., *Geophys. Res. Lett.,* 19, 215-218 (1992).
35. Jones, P.D., Wigley, T.M.L., and Wright, P.B., *Nature,* 322, 430-434 (1986).
36. Budyko, M.I., and Izrael, Y.A., Eds., *Anthropogenic Climate Change,* University of Arizona Press, Tucson (1991).
37. Larcher, W., Ed., *Physiological Plant Ecology,* Springer-Verlag, New York (1980).
38. Harvey, L.D.D., *Global Biogeochem. Cycles,* 3, 137-153 (1989).
39. Enoch, H.Z., and Sacks, J.M., *Photosynthetica,* 12, 150-157 (1978).
40. Webb, W.L., Lauenroth, W.K., Szarek, S.R., and Kinerson, R.S., *Ecology,* 64, 134-151 (1983).
41. Woodwell, G.M., in *Changing Climate, Carbon Dioxide Assessment Committee,* National Academy of Science Press, Washington, DC pp. 216 251, (1983).
42. Running, S.W., and Coughlan, J.C., *Ecol. Modelling,* 42, 125-154 (1988).
43. Reuss, J.O., and Innis, G.S., *Ecology,* 58, 379-388 (1977).
44. Jansson, P.E., and Berg, B. *Can. J. Bot.,* 63, 1008-1016 (1985).
45. Carlyle, J.C. and Than, U.B.A., *J. Ecol.,* 76, 654-662 (1998).
46. Crill, P.M., *Global Biogeochem. Cycles,*5, 319-334 (1991).
47. Raich, J.W., and Schlesinger, W.H. *Tellus Ser. B,* 44B, 81-99 (1992).
48. Born, M., Dorr, H. and Levin, I., *Tellus Ser. B,* 42E, 2-8 (1990).
49. Kwon, O. Yul, and Schnoor, J.L., *Global Biogeochem. Cycles,* 8, 295-305 (1994).
50. Broecker, W.S., and Peng, T.H., in *Gas Transfer at Water Surface,* W. Brutsaert et al., Eds., D. Reidel, Norwell, MA, pp. 479-493 (1984).
51. Takahashi, T., Broecker, W.S., and Bainbridge, A.E, in *Carbon Cycle Modelling. SCOPE 16,* B. Bolin, Ed., Wiley, New York, pp. 159-199 (1981).
52. Oeschger, H., in *Carbon Dioxide and Other Greenhouse Gases: Climate and Associated Impacts,* R. Fantechi and A. Ghazi, Eds., Kluwer Academic, Norwell, MA, pp. 40-54 (1989).
53. Barnola, J.M., Raynaud, D., Korotkevich, Y.S., and Lorius, C., *Nature,* 329, 408-414 (1987).
54. Intergovernmental Panel on Climate Change (IPCC), *Climate Change*

1994 Working Groups I and III of the IPCC, Cambridge University Press, Cambridge, United Kingdom (1994).

55. Galloway, J.N., Schlesinger, W.H., Levy, H. II, Michaels A., and Schnoor, J.L., *Global Biogeochem. Cycles,* 9:2, 235-252 (1995).
56. Hudson, R.J.M., Gherini, S.A., and Goldstein, R.A., *Global Biogeochem. Cycles,* 8:3, 307-333 (1994).
57. Warnek, P., *Chemistry of the Natural Atmosphere*, Academic Press, London (1988).
58. Schlesingerr, W., *Biogeochemistry: An Analysis of Global Change,* Academic Press, New York (1991).
59. Paterson, K.G., Ph.D. Dissertation, The University of lowa, lowa City (1993).
60. Yan, Y.L., Ph.D. Dissertation, The University of lowa City (1993).
61. David, M., *Estimation of the Yields of Tropospheric Degradation Products of HCFCs and HFCs,* EAWAG No. 1800, Swiss Federal Institute for Environmental Science and Technology, Duebendorf, Switzerland (1993).

3

Scientific Evidence on Assumed Greenhouse Warming

This chapter is a component of experimental evidence on the likely global greenhouse warming by Jessica T. Mathews, the vice-president and Research Director of World Resources Institute. In the present chapter, she also varies policy options as recommendations. With in the past few years a scientific consensus has begun to emerge on the causes and likely impacts of the expected warming of the earth's climate due to rising concentrations of greenhouse gases. There is little agreement, however, on what, if anything possible to do about it. Do we continue with research to reduce the scientific uncertainties? Do we act now to avert or slow the warming trend? Or do we take steps to adapt to it? The temperature rise expected by the mid-2000s (a 1.5 to 4.5°C rise) would change most characteristics of global climate, she writes, changing rainfall patterns and growing seasons and leading to a substantial rise in sea levels. A 3°C rise would put global environment beyond the range of human experience.

Mathews concludes that the costs of waiting for scientific certainty are too great. Instead, she urges the United States to act now to avert an unacceptably large greenhouse warming. Along with these, she also proposes steps to increase energy efficiency, reduce the use of carbon-rich fuels, phase out the use of chlorofluorocarbons (one of the major man-made contributors to global warming), and finally, to start international discussions on the greenhouse effect and on long-range energy strategies.

About her achievements and academic profile, Jessica Mathews received her B.A. from Radcliffe College in 1967 and her Ph.D. in biochemistry and biophysics from the California Institute of Technology in 1973. From 1977 to 1979 she has been the director of the office of global issues on the National Security Council. Before joining WRI, she was on the editorial board of the *Washington Post,* where she covered science, technology, energy, environment, health, and number of other issues.

I

"If the Lord Almighty had consulted me before embarking on the Creation, I would have recommended something simpler," wrote Alfonso X of Castille, a medieval patron of astronomy. For better or worse, the Lord did not, and several centuries later we are becoming ever more aware of the earth's complexity. Scientists still understand little of the workings of the atmosphere and the oceans, of their interactions that drive the planet's climate machine, and of the biogeochemical cycles of carbon, nitrogen, sulphur, and the few other elements essential to life. And while nature is complex and dynamic enough in itself, natural forces are now being changed by man's own activities, whose effects reach from the oceans to the top of the stratosphere. In generating a global "greenhouse" warming, man has embarked on a vast, unplanned planetary experiment that poses unprecedented challenges to his wisdom, foresight, and scientific capacity.

The theory of a greenhouse effect was first proposed almost a century ago. The earth's atmosphere, it was pointed out, is largely transparent to incoming solar radiation but absorbs the lower energy (longer-wavelength) radiation that is reradiated by the earth. The extra energy that remains in the atmosphere warms it in a manner akin to the warming of a greenhouse. The major atmospheric gas responsible for this effect is carbon dioxide, though several other gases are also involved.

The greenhouse theory is supported by many lines of evidence. Climatologists now know that without the natural greenhouse effect, the planet would be permanently covered with ice and, presumably, lifeless. Astronomers have discovered that Venus, which has greenhouse gases in its atmosphere, is much warmer than one would expect on the basis of its distance from the sun. The atmospheres and climates of the other close-in planets are also consistent with the theory. More recently, computer climate models of increasing sophistication have yielded consistent estimates of the expected warming of the earth's climate over the coming decades from rising concentrations of greenhouse gases. Finally, within the past few months, the strongest empirical evidence obtained to date that a greenhouse warming is actually under way has become available.

This evidence comes from three sources. First, researchers at the

University of East Anglia in Great Britain combined temperature readings obtained over the land and in the oceans during the past 130 years to produce the first comprehensive estimates of global mean temperature.[1] The readings show a marked warming trend beginning about 1890. The three warmest years of the 134-year record are 1980, 1981, and 1983, and five of the nine warmest years have occurred since 1978. The overall warming of about 0.5°C is consistent in magnitude with what is predicted by the most sophisticated greenhouse projections. Second, temperature readings taken in the Arctic permafrost show that the temperature there has risen about 2 to 4°C over the past several decades to a century.[2] This larger temperature rise in the Arctic is also consistent with theoretical predictions, which show a warming at high latitudes several times greater than the global average. A third line of evidence is the sea-level rise of 2.0 to 2.5 millimetres per year measured over the last 50 years, which is in part due to thermal expansion of the water.[3]

II

There are five principal greenhouse gases. Carbon dioxide, the best known, accounts for about half of the current effect. Its atmospheric concentration has risen by 25 per cent over the past 100 years. Recently, the rate of growth has accelerated; the concentration of carbon dioxide has increased 10 per cent in the past 30 years. The principal cause of this increase is the combustion of fossil fuels. An additional, though uncertain, component of the rising concentration is tropical deforestation. The other four greenhouse gases—methane, nitrous oxide, tropospheric (lower atmosphere) ozone, and a collection of closely related compounds known as chlorofluorocarbons (CFCs)—together account for the other half of the current effect. Although present in very small concentrations, each is a far more potent greenhouse gas than is carbon dioxide, so that rising concentrations have a correspondingly greater effect.

Analysis of air bubbles trapped in glacial ice has made possible the measurement of long-term trends in atmospheric methane, which apparently began increasing about 300 years ago. Very recently—during the past 20 years or so—the rate has increased sharply to about 1 per cent per year. The reasons for this increase, however, are unknown. Among the many suspected causes are larger cattle population and growing areas of rice paddies, both of which release methane. Nitrous oxide is also increasing steadily, though much more slowly. The causes are also unclear because its natural cycle is little understood. However, increasing fertilizer use and combustion of fossil and biomass fuels are suspected. The tropospheric ozone concentration may be on the rise by as much as 1 per cent per year. Ozone is produced in the presence of sunlight from hydrocarbons and nitrogen oxides, the concentrations of which are also increasing due to greater fossil fuel combustion and industrial activity. Only in the case of the CFCs is the reason for the increasing concentration absolutely clear, since all CFCs are manmade. The atmospheric concentration of the principal CFCs has recently been growing very rapidly, at an annual rate of about 7 per cent.

What is important to note from this brief review is that, with the exception of CFCs, the sources of all the greenhouse gases are either uncertain, diffuse (and therefore difficult to control), or principally the result of energy use. Therefore, if or when control of emissions of greenhouse gases is required, the options are principally two: limit or eliminate CFC use and control energy use, particularly fossil-fuel burning. Slowing or reversing deforestation may also help.

How likely is it that such actions will be needed? Despite many uncertainties about the detailed impacts of a greenhouse warming, a broad consensus exists on many of its features. A greenhouse effect equivalent to that which would be caused by a doubling of the preindustrial level of carbon dioxide in the atmosphere is expected to cause a rise in average global surface temperature of 1.5 to 4.5°C (or about 3 to 8°F), with the more recent projections near the high end of this range.[4] A 3°C rise would put the global climate beyond the range of human experience, in the same neighbourhood as the climate that prevailed 13 million years ago. An atmospheric commitment to such an increase is now expected as early as the 2030s.

The expected warming is projected by the date of its "atmospheric commitment" rather than its actual appearance because of the substantial lag between the time higher greenhouse gas concentrations occur and the time the global average temperature reaches its new (warmer) equilibrium. The length of the time lag, which is influenced by the moderating effect of the oceans, is not known but is believed to be a few decades. Although the locution is awkward, the distinction in the way warming is measured is important. This measure of how much warming the atmosphere is committed to is the meaningful one, of course, because once the greenhouse gases are emitted, the eventual effects are inevitable.

A 1.5 to 4.5°C rise would almost certainly alter most characteristics of the global climate. Rainfall patterns are expected to shift, perhaps causing Dust Bowl-like conditions in the U.S. grain belt. Ocean currents are also projected to shift, dramatically altering the climates of many areas. A diversion of the Gulf Stream, for example, would transform western Europe's climate, making it far cooler than it is today. The timing and patterns of monsoons would likely change. The extent of sea-level rise is somewhat more uncertain. Most estimates project a rise of about one meter over 100 years. Such a rise would inundate many coastal regions, erode breaches, damage water supplies through saltwater intrusion, and destroy ecologically vital swamps, marshes, and estuaries. The fishing industry would be affected. Growing seasons would change, and this, together with altered rainfall, would force the relocation of some agricultural areas. Even the local effects of warmer temperatures would be considerable. Washington, DC, for example, is projected to experience twelve days of 100°F or hotter temperatures, instead of one, the current average. And instead of thirty-six days of 90°F or hotter, the capital would swelter through eighty-seven. Patterns of energy demand, construction, transportation, water management, and coastal engineering would all be affected. Over a longer period, perhaps one to two centuries, a large global warming could melt the land-based ice over Greenland and Antarctica. Estimates of the resulting sea-level rise are very uncertain, ranging up to 24 feet. After just a 15-foot rise, however, major parts of San Francisco, New Orleans, Boston, Miami, New York, and most of the rest of the US coastline would be underwater.

Positive consequences are also expected. Some plants would grow more quickly, stimulated by the additional carbon dioxide. Rainfall might increase in what are now arid but potentially fertile regions, especially sub-Saharan Africa. Conditions for agriculture would also improve in northern areas with appropriate soils and adequate rainfall or irrigation. As profound as these effects are, consequences we cannot now predict—either positive or negative—may well have the greatest impact.

Some climatologists believe that another characteristic of a rapidly warming climate could be larger and more frequent weather extremes, hurricanes and other violent disturbances, droughts, and extremely wet periods might all occur more frequently. This past year's drought in the Southeast, which caused an estimated $ 1.75 billion in damage in just 6 of the 11 affected states, is a sobering reminder of the extremely high costs of such weather anomalies.[5] The Great Lakes region, meanwhile, has experienced above-average rainfall in 17 of the last 18 years, perhaps due to change in the path of the jet stream.[6] The rising water level in the lakes is projected to cause $ 100 million to $ 150 million in damage this year and far greater consternation and political manoeuvring as lakeshore governments struggle to anticipate the effects of future higher levels.[7]

A climate in disequilibrium is in itself a costly and socially difficult situation.

There are many areas of great uncertainty about greenhouse mechanisms. In particular, the behaviour of clouds, the mechanisms of ocean circulation, and various oceanic and atmospheric feedback loops may change some of these projections. However, scientists are reasonably confident of the probable effects over large areas. For example, mid-continental regions of the United States are likely to become drier. But predictions of more localized effects—for example, the likely climate in Nebraska—are highly uncertain. But at least in their broad outlines, the theory, causes and impacts of the greenhouse warming described here appear reliable.

III

The greenhouse warming is part of a bigger picture, it is closely linked to stratospheric ozone depletion and acid deposition. These three phenomena are tied together by many of the same chemical species, by the same human activities that generate them, and by the effects of one phenomenon on the timing and severity of the others. The leading parts in each are played by the same actors, though sometimes in different roles: carbon dioxide, nitrous oxide, methane, carbon monoxide, ozone, nitrogen oxides, sulfur oxides, the hydroxyl radical, and CFCs. These interconnections have important implications for control strategies.

For example, as noted earlier, carbon dioxide is the largest contributor to global warming. At the top layer of the atmosphere, however, it cools the stratosphere and slows the rates of certain reactions that determine the rate of ozone depletion. Methane's role is more complicated. In the stratosphere it acts as a chemical "sink" for chlorine atoms, thereby reducing ozone depletion. It also reacts with other compounds in the stratosphere to form carbon dioxide and water, thereby amplifying the greenhouse effect because water vapour is also a greenhouse gas. In the troposphere methane leads to higher ozone levels, though by different chemical pathways depending on the concentration of nitrous oxides. Sulfur oxides are converted by ozone, hydroxyl, and other chemicals to sulfates, which cause acid deposition. Sulfur oxides also affect the fate of many other of the leading actors. Ozone in the troposphere acts as both a greenhouse gas and as pollutant, affecting plant growth and human health. In the stratosphere however, it absorbs incoming ultraviolet radiation, playing a vital role in protecting human, plant, and animal life.

Moreover, many of the same human activities are involved in these phenomena. For example, a refrigerator eventually release CFCs, which contribute to both stratospheric ozone depletion and global warming. And if the refrigerator runs on electricity produced by coal burning, its use also

(a) produces carbon dioxide (which contributes to warming) and nitrous oxide (which contributes to both warming and to ozone depletion);

(b) produces sulfur and nitrogen oxides, the precursors of acid deposition (nitrogen oxides also contribute to warming by increasing the concentrations of tropospheric ozone);

(c) produces carbon monoxide, which enhances warming by reacting with hydroxyl radicals, which are the principal tropospheric sink for methane, a greenhouse gas.

As these examples of the mind-numbing chemical complexity of the atmosphere illustrate, the use of names to designate individual phenomena creates an illusion that these are distinct changes. They are not. Acid deposition is just one of the results of a far more complex mix of air pollutants that interact in many ways to affect plant, animal, aquatic, and human life. Greenhouse warming and ozone depletion are so closely tied together that they should be treated as a single phenomenon. In fact, the atmosphere might most usefully be visualized as a volume of fluid in which all the chemicals mix. Above all, as the costs and benefits of controlling any one of these problems are weighed in the political arena, the effects on the other two must also be considered. Luckily, most emission reductions work in the same direction, helping to solve all three problems.

IV

Beyond this intimacy with ozone depletion and acid deposition, the key factor in considering a policy response to global warming is the question of timing. Is the greenhouse effect a problem for our children? Given the scientific uncertainties, is it too soon to act, or might we wake up one day and find that it is too late? What are the consequences of acting later rather than sooner? Can we expect to have significantly reduced the uncertainties in time to significantly affect the outcome? Paraphrasing Senator Howard Baker's immortal question: What will we know, and when will we know it?

The answers begin with where we stand today. As noted earlier, the correct measure is not how much warming has already occurred but rather what warming the atmosphere is committed to, because the time greenhouse gases are emitted is the point of irreversible (so far as we know) commitment. Veerabhadran Ramanathan and his colleagues at the National Centre for Atmospheric Research have estimated the effect of emissions from 1860 to 1980 to be approximately 0.8°C—that is, a commitment to this much warming has already occurred.[8] Allowing for the uncertainty caused by various feedback effects, this translates to an eventual warming in the range of 0.5 to 1.5°C above the preindustrial global average temperature.

Irving Mintzer at the World Resources Institute has constructed a tool that can illuminate future warming trends.[9] His computer model combines the climate-altering effects of all the major greenhouse gases. Individual components of the model can be separately manipulated, reflecting hypothetical policy and economic changes. Mintzer's "base-case" scenario reflects conventional wisdom regarding population, economic, and energy growth from 1980 to 2075. No policies are introduced to slow the rate of a greenhouse gas buildup: no major effort is made to arrest tropical deforestation or to improve the efficiency with which energy is used. In this scenario, environmental concerns have little effect on energy policy. The model is quite conservative in projecting substantially lower rates of growth in CFC emissions than are occurring today, even though it envisions no policy steps to limit these emissions.

For this base-case scenario, the model predicts a commitment to an average global warming of 0.9 to 2.6°C above preindustrial temperatures by the year 2000. A warming well within this range—2°C—would put the global average temperature beyond that experienced in recorded human history. Yet, politically speaking, 13 years is the blink of an eye for reaching and implementing a global agreement. The Nuclear Non-Proliferation Treaty took only seven years to negotiate and secure sufficient ratifications to enter into force, but it is a notable exception. The Law of the Sea Treaty, more the norm, took 12 years. Perhaps the best comparison is to the Vienna Convention to Protect the Ozone Layer, it took 10 years to reach an agreement on a framework, and the convention's regulatory teeth are still being negotiated. The convention is a notable precedent in that it has been negotiated in the context of considerable scientific uncertainty and it, like a possible greenhouse agreement, is an effort to anticipate and avert—rather than clean up— an environmental problem.

Looking a little further ahead, Mintzer's model predicts that by 2030 the commitment to global average warming will be 1.6 to 4.7°C, or about 3 to 8°F, above preindustrial temperatures—that is, the equivalent of a doubled preindustiral carbon dioxide level. The warming commitment will be substantially greater at the poles. This is a very different climate regime than today's, and it is only as far ahead as World War II is behind us. While immense changes can occur in 45 years, it is not a long time for certain transformations. For example, it has generally taken 50 years for new energy supply technologies to capture half of the global market.[10]

Mintzer has also used his model to investigate two scenarios that are significant diversions from current trends. In his "high-emissions" scenario, the use of coal and synfuels is encouraged, the deforestation of tropical forests continues unabated, and minimal environmental costs are reflected in the price of energy. CFC emissions rise with income growth at the high historic rate at which they grew in the United States over the past few decades. By contrast, in the "slow-buildup" scenario, strong policies are adopted to implement solar energy, improve energy efficiency, discourage solid fuel use, and arrest deforestation. CFC production is frozen by international agreement at the 1985 level. In the high-emissions scenario the date of commitment to the equivalent of a doubled preindustrial carbon dioxide level advances from 2030 to 2015, whereas in the slow-buildup case it is delayed until about 2080. Thus, if the model is correct, this particular set of policies, hypothetically implemented in 1980, would mean a difference of six decades before the planet is committed to this benchmark warming level.

A different way to approach this question is to ask what are the consequences of delaying action until a significantly higher degree of scientific certainty about greenhouse mechanisms and impacts becomes available. Two decade is a reasonable guess for how long this might take. If an additional decade is then needed to reach international agreement on a set of policies, 2015 might be the earliest date for more confident action. According to Mintzer's projections, the planet would then be committed to a 0.25 to 0.8°C greater warming than would be the case had the policies envisioned in the slow-builup scenario been adopted in 1985. Thus, if no action is taken to alter current trends, over the next 30 years the planet will become committed to an additional warming about half again as great as that believed to have been committed to during the entire 125 years of the industrial age.

In sum, the greenhouse clock is ticking. A substantial global warming (0.5 to 1.5°C) is already inevitable. Since the rate of greenhouse gas emissions is accelerating, additional warming increments will be committed to much faster than in the past, meaning faster climate change and less time for societal and ecological adaptation. A reasonable estimate of the path we are now travelling shows a warming commitment of 0.9 to 2.6ºC above preindustrial temperatures by 2000, and 1.6 to 4.7ºC by 2030. On the other hand, history is not necessarily destiny. Politically optimistic but economically realistic policy changes undertaken now could significantly slow the anticipated warming. Waiting for greater scientific certainty would probably mean a 0.25 to 0.8ºC additional average warming to cope with— a not insurmountable, but by no means insignificant, difference.

V

The rough outlines of a greenhouse policy debate are becoming clear. There are three dominant views. One holds that it is too soon to begin to think about doing anything other than intensive research. This is the position, for example, of the US Department of Energy and of many scientists. Without question, the current scientific uncertainties are very large. On the other hand, there is highly suggestive evidence that a greenhouse warming is already under way; there is even stronger evidence that the rate of greenhouse emissions is accelerating; and there is ample evidence to indicate that the costs of a rapidly changing climate are very high. Moreover, scientific confidence on the greenhouse issue is an elusive goal. My estimate that scientific confidence on the greenhouse issue is an elusive goal. My estimate that scientific uncertainties may be resolved within two decades might be optimistic. And Mintzer's analysis suggests that there could be a high cost associated with waiting. Thus, a strong case can be made in favour of acting now, if economically sensible and politically feasible steps can be identified.

Among those favouring some kind of action, one group, who might be termed "adaptionists," emphasizes learning to live with the greenhouse warming. Another group emphasizes the need to slow and eventually halt the warming. This latter group might be called "preventionists", although this is obviously a misnomer because, as we have seen, the warming is apparently under way and would continue for decades even if all greenhouse emissions were halted tomorrow.

Some adaptionists proceed from the belief that because unilateral action to avert a warming is infeasible, and international cooperation impossible, adapting is the only option. Other adaptionists believe that climate warming will likely yield net positive benefits, and that because some nations will gain and others lose from the effects to climate change, strategies based on independent adaptation make the most sense. Heavily represented in this group are climatologists who have argued for years in favour of policies to build greater societal adaptability to natural climate fluctuations.

There are five principal problems with an adaptionist approach. First, adaptionists usually underestimate the likely negative effects of a warming, or at least the risks of such. Most such calculations give short shrift to the human costs that would accompany, for example, flooded coastal zones or shifts of hundreds of miles in areas suitable for farming. Although roads and dikes might be built and new crops bred, the human costs of disruption, dislocation, and retraining are unavoidable. The ecological risks are also generally not considered. Unmanaged ecosystems are less able to adapt, especially to unnaturally rapid changes, than human society. Abundant geologic evidence links periodic mass extinctions in the oceans to decreasing temperatures.[11] Populations within parks and conservation preserves that could not migrate or adapt would be lost, and biologically vital coastal communities would be severely at risk.[12] Similarly, adaptionists generally do not factor in the likelihood of unpredictable, unpleasant surprise. The stunning discovery in 1985 of a "hole" in the Antarctic ozone layer underscores the potential for sudden threshold effects instead of smooth incremental change. In recent Senate testimony, Wallace Broecker, a professor of geochemistry at Columbia University, raised the possibility, based on new evidence, that "future climate changes may come in sharp steps, and these steps may have complicated geographic patterns. If so, then we must begin to think in terms of climate surprises that may, without warming, cause shifts in temperature and rainfall patterns."[13] In light of these and the other risks described earlier, it is a poor bet for any government to count on emerging from a rapidly changing climate as a "net winner."

A second difficulty with the adaptionist approach is that it either depends on being able to predict the specific regional (or even local) impacts of changing climate or else requires that steps be taken to adapt to change without knowing, for example, whether the new climate would be wetter or drier. Current ability to model and predict geographically specific impacts is very limited, and the ability to do so with confidence is generally thought to lie far in the future. Hence, the lead time for action under this approach may simply be too short (and certainly shorter than for a preventionist strategy, which relies on the ability to predict the broad outlines—rather than the local or regional impacts—of global climate change). Adaptation without knowing the likely regional impact is possible. For example, a region could at the same time conserve water supplies and develop reservoir and flood control systems. However, building margins of safety in both directions is expensive and would certainly be politically hard to swallow.

Third, adapting may widen the already yawning gap between the developed and developing countries. Adaptation requires strong research capabilities, heavy capital investment, and a government that can mobilize and direct resources. All of these are extremely scarce in the developing world. Thus, unless the developing countries as a group are net winners from a changed climate, a "go-it-alone" adaptionist approach is likely to leave these nations worse off relative to the developed countries than they now are.

Fourth, adaptionists must at some time in the future become preventionists. No one believes that society as we know it can adapt to, say a 15°C global average warming. Thus, the planet's warming trend must eventually be slowed and then stopped. The longer society waits, the more rapid and disruptive the slowdown might have to be. It could also be much more expensive than it would be today if, in the interim, a heavy commitment had been made to coal, tar sands, oil shales, and other carbon-rich fuels. This would be especially true—and tragic—for developing countries, which have the choice, now, of choosing a more energy-efficient path than that travelled by the now-industrialized nations. Later actions to halt the warming might also be far more internationally divisive than cooperative action would be today. Assume for the sake of argument that in a warming world some countries experience net gains. There would also be—perhaps next door—net losers. International cooperation is difficult to imagine today in the presence of so much uncertainty about which nations, if any, stand to gain, but it would be infinitely more difficult in a world spilt into countries with demonstrably opposed interests in continuing a climate-altering regime. Suppose, as some have suggested, that the Soviet Union would be a net winner and the United States a net loser. (Soviet scientists, it should be noted, do not on the whole share this view.[14]) The prospects for international cooperation would be far dimmer than in today's shared uncertainty.

Finally, even today, the adaptionist strategy poses political challenges at least as formidable as the preventionist approach. As one adaptionist report puts it: "A country with stable government, balanced budgets and low unemployment is in a strong position to adapt to a warming; a political entity that harbors autocratic or corrupt leadership or one with excessive numbers of people living in hunger and poverty has small reserve to meet the further stresses of a changing climate."

Moreover, this strategy "will require fundamental changes—in the economic and political goals and procedures" of nations, and "a shift of priorities and incentives from short term performance towards the identification and pursuit of long term goals for society."[15] By these criteria few governments would qualify, and the prospects look dim indeed.

VI

If a research-only strategy is unwarranted, given the high costs associated with waiting for scientific certainty, and an adaptionist focus is flawed, are there preventive measures that could significantly affect the greenhouse trend, that make economic sense, and that seem politically realistic? Each of these conditions is essential, and the criteria for meeting them should be stringent. Because of the scientific uncertainties, any preventive measure should be either inexpensive, given the context, or economically justifiable on its own merits.

There are, in fact, preventive measures that meet all three conditions. As Mintzer's analysis suggests, a policy based on increasing efficiency and phasing out CFCs would significantly slow the warming trend. It could delay the commitment to the equivalent of a doubled atmospheric carbon dioxide level for many decades beyond current trends, thereby buying time for the development of alternative energy supplies and for taking the adaptionist steps that will inevitably be necessary. This last is an important point. The two strategies are not mutually exclusive. Adaptionists point to energy conservation as a prime step, just as preventionists do, and some adapting will be necessary under even a fairly aggressive preventionist approach. There is, nonetheless, a significant difference in policy emphasis between the two approaches, and an important choice to be made. Because of its global scope and long time scale, dealing with the greenhouse effect will take an usual degree of political will. Certainly, a general consensus on the overriding goals for action—either to avert climate change or adapt to it—will be a necessary precondition.

Research in many countries and economic sectors confirms that energy efficiency improvements remain a very large resource, and by far the lowest-cost source of new energy supply at least for the short-and mid-term future.[16] Although generally unrecognized, the potential for energy savings is as great in the developing countries as it is in the industrialized ones; poverty is as great a cause of wasteful energy use as is great wealth.

The poor who light their homes with a wick dipped in kerosene, for example, get one-hundredth the illumination of a 100-watt electric bulb for the same amount of energy. At the other end of the spectrum, countries just now building large energy supply systems can capitalize on the insights gained in the industrialized nations over the last decade and save literally billions of dollars. For example, a detailed study of Brazil shows that an investment of $4 billion in high-efficiency technologies (such as refrigerators, lighting, and motors) would supplant construction of 21 large power plants for a net saving of $ 19 billion between now and 2000. Cutbacks in fossil-fuel use that are achieved through strategies to conserve energy will also ameliorate acid deposition and related air pollution problems.

The first step in a global greenhouse strategy, then, is a concerted push toward national energy plans built on energy efficiency and, to the extent possible, fuel switching to the less carbon-rich fuels, especially natural gas. At the international level this entails a major shift in bilateral and multilateral assistance programs, which now do not encourage efficiency investments.

The second step is a prompt agreement to phase out CFC use. Analysis has shown that it would be technically easy and inexpensive to halt the current rapid growth in emissions and actually to cut use by one-third in about five years.[17] The U.S. government has taken a step in this direction by formally producing a precaution freeze at current levels and a phase-out over the next 10 to 20 years. As of this writing, there is considerable momentum for a far-reaching international agreement to reduce CFC use; the motivation so far, however, has been dominated by the need to protect the stratospheric ozone layer. If the case for slowing the greenhouse warming could also be factored in, a phase-out agreement seems not at all visionary.

It is not too early to begin international discussions on the greenhouse effect and on long-range energy strategies. A scientific exchange on this subject between the United States and the Soviet Union is already under way and could rather easily be elevated to the political level.[18] Considering that between them these two nations account for 40 per cent of global carbon dioxide emissions (and 52 per cent of global coal reserves), this would be a significant step. The United States should also seek to engage China in discussions of that country's energy options. China currently sees few alternatives to a heavy reliance on coal, but the government has also shown itself to be receptive to major policy shifts—if they will save money. Two other regional discussions should also begin—among the Organization for Economic Cooperation and

Development nations and among developing countries. A conference exploring alternative energy strategies in developing nations would be a sensible first step, especially if it explored the foreign exchange implications of the various alternatives. Energy efficiency improvements generally have the triple advantage of costing less, generating more jobs, and requiring less foreign exchange than new supply options. Given many countries' urgent need to ease their foreign debt burden, this last is a major advantage.

Finally, greater efforts must be made to slow tropical deforestation. Although the size of the contribution of deforestation to the warming trend is the subject of much debate, the possibility that the biota are a significant source of carbon dioxide, combined with the overwhelming human and ecological reasons for saving the tropical forests, makes a sufficient case for immediate, high-priority action.[19]

In the research realm, a far more vigorous research and development program on nonfossil energy alternatives should be launched in the United States and elsewhere. Solar energy options need consistent long-term funding, as do the wide variety of technologies for increasing the efficiency of energy use. Improved nuclear reactor designs should be further explored on paper to see what contribution they can make toward solving nuclear energy's formidable economic, safety, waste, and proliferation problems. It goes without saying that basic research on the greenhouse phenomenon deserves the highest priority. And, finally, further policy analysis of most of the issues raised in this discussion is badly needed.

If all this is begun in the next few years, prospects for averting an unacceptably large greenhouse warming might soon appear dramatically better than they do today. The task itself will be easier to accomplish now than later. And if, by some completely unexpected turn of events, the greenhouse warming disappears as a global concern, the world will still be better off.

References

1. P.D. Jones, T.M.L. Wigley, and P.B. Wright, "Global Temperature Variations Between 1861 and 1984," *Nature* 3 (July 31, 1986): 430-34.
2. A.H. Lachenbruch and B. Vaugh Marshall, "Changing Climate: Geothermal Evidence from Permafrost in the Alaskan Arctic." *Science* 234 (Nov.7, 1986): 689-96.
3. T.P. Barnett, *Estimates of Global Sea Level Change: A Problem of Uniqueness* (New York Van Nostrand Reinhold, 1984).

4. J.R. Trabalka, ed., *Atmospheric Carbon Dioxide and the Global Carbon Cycle* (Report No. DOE/ER-0239) (Washington, D.C.: Department of Energy, 1986).
5. Data compiled by M. Valentine, World Resources Institute, for Maryland, Virginia, North Carolina, South Carolina, Georgia, and Alabama from state departments of agriculture and independent studies.
6. Jim Fish, Great Lakes Commission. Personal communication, 1986.
7. "The Great Lakes Water Levels." Report to Congress by the U.S. Army Corps of Engineers, 1986.
8. V. Ramanathan, et al. "Trace Gas Trends and Their Potential Role in Climate Change." *Journal of Geophysical Research* 90. no. D3 (1985): 5547-566.
9. I. Mintzer, *Colling Down the Hothouse: An Exploration of the Potental to Limit Global Warming* (Washington, D.C.: World Resources Institute, 1987).
10. C. Marchetti, *The Dynamics of Energy Systems and the Logistic Substitution Model* (HASA Report RR-79-13) (Laxenburg, Austria: HASA, 1979). Also J. Laurmann, "Market Penetration as an Impediment to Replacement of Fossil Fuels in the CO_2 Environmental Problem." Paper presented at the Symposium on Greenhouse Problem Policy Options. Hubert Humphrey Institute of Public Affairs. Minneapolis, Minnesota, May 1984.
11. Steven M. Stanley, "Mass Extinctions in the Ocean," *Scientific American* (June 1985), 64-72.
12. Robert L. Peters and Joan D.S. Darling, "The Greenhouse Effect and Nature Reserves." *Bioscience* 35. no. 11 (1985): 707-717.
13. Wallace S. Broecker. Testimony Before the Senate Subcommittee on Environmental Pollution, June 10-11, 1986.
14. See M.I. Budyko and M.C. MacCracken, "US/USSR Meeting of Experts on Causes of Recent Climate Change," Lawrence Livermore National Laboratory, Aug. 1986.
15. Wallace Orr Roberts, "The Coming Global Greenhouse Warming: What We Can and Should Do About It." Report of teleconference sponsored by the Western Behavioral Sciences Institute, Aug. 1985.
16. See, for example, Jose Goldemberg, Thomas B. Johansson, Amulÿa K.N. Reddy, and Robert H. Williams. *Energy for a Sustainable World* (Washington, D.C.: World Resources Institute, 1987).
17. A.S. Miller and I.M. Mintzer, *The Sky Is the Limit: Strategies for Protecting the Ozone Layer* (Washington, D.C.: World Resources Institute, Nov. 1986).

18. See Budyko and MacCraken, "U.S./USSR Meeting"; and for example, speech by Sen. John Chafee to the Fifth U.S./USSR Symposium on Comprehensive Analysis of the Environment, Washington, D.C., Dec. 10, 1986.
19. See World Resources Institute, World Bank, and United Nations Development Programme. *Tropical Forests: A Call for Action* (Washington, D.C: World Resource Institute, Oct. 1985).

4

Aftermath of Kyoto: Application of Economics and Polity

In environmental efforts of Global level, Kyoto Conference holds an important place. But even more important is the follow up at regional and global platforms in economic and political terms. The same has been highlighted in the present chapter. After the completion of December 1997 Kyoto Conference, participating nations are now grappling with the realities of a negotiated agreement to cut future carbon emissions below 1990 levels. Expressions of passionate concern about climate change and the prospects for doing something to shed fears of global warming have given way to tough political bargaining over which countries, which industries, and which firms will actually bite the carbon emissions reduction bullet.

Analyzing has opened vistas to 'strategizing'. Kyoto policies defining US relations with the rest of the world are now being transformed to domestic industrial policy in worldwide. Countries the evolving policy we observe diverts attempts from meeting smaller but difficult challenges of managing the local commons to the ultimate challenge of managing the global commons.

This shift of attention from local to global has been related to with crises that seem always to be a prerequisite to formal governmental action. The need to manage the commons, whether it be common hunting territories, fisheries, or a common air mantle that sustains life, defines a need for property rights and government execution of those rights (Anderson and Leal, 1991).

The commons management imperative is a centralizing force in all human communities. Decentralized spheres of private action and exclusive private rights, what might be termed individual or local sovereignty, are reduced as government spreads feet. Each step taken along the way involves collective decision making that unavoidably encounters special interest struggles to have wealth redistributed in favourable ways. And each step can facilitate social gains by denying a tragedy of the commons.

As the dimensions of the commons to be managed expand beyond community, state, region, and nation, rules that govern heterogeneous communities open up tracks for ever more homogeneous regulations. Customs, traditions, and institutions like common law tend to be pushed to one side as statues and treaties from a more extensive social order.

Local sovereignty is compromised as joint decision making becomes delegated to state, national, and then international bodies. When nations collectively agree to pursue global·environmental goals, state and national sovereignty is of need compromised. An inevitable trade off accompanies the transfer of sovereignty from smaller to larger communities (Yandle, 1997, p. 29-30; Ostrom and Schlager, 1996, p. 46). When remotely determined homogeneous regulations are imposed on diverse communities, some efficiencies in resource use, where more readily measured costs are weighed against locally perceived benefits, are exchanged for the avoidance of more remote costs, not observed with ease at local levels. As control becomes more remotely determined, the efficiency losses tend to increase. It is obviously important that the marginal benefits from avoiding global costs exceed the ever-increasing marginal costs of efficiency failures. The Kyoto Protocol is a case in point.

The December 1997 agreement to reduce greenhouse gases, endorsed by representatives from 174 nations, joins an estimated 180 other environmental treaties on submit with the UN Secretary General (Committee to Preserve American Security and Sovereignty, 1998). Kyoto, if ratified, and the other treaties are fundamentally different from national decisions to legislate in the interest of better air or water. First off there is the remoteness issue. The Kyoto Protocol seeks to impose a homogeneous rule—greenhouse gas reductions based on 1990 emissions—on a diverse and heterogeneous group of communities.

Just the task of getting 174 nations, let alone 174 people, to agree on substantive issues staggers the mind. Next, constitutional constraints and domestic rules of law and property that normally safeguard property rights and force competitive behaviour in domestic economics can be compromised more readily at the post-Kyoto negotiators' table. National legislative bodies accustomed to writing statutes and directing the ship of state find themselves subject to political pressures from far-flung governing bodies as nations prepare to engage in trade with other nations.

The items to be traded vary fundamentally from the array of goods and services that normally describe exports and imports. The Kyoto trade involves bartered off-setting actions to reduce greenhouse gases; the exchange of still undefined marketable emission grants and bilateral agreements to engage in clean technology transfers and development assistance.

Finally, actions that might otherwise be seen as attempts by industries to cartelize, restrict output, and enhance competitors' costs are encouraged in the name of global environmental protection. National policies that affect the new tradeable goods that might otherwise be seen as violations of GATT are viewed benevolently. Kyoto offers extraordinary opportunities for all-encompassing cartelization that converts foreign policy to world industrial policy. Those interest groups concerned about the environment may still receive comfort in all this. Carbon emissions may be reduced and the prospect for global warming, if it exists, may be marginally diminished. Those who see Kyoto as an opportunity to aim a stronger toehold in markets will be comforted as well. Relative prices of major energy commodities will change. For example, the demand for natural gas will rise while the demand for coal plummets. Certain ozone-depleting chemicals will be restricted and comparative advantage enjoyed by nations worldwide will be altered.

In short, there will be winners and losers in the post-Kyoto movement. But as much as anything else, the Kyoto Protocol magnifies the pressure of well-organized interest groups to obtain transferred wealth and resources from the politically weak and unorganized sections. Kyoto, global warming, and greenhouse gas containment can be used as justification for accomplishing special interest goals. To the extent that the justification becomes accepted, Kyoto decreases the cost of political favour seeking.

Apart from the more traditional political favour seeking, the Protocol establishes an enhanced stage for nations to pursue special interest benefits. The last major section of the chapter examines the political bargaining now underway in Europe, where emission allocations are being fixed for member nations, and in the process, potential beneficiaries of some preliminary statistical modelling reported in the section throw some light on the potential winners and losers. The chapter ends with some final thoughts on Kyoto and sovereignty.

I

Impact of Economic Aspects

The Kyoto Protocol is an evolved agreement relying in the notion that developed countries, which are automatically large energy users and greenhouse gas producers, should bear the brunt of reducing emissions in the name of avoiding costly climatic changes. This idea was first argued formally in Toronto in June, 1988. It was then addressed by Congress in 1989 in proposed bill—the Global Warming Prevention Act—and later became fundamental to commitments sought in 1992 when representatives of 160 nations attended the Rio de Janeiro Conference on Environment and Development (Manne and Richels, 1991).

Attempts for the purpose to contain greenhouse emission were bolstered further at a second Conference of Parties to the Rio de Janerio Agreement held in Berlin in 1995, yielding the Berlin Mandate, which stressed the importance of gaining national commitments to greenhouse gas arts.

Then, an ad hoc group meeting in Geneva in 1995 and again in 1996 called for binding mandates for developed countries, 38 in number known as Annex I and including primarily the OECD and Eastern European states. Fruitful co-operation and emission reporting were expected of developing countries, but no quantifiable emission reduction commitments were called for. Just what are the relative emission magnitudes involved here? In 1990 the Annex I countries, with the USA leading the pack, produced roughly 64 per cent of all greenhouse gases, which then aggregated six billion tons annually. (The data here, from Antonelli and Schaefer, 1997, p. 18, were drawn from reports of the Intergovernmental Panel on Climate Change.) The developing countries, led by China, generated the remaining 36 per cent. Forecasts of emissions for the year 2015 predicted total emissions to be 8.45 billion tons, with the developing countries producing 52 per cent of the total. At that point, the developed states would become minority players. By the year 2100, the forecast called for 19.8 billion tons of greenhouse emissions, with the developing world producing 66 per cent of the total. Seen in this context, the Protocol is a very odd agreement, if reducing total greenhouse gases is its primary purpose. Under the Protocol, developed countries have agreed to reduce emissions by the period 2008-2012 so that their aggregate will be five per cent less than 1990 levels.

Meanwhile developing countries will be expanding emissions at roughly three per cent per year. With these opposing trends, it is impossible to see how 1990 targets can ever be attained overall. Obviously, there is far more to Kyoto than reducing the threat of global warming. A review of research on the economic effects of greenhouse gas containment may provide some clues regarding other goals.

II

Existing Literature on the Subject

Much before Kyoto, academic economists were busy turning out studies on the economic effects of controlling greenhouse gases (Manne and Richels, 1991; Nordhaus, 1991; Peace and Barbier, 1991; Whaley and Wigle, 1991; Jorgenson and Wilcoxen, 1993; Kosobud, and others 1994; Larsen and Shah, 1994; Sinclair, 1994; Holz-Eakin and Selden, 1995; Carrato, Galeotti, and Gallo, 1996; Chen, 1997). Some of the studies represent the economist's most sophisticated techniques for shaping national economies.

Others focus solely on European issues. Still others compare various government instruments for reducing carbon emissions—taxes, regulation, and marketable permits. The Jorgenson-Wilcoxen (1993) study follows major macro model of the US economy that accounts for 35 industrial sectors, consumer behaviour, investment, and trade.

The authors assume a policy goal of holding US carbon emissions constant at 1990 levels. As it turns out, they incorrectly assume that a 14.4 per cent reduction in year 2020 emissions will achieve 1990 levels. Recent data show reductions in the range of 36 per cent are necessary. Nonetheless, the Jorgenson-Wilcoxen model shows the level of taxes required on various fuels to achieve their stated goal. For example, one of their simulations demands coal to be taxed at $US11.01 per ton; oil at $US2.31 per barrel, and natural gas at $US0.28 per thousand cubic feet. The resulting revenues will yield $26 billion annually to the federal government.

The authors conclude that the tax policies considered will have effects on GDP (Gross Domestic Product) increase that range from fractions of a percentage point reduction to a one percentage point reduction from baseline growth. However, they show dramatic changes in the relative prices of energy, with coal sustaining a 40 per cent price hike and an associated 26 per cent reduction in production. In a similar study that focuses on the United Kingdom, Pearce and Barbier (1991) estimate a 67 per cent hike in coal taxes, 40 per cent for gas, and 54 per cent for oil will be required to reduce UK carbon emissions by 20 per cent in the year 2005.

They note that unilateral action can accomplish very little; domestic energy use and carbon emissions may fall, but importation of substitutes from elsewhere can cause carbon emission replacement by exporting countries. These prospects for massive changes in relative prices and altered trade patterns provide clues for identifying players in Kyoto's exclusive interest struggle. '

Manne and Richels (1991) take a global approach in their study of emission reductions. They assume that countries worldwide seek to reduce carbon emissions 20 per cent by the year 2000. They correctly assume that the industrialized world will accept the 20 per cent reduction goal, but that the rest of the world will not.

They calculate GDP losses associated with the carbon constraint and realise that the USA would sustain rising GDP losses across the control period, hitting a net loss in growth of 3 per cent by the year 2030. Losses for the OECD countries are shown to be much lower, reaching 1-2 per cent in 2030. The estimate helps us to learns now the EU countries could push so hard for US emission reductions. Mexico and oil producing countries would sustain even larger losses, and China the largest of all, losing 10 per cent of GDP in the later half of the twenty-first century.

In the most stringent set of circumstances, the price of coal would increase fourfold, and the demand for oil would accordingly enhance not decrease. (Is it possible that some oil producers would favour Kyoto?). Other studies reported in professional journals follow along the lines of these just summarized. The academics appear to agree that curtailment of carbon emissions to 1990 baseline levels places the brunt of the adjustment cost on the coal and coal-related sectors, that GDP growth rates in the industrial world will be affected by useful amounts. (For example, a loss of 1 per cent in US GDP is not small potatoes.) The studies also demonstrate the potential benefits to permit trading, as opposed to taxation and regulation. Of particular relevance to this chapter, the research tell us:

(1) that the potential rate of the Kyoto Protocol to the USA is far greater in total and in relative terms than that for other industrialized countries;
(2) that lot of major European countries (UK and Germany) have already experienced adjustments that lighten their load;
(3) that substitutes for coal have much to gain,; and
(4) that how control instruments and permit markets are defined will offer significant differential effects across countries.

III

Research and Observations by Public Sector, Consultants and Trade Units

With time for the Kyoto conference drew near, a number of major economic studies were produced at the behest of trade associations, organized labour, and government. In most cases, these studies were performed by widely recognized and respected consulting firms whose reputations represent great investments in brand-name capital.

As might be expected, the studies focused on sectors or elements of the US economy that were of greatest interest to the sponsors. The observations help us to understand more about the stakes involved for special interest groups. DRI/McGraw-Hill provided a major economic impact study for the United Mine Workers/Bituminous Coal Association, itself important alliance (*The Impact of Carbon Mitigation Strategies,* 1997). The study, which was reviewed by the Economic Policy Institute, provides insights into estimates of the macroeconomic and sector impact of stabilizing greenhouse gas emissions at 1990 levels and reducing emissions by 10 per cent below 1990 levels by the year 2010. The study assumes government-issued marketable permits will constrain carbon emissions. These permits are predicated to catch prices that range from $US180-280 per ton of emissions across the year 1995 through 2020 for the containment case. Permit costs will be higher in the 10 per cent reduction case. The study shows a seven-fold price increase for coal, electricity prices increasing about 100 per cent, and retail gasoline prices rising, 40 to 50 per cent. Coal which now, offers 24 per cent of US energy will provide 18 per cent.

Petroleum's share increases, and natural gas maintains its current market share. The government's revenue from permit sales rises to $US776 billion in 2020, and yields a budget surplus of $US388 billion by 2020. Yearly losses in employment reach 1.4 million for the years 2000-2020, and GDP growth is reduced by one percentage point as the economy adjusts to the constraints. Coal output is predicted to come down 45 per cent, rubber and plastics by 50 per cent, and electricity production by 18 per cent. A major study by WEFA sponsored by the American Petroleum Institute guess US carbon emissions will stabilize at 1990 levels by the year 2010. The study realistically rejects the State Department's proposal for inter-country trade permits due to the absence of institutional infrastructure (National Impacts, 1998).

WEFA assumes a US permit market instead. The analysts assume uncontrolled emissions will be 27 per cent above 1990 levels by 2010, and 46 per cent above the target by 2020. To ensure the necessary reductions, carbon permit prices would rise across the control period from $US100 per ton/per year to $300 per ton. The economic effects of the reductions would cause a 30 to 55 per cent increase in consumer prices, with energy-intensive sectors sustaining shocks comparable to those associated with the Arab oil embargoes of the 1970s. Real GDP would fall 2.4 per cent less than baseline 2010 estimates, with that loss alone amounting to $US227 billion 1992 dollars. Cumulative GDP losses across the years 2001 to 2020 would total 3.3 trillion dollars, which is roughly 48 per cent of 1996 GDP. Employment downfall would exceed 22.8 million workers by the year 2010. Addressing international competitiveness and trade, the WEFA study noted:

> "One key reason for the lower level of real GDP is reduced global competitiveness. Because the imposition of the carbon target and permit system is not borne equally by all countries . . . US exports are relatively more expensive on the world market, while the prices of many imported products will fall. As a consequence, exports are lowered dramatically, while imports are increased substantially."
>
> (National Impacts, 1998)

Findings say that chemicals, paper, textiles and apparel, and computer and electronic parts production will be severely affected. The US Department of Energy prepared an exhaustive study of Kyoto effects (Office of Policy and International Affairs, 1997). Same report also assumes a control target of achieving 1990 emission levels by 2010 and considers both a US and international market for tradeable permits. If the market is clearly domestic, permit prices rise to $US150 per ton of carbon emissions. With a world market, the price falls to $US40. Assuming a domestic control scenario, US coal consumption will reduce by 50 per cent by 2010, with the price tripling. Total GDP losses across the period will have a present value of $US418 billion. Revenues from permits will reach $US400 billion by the year 2010.

Ronald J. Sutherland, Senior Economist for the American Petroleum Institute, prepared an interesting analysis of Kyoto policy options.

Using a simple econometric model for describing carbon emissions, Sutherland (1998) shows that it is practically impossible for the US to achieve Kyoto's goals, especially if nuclear energy production is ultimately replaced by gas-fired turbines, which is now forecast. Three things happen. Clean nuclear is replaced with dirtier natural gas. Income growth leads to a predictable increase in the demand for energy, and thus more carbon emissions. The price increases necessary for achieving Kyoto goals will not be accepted. For example, based on estimates of price elasticity of demand from 10 large-scale studies, gasoline prices would necessitate to rise from $1.25 per gallon now to $4.23 per gallon in 2010, just to achieve Kyoto levels.

After that, prices would have to rise continuously to offset increases in demand generated by rising incomes. Sutherland findings demonstrates the hopelessness of relying on technical change, prices and controls for reaching Kyoto's US goal for 2010. In a few words, the target date for achieving the goal comes too soon.

Faced with an array of studies forecasting important Kyoto burden, the US Congress held hearings on the matter in March, 1998, and heard from Dr Janet Yellen, Chairperson on the Council of Economic Advisors (Testimony of Dr Janet Yellen, 1998).

Dr Yellen indicated that the price imposed by Kyoto on the US economy would be quite small. Putting the burden in terms of the cost of reducing a ton of carbon emissions, she explained how the cost could fall from $US240 per metric ton to $US23 per ton. Her positive estimate assumed large gains in energy-production efficiencies, obtained through deregulation, expanded emission credit trading with developing and developed countries, and carbon fall gains from natural sinks, such as the ocean and forests. She indicated that her estimates were not based on a single formal model of the economy, but were derived from assumptions applied to several major studies.

It is worth noting that for Dr. Yellen's prediction to obtain, all her assumptions would need to be met in a matter of 10 years, assuming the US Senate ratifies the Protocol this year.

There are other notable studies that might be mentioned, still the reports surveyed here serve the purpose of identifying strategic issues that motivate special interest groups either to rally around Kyoto or to take costly steps to stop the ratification process. Farthermore, the relative effects on energy-intensive sectors are emphasized, with coal production carrying the brunt of the load. International competitiveness for identifiable sectors is at issue. And the scope of the permit market either domestic or international—is shown to have significant effects on the ultimate cost projected for the US economy.

IV

Theory of Bootleggers and Baptists

During the year April, 1998, the European Union members officially ratified and signed the Kyoto treaty, accepting an 8 per cent reduction in carbon emissions below 1990 levels over the next 15 years (Leopold, 1998). The USA, which had accepted a 7 per cent decrease had still not ratified the agreement, and the prospects for doing so were dim. In the same month, Japan, Austalia, Brazil, Canada, Norway and Monaco signed. Argentina and Pacific island nations had signed earlier.

As of January 2000, 84 countries have signed the Protocol, although only 22 have ratified. Perhaps the most notable non-ratifier is the United States (Status of Ratification, 2000). With 36 per cent of emissions among industrialized nations, and 23 per cent worldwide, the USA only can prevent the agreeing nations from reaching the requisite 55 per cent reduction in emissions required for the agreement to be binding.

(a) *Some theoretical considerations*

It is useful to consider some theories of regulation when seeking to understand events related to the implementation of the Kyoto Protocol. The review of economic effects identified potential winners and losers and highlighted the exceptionally great value of wealth transfers that are at stake. Armed with the information, consider some theory.

We can say that there are three basic theories of regulation that may assist the analysis (see further Yandle, 1989) : (1) The first is called the *public interest* theory, which simply states that governments attempt to maximize the collective well being of citizens. Political actions, according to this theory, are efficiency drawn, always weighing benefits and costs and attempting to maximize net benefits. If taxes are to be imposed to reduce quantifiable harms from global warming, the politicians will carefully calibrate and levy the taxes so that least-cost solutions emerge. When things turn out differently, the proponents of this theory respond that politicians, like everyone else, are fallible.

(2) This theory carries a note of political realism. The *capture* theory tells us to expect dedicated politicians attempting to serve the public interest to encounter persuasive special interest groups who have a substantial impact on political action. In effect, the political decision maker, though committed, is captured by the special interest group. Unfortunately, this theory does not help determine which of many special interest groups may succeed in gaining the struggle.

(3) The third theory, called the *economic* theory of regulation (Stigler, 1971; Posner, 1974; and Peltzman, 1976), asks us to consider the political arena as a market place where favours are brought and sold. Interest groups who have the most to gain or to lose will bid the highest

prices for favours. Politicians dedicated to preserving their jobs, and needing large amounts of campaign funds to do so, auction off the favours. If carbon emissions have to be controlled, the politician, by this theory, will find the group with the largest economic stake in the outcome and favour that group. Other competing groups will try to outbid the winner. Special interest groups with large markets and revenues that can be enhanced by regulation can outbid other less organized groups that have smaller to offer.

The smaller the group, holding the prize constant, the more each member can gain. The larger the group that bears the cost of the prize, the less likely it is that they will mount meaningful criticism. Theory of *bootleggers and baptists*, a subset of the economic theory, calls attention to coalitions that seem to prevail when environmental and other social regulation is being formulated (Yandle, 1983). Though powerful interest groups still matter, this theory tells us that there must be at least two interest groups working in the same the direction. Bootleggers like Sunday Closing laws that close legitimate sellers of alcoholic beverages; they get the market to themselves. Baptists support the same laws, but for entirely different reasons.

Kyoto promises to be rich with Bootlegger/Baptists coalitions. Every group is necessary for successful outcomes; if one defects, the other will lose benefits.

During the post-Kyoto period, we should expect to find environmentalists pushing for ratification, enforcement, and working to prevent backsliding. These are the 'Baptists' in the theory. They demand regulation of particular kinds. They do not support voluntary action and co-operation. Traditional regulation theories tell us that we should search for other special interest groups who either are positioned to gain from regulatory enforcement and stringency or who must fend off losses that stems from proposed rules. Within industries, there may be firms that have specialized assets or output that are favoured by rules raising the cost of competing assets and products. With Kyoto, there are nations positioned to exploit carbon reductions already made; they are in a position to raise the cost of competing economies.

There are other countries that can become lower cost suppliers of carbon reduction offsets. But unlike conventional regulatory incidents that involve one national government regulating domestic industries, Kyoto presents us with the unusual situation of countries behaving like firms strategically positioning themselves to benefit while seeking protection and credibility from international environmental groups that embrace Kyoto as a necessary part of their environmental cause.

V

Episodes in the Post-Kyoto Period

In tune with the Bootlegger-Baptist theory, the Kyoto Protocol provides environmentalists to run interference and reduce favour-seeking costs for interest groups already working to obtain political favours. For example, in January 1997, Enron Corporation, a leading provider of low-carbon natural gas, announced the formation of Enron Renewable Energy Corporation indicating that it was 'preparing to take advantage of the growing interest in environmentally failed alternatives of power in the $US250 billion US electricity market' (Salisbury, 1998). The new division faces the difficult challenge of producing solar and other non-traditional energy products at costs that can compete with traditional energy sources.

As a result, Tom White, Enron Renewable Energy CEO, understandably endorsed President Clinton's $US6.3 billion plan to fight global warming, which includes $US3.6 billion in tax credits to spur the manufacturing and purchase of renewable energy and related technologies (Salisbury, 1998). Kyoto justified taxpayer subsidies will make life easier for firms like Enron. Other US producers have for long time enjoyed federal subsidies they now hope can be global-warming justified. On 9April, 1998, the National Corn Growers Association launched a campaign hoping to stall congressional efforts to eliminate the 5.4 cents per gallon federal tax incentive given to producers of corn-based ethanol (National Corn Growers Report, 1998).

Originally enacted on the dubious basis of providing energy self-sufficiency, the large ethanol subsidies were on shaky ground. A few days after the Renewable Fuels Association joined forces with ethanol producers to celebrate Earth Day, calling attention to ethanol's beneficial influence on global warming (Renewable Fuels Association, 1998b). On 20th April, Secritary of Agriculture Dan Glickman indicated his strong support for extending the ethanol subsidy, noting that 'renewable fuels provide an important opportunity . . . to smaller greenhouse gas emissions (Renewable Fuels Association, 1998a). Immediately after Kyoto, Mary Nichols, US EPA Assistant Administrator for Air and Radiation, spoke at the National Ethanol Conference in Des Moines, Iowa, in January, telling the audience: 'One area where I think we do more together is the area of climate change and global warming' (Stark, 1998). Sufficiently understandably, no one mentioned that ethanol production was so costly that it might be a net destroyer of energy, or that the federal government's $US600 million yearly ethanol subsidy, half of which went to one ethanol producer, Archer-Daniel-Midland ($US7 billion in the last 16 years). Nor was a literal Bootlegger-Baptist connection explained.

The taxpayer subsidy assists the production, of beverage as well as industrial alcohol (Bandow, 1997). On 6 May 1998, House Speaker Gingrich successfully salvaged the ethanol program, much to the disappointment of Senator Bill Archer (Republican, Texas) who sought to level the playing field for oil produces in his state by ending the programme (Pianin, 1998). Global warming helped save the day for the corn producers. Following in their American cousins 'ways the Canadian Commercial Alcohol Association trumpeted the products' carbon reducing virtues, suggesting that any CO_2 produced by burning ethanol would be recycled into corn plant tissue, thereby yielding a net decrease in atmosphere carbon dioxide levels (Canadian Commercial Alchol Association, 1998). Not to be outdone, the National Biodiesel Board, representing farmers nationwide who produce soybean and other vegetable oil goods testified before Secretary of Energy Frederico Pena on 19 February 1998, pointing out the environmental benefits of blending farm-produced oil products with diesel fuel (National Biodiesel Board, 1998).

Lobbying to persuade the Department of Energy (DOE) to give regulatory approval to biodiesel as an officially consented alternative fuel, insuring a market through DOE programmes, the trade association officials indicated 'biodiesel helps decrease the effects of global warming by directly displacing fossil hydrocarbons'. Although corn producers with specialized assets for producing ethanol see a pot of gold in Kyoto, farmers who must fare in worldly competitive market generally oppose Kyoto.

Dean Kleckner, president of the 4.8 million member American Farm Bureau Federation, opposed the signing of the protocol 'because of its potential loss to US farmers' (Farm-state senators sceptical, 1998). Reinforcing his concern, Mary Novak, senior vice-president of WEFA, a major enconometric consulting firm, predicted a Kyoto-induced 10 per cent increase in the cost of food, and substantially more fertilizer taxes and fuel prices. There are winners and losers within the same economic sector.

Although the ethanol and biodiesel 'bootleggers' were rapidly putting on the green, a coalition of major oil producers and thousands of other firms were having trouble keeping members on the anti-Kyoto reservation. Calling their trade group the Global Climate Coalition (GCC), leading oil producers attempted to speak with one voice in debunking Kyoto's recognized shaky scientific underpinnings, calling attention to the economic effects of the protocol. In June 1998, Shell Oil declared it was leaving the GCC. Claiming credit for Shell's green conversion, Friends of the Earth spokesperson Anna Stanford indicated:

'We're delighted that our hard work has paid off, that Shell has bowed to public pressure and found that the future lies in fighting climate change and investing in green energy. Now is the time to turn our attention to Exxon to make them follow Shell's lead' (Friends of the Earth, 1998).

As to Shell's reply the firm indicated that 'there are enough indications that CO_2 emission are having an effect on climate change' (Magada, 1998). Being more specific about the firm's strategy, Mark Moody-Stuart, Chairman of Shell Transport and Trading, showed that Shell was 'promoting the development of the gas industry particularly in countries with large coal reserves such as India and China' (Magada, 1998). Obviously tough support of Kyoto, at the margin, would imply increasing demand for cleaner natural gas. Shell's departure from GCC was made easier by an earlier defection by British Petroleum.

John Browne, CEO of BP, said that industry must play a 'positive and responsible part in identifying solutions' to the global warming problem (EDF, 1997). His comments came after having serious discussions with members of the Environmental Defence Fund and also World Resources Institute, the 'Baptists' in the theory. BP, expecting to see increase in demand for oil as a cleaner substitute for coal, also announced a significant investment hike in solar and alternative energy technology development. Support of Kyoto by environmentalists is certainly to be expected, even if global warming is purely a spurious event that will pass. Strict guardians of the environment are criticised to the any human action that might despoil the environment. Any discharge that can be counted in tons must therefore be opposed on principle.

However, the Kyoto Protocol enjoys a 'Baptist' supporter that gets very near to the name itself. It is the United Methodist Church. On 17 December, just a few weeks after the Kyoto meetings, Jaydee R. Hanson, assistant general secretary of the United Methodist Board of Church and Society, declared his denomination's support for Kyoto ('Church executive calls for ratification', 1997). Hanson urged the US Senate to 'protect God's creation' by ratifying the agreement. Despite the potential benefits others find by teaming up with 'Baptists' to support the protocol, many major industries oppose Kyoto, or at least major firms in those industries do so. Coal producers and related unions are among the most vocal in their opposition. Truely, coal interests in West Virginia were successful enough to obtain state legislation prohibiting the state's division of environmental protection from 'proposing or implementing rules monitoring greenhouse gas emissions from industrial sites' ('Governor signs bill, 1998).

On signing the bill, Governor Cecil Underwood indicated that while 'actions like the Kyoto Protocol must be opposed, we 'should continue to support the development and implementation of technologies that allow the clean burning of coal' (ibid). Governor Underwood was joined by Kentucky's Governor Paul Patton in successfully gaining a Southern Governors Association resolution saying originally the same thing. The Kyoto Protocol promotes an unusual trading environment, one that has governments, not individuals or firms, trading with other governments. Even before ratification, measure were already underway to capitalize on the protocol. Some found it possible to gain additional wealth for actions they were going to take anyways.

In April 1998, Costa Rica declared a new version of its programme to save 1.25 million acres of rainforest by selling CO_2 allowances to industrial firms elsewhere (Allen, 1998). Announcing the programme, to be managed by the prestigious Swiss commercial inspection agency SGS, Costa Rican President Jose Maria Figueres described environmental bonds called Certified Tradeable Offsets, each one corresponding to one ton of carbon to be absorbed by trees. The planned offsets will adjust one million metric tons of carbon annually.

The zero cost programme generated an estimated $US20 million in revenues in 1998, or $US20 per ton of carbon emissions offset, and $US300 million over the life of the project, which has became the life expectancy of the Kyoto Protocol. In April 1998, Japan and Russia engaged in what is believed to be the world's first greenhouse gas emissions swap, which included two countries, not two private parties (Takenaka, 1998).

The alliance provides Japanese technicians to Russian power plants and factories who assist in cutting carbon emission at some 20 facilities. As part of the said agreement, Japan and Russia will share information on nuclear energy production. Both have something to offer. Japan is a leading producer of nuclear energy technology, and Russia a leader in the development of breeder reactors. Japan will become a larger investor in the search for offshore gas and oil in Russian waters.

This Kyoto type arrangement is facilitated by the fact that Russia has no difficulty in meeting its zero carbon emission hike over the 1990 baseline. The Russian economy is in shambles. However, Japan, which promised to cut baseline emissions by 6 per cent, faces a real challenge.

VI

Permits for Reducing Costs of Protocol Goals

Permits for marketable greenhouse gas emission the centrepiece of the Kyoto Protocol, offer the prospect of significantly reducing the cost of achieving protocol goals and created meaningful support for the protocol among major interest groups. Indeed, at times it appeared that having a permit market was justification enough for taking actions to address global warming, no matter what the economics or science have to say. In any case, an unfettered permit market theoretically would provide countries such as the USA, which faces high incremental control costs, the opportunity to shop world markets for lower cost providers of emission cuts. Given Kyoto's constraints, incentives would be large for securing trades, wherever they might take place. Apparently, the prospect of having the USA provide reductions through the market, instead of internally, is more than some international politicians can bear.

(*a*) *Trade Threats*

England, then Deputy Prime Minister, John Prescott, for one, wants to make certain the USA feels the pain of implementing the Kyoto accord, that more cost solutions be imposed rather than lower cost ones. In an obvious move to raise rivals costs, Prescott expressed concern that Washington would 'buy tradeable greenhouse emission permits from Russia' ('EU urges US to implement Kyoto', 1998).

As he stated 'Europe has always been clear that while we accept the trading possibilities in this matter, they should not be used as a reason for avoiding taking action in your own country'. It so occurs that Russia's emissions have fallen 30 per cent below the country's target level of zero reduction. Russia can actually increase emissions to offset higher cost reductions that might be taken elsewhere, which is exactly what tradeable permits can do.

But Prescott is disturbed by the prospect of gains from trade for the USA. First off, he is simply opposed to an international market in carbon emission offsets. In addition, his idea of trade requires that one party always decreases emissions so that another party can increase them. In the present situation, where Russia is actually cleaner than necessary, both parties can increase emissions, and both will gain by acting in this manner.

VII

Help from Traders

Again the European Commission's 3 June 1998 Communication

setting out principles for the November Buenos Aires meeting of Kyoto Parties makes it evident that Europe's member states hope to minimize their emission reduction costs while limiting gains from trade for the USA (Climate Change, 1998). Noting the EU plan to use a bubble concept in achieving overall emission reductions for the member countries, the Communication states:

> "It is recognized that the flexible mechanisms can play an important role in meeting commitments at least cost, thereby safeguarding the competitiveness of EU industry. The existence of the EU bubble does not prevent the Community from fully participating in international emission trading"
>
> (Climate Change, 1998)

European Commission expects to gain internally with its bubble and externally through emission trading. However, the Communication endorses Prescott's position regarding US trading strategies:

> "At Buenos Aires, discussions on emission trading should focus on ensuring the establishment of strict rules and for setting minimum requirements that any Party or private entity needs to fulfil in order to participate in international trading . . . It is also necessary to define the Protocol's use of the world 'supplemental' in respect to the contribution of the flexible mechanisms. In principle a ceiling should be set for trading to ensure that the main reduction in emissions are by domestic efforts."
>
> (Climate Change, 1998)

Bubble of Europe an item of contention during the Kyoto discussions. Playing the 'increase competitors' cost game', the USA pushed for each European state to have specific reduction goals to be met internally. This strategy put a heavy burden on southern European countries, such as Spain, Portugal, and Greece, lower income but high carbon emitters that are rapidly industrializing.

Countries such as the UK, Germany, The Netherland, and France were already comparatively clean, having transformed their coal-based energy economies to cleaner fuels. If uniform reductions were imposed on each European member state, the EU would lose a cross-subsidization advantage of allowing some countries to actually enhance emissions while others offset those emissions at relatively low cost. The Kyoto Protocol itself showed uniform reduction goals of eight per cent for each member country that were to be converted later to bubble-based cuts.

(a) *Allocation Scheme of EU on Analysis*

In June 1998, EU leaders met to negotiate each member's reduction allocation (EU Greenhouse Deal, 1998). The draft proposal called for individual reductions shown in the accompanying table, which lists emission reductions in ascending order.

(b) *Proposal being Modelled*

In order to explain these proposed targets, and recognizing the limitations of a small data set. I Regression using as a dependent variable the number of tons of CO_2 emissions to be released or reduced in the 1990-2010 time period for each EU country was run. This was calculated by using the percentages in the table applied to each nation's 1987 level of CO_2 emissions. (The data on emissions is taken from Larsen and Shah, 1994, p. 843; 1995 data for Luxemboug were not available in The World Bank Tables and were prepared by interpolation from Larsen and Shah, 1996.)

Independent variables included in the linear model were 1995 per capita GDP is US dollars, the 1995 ratio of carbon emissions to GDP (kg/$US), 1998 country population, and the year when each State joined the European Union. (Data for the independent variables are for 1998, and are taken from *World Resources: 1998-99*)

Table 4.1. EU Member State Emission Decrease Goals 1990-2010

Sl.No.	*Country*	*Per cent change from 1990 levels*
1.	Luxembourg	28.0
2.	Denmark	21.0
3.	Germany	–21.0
4.	Austria	–13.0
5.	UK	–12.5
6.	Belgium	–7.5
7.	Italy	–6.5
8.	Netherlands	–6.0
9.	France	–0.0
10.	Finland	–0.0
11.	Sweden	–4.0
12.	Ireland	+13.0
13.	Spain	+15.0
14.	Greece	+25.0
15.	Portugal	+27.0

Source: Friends of Earth Press Release (1998).

Testing of the carbon emissions per GDP unit and per capita GDP, shown in the accompanying chart, indicates that CO_2 emission intensity decreases with the level of per capita GDP. At first blush, the data and recession line recommend that the attainment of higher per capita GDP levels could reduce total worldwide carbon emissions.

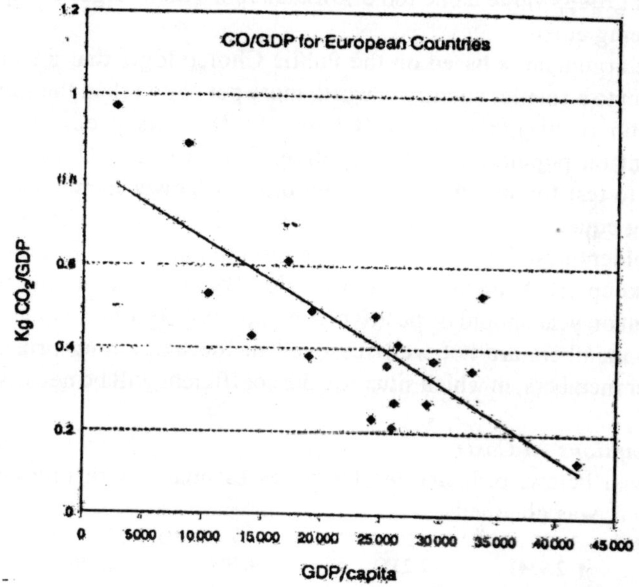

Fig. 4.1. Relationship of carbon dioxide emissions to GDP per capita in European countries.

However, this conclusion is incorrect, at least on a historical basis. Higher income levels do lead to lower CO_2 intensity, but greater total carbon emissions.

Here, we now turn to the underlying theory of the statistical model. The politics of redistribution suggest that richer countries will absorb more of the environmental load than poorer countries. All else equal, the coefficient on per capita GDP should be negative, lesser tons of emission allowances. However, the cost of emission reductions will be higher for those countries that have 'cleaner' GDP. Generally speaking, the lower the amount of CO_2 per dollar of output, the more costly it will be to decrease a ton of emission. A positive coefficient on the carbon/GDP ratio will imply that countries with 'dirtier' GDP, which are the poorer countries, receive more allowances.

A negative coefficient on the carbon/GDP ratio implies that richer nations deflect control costs to poorer countries. That is, those countries that face lower control costs (dirtier emissions) will be considered less favourable when emission allowances are distributed. The results of the modelling exercise will tell us just how generous the wealthier countries really are. Population size tests for a redistribution argument that small groups value a one ton allowance more than larger groups, all else being equal.

The argument is based on the Public Choice logic that a small concession to a smaller country is worth more per capita than the same concession to bigger country (Chen, 1997). This predicts the coefficient on population to be negative. The year of EU entry is included to test for side payments from older to newer members, all else being equal. The out of new members is always a greater threat than for older ones. Side payments in the form of emission allowances help to keep fresh members in the fold. By this argument, the coefficient on year should be positive. A competing argument suggests that new members are not well-seasoned in the bargaining process with older members, in which situation the coefficient will be negative.

(c) Assumptions on Costs

Given below, ordinary least squares estimate, with intercept suppressed, was obtained:

$$\text{TONS} = -1.477\ \text{PERCAP} - 52046\ CO_2/\text{GDP} - 449.128\ \text{POP} + 31.173\ \text{YEAR}$$
$$(-2.934) \qquad (2.255) \qquad (-4.707) \qquad (2.980)$$
$$R^2: 0.63 \quad F(3,11): 9.04$$

Below the coefficients are show T-ratio, along with other relevant statistics. As indicated, the proposed reductions follow a rough pattern that yields lower tons of emission growth for higher income countries. All else equal, fewer tons are permitted for countries with high carbon to GDP concentrations, which means countries like Portugal and Spain will clean up more, at the margin. Fewer allowances are provided to higher population countries, and more allowances are sanctioned to newer members of the European Union. For example, Spain, a recent EU member, has lower income, and a 'dirtier' GDP than France does. Even though penalized for its 'dirtier' GDP, Spain is allowed to enhance emissions over the 1990 baseline by 15 per cent. France is to achieve and then maintain the 1990 emission level. At the mean of the estimate, which has large confidence intervals given the small sample, a $US1000 hike in per capita GDP yields a 1.47 ton reduction in carbon emissions. An increase of 1g per GDP dollar of carbon emissions (the sample mean is 420g) predicts 52 fewer tons in emission growth.

An increase of one million in population is linked with a loss of 449 tons of emission allowances, and an increase of one year in the year of membership, say from 1974 to 1975, yields an increase of 31 tons in allowances. Since it is always less expensive to reduce emissions when concentrations are higher, the EU proposal establishes future sellers and buyers of tradeable emission reduction permits. Populous nation states with lower emission allowances will buy permits from states with more dirty carbon streams and larger allowances for emission growth. The allocation scheme enables us to predict that wealth will flow generally from northern to southern European nations at least for trades within the European bubble.

The EU plan of encouraging bubble trading within the EU and managing external trades places the central government is the traditional protectionist position of restricting exports and imports. But in this case the items traded are permits (emission reductions), not commodities. Along these lines, an examination of the residuals for emission allowances, those larger than one standard deviation from the mean value, reflects France gaining—being a potential seller—and Germany and Portugal losing disproportionately in the political process that determined emission allowances. The outcome also confirms the Public Choice notion that a concession to a less populous groups is worth more per member than the same concession to a larger group. Population size exercises a significant and independent effect in explaining the proposed EU sanetioning of future greenhouse emissions.

VIII
Safeguarding the Tradeable Rights

With post-Kyoto bargaining continues, there are at least two major institutional problems to be settled. The first relates to permit markets, how they will be defined put to function and the extent to which this budding market will be unfettered by international rules and regulations.

The second problem relates to enforcement of agreements within and among countries that ratify the Kyoto Protocol. While the first problem is put at discussion at the fall meeting in Buenos Aires, the second has already been discussed (Morrison, 1998). In efforts to clamp down on all forms of environmental cheating, ministers from the Group of Seven and Russia met some time back to line up co-operation against environmental crime. Britain's Deputy Prime Minister John Prescott stated that he 'wanted to see the equivalent of Interpol to allow police, customs and enforcement agencies to combat . . . global illegal trade' (Morrison, 1998).

While many issues were at stake in the discussion, the bootleg trade in chlorofluorocarbons, one of the greenhouse gases, was singled out for attention. Probably an international environmental police force is in the making.

Ultimate Considerations

Probably, the Kyoto Protocol is on of the most far-reaching international accords to be settled in modern times. And for all we know, global climate change may be one of the most far-reaching threats faced in modern times. But while the theory and proof of global warming is considered to be shaky or at least controversial (Lindzen, 1997), the theory and evidence that helps explain changing rules of sovereignty is rather well-established. Sovereighty modification concerns changing the locus and means of collective decision making.

Human efforts to manage the commons have always involved sovereignty issues. Kyoto is no different. While the principles are no different, the scope of Kyoto and the concerned magnitude of affected wealth are different indeed. When countries become substituted for firms and conventional interest groups in struggles over politically determined favours, totally different set of forces is unleashed.

There are no guiding rules of law, no overriding constitutional constraints, and no impartial judge to hear appeals and grievances. There is no international government, and if they were there by definition it would have extraordinary monopoly power. Since orthodox constraints are absent, Kyoto bargaining will involve the messy but beneficial activity of ministers of state and competing legislative bodies that must deal with expensive proposals. This chapter has examined Kyoto through the lens of Public Choice economics. Doing so enabled the identification of potential winners and losers in the political process that heads toward last ratification of a global greenhouse gas emission control system.

There is ample evidence that Kyoto is already being used as a crutch for conventional special interest groups to secure political favours. There is some fact that some nations and communities of nations are acting in strategic ways to enhance their positions relatives to other nations. We should expect no less. In the final analysis, we should expect that fears of global warming will subside and that efforts to control the world's energy economies will gradually dissipate. Yet while we might cling to these hopes, history teaches us that once a major concern gets transformed into institutional rules, interest groups that invested in those rules will work to maintain them. The compromise of sovereignty delivered by Kyoto will tend to last. When efforts are made to handle a global commons, prior property rights and spheres of private action will of necessity be compromised.

References

National Biodiesel Board (1998). Agricultural products are key to national energy security, 24 February.

Allen, V. (1998). Costa Rica to save forest with carbon credits. Reuters.

Anderson, T. and Leal, D.R. (1991). *Free Market Environmentalism.* San Francisco: Pacific Research Institute.

Antonelli, A. and Schaefer, B.D. (1997). The road to Kyoto. *Backgrounder.* Washington, DC: The Heritage Foundation (6 October).

Banbow, D. (1997). Ethanol keeps ADM drunk on tax dollars. Washington, DC: Cato Institute

Canadian Commercial Alcohol Association (5 May 1998). Fuel ethanol.

Carrato, C., Marzio G., and Massimo G. (1996). Environmental taxation and unemployment: some evidence on the 'double dividend hypothesis in Europe'. *Journal of Public Economics,* 62 (1/2), 141-81.

Chen, Z., (1997). Negotiating an agreement on global warming. *Journal of Environmental Economics and Management,* 32, 170, 178.

Chruch executive calls for ratification (17 December 1997). Washington, DC: United Methodist News Service.

Climate change (28 July 1998). European Union, DN: IP/98/498.

Committee to Preserve American Security and Sovereignty (1998). *Treatics, National Sovereignty, and Executive Power: A Report on the Kyoto Protocol.* Alexandria, VA (18 May).

EDF (1997). British petroleum to take action on climate change. Letter, September. http://www.edf.org (2 March 1998).

Friends of the Earth (1998). EU greenhouse gas deal too much hot air. Press Release.

Farm-State senators skeptical of climate plan (1998). Reuters.

Governor sings bill critical of Kyoto Protocol (1998).

Holtz-Eakin, D. and Selden, T.M. (1995). Stoking the fires? CO_2 emissions and economic growth, *Journal of Public Economics,* 57:85-101.

UMWA/BCOA (July 1997). The impact of carbon mitigation strategies on energy markets, the national economy, industry and regional economies. Prepared for UMWA/BCOA by DRI/McGraw-Hill.

Jorgenson, D.W. and Wilcoxen, P.J. (1993). Reducing US carbon dioxide emissions: an assessment of different instruments. *Journal of Policy Modeling,* 115 (5/6), 491-520.

Kosobud, R.F., Daly, T.A., South, D.W. and Quinn, K.G. (1994). Tradeable cumulative CO_2 permits and global warming control. *Energy Journal,* 15 (2), 213-32.

Kyoto Protocol to the United Nations framework on climate change (1997). http://www.cnn.com (27 July 1998).

Kyoto Protocol Status of Ratification (2000).

Larsen, B. and Shah, A. (1994). Global tradeable carbon permits, participation incentives, and transfers. *Oxford Economic Papers,* 46 (5), 841-56.

Leopold, E. (1998). European nations sign Kyoto global warming treaty. Reuters.

Lindzen, R.S. (1997). Can increasing atmospheric CO_2 affect global climate? *Proc. Natl. Acad. Sc.,* 94, 8335-42.

Magada, D. (21 April 1998). Focus: Shell revamps image. Reuters.

Manne, A.S. and Richels, R.G. (1991): Global CO_2 emission reductions: the impacts of rising energy costs. *Energy Journal* 12(1), 87-107.

Morrison, J. (1998). G8 countries to act against environmental crime. Reuters.

National Biodiesel Board (21 February 21, 1998). Agricultural products are key to national energy security.

National Corn Growers Assocation (1998). National Corn Growers Report.

National impacts (1998). WEFA National Impacts Link.

Nordhaus, W.D. (1991). The cost of slowing climate change: a survey. *Energy Journal,* 12 (1), 37-65.

Office of Policy and International Affairs (1997). Analysis of carbon stabilization cases. SR-OIAF/97-01. Washington, DC: U.S. Department of Energy (October).

Ostrom, E. and Schlager, E. (1996). The formation of property rights. In *Rights to Nature* (S.S. Hanna, C. Folke, and K.-G. Maler, eds.). Washington, DC: Island Press.

Pearce, D. and Barbier, E. (1991). The greenhouse effect: a view from Europe. *Energy Journal,* 12 (1), 147-161.

Pianin, E. (1998). Gingrich halts move to end ethanol subsidy. *The Greenville News,* 7 May, 6D.

Posner, R.A. (1974). Theories of economic regulation. *Bell Journal,* Autumn, 335-58.

Raven, G. (1998). EU urges US to implement Kyoto global warming deal. Reuters.

Renewable Fuels Association (1998a). RFA Ethanol Report Issue 72.

Renewable Fuels Association (1998b). Ethanol's contributions to 'clean air celebrated on Earth day'. Press Release, (21 April).

Salisbury, L. (1998) Enron exec wants clean energy tax break. Reuters (26 February).

Sinclair, P.J.N. (1994). On the optimum trend of fossil fuel taxation. *Oxford Economic Papers* 46 (5), 869-77.

Stark, C. (1998). Inventory of greenhouse gases. *Iowa Energy Bulletin.*

Stigler, G.J. (1971). The economic theory of regulation. *Bell Journal,* Spring, 3-21.

Sutherland, R.J. (1998). Achieving the Kyoto Protocol: an analysis of policy options. Washington: American Petroleum Institute (March).

Takenaka, K. (1998). Japan, Russia conclude landmark greenhouse gas swap. Reuters.

Testimony of Dr. Janet Yellen, Chair, Council of Economic Advisers Before the House Commerce Committee on the Economics of the Kyoto Protocol (1998). Washington, D.C.: Council of Economic Advisers (4 March 1998).

Whaley, J. and Wigle, R. (1991). Cutting CO_2 emissions: the effects of alternative policy approaches. *Energy Journal* 12 (1), 109-24.

The World Bank (1998). *World Resources: 1998-99.* Washington: The World Bank.

Yandle, B. (1983). Bootleggers and Baptists: the education of a regulatory economist. *Regulation,* May/June, 12-16.

Yandle, B. (1989). *The Political Limits of Environmental Quality Regulation.* Westport, CT: Quorum Press.

Yandle, B. (1997): *Common Sense and Common Law for the Environment.* Lanham, MD: Rowman & Littlefield Publishers.

5

IIAM and the Carbon Abatement Policy

When we talk about restricting ourselves on every use in order to have sustainable development and least harmful change in environment, it also means same sacrifices at domestic level for each country. Major constraints can affect the production of Industrialised nations in particular, and thus affect the economic growth. Therefore, the need is to see how the two can be balanced which has been discussed in the Chapter in the light of IIAM policy.

"In December 1997, parties to the FCCC were to assemble in Kyoto, Japan. At that meeting, they may adopt legally binding targets and timetables of limiting carbon emissions from industrial countries. During the negotiations leading up to Kyoto, the United States government endorsed the idea of setting firm emissions abatement goals that countries must meet sometime in the medium term (probably between the years 2005 to 2015). The US government, however, stopped short of announcing support for any specific target or timetable."

In the process to assess the economic costs of a greenhouse gas abatement policy within the parameters of what the US government announced a willingness to support, this chapter paper uses the International Impact Assessment Model (IIAM) to analyze a representative cabon abatement policy, under which the OECD countries would be needed to reduce their emissions to 90 per cent of 1990 levels, by the year 2010 and then maintain these emissions targets through 2030. This target is less ambitious than the proposal of the European Union, for a limit of 85 per cent of 1990 emissions in 2010.

The IIAM has been designed to analyze the impacts of climate policies on 80 individual countries and regions within a broader context of world trade. The IIAM builds on an extensive body of study on the economics of climate change and international trade theory. It uses a computable general equilibrium model of each country coupled with a model of international trade. The model is based on trade data from the United Nations, energy data from the bodies like International Energy Agency (IEA), and national economic data from a variety of sources. Since energy use must be reduced significantly in a relatively short-time period, either proposal would came substantial GDP losses in the industrial countries undertaking emission limits. Other countries' GDP would also be reduced. The energy exporting countries would suffer losses comparable to the Organization for Economic Cooperation and Development (OECD), even though, in case they did not undertake emissions limits, because of stressed international markets for fossil fuels. The ground rules for the current international negotiations on climate policy call for no additional commitments from developing countries. The entire world, however, is linked through international trade, and all countries will be affected if economic growth slows in the industrial countries. Therefore, the adoption of emissions limits by OECD countries would negatively impact most developing countries. Developing countries would bear losses on average 10 per cent as large as those affecting the OECD.

These losses would arise because OECD countries would demand fewer exports from developing countries, shifting the terms of trade against developing countries, thus reducing their gains from trade. Losses could exceed one per cent of GDP for nations that are highly dependent upon trade with OECD countries and have little scope for benefiting from lower-energy costs. Potentially, some energy-importing developing countries, including South Korea and India, could benefit from having energy costs less than those of the industrial countries with which they compete in world markets. Such countries would then be able to expand their energy-intensive in the OECD. Any way, the IIAM finds that these benefits of lower energy costs are strong enough to offset the shrinkage in export markets for only a very few countries. Losses to developing world would be much larger if the industrial countries protected their energy intensive domestic industries from competition with exports from countries enjoying the benefits of lower energy costs. All developing countries would bear economic losses under these scenarios, while the costs to industrial countries would be reduced.

There are also likely to be significant differences among OECD countries in the size and nature of impacts. For reasons unrelated to climate policy, Germany and the United Kingdom might find it much easier to achieve their emissions goals than will other members of the OECD. As a result, these countries will not encounter the kind of energy cost increase likely to occur in other OECD countries and will attain a competitive advantage over their OECD trading partners. Canada will suffer larger losses than other OECD countries because it has a more energy intensive economy and a large share of its GDP is generated through exports of oil and more energy intensive goods. The United States will be near the OECD average.

Talks for Global Climate Change

Growing concern about global climate change has resulted in several international initiatives that could ultimately result in the adoption of policies designed to reduce greenhouse gas emissions. The first important milestone in international negotiations was the signing of the UN FCCC in Rio de Janeiro in 1992, where participating governments agreed to non-binding goals for reducing greenhouse gas emissions. Three years later, the first session of the Conference of the Parties (members) to the Convention on (COP-1) met to explore the "adequacy" of commitments made at the 1992 Framework Convention. At COP-1, participating governments decided that the nonbinding commitments to decrease greenhouse gas emissions agreed to in Rio de Janeiro were not sufficient. Therefore at COP-1, government representative produced a decision document (known as the "Berlin Mandate") to set up a process that would "aim to elaborate policies and measures," as well as "set quantified limitation and reduction objectives within specified time frames, such as 2005, 2010, and 2020" for greenhouse gas "emissions by sources and removals by sinks," Numberous proposals—each calling for some type of commitment from industrial countries to reduce emissions below 1990 levels during the 2000-2010 time frame—were tabled at COP-1. Environmental ministers met again at COP-2 during the summer of 1996; among the stated goals of the COP-2 meeting was to "give fresh political impetus to the negotiations process."

At COP-2, the US government first articulated support for strong ("legally binding") targets for reducing emissions. At that time, the US government did not propose any specific targets or timetables, but indicated support for "medium-term goals," which implied that policies would possibly become binding between the years 2005 and 2015.

Decisions on these proposals will be made at a meeting in Kyoto, Japan, in December 1997.

Evaluating Economic Impacts of Climate Change Policies

Research studies of the economic impacts of global climate change policies in the past several years suggest that adoption of the various proposed emissions reduction plans over the next two decades could entail high economic costs for all countries. However, costs to developing countries have been downplayed because the focus of international negotiations has been on industrial countries that are assumed to admit carbon limits. To examine the consequences of carbon abatement policies on individual countries, particularly developing countries, Thomas Rutherford and Charles River Associates prepared the International Impact Assessment Model, which is a computable general equilibrium model. The IIAM provides a new method for analyzing the impacts of greenhouse gas abatement policies: It allows users to examine the consequences of emissions abatement policies for 80 nations and regions.

The model divides the world into five geopolitical regions: the Organization for Economic Cooperation and Development (OECD) nations, Non-OECD Asia (ASIA), Eastern Europe and Former Soviet Union and Centrally Planned Emerging Economies (CPEE), Middle East and North Africa (MIDE), and the rest of the world (ROW). By looking at the world as a whole, the model accounts for how countries are linked through international trade and energy markets. The IIAM builds on an extensive body of study on the economics of climate change and international trade theory. Papers based on this research are listed in the bibliography at the end of this report.

Consequences of Executing Possible Emission Limits

While the US government has not yet proposed specific policies, it has, as noted above, expressed support for setting target limits. Two proposals have been prominent in presentations made by the US administration. The first requires that OECD nations return their emissions to 1990 levels by the year 2010 and maintain them at this level through 2030 (hereafter we refer to this proposal as the "Stabilization" proposal).

Under the second proposal, known as the "Reduction" proposal, OECD countries would be needed to reduce their emissions to 90 per cent of 1990 levels by the year 2010 and then maintain these emissions targets through 2030. This proposal goes less far than the current position of the European Union, which is calling for decrease to 85 per cent of

1990 levels by 2010. Since it occupies a middle ground, we focus in this paper on the Reduction proposal. For many policies that are currently being tabled, all Annex I countries (OECD countries plus economies in transition, known as the Former Soviet Union and Eastern Europe) would be required to reduce their emissions. For this study, however, it is assumed that only OECD countries adopt carbon limits. Because the former Centrally Planned Emerging Economics are undergoing many financial difficulties, this study assumes that these countries would not be forced to adopt emissions limits.

Using the IIAM, we estimate the economic impacts of these two proposals on both major world regions and individual countries.

This study reports how these two proposals impact a country's gross domestic product (GDP), non-energy exports, terms of trade, and carbon emissions. It also accounts for a carbon tax necessary to achieve the goal. These impacts are measured relative to a business-as-usual scenario in which carbon abatement policies are absent. The rest of this study is organized as follows: one, an explanation of the probable impacts on different country types is presented; next, results of these two proposals on world regions are discussed followed by an explanation of the effects on individual countries; and two sensitivity analysis on many of the key assumptions is formulated. In general, the impacts are reported as a percentage change from the levels in the business-as-usual scenario. This paper concentrates on the Reduction proposal, which lies between Stabilization of emissions and the decrease proposals put forward by the European Union.

Impacts on leading parts of the world

In order to understand the impact on different regions and countries, we first discuss the likely impacts on three country types and explore the reasons why different impacts can be expected. A carbon abatement policy's impact on a specific country first relies on how that country is categorized: OECD member, energy exporter, or developing country. The economic impact on the OECD countries should be negative. It is only OECD countries that must adopt carbon limits.

These limits need them to reduce their consumption of fossil fuels by substituting more expensive fuels or employing more expensive manufacturing and production techniques. This would raise the costs of their domestically produced goods and make these goods less competitive internationally. Moreover, fuel for final consumption would become more expensive; therefore, households would change their consumption mix.

This would result in a loss of welfare (consumers' surplus) and genuine income for households. Energy exporting nations would be adversely affected by carbon abatement policies. The price of fossil fuels would drop with a decline in the OECD countries' demand for these fuels. In this manner, energy exporting countries would experience a loss of revenues from energy sales. Since these countries undertake no carbon limits, their domestic industries would benefit from lower energy prices. If an energy producing nation such as Venezuela also has energy-intensive domestic industries, then its production costs could decline relative to the OECD and, therefore, make its goods more competitive internationally. Also, households would benefit from the less energy prices. None of these potential benefits should be large enough to offset the loss in revenues from energy exports, but they should moderate GDP losses in energy exporting countries. The effect of carbon abatement policies on developing countries is ambiguous. These countries would not be required to undertake any carbon limits; thus, they would receive the benefits of lower energy prices. But there are two offsetting effects: an "income effect" and a "substitution effect." About the income effect, as the OECD's income declines, OECD purchasing power decreases, and the OECD countries can only afford to purchase fewer imports from the developing countries.

Number of these countries conduct approximately 60 per cent to 75 per cent of their trade with OECD countries. Therefore, the developing countries could experience a loss in export revenue. On the other hand, they benefit from the substitution effect. It means, since these countries do not undertake any carbon limits, they receive the full benefit of lower world energy prices and their domestic industries receive a competitive advantage relative to those in the OECD. Therefore, the non-OECD countries export, more goods to other non-OECD nations countries which displaces OECD exports to these countries. The net impact depends on which effect dominates and consequently whether the terms of trade for a particular specific country improves or deteriorates.

The Consequences

In order to compute the impacts of the two proposals, the model is first run under the business-as-usual scenario with a common set of assumptions. Using these same assumptions (these assumptions include using accepted elasticity values as well as IPCC reference scenarios), the model is after that run under the proposed carbon limits. We report economic impacts on world regions and then on individual countries. In general, the impacts are reported as a percentage change from the levels in the business-as-usual scenario. All dollar figures are found to be 1992 US dollars.

I. Consequences for World Regions

(a) Emissions of carbon dioxide

As per model's results, in 2010 the OECD region as a whole must reduce its carbon emissions by 30 per cent from business-as-usual levels in order to comply with the emission limit (see Exhibit 1). In the year 2030, OECD countries must reduce their emissions further, by 47 per cent. This growth in required emissions abatement over time occurs because, in the business-as-usual scenario, emissions in the OECD region are forecasted to grow from 2.8 billion metric tons in 1990 to 4.7 billion metric tons in 2030. Thus, the gap between the OECD's emissions in the business-as-usual (BAU) scenario and the constant target of 90 per cent of 1990 emissions levels continues to grow.

Exhibit 1: % age Change in Carbon Emissions for the OECD and the World Reduction Proposal

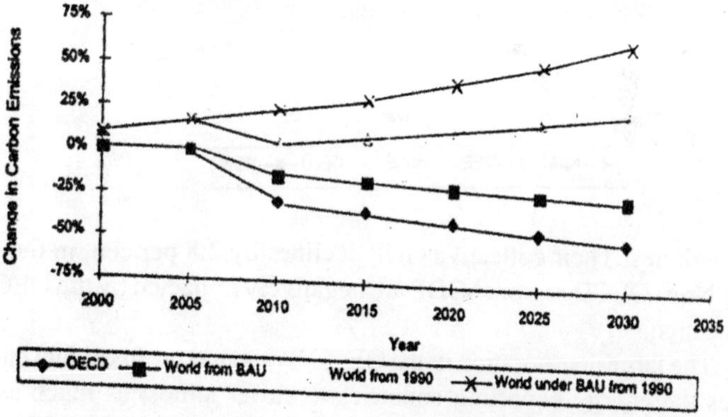

Cuts in OECD energy consumption and hence, emissions could be offset, at lest in part, by increase in energy consumption and emission in the non-OECD countries. First, because of the lower world energy prices under a carbon abatement policy, non-OECD countries are possible to consume more energy. The reduction in OECD fuel consumption causes a decline in world energy prices and induces the non-OECD countries to consume more fossil fuels. Second, because non-OECD countries experience lower fuel rates, some industries may relocate from OECD to non-OECD countries. Even with OECD emission limits, world emissions would continue to increase from 1990 levels. Since non-OECD countries have no emissions restrictions placed upon them, their carbon emissions continue to grow (see lines denoted "World from 1990").

Under the Reduction proposal, there is an increase in world carbon emissions from 1990 levels of 6 per cent in 2010 and 28 per cent in 2030.

(*b*) *GDP*

As per both the proposals, the required reduction in OECD carbon emissions causes a reduction in GDP in all regions (see Exhibit 2). Even though the proposals require only the OECD countries to accept carbon limits, other countries are impacted through international trade in energy and non-energy goods. The OECD is directly affected by the carbon abate-

Exhibit 2: % age Change in GDP

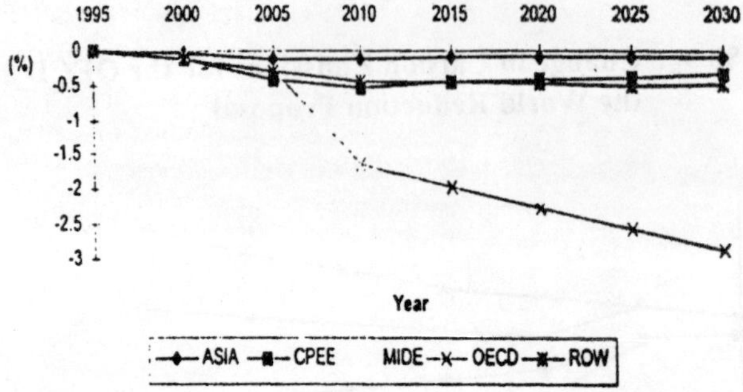

ment policies. Their collective GDP declines by 2.8 per cent in the year 2030. Non -OECD regions' GDP are negatively impacted by the OECD's loss of income.

The large deterioration in the OECD's demand for fossil fuel energy causes the energy exporting countries to suffer almost as much as the OECD countries. In 2030, these nations experience a loss in GDP of 2.3 per cent.

The earlier Centrally Planned Emerging Economies (CPEE) and rest of the world (ROW) regions experience GDP losses in the range of 0.3 per cent to 0.5 per cent. These losses are greater than the losses in the ASIA region because the CPEE and ROW regions carry some countries that are significant energy exporters, whereas ASIA is dominated by countries that are non-energy exporters and energy importers.

For all three of these regions, the decline in GDP come down in the more distant years because each region has significant time to recognize its economy and make use of competitive advantages from lower world energy prices.

In addition, in each future year, the OECD must use less energy per unit of output; this keeps on to raise their production costs. Therefore, the developing countries gain more of a competitive advantage and begin to benefit more from this advantage.

(*c*) *Impact of Trade*

In case, the OECD countries were to adopt either the Stabilization or Reduction proposal, each region would experience significant impact on trade. The changes in each region's non-energy exports and terms of trade provide insights into how these proposals impact each region's GDP.

Under either proposal, non-energy exports from all non-OECD regions increase from their business-as-usual levels, whereas the OECD's non-energy exports came down (see Exhibit 3). This occurs because as OECD countries are required to further reduce emissions from business-as-usual levels, they must continue to substitute away from energy to produce their goods. These inefficient changes in production enhance the price of OECD goods relative to those of non-OECD goods resulting in a decline in OECD exports and an increase in non-OECD exports.

Exhibit 3. % age Change in Non-Energy Exports

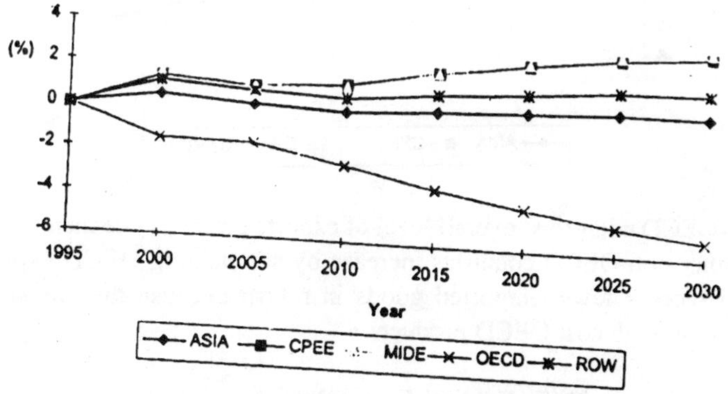

Modifications in terms of trade can be used to evaluate the relative change in a country's trade pattern. Terms of trade is measured as the ratio (in value terms) of a country's exports to its imports.

Therefore, the change in a region's terms of trade from the business-as-usual secenario dominates the change in the relative value of goods that it exports to the value of goods that it imports. For example, if the value of a country's exports increase and its imports decrease, the country's terms of trade improves and its trade position improves. The terms of trade in non-OECD regions, relative to that of OECD countries, declines for two reasons (see Exhibit 4). First, the cost of imports from the OECD increases because production costs are more in the OECD under carbon emissions limits. Second, the decline in OECD income under either of these proposals means that OECD expenditures on the combination of domestically produced and imported goods will decline similar to the business-as-usual scenario.

However, depending on the change in the cost of imports relative to domestic goods, the OECD countries' expenditures on imports could either increase or decrease. Since the percentage change in terms of trade for these non-OECD nations negative, the cost advantage achieved by non-OECD countries is not, on balance, large enough to induce the OECD countries to increase their expenditures on imports. Although the

Exhibit 4. % age Change in Terms of Trade Relative to the OECD

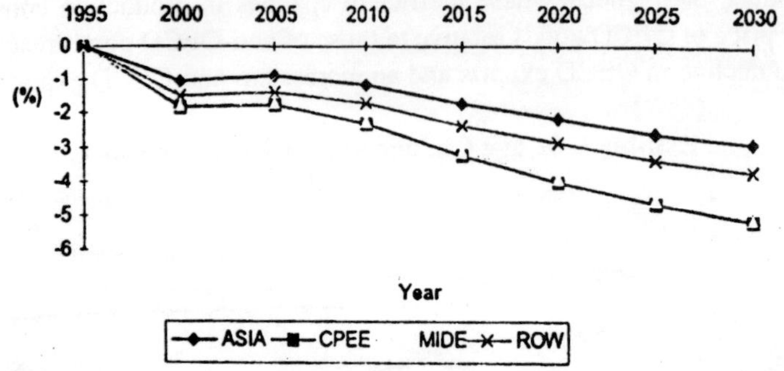

non-OECD countries' overall level of exports grows (since their exports to other non-OECD countries increase by supplanting OECD exports), they receive fewer imported goods in return because they must still purchase high cost OECD products.

Consequences for Individual Countries

In this section are described the differences among countries within the various regions. First is a comparison of the economic impacts on the following seven OECD countries: Canada, France, Germany, United Kingdom, Italy, Japan, and the United States. Next, the economic impacts on developing countries are studied, determining the economic profile needed for a developing country to benefit when carbon limits are placed on OECD countries. Lastly, the paper analyzes impacts on energy exporters of the Reduction proposal. The Stabilization proposal would have a similar pattern of impacts, but they would be somewhat smaller. The European Union proposal would have similar but higher impacts.

(*a*) *OECD Nations*

All these seven OECD countries experience very different GDP losses. Four major factors influence the varying degree of impacts among OECD countries: growth in emissions in the baseline, levels of pre-existing energy taxes, energy intensity, and exposure to competition in world trade.

1. Baseline emissions world growth of : Factors affecting baseline emissions growth such as population growth, output growth, and relative shares of fossil fuel use, differ across countries. Higher required reductions in carbon emissions, expressed as a percentage of baseline emissions, imply larger GDP losses (see Exhibit 5).
2. Already existing energy taxes: Since pre-existing taxes in Italy, France, and Japan are much higher than in the US and Canada, the carbon taxes required to achieve a given reduction are also much higher in the former nations.
3. Intensity of Energy: Countries in the OECD that have relatively energy-intensive industries or economies will face higher costs of reducing emissions, in absolute terms and as a share of GDP.
4. Structure of Industry: Countries with energy-intensive processes or industries that are also heavily involved in international trade, and trade mostly with other OECD countries, will be harmed more than others. These countries will face greater than average increases in the costs of producing goods that compete in international markets, and greater imports and exports as a share of GDP make global competition more important in the overall economic picture. Moreover, trade competition among OECD countries is treated as being more intense than trade competition between OECD and non-OECD countries. Therefore, countries whose trade is focused toward other OECD countries will be hurt more than countries whose trade is more oriented toward non-

OECD countries. Most OECD countries benefit from lower global oil prices, but oil-exporting OECD countries also suffer from lower world oil demand and lower prices.

Exhibit 5: Necessary Reductions in Emissions from Baseline

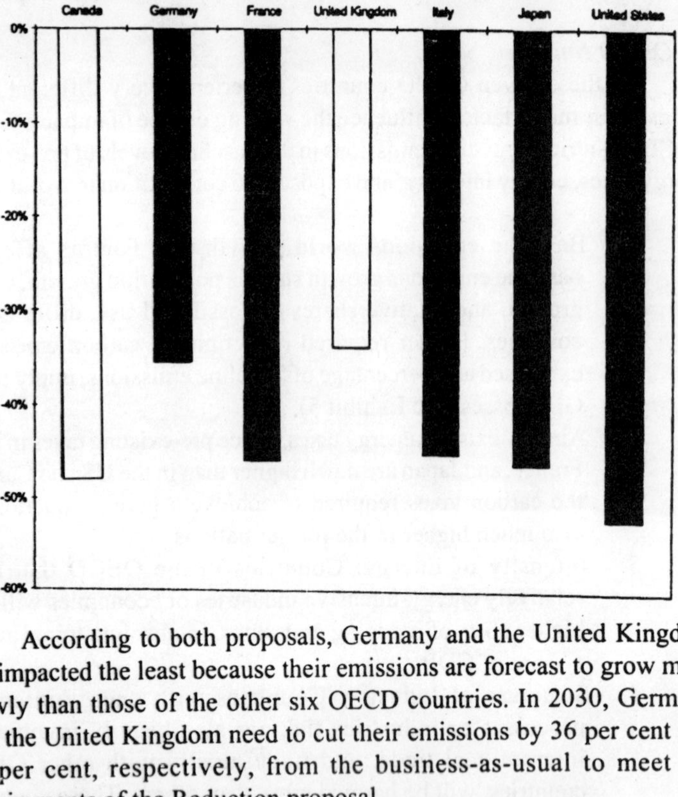

According to both proposals, Germany and the United Kingdom are impacted the least because their emissions are forecast to grow more slowly than those of the other six OECD countries. In 2030, Germany and the United Kingdom need to cut their emissions by 36 per cent and 34 per cent, respectively, from the business-as-usual to meet the requirements of the Reduction proposal.

Canada and the US, however, need to reduce their emissions by 48 per cent and 52 per cent, respectively, from the business-as-usual in order to match with the Reduction proposal (see Exhibit 6). Both Germany and the United Kingdom have announced that they will be able to meet target of holding emissions at 1990 levels through 2000 because of policies and events *independent* of climate policy. Germany's emissions growth is halted for a time because its base year included the former East Germany. Energy use was dominated by highly inefficient use of coal in that country. Contraction of the former East German economy and replacement of its inefficient patterns of energy use have reduced emissions from that part of Germany and held total emissions for the reunited country down relative to the remaining Europe.

In the United Kingdom, policies to reduce subsidies to the coal industries and deregulation of energy industries, both of which began independently of climate change concerns, have also served to hold down emissions by promoting substitution of natural gas for coal. Britain's somewhat higher costs, compared to Germany, are partly explained by the losses in oil export revenue that Britain faces. Due to these developments in the German and British economies, their costs of near-term limits on carbon emissions are significantly smaller than in the rest of the OECD. The percentage increase in energy costs (measured by the implied carbon tax) is less than in other OECD countries because the required percentage reduction in emissions is smaller, and both countries therefore, achieve trade benefits at the expense of other OECD countries. Nations like France, Japan, and Italy experience less GDP loss than the US and Canada because those three countries use less energy per unit of GDP and have lower growth in baseline emissions than the latter two countries. Nuclear energy supplies more than a third of France's energy requirements. This means that more than a third of France's energy is already a carbon-free energy source.

Exhibit 6: Losses in GDP in 2030 from Proposals of Reduction

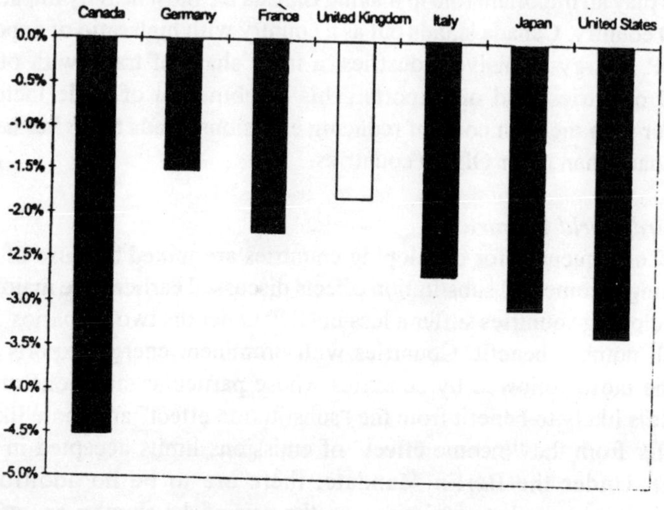

This produces two opposite effects on the costs of carbon limits. France has less scope to replace fossil fuels used for electric power production with other fuels, and therefore must rely on more expensive options to curtail growth in emissions. In the baseline, France is assumed to continue to expand its nuclear power industry so that about one-third of baseline growth in energy demand is also fulfilled from non-carbon sources. If, however, France were to move away from nuclear power in the baseline, then its costs would be greater than estimated. Present energy prices in France, Japan, and Italy are much higher than in the US and Canada therefore, it takes a large carbon tax to produce the same proportionate increase in delivered energy prices to bring about the required reduction from baseline absorption of fossil fuels. The required level of the carbon tax becomes so high that the price of fossil fuels (including their associated carbon taxes) equals the cost of the backstop fuel (a new, carbon-free energy source which is assumed to be available in unlimited quantities at a multiple of today's price for fossil fuels).

In other words, the backstop fuel becomes cost-effective in the year 2015. If no backstop fuel existed, these nations would require carbon taxes that were two to three times more than those in the US and Canada. Since the model assumes that each country produces its own backstop fuel, the model underestimates the GDP loss in countries like Japan that are expected to do this. To address this issue, we made the price of Japan's backstop fuel 20 percent higher than that of the United States. Trade effects play an important role in making Canada the most heavily impacted OECD country. Canada stands out as a country with high ratio of exports to GDP, energy-intensive industries, a large share of trade with other OECD countries, and oil exports. This combination of trade factors, together with the high costs of reducing emissions, leads to higher harm for Canada than other OECD countries.

(*b*) *Third World Countries*

Consequences for developing countries are mixed because of the offsetting income and substitution effects discussed earlier. The majority of developing countries suffer a loss in GDP under the two scenarios, but a small number benefit. Countries with prominent energy exports are hurt the most, followed by countries whose particular situations make them less likely to benefit from the "substitution effect" and more likely to suffer from the "income effect" of emissions limits accepted in the OECD. Under the Berlin Mandate, there are to be no additional commitments to reduce emissions on the part of developing countries.

But the markets in the OECD to which these developing countries sell a big share of their exported goods will shrink, so that most developing countries would also be harmed by the adoption of emissions limits in the OECD.

Under either proposal, developing countries would face losses on average of about ten per cent as high as those experienced by the OECD. These losses would come about because OECD countries would demand fewer exports from developing countries, shifting the terms of trade against developing countries and causing a decrease in their gains from trade. In addition, imports from the OECD would become more expensive. Losses could exceed one per cent of GDP for countries that are highly dependent on trade with the OECD and have little possibility for benefiting from lower energy costs. Developing countries that are not members of OPEC but do have significant oil exports suffer greater economic impacts than most developing countries.

For example, under the Reduction proposal, Ecuador and Mexico experience downfall in GDP of 1.6 per cent and 1.0 per cent, respectively, versus developing, non-oil exporting countries like China, which suffers a loss of only 0.05 per cent in the year 2030. Furthermore, developing countries that are leading oil importers, such as South Korea, benefit from the reduction in lower-energy prices and experience a slight increase in GDP from the two emissions abatement proposals.

(c) *Leading Oil Exporters*

All the economic impacts on most major oil exporting countries are fairly uniform. These countries experience larger GDP losses under the Reduction scenario that under the Stabilization scenario as the price of oil declines more in the latter scenario. There is a dramatic drop in each country's terms of trade because of each country's loss of revenue from its primary export, oil.

(*d*) *Countries who Benefit from Abatement Proposals*

Amongst the non-OECD, there are some countries that might benefit if the OECD countries were to adopt either the Stabilization or Reduction proposals, including India, Jamaica, Jordan, Philippines, and South Korea. Jamaica prospers the most. It is an oil-importing developing nation that exports a very energy-intensive product, bauxite, to the OECD countries.

Its potential benefits thus illustrate the necessary conditions for a gain in comparative advantage. Korea is also an oil importer, and it is a relatively wealthy country that has the industrial base to take advantage of lower costs in a broad range of universally competitive industries.

The above impacts are estimated assuming that capital flows freely into the developing countries to finance the conversion of their industries to take advantage of energy price differentials, and the OECD countries do nothing to limit or offset imports of energy-intensive goods from countries not following carbon limits. As discussed below, trade protection by the OECD turns impacts on all developing countries negative.

Case of Trade Protection

As per the carbon abatement proposals, many individual countries increase their non-energy exports because of their cost advantage over the OECD in markets inside and outside the OECD. However, the OECD may choose to protect some of its industries. To account for this feasibility, CRA ran a trade protection case. In the trade protection case, it is assumed that the OECD countries adopt some combination of measures to protect domestic industries against competition from countries that do not accept carbon emissions limits.

These policies could be overt, in the form of border adjustment taxes based on approximations of the carbon content of different imports, or more readily concealed actions to benefit industries bearing with such competition, such as tax subsidies or exemption from carbon taxes or other policies designed to reduce emissions. For the purposes of this analysis, these trade restrictions are implemented by limiting imports from non-OECD countries to baseline levels (a form of quotas). Under such assumptions, all developing countries face negative impacts, and the average loss in developing countries increases (ASIA and ROW) from 0.3 per cent to 0.6 per cent of GDP in 2030 under the Reduction scenario.

To conclude the Chapter, it can be said that the bottom line of this research is that any significant reductions in greenhouse gas emissions will produce significant economic dislocations throughout the global economy, even if undeveloped nations are exempted or given a longer timetable to meet emission reduction goals. Excluding such nations from treaty commitments does not exclude them from the treaty's impacts, and it could trigger other policy changes that would have an even more deleterious impact upon the global economy.

References

Boehringer, C., and T. Rutherford. "Multi-sectorial Framework for Analysis of Carbon Emission Restrictions and Bilateral Trade in the European Union," (*Journal of Energy and Resource Economics forthcoming*).

Charles River Associates and DRI McGraw Hill, "Economic Impacts of Cabon Taxes: Overview," Electric Power Research Institute, November 1994.

Felder, N., and T. Rutherford, "Unilateral CO_2 Reductions and Carbon Leakage," *Journal of Environmental Economics and Management,* 1993.

Harrison, N., T. Rutherford, and D. Tarr, "Quantifying the Uruguay Round," *Finance and Development,* 1995.

Jacoby, H.D., R.S. Eckaus, A.D. Ellerman, R.G. Prinn, D.M. Reiner, and Z. Yang, "QERLRO Impacts: Domestic Market, Trade and Distribution of Burdens, and Climate Change," Joint Program on the Science and Polity of Global Change, Massachusetts Institute of Technology, 1996.

Kennedy, D., M. Hinelry, and B. Zisher, "Effects of Greenhouse Gas Abatement in OECD Countries on Developing Countries," Presented at the IPIECA Symposium on Critical Issues in the Economics of Climate Change, October 8-11, 1996.

Lindbeck, A., "The Recent Slowdown of Productivity Growth," *Economics Journal,* 1983.

Manne, A., and T. Rutherford, "International Trade in Oil, Gas and Carbon Emission Rights: An International General Equilibrium Model," *Energy Journal,* 1993.

Oxford Economics, "Controlling Carbon Emissions in the G7 Countries," *World Economic Prospects,* Summer, 1996.

Perroni, C., and T. Rutherford, "International Trade in Carbon Emission Rights and Basic Materials," *Scandinavian Journal of Economics,* 1993.

6

Global Concerns of European Policy

Although there have been significant advances in aspects of our scientific understanding, for policy purposes we remain uncertain but concerned about the following:

1. Vagueness of Feedback on Water Cycle

Although the science is beyond dispute at the most fundamental level (i.e., that greenhouse gases such as CO_2 act to warm the earth's bottom and that human emissions are increasing their concentration), we do not understand adequately the various positive and negative feedbacks associated with the cycle of water and longer-term responses associated with natural carbon and methane cycles; nor do we understand the critically significant issue of ocean-current behaviour.

2. Disturbance in Flow of Greenhouse Gases

We know that CO_2 and (to a lesser extent) other greenhouse gas emissions are making big perturbation to the natural balance of flows of greenhouse gases and that this must ultimately affect climatic patterns and possibly the ocean-current flows that we think have been implicated in past climatic instabilities.

As it is clear that the concerns about human-induced climatic change first emerged as a major political issue in the mid-to late 1980s, governments in the European Union and Scandinavia have been in the forefront of attempts to start addressing the problem. Some EU countries, and later the EU itself, adopted unilateral emission goals and sought to follow these through with policies to limit specifically CO_2 emissions.

Building upon this, the EU sought to lead the international process established by the UN General Assembly towards a bold Framework Convention on Climate Change. The Convention which emerged from this process, signed by 153 nations at the UN Conference on Environment and Development at Rio in June 1992 (and by several more since), now forms the legal basis for the international development of responses to the environmental problem.

Global Significance of EU Climate Strategy

(a) EU Emissions in the Global Context

Following Fig. 6.1 shows the contribution of different regions to fossil-fuel CO_2 emissions in 1993, in terms of emissions per capita compared with population (the product—the area of the blocks—is thus proportional to total emissions). The USA was the biggest emitter, accounting for 25 per cent of the global aggregate; the countries of Central/East Europe including Russia, in total accounted for another 17 per cent, but following the breakup and economic contraction of this region, the EC is left as the second largest cohesive economic group, emitting 14.5 per cent of global CO_2 emissions (the accession of Austria and Scandinavian countries will add another per cent or so).

Emissions from developing states are rising rapidly, and now account for over a quarter of the global total. On a per capita basis, the USA is again the most profligate emitter and forms a separate group along with Canada and Australia; European per capita emissions are in a range similar to Japan and (now) to the former USSR, at about half this level. On this measure there is a huge gulf compared with most developing countries, where emissions per capita are typically several times lower than in developed countries. Due to this and differences in wealth, and the fact that the developed countries have dominated emissions historically, developing countries have taken the attitude that stabilization of emissions from industrialized nation is a precondition for them to consider any substantive abatement action.

The economic collapse of the former Soviet Union conveys that emissions are contracting there anyway, and precludes them from taking a more active position. The focus is thus upon OECD countries. The US Clinton Administration published its national plan for 1990-2000 stabilization[1] of greenhouse gases relatively early, as did the United Kingdom. Japan has committed to a target of per capita 1990-2000 CO_2 stabilization, released an Action Plan to Arrest Global Warming, and is working on more detailed measures. Japan has also emphasized the long-term nature of the problem, and technological strategies for this long term.

Action in all three of the OECD's major economic groupings is important, but there is a particularly strong spotlight upon Europe, which caused declarations of emissions stabilization by which has yet to agree on any coherent strategy for achieving it.

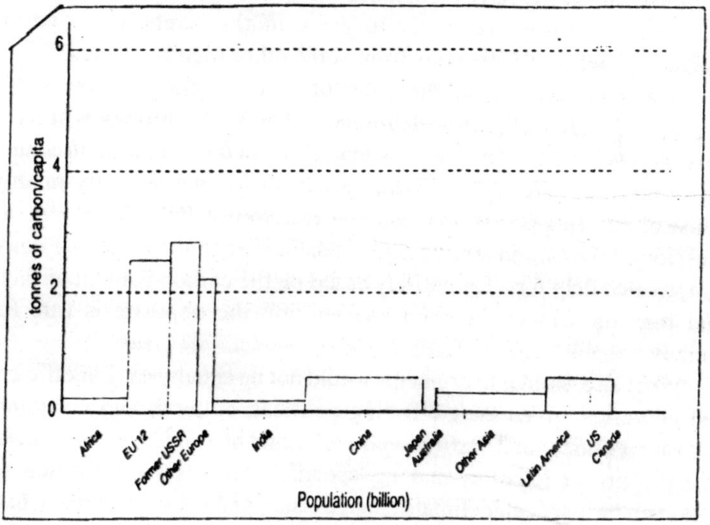

Fig. 1 Carbon emissions per capita and population, 1993.
Source: Extracted by the author from BP Statistical Review of World Energy (1994) and World Population Prospects, UN.

(*b*) *Domestic Controversies: The EU as a 'Test Case' and Nucleus*

Second reason why the EU position is important is because in several ways the EU represents a microcosm of the global problem. EU member countries differ with respect to economic and institutional factors, and some of the problems faced by the EU reflect those that could arise, on a larger scale, at the global level in the talk of a co-ordinated climate change strategy. There is a 'North-South' dimension, with four countries in a markedly less advanced development stage; Spain, Portugal, Ireland, and Greece.

Their comparatively homogeneous economic situation is the basis for their common position on some aspects of climate change policy:

these 'cohesion countries' do not want to hold the responsibility for past emissions of other EU countries, and they fear any constraint on energy consumption as an obstacle to the main objective of economic growth. Moreover, the economic costs of limiting emissions to 1990 levels would be higher for the currently less-developed countries as their economies are likely to grow faster, and begin from a lower basis. Climate policy declarations in the EU have recognized the disparity, and that emissions from these countries are likely to grow in the context of overall stabilization, needing reductions from some other member states.

Apart from decision on the extent of action, economic factors also influence the choice of policy instruments. The same strategy will have different costs for different countries depending on the economic structure, existing taxation (average fossil-fuel prices in EU nations vary mainly because of differing taxes), and resource availability. For example, in the discussion on the carbon tax, the size of the nuclear contribution in France has motivated help for a tax entirely based on the carbon content of fuels rather than on a mix of carbon and energy; the opposite is true for Germany.

What else, similar instruments would not be equally easy or efficient in all countries, given their differing political, cultural, and economic situations. Political and institutional variations also include the general national approach to policy-making; specific elements that influence the position on the particular climate change issue; and the state of the debate upon sovereignty, subsidiarity, and the strength of EU decision-making powers. Wynne[2] draws a distinction between a 'top-down' approach centred around formal policy institutions (e.g., the Netherlands, Germany), and a 'bottom-up' approach (e.g., the United Kingdom) in which diverse actors except the formal institutions play an important role in policy development and implementation, rather than simply adapting to it.

Acceptance of policies can also be influenced by other developments; for instance, the United Kingdom population is most unlikely to accept additional energy taxation just after the government has fought to introduce VAT on domestic energy use. All these differences complicate the process of achieving agreement among EU countries, but they are small compared with the differences that prevail at the global level. Compared with the differences between the USA, Russia, and China, for example, the EU is quite a homogeneous group, with strong co-ordinating institutions already there.

If concrete international action to counteract global warming has any change of being taken in the near future, it will be easier for a small group of relatively homogeneous nations such as EU member states to take the lead. Such action may also demonstrate possible avenues for implementing agreements between states with various economic conditions, cultures, and sensitivities. The demonstration effect of EU policy may thus strongly influence the approach taken at the global level. Moreover, there exist various ways in which an initial coalition—such as the EU—may itself form a nucleus for an expanding regime, over and above the fact and impact of political leadership.[3] Thus, the importance of EU climate policy for the world.

Growth of EU Climate Policy[4]

(*a*) *The EU CO_2 Stabilization of Declaration*

Now, the European Community has taken a forward stance on the issue of climate change, and CO_2 emissions in particular. EC member countries were amongst the first to adopt targets for limiting CO_2 emissions, and desire the international community to negotiate a binding Convention including emission constraints. The decision with the single greatest influence on the developement of the issue, both within the EC and on the broader international discussions, was the declaration by the joint Council of EC Energy and Environment Ministers of Member States, dated 29 October, 1990, that: 'The European Community and Member States assume that other leading countries undertake commitments along [similar] lines and, acknowledging the targets identified by a number of Member States . . . are willing to take actions aiming at reaching stabilization of the total CO_2 emissions by 2000 at 1990 level in the Community as a whole.'

All this comes into the pattern of 'constructively ambiguous' declarations that mark many stages of the development of climate policy, most notably the Convention itself; it reflects 'willingness to take action aiming at . . .', and 'assumes' that other countries will take similar measures, but does not make the goal explicitly conditional upon such action. The UN Climate Convention, as the European Union signed some twenty months later at Rio, reiterates this 'aim' for all industrialized country signatories. The EU's CO_2 stabilization aim has been repeatedly reaffirmed, most importantly with the EU Council's Monitoring Decision—a legal instrument in terms of EU law—that carries a preamble highlighting repeated reaffirmations of the goal (see below). Also, both the process and outcome of developing the Convention have added greatly to the status significance of the EU's commitment.

To renege upon it now would undermine the UN Convention in the very area in which the EU fought hardest for stronger wording, and would be used by developing states as a prima facie reason why they should not take significant action. Given that the target has already been reaffirmed by the Union's Council of Ministers, it would also prove the EU look foolish, if not actually devious. Accordingly, there are now strong pressures to ensure that the EU stabilization goal is not abandoned, and to find altenatives of achieving it.

Stabilization by the EU is not the same thing as stabilization by all individual states, since the former allows emissions by some countries to increase if others come down accordingly. The less-developed Cohesion countries—notably Spain, Portugal, Greece, and Ireland, which start from a base of per capita emissions far less than the EU average—made it plain that they would not stabilize their own emissions.

They signed the Convention on the same basis, drawing on the provision for joint implementation of the stabilization goal—called their participation in the EU goal—as their commitment. The Council Declarations, and the Monitoring Decision, clearly recognize that these countries are likely to enhance emissions—and by implication that others in the EU must reduce correspondingly to achieve the collective goal. To meet the legal requirements of the Convention, a full EU report, detailing strategy in place to attain stabilization, should be lodged with the Secretariat by 21 September, 1994. The difficulties in preparing this—which at the time of writing seem unlikely to be resolved well in time to meet the deadline—reflect the fundamental dilemmas and unresolved tensions in EU climate policy.

(b) Ensuring Stability of EU CO_2 Emissions: National Composition

The EU's stabilization aim was not a random choice. Nor did it reflect simply a recognition that such 1990-2000 stabilization was fast becoming a standard symbolic and psychological demonstration to the developing sector that developed countries could, and intended to, start addressing the problem by at least ensuring that their CO_2 emissions did not continue to go up. It was also a reflection that the targets already declared by member countries, if achieved, would be almost sufficient to achieve 1990-2000 stabilization across the EU.

Set against these are the emissions projected in the absence of a abatement measures for the Reference Scenario calculated by the European Commission's Energy Directorate.[5]

In essence this would cause an internal EU 'market' in entitlements to emit CO_2 and harness market incentives for the purpose of achieving the stabilization goal. There would be a direct incentive on all nations to minimize emissions (either to minimize the payment for quotas or to maximize the revenue from selling them) irrespective of whether they were meeting some already defined national target.

National bureaucracies—and in particular finance ministries—would be faced directly with the fact that CO_2 emissions involve a tangible cost, and could thus balance internally the uses of constraint against more-traditional energy policy goals. Ultimately, the 'price' of such quotas should settle at a point which reflects the least expensive of meeting the stabilization target anywhere in the Union. The efficiency benefits could be considerable; one study suggests that the costs of an approach that allows such inter-country flexibility could be just one-fiftieth of the costs involved if each country were bound to stabilizing CO_2 emissions individually. Such a system ensures that the collective objective of stabilizing total emissions is attained, because this is established by the total number of quotas issued. But it is much more flexible than the allocation of fixed deadlines.

It is also fully consistent with the 'polluter pays' principle by ensuring that increases in emissions above the agreed initial quotas are paid for, and additional constraint is acknowledged. Governments would retain control over the policies used to limit emissions, but components could be adjusted for mutual benefit under the vast thrust of overall EU harmonization. The Commission could still promote Europe-wide components to energy and climate policy; indeed, governments might be more receptive to them since the benefit of limiting emissions would be more tangible. Energy pricing is important, and reform tax systems to place greater weight on energy/carbon taxation over period is an important strategic component of climate policy; such measures could and should continue to be promoted in concert with a tradable quota provisions.

But many other measures would be relevant, and a harmonized tax agreement across the EU would not be the focus of success or failure to ensure the stabilization goal. The approach would therefore provide an efficient and feasible way of meeting the declared goal, whilst being consistent with two major policy principles enunciated by the EU and consented by the Member States: the subsidiarity principle, by devolving the detailed energy policy decision-making as far as is consistent with Union objectives; and the polluter-pays principle.

(c) *Practical Aspects of Tradable Emission Quotas*

Certainly, setting up such a system would be complex and would require both analysis and negotiations to address a range of complex questions concerning allocation, management, and practical working of such a system, as compared with the alternatives. Many of these are considered elsewhere, in a more detailed study conducted between lot of European agencies. Negotiating the initial allocation of quotas would inevitably be a politically fraught and difficult process, though as experience to date shows it is not unique in facing the problem of negotiating 'burden sharing', which ultimately has to be faced in any substantive EU effort. As compared with fixed targets, the problems might be eased by the added flexibility: countries would no longer have to err on the side of extreme caution because of uncertainties about being able to meet specific emission targets. It could also, offer a politically feasible way out from existing declarations about the unacceptability of particular targets. While this is introduced in the context of the 1990-2000 stabilization goal, in practice it makes most sense if developed as an instrument for emissions control over a longer duration. This recognition could also ease the initial development of the system. Countries would negotiate in the knowledge that the goal of 1990-2000 stabilization is about to be but the first step, and that if a tradable quota system is established as an effective and efficient mechanism, there are likely to be further rounds of allocation.

A country which ends up with a huge surplus of quotas in the year 2000 would be pressured to a lower allocation in subsequent rounds; and if the situation arises because it held out for an unreasonably high allocation, based on implausibly large projections of CO_2 emissions, the credibility of its negotiation position for subsequent rounds would be seriously weakened. Furthermore, this generates the possibility of 'banking' quotas for future use. In other words, if, under the incentive of the system, it proves possible to do better than the stabilization goal, and the price of quotas drops correspondingly to smaller levels, parties with spare quotas could elect to 'bank' them for later use—or for selling in the future—based on their expectation of how much emission constraints may further tighten after 2000. This both improves the stability of the system and improves the prospects for exceeding and stengthening the environmental goal.

The significance of allowing such banking has been clearly demostrated in US experience with tradable permits. The benefits of designing a system which can, needed, be extended over time raises a number of other possible design issues. Grubb and Sebenius develop a proposal for a system of permits with more lifetime, of which a fraction are retired every few years and reissued according to the need to tighten the emissions control and/or expand the level of participants.

Also, it is this possibility which points to the real importance of finding a workable and flexible solution to the EU's climate dilemmas. It must, in any case, be an approach that can cope with expansion of the Union. Implicitly, it could also form the practical basis for an expanding regime of climate control, that could enlarge to include non-member nations, OECD countries like Japan that may only be able to meet their commitments as part of a larger group; and perhaps beyond that, developing nations who see it as an effective and practical means of developing a global regime with mutual benefits.

This possibility brings us back to the starting-point of this article: if the EU system can get a way of implementing its emissions commitment in an effective and efficient manner, its greatest value may be as a demonstration and nucleus for a global alternative. As indicated, there are many practical and political issues that would need to be resolved. But what is needed at present is political recognition that this type of approach could offer an effective way forward for implementing the European Union's CO_2 commitment, and a commitment to open high-level discussions on the feasible design of such a system as part of the EU strategy.

To Conclude

Climate change remains as a real concern. The institutional regimes established globally and within the EU during the past three years partially insulate public policy from the ebb and flow of popular concern, and generate internal pressures which force governments to keep addressing the issue and reviewing whether progress appropriate is adequate. These developments have strongly reinforced the original EU undertaking to stabilize CO_2 emissions at 1990 levels by the year 2000, and the Monitoring Decision forms the formal and institutional basis for achieving this. But the national programmes are not all convincing; nor do they fully achieve the declared goal, which is but the initiation of likely longer-term needs. With the effective collapse of the carbon/energy tax and drastic weakening of the SAVE programme, Europe does not have a strategy to atteion its CO_2 undertaking.

The first meeting of the UN Conference of Parties will be held in Germany, and the submission of the European strategy has to be made during the course of the presidency of Germany.

At present, unless there are very rapid developments, Germany and the EU face a politically and environmentally damaging failure. The basic cause of this failure would lie in the same elements that underlie the global endeavour: how to implement collective commitments among diverse and jealously sovereign nations in an area as fundamental as energy policy. Yet there are substantial pressures to find some convincing strategy. If there is substantive political will, probably during the time of the sequential German-French-Spanish presidencies, then political realities may force Member States to launch negotiations on buildings targets or, more promisingly, tradable national-emission quotas—to make possible the 1990-2000 goal, and/or for implementing longer-term emission constraints. At presents the omens are not promising; but if Europe can successfully involve effective system for collective control of its emissions, it may yet fulfil its claim to lead the world in combating the threat of environmental change.

References

1. I use this term to describe the aim that emissions in the year 2000 should not exceed 1990 levels. Stabilization in full implies a commitment that emissions should not rise again thereafter.
2. B. Wynne (1993), 'Implementation of Greenhouse Gas Reductions in the European Community: Institutional and Cultural Factors', *Global Environmental Change,* 3/1, 101-28.
3. C. Carraro and D. Siniscalco (1993), 'Policy Coordination for Sustainability: Commitment. Transfes and Bandwagon Effects'. in I. Goldin and L.A. Winders (eds.), *Sustainable Development* (CEPR and Cambridge University Press); C. Carraro, A. Lanza, and A. Tudini (1993), 'Technological Change, Technology Transfer and the Negotiation of International Environmental Agreements', *International Environmental Affairs* (forthcoming).
4. An earlier but more extensive account of the development of EU climate policy and the implications of the UN Climate Convention is given in Pier Vellinga and Michael Grubb (eds.) (1993), *Climate Change Policy in the European Community* (London: Royal Institute of International Affairs).
5. Commission of the European Communities (1992), 'A View to the Future', *Energy in Europe,* special issue (Sept.) (Bussels: CECDGX VII).

7

Energy Policies in Asia in Light of Climatic Change Impact

The present chapter is a draft document about the implications of global climate changes in view of energy policies in Asia continent. It has been prepared by Toufiq. A. Siddiqi, Environment and Policy Institute, East-West Centre, Hawaii to be presented at a workshop "Responding to the Threat of Global Warming: Option for the Pacific and Asia." held at Honolulu, Hawaii from 21st to 27th June, 1989. Special feature of their paper is that it also discusses illustrative options for selected countries of Asia continent.

Introduction

The 1980s have seen a dramatic change in the nature of the environmental issues in which decision-makers are interested. Almost exactly a decade ago, we (EAPI/EWC) organized a meeting to help identify priorities for a new program dealing with "The Environmental Dimensions of Energy Policies." A group of distinguished persons from eleven countries in Asia, the Pacific, and North America suggested that we concentrate our initial efforts on developing environmental guidelines for offshore oil and gas exploration and production, and for the mining, transportation, and combustion of coal (Siddiqi, 1979). There was some discussion of the longer-term climatic effects of the increased use of fossil fuels, but the view expressed by the group was that it was too early to try to get policy-makers interested in the subject.

As recently as three years ago, when I submitted a paper on a possible "Law of the Atmosphere" to a well-know law journal, the paper elicited no response for several months, and was then returned with more or less of a yawn!

In this closing year of the decade, the situation has changed so drastically that there is a conference or a workshop almost every week dealing with some aspect of climate change. If one might be permitted to borrow a phrase from the heyday of the Energy Crisis of the 1970s, "The sun never sets on Climate Change conferences." Even though there is a great deal of redundancy in having so many meetings on the same topic, there are significant benefits as well. One of them is that awareness of the "Greenhouse Effect," and of its implications for the earth's climate, has become widespread amongst the public and decision-makers in a large number of countries.

It is no longer necessary to describe the nature of the "Greenhouse Effect," and the role played by human activities in contributing to it. With your permission, then, I shall simply summarize here the relative importance of different gases in terms of contributing to global warming, and then focus on efforts to reduce the one most directly related to energy use, that is, carbon dioxide (CO_2). According to current estimates (Enquett Commission, 1988), carbon dioxide is responsible for about half the "Greenhouse Warming" at present.

In subsequent sections of this paper, I shall discuss present energy use in Asia, and possible changes in the relative importance of different sources of energy on that continent in response to climate change concerns.

Energy Use and Levels of Affluence

The relationship between energy use and affluence is well-established. In general, rich societies use large amounts of energy per capita, whereas poorer societies are also those that have low use of energy per person. Even though the Gross National Product (GNP) is an unsatisfactory indicator of welfare, the relationship between per capita GNP and energy use provides an illustration of the link between the two. (The GNP numbers are from the World Bank, 1987, and the energy numbers from the United Nations, 1988.)

The major implication of this disparity in per capita energy use numbers for strategies to deal with climate change concerns is that *it is unrealistic to expect the less-industrialized countries of Asia to cut back on their energy use. In fact, it is very likely that energy use in these countries will increase several-fold, before levelling off or beginning to decline.* This is not to argue that countries in Asia should not practice energy conservation, or attempt to use energy more efficiently.

Each of the two approaches mentioned above has significant difficulties associated with it, which should not be under-estimated. Even though natural gas emits thirty to forty per cent less CO_2 than oil or coal for the same amount of heat generated, its main constituent is methane (CH_4), a gas that is an order of magnitude worse than carbon dioxide in terms of the "Greenhouse Effect." Unless strict measures are taken to ensure against leaks in the system, the benefits of switching to this source could be negated.

The technical and perceptional problems associated with the use of nuclear power, such as the long-term storage of nuclear wastes, reactor accidents, and nuclear weapons proliferating (see, for example, Albright and Ferveson, 1988), are too well-known to need a detailed discussion here.

Although solar-and wind-energy are already in use in a number of locations, their use on a large scale is still not competitive with fossil fuels. The expected large costs to essentially all countries that could result form a global climate change might provide an adequate rationale for investing heavily in the development of new (such as nuclear fusion) and renewable energy sources. Many in the scientific and technological communities has lamented the cut-backs in such research and development that occurred during the early years of this decade, when oil prices declined. Those charged with decision-making respond, unfortunately, to short-term needs, whereas the development of new energy technologies requires long-term commitments.

Several factors are contributing to the deforestation taking place in Asia and much of the developing world. Firewood is often the only source of energy available for cooking or heating in many rural areas of South-and South-East Asia. The need for agricultural land as populations expand has been another major cause of deforestation. The export of timber has been an important source of foreign currency in many countries, and the practice continues, although on a smaller scale, even when it is officially banned.

In the limited space available here, we shall focus our discussion on energy-policy related concerns. In particular, we shall examine the extent to which countries in Asia might be able to switch from coal or oil to energy sources that emit less carbon dioxide.

Sources of Commercial Energy in Asia

The amount of commercial energy supplied by the individual fossil fuels, and by non-fossil sources (mainly hydo-, nuclear-, and geothermal-power) during 1986 in each of the countries in Asia (United Nations, 1988).

As we see from the Table, the energy supplied by various energy sources in the different countries of Asia reflects the full diversity of that vast continent. The two most populous countries of the world—China and India—depend on coal for the largest share of commercial energy. A similar situation prevails in North Korea, Mongolia, and Vietnam. The relative contribution of different energy sources to the total commercial energy in these countries.

The countries of West Asia (the "Middle East"), and the ASEAN countries rely on oil for most of their energy. The share of total commercial energy supplied by different energy sources in some of these countries is shown in Fig. 1.

In several countries of West and South Asia, natural gas is the largest contributor to energy supplies, as shown in Fig. 2.

Nuclear power is supplying more than 1/4 of the total electricity generated in Japan, and about 45 per cent of the total electricity in South Korea and Taiwan. Hydropower supplies a substantial portion of the electricity used in Nepal, Pakistan, and Sri Lanka, and has been a major energy source in China, India, and Japan.

Designing Energy Policies for Reducing CO_2 Emissions

In designing energy policies to reduce the emissions of carbon dioxide, the degree of difficulty faced by different countries in the region will vary greatly. Countries which derive most of their energy supply from domestic reserves of coal or oil, and which have limited potential for replacing it with other domestic energy sources will face the largest challenge. Countries with substantial untapped hydro-electric capacity would normally have fewer (but definitely not negligible) problems in meeting any longer term goals for carbon dioxide emissions. The balance of trade for individual countries will also have a major impact on the ability of the countries to substitute less-polluting imported energy sources for more-polluting domestic sources. The relative level of difficulty faced by different countries in lowering carbon dioxide emissions is illustrated in Fig. 3.

Nuclear power and renewable energy sources are highly desirable from the perspective of reducing carbon dioxide emissions. The type of nuclear power plants that are in widespread use today do not enjoy a great deal of public confidence in many countries, particularly since the accidents at Three-Mile Island and Chernobyl. A number of potentially safer designs have been suggested during the past few years (Spiewak

Figure 1.

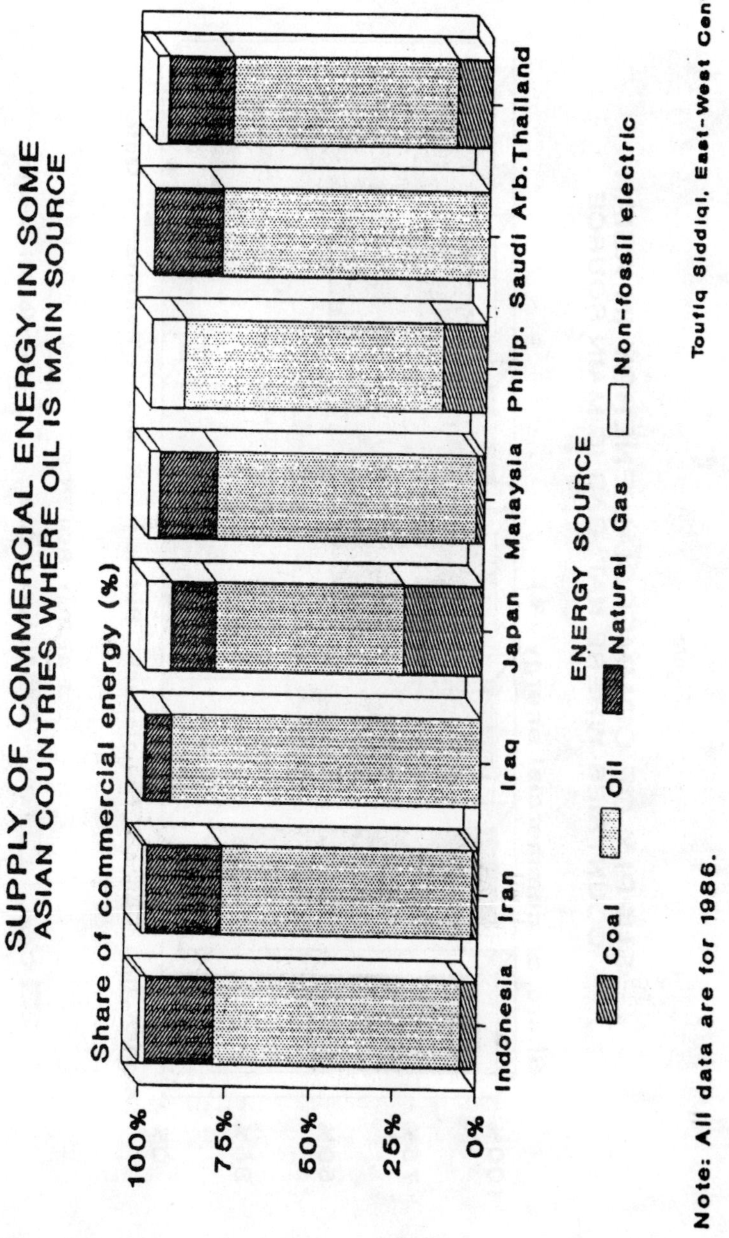
SUPPLY OF COMMERCIAL ENERGY IN SOME
ASIAN COUNTRIES WHERE OIL IS MAIN SOURCE
Share of commercial energy (%)
100%
75%
50%
25%
0%
Indonesia
Iran
Iraq
Japan
Malaysia
Philip.
Saudi Arb.
Thailand
ENERGY SOURCE
Coal
Oil
Natural Gas
Non-fossil electric
Note: All data are for 1986.
Toufiq Siddiqi, East-West Center

Figure 2.

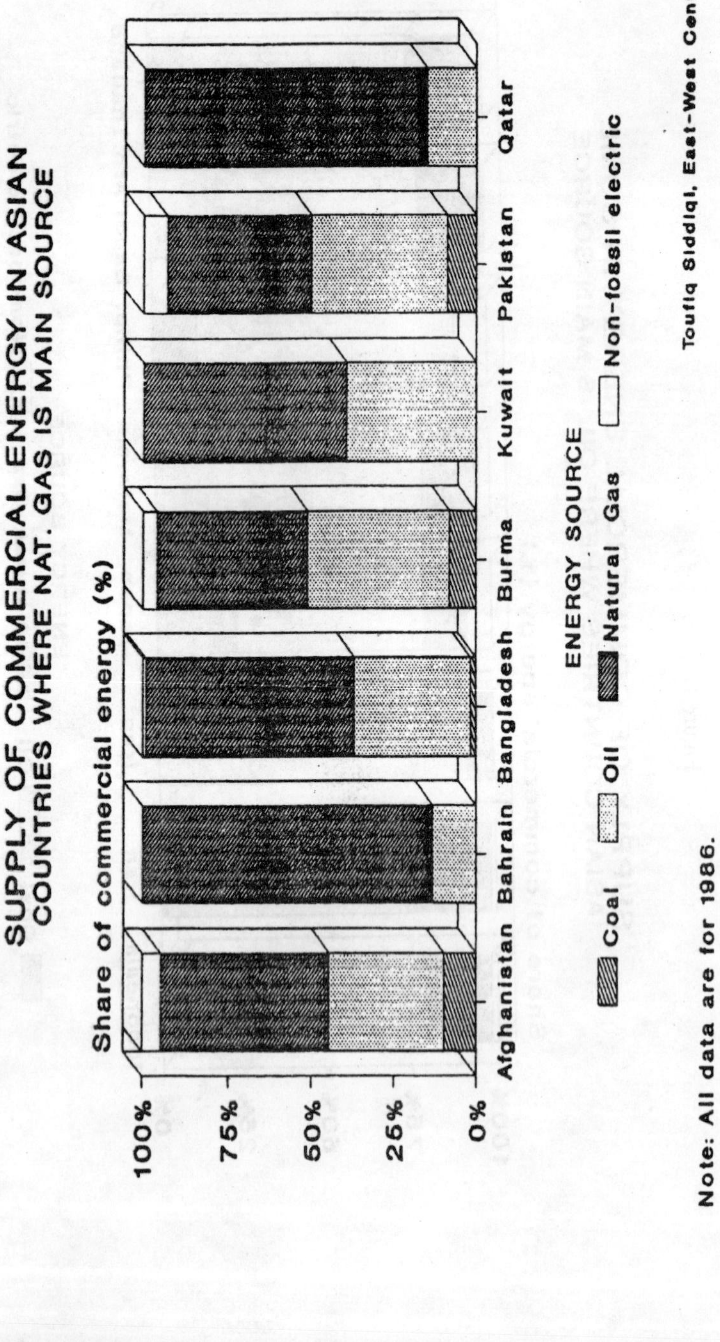
SUPPLY OF COMMERCIAL ENERGY IN ASIAN
COUNTRIES WHERE NAT. GAS IS MAIN SOURCE
Share of commercial energy (%)
100%
75%
50%
25%
0%
Afghanistan
Bahrain
Bangladesh
Burma
Kuwait
Pakistan
Qatar
ENERGY SOURCE
Coal
Oil
Natural Gas
Non-fossil electric
Toufiq Siddiqi, East-West Center
Note: All data are for 1986.

Figure 3.

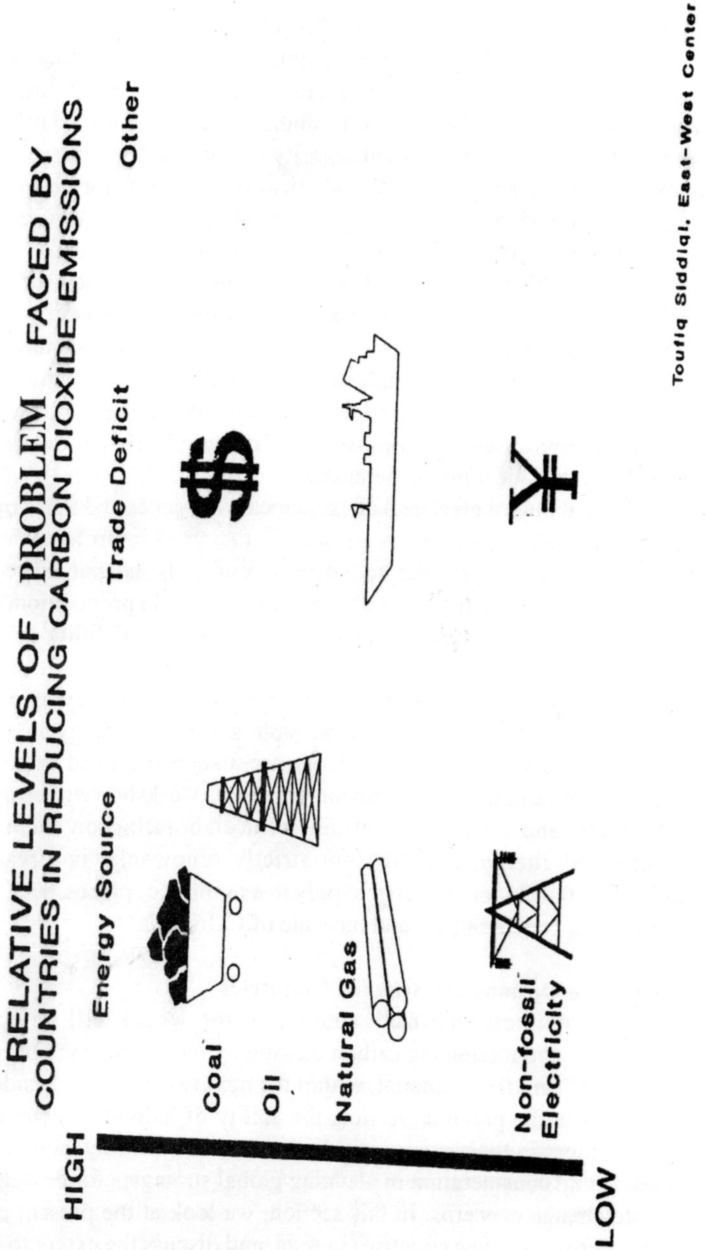
RELATIVE LEVELS OF PROBLEM FACED BY
COUNTRIES IN REDUCING CARBON DIOXIDE EMISSIONS
Energy Source
Trade Deficit
Other
HIGH
LOW
Coal
Oil
Natural Gas
Non-fossil
Electricity
Toufiq Siddiqi, East-West Center

and Weinbergy, 1985), and some of them may become commercially viable during the early years of the 21st century.

Further, the 1000 Mwe power plants that have become the preferred size in the industialized countries are too large for many developing countries. In general, the size of any single plant should not be more than about a tenth of the total installed capacity in that country or region. Large nuclear power plants are thus a practical option only for countries or regions where the total capacity exceeds about 10,000 Mwe. This excludes the vast majority of the less-industialized countries at present.

The problems associated with the long-term storage of highly radioactive wastes from the nuclear industry are well known. The risks of transporting and storing such wastes for hundreds of thousands of years can be reduced, but not completely eliminated. Thus, societies would have to decide how such risks compare with the risks from global climate change. In both cases, societies would be making decisions not only for the present, but for future generations.

Even though a great deal of excitement was generated a few months ago by the apparent discovery of nuclear fusion at room temperatures, the consensus amongst the scientific community is that large-scale generation of energy from this process is not a viable proposition. Other routes to nuclear fusion also do not promise the availability of a new energy source during the next two or three decades.

Renewable sources of energy are already in use to varying extents. Hydropower has been a major renewable source of energy in several countries, and wind-and solar-energy are also being used in selected locations. Some of the other presentations in this workshop will be dealing with these, and I will thus refrain from elaborating on them here. Geothermal energy, although not strictly renewable, is already an important contributor to energy supply in a number of places, such as the Philippines, New Zealand, and the state of California.

Illustrative Options for Selected Countries

It is unlikely that each country in the world will be equally enthusiastic about reducing carbon dioxide by twenty per cent or by any other significant fixed amount, within the next two or three decades. As mentioned in the previous section, the ability of individual countries to make changes in their energy supplies varies considerably, and needs to be taken into consideration in planning global strategies for dealing with climate change concerns. In this section, we look at the present energy supply system in a few countries in Asia, and discuss the extent to which energy sources that emit less or no carbon dioxide can be utilised during the next two decades.

China

China relies almost entirely on fossil fuels for its commercial energy. Coal alone supplies about 82 per cent of the total, and oil about 14 per cent (United Nations, 1988). The share of energy supplied by each of the commercial sources.

A substantial amount of coal is used in small and inefficient boilers in small industries, offices, and homes. There is thus good potential for improvements in energy efficiency. Given its presently low level of per capita energy consumption, it is unlikely that total energy use in China will decline due to more efficient energy use. It could, however, lead to a slower rate of growth than would be the case otherwise.

The reserves of natural gas in China are small. Proven reserves at the end of 1987 amounted to 30.7 trillion cubic feet (tcf; in terms of heat content, 1 tcf is equivalent to approximately 35 million tons of coal), representing about 0.8 per cent of the world total (British Petroleum, 1988). By way of comparison, the proven reserves of the USA are 186.7 tcf, and of Iran 489.4 tcf. China's proven reserves of natural gas are thus too small (equivalent to less than 2 years of coal production) to permit large-scale switching from coal. This avenue for reducing carbon dioxide emissions is thus not a viable option for China at present. However, the country has not been adequately explored for natural gas, and future discoveries might permit this fuel to play a more important role. In addition to the benefits in terms of carbon dioxide reductions, greater use of natural gas for space heating and cooking could reduce the high levels of particulates and sulfur oxides in the air of many Chinese cities.

The hydro-power potential of China has not been fully tapped, and could make a much larger contribution to China's energy supply than the approximately 2 per cent it provides today. The total capacity for hydropower generation has been estimated (Ling Peihong, 1989) at 680,000 Mw—the equivalent of about 650 large nuclear power plants! Only about four per cent of this capacity has been tapped so far. Even though much of this capacity lies in remote locations in Southwest China, the potential for increasing the contribution of this environmentally preferred source is large. Inevitably, there are some environmental costs associated even with hydro-power facilities. These could include loss of agricultural land, extinction of rare species of flora and fauna, and other effects arising from changes in patterns of land use and water supplies.

Other renewable sources of energy could also make a useful contribution towards reducing carbon dioxide emissions. Solar heating could meet some of China's needs for space heating and hot water. Wind and geothermal energy are viable options in many locations. Windmills have been used in China for centuries, primarily for pumping water. Small-scale wind generators have also been used in the prairies of Inner Mongolia. Fast-growing trees could be a source of energy, but would not provide much of a benefit in reducing carbon dioxide emissions when used as fuel.

Reactors for nuclear research have been in operation in China for two decades. China is presently building its own nuclear power units (Ling Peihong, 1989) at Qinshan in Zhejiang province (600 Mwe), and in Jiangyin county, Jiangsu province (2000 Mwe). Further, a 1000 Mwe nuclear power plant is under construction at Daya Bay near Hong Kong. It has been designed, and is being built by a French-British group.

With its experience in nuclear research, as well as its status as a member of the "Nuclear Weapons Club," China has the trained manpower to expand the use of nuclear power. Since the present per capita use of electricity is still small compared to that in the industrialized countries, it is more realistic to think of nuclear power as a contributor to future power plants, than as a replacement for present ones.

There has been substantial deforestation in China over the past century. Efforts have been made during the past few years to reverse this trend, but the potential for bringing substantial additional land under forest cover is still great. Thus, in common with most other developing countries, it would be more realistic in the near-term to expect China to make its contribution to a global carbon dioxide reduction strategy through *afforestation* rather than through an actual reduction in emissions from the combustion of fossil fuels.

Japan

In the process of becoming one of the world's leading industrial nations, Japan has made use of a number of energy sources. During the 1930's, coal provided about half of the total energy used, and hydropower most of the remainder. As recently as 1950, hydropower supplied about 40 per cent of the total energy used in Japan (Ginsburg, 1989). Rising environmental concerns and the availability of cheap oil during the 1960s led to the dominance of that energy source in Japan's supply picture during the past quarter of a century.

The sudden rise in petroleum prices in 1973 and 1979, and concerns about the reliability of supplies led Japan to a strategy of greatly diversifying the sources of energy. The relative contribution of the different energy sources is shown in Fig. 1.

The country has the largest nuclear power program in Asia, which supplied 186 billion kilowatt-hours of electricity during 1987 (IEEE, 1989). The industry is capable of considerable additional expansion. However, rising public concern about the location of nuclear power plants has made it more difficult than in earlier times to find suitable locations in this land-scarce country. Also, the occurrence of frequent earthquakes makes it difficult to find suitable sites for the long-term storage of nuclear wastes.

Japan is also the largest importer of liquefied natural gas in the world. Even before the concerns for reducing global emissions of carbon dioxide had become widespread, Japan had decided to make greater use of imported LNG to improve air quality in selected areas. As a country with the largest trade surplus in the world, Japan is in a good position to increase use of LNG as a part of its contribution to reducing carbon dioxide emissions.

Geothermal energy has been used in Japan on a small scale for several decades, but the potential for expanding its share of the total energy supply in the country is rather limited. In terms of using renewable energy sources, Japan could make some additional use of hydropower.

The present emissions of CO_2 in Japan are estimated to result in about 250 million tons per year of carbon being put in the atmosphere (Nitta and Yamaji, 1989). Using the long-term energy forecast made by the Ministry of Trade and Industry (MITI), about 300 million tons of carbon per year would be emitted by 2005 A.D. Nitta and Yamaji have examined the effect of taking steps to reduce CO_2 emissions in the individual sectors consuming fossil fuels. Pursuing CO_2 reduction strategies could lower the annual emissions in 2005 to about 232 million tons of carbon, or a seven per cent reduction from current levels. They have estimated that the forests in Japan are absorbing about 10.4 million tons of carbon per year, and believe that this amount could be double by 2005 A.D.

The country's largest longer-term contribution to reducing carbon dioxide emissions may well turn out to be in the field of photovoltaic cells for the direct conversion of sunlight into electricity. Along with the USA and some European countries, Japan is a leader in research towards making this proven technology more competitive with electricity from fossil and nuclear sources. Japan is also in a good position to provide financial and technical assistance to developing countries that are pursuing policies for reforestation and afforestation.

India

India relies on coal for about two-thirds of its supplies of commercial energy. The pattern of energy supply and reserves bears many similarities to that of China. The country has substantial coal resources, whereas the proven domestic reserves of natural gas, estimated at 17.6 tcf (British Petroleum, 1988) are too small to permit a large switch from coal.

The potential for more efficient use of energy exists, particularly in transportation-related fields. As in many other developing countries, the buses, trucks, and automobiles in India do not usually operate at maximum efficiency. Also, Indian coals have a very high ash content—frequently above 30 per cent. This coal is usually transported by rail, sometimes to demand centres over a thousand kilometres away. Additional efforts could be made to reduce the ash content prior to transportation.

Another opportunity for conserving energy lies in locating more power stations closer to the coal fields, most of which are located in the eastern part of the country. Developments in reducing losses in the transmission of electricity could be very helpful in this context.

Nuclear power plants have been in operation in India for two decades, but the total installed capacity is still rather small—less than 3000 Mwe out of a total installed capacity of 55,000 Mwe (Pachauri, 1989). The newer plants have been designed and built by Indians, and future plans call for a significant increase in the generation of electricity from nuclear reactions.

Hydroelectric power has been an important component of the Indian energy system since the early part of this century. Many of the more practical sites have been tapped, but considerable potential still exists. Also, if a satisfactory regional agreement can be worked out, it would be possible to make use of the enormous possibilities for generating hydropower in Nepal for the use of both countries, and possibly Bangladesh.

Thinking in this bold vein, an agreement by the South Asian countries to cooperate in the field of energy would also make it possible to construct a pipeline for bringing natural gas from Iran across Pakistan to India. It would also enable some of the natural gas in Bangladesh to be transmitted for use in Eastern India. Such arrangements could be beneficial not only in financial terms, but also contribute to improving the air quality in many Indian cities, as well as reducing the global emissions of carbon dioxide.

Iran

Iran, along with a few other countries in the Middle-East, is in the unusual position of not being adversely affected by any worldwide efforts to reduce CO_2 emissions. It has the second highest proven resources of natural gas in the world, amounting to 489.4 tcf (British Petroleum, 1988). This represents about 13 per cent of the total world reserves of natural gas, and roughly equals the combined reserves of North America and Western Europe!

Even though a switch from coal and oil could hurt Iran financially, since the country is a major exporter of oil and a leading member of OPEC, increased exports of natural gas could make up for the revenue loss.

For its domestic use, Iran relies on oil for 75 per cent of its commercial energy, with natural gas providing most of the remainder (Fig. 1). The country is in an excellent position to vastly expand the role of natural gas in its energy supply, if it decides to pursue a strategy to reduce CO_2 emissions.

During the 1970s, Iran had initiated a program of nuclear power. Two reactor units were under construction by a consortium of West German companies, but the program was discontinued after the Iranian revolution. However, the country has the financial resources, and a large enough demand for electricity, to enable it to proceed with nuclear power as part of its contribution to slow global warming.

Hydropower presently contributes about 1.5 per cent of the total commercial energy used in Iran (United Nations, 1988). There is some scope for additional use of this source, as well as other renewable energy sources. Selected areas in the country also provide opportunity for fixing additional carbon through afforestation.

Bangladesh

Bangladesh is probably the most populous of a group of countries that make a relatively small contribution to the global emissions of carbon dioxide, while being one of the most vulnerable to the likely consequences of global warming. The areas lying in the delta formed by two great rivers—the Ganges and the Brahmaputra—are prone to frequent flooding from the rivers, and from cyclones. Any worldwide rise in sea-levels could have serious consequences on Bangladesh, such as displacing a large part of the population, and much of the mangrove areas (ESCAP, 1988).

Bangladesh obtains over 60 per cent of its total commercial energy from natural gas, with oil supplying most of the remainder (Fig. 2). The reserves of natural gas are adequate (12.7 tcf) to permit an increase in natural gas production, either for domestic use, and possibly some export to India. Further, as discussed earlier in the section on India, a suitable agreement might open up the possibility of tapping Nepal's large hydropower capacity for the benefit of Nepal, India, and Bangladesh.

In common with other parts of South-and Southeast-Asia, there has been substantial deforestation in the upland areas of Bangladesh. The country could make its contribution to the global efforts to stabilize CO_2 levels by reforestation. However, Bangladesh has one of the highest population densities in the world, and it would be difficult to take land away from agricultural production and designate it solely for forest use.

Conclusion

On a global level, steps need to be taken to initially slow down the rates of increase in the emissions of CO_2 and other greenhouse gases, and subsequently to stabilize and possibly reduce the atmospheric concentrations of these gases. In pursuing a strategy to achieve this goal, one may have to use a modified version of the saying, "From each according to his ability, to each according to his needs." The contribution each country could make to the common goal may have to differ, based on circumstances. The level of industrialization, the availability of resources and infrastructure to switch from one energy source to another, and the potential for reforestation and afforestation are some of the important factors that could affect the nature of each country's contribution.

In this paper, we have briefly examined the present patterns of energy supply in the countries of Asia, and the potential in a few countries for switching to energy sources that emit less carbon dioxide. More detailed studies need to be undertaken, and have been initiated at a number of institutions. We'll be hearing about some of them later on in the workshop. We will also be learning about the policies under consideration in different countries regarding energy conservation strategies, and the outlook for adding to the global fixing of carbon through increased forestation.

I would like to conclude this paper with a request to the participants at this workshop. There is a great deal of knowledge and expertise present in this room, and we would like to benefit from the opportunity. In the table below (Table 1), I have listed the total commercial energy used in several countries (or geographic entities) of the region, as well as the percentage contribution of the different energy sources, during 1986. A part of the Table has been left blank, for your input. It would be very helpful, if you could write down for your country, or other geographic entities that you are particularly familiar with, your estimates of:

(a) The total percentage increase in commercial energy consumption in the country expected in the year 2010.

(b) The percentage contribution of each of the energy sources to the total energy supply of the country.

Please also indicate on the Table whether or not your estimate is based on the country's implementing policies to reduce emissions of carbon dioxide.

Additional copies of the Table are being distributed, so there is no need to remove the Table from the complete paper.

We would like to incorporate your input in the workshop summary we shall be preparing during the next few days. Thus, it will be very helpful, if we could get back the Table, with your estimates, prior to your departure from Honolulu.

In conclusion, I would like to add my welcome to that of Dr. Ginsburg and Dr. Drucker, and to thank you for taking the time from your busy schedules to share your insights with us.

Table 1. Present and projected contribution of various energy sources

		1986 A.D.						2010 A.D.				
		Total Commercial Energy Consumption (Mtce)		Percentage Contributed By				Total Commerical Energy Consumption (Mtce)	Percentage Contributed By			
Sl.No.	Country *			Coal	Oil	Nat. Gas	Electricity (Non-Fossil)		Coal	Oil	Nat.Gas	Non-Fossil
1.	Australia	106.52	41.5	38.3	18.3		1.9					
2.	Bangladesh	6.40	1.7	35.3	62.2		0.9					
3.	Canada	249.07	13.6	39.9	29.3		17.2					
4.	China	742.85	82.0	13.8	2.5		1.7					
	-Mainland											
	-Taiwan											
	-Hong Kong											
5.	Fiji	0.27	5.5	79.4	15.1		0					
6.	India	210.19	67.8	25.4	3.4		3.4					
7.	Indonesia	47.48	4.7	73.5	20.0		1.9					
8.	Japan	440.17	23.7	56.3	12.8		7.2					
9.	South Korea	68.17	45.7	48.4	0.2		5.8					
10.	Malaysia	16.68	2.4	77.9	16.7		3.0					
11.	New Zealand	13.09	11.9	30.1	36.4		21.5					
12.	Pakistan	25.26	8.8	42.3	43.5		6.9					
13.	Philippines	13.74	13.1	77.4	3.0		9.5					
14.	Singapore	10.75	0.1	99.9	0		0					
15.	Thailand	23.56	10.3	67.5	18.9		3.3					
16.	U.K.	302.25	37.1	35.2	24.9		2.7					
17.	USA	2278.10	26.2	44.8	24.9		4.1					
18.	Vietnam	7.30	68.7	27.9			3.4					

* The word "Country" is used in this paper to indicate a geographical entity for which separate data are reported. No statements regarding political boundaries are applicable.

References

Albright, D., and H.A. Feiveson (1988). "Plutonium Recycling and the Problem of Nuclear Proliferation," in *Annual Review of Energy,* edited by J.M. Hollander, H. Brooks, and D. Steinlight, Vol. 13, pp. 239-65.

British Petroleum (1988). *BP Statistical Review of World Energy,* London: British Petroleum, Government and Public Affairs Department, 36 pp.

Enquete-Kommission (1988). *Schutz der Erdatmosphare: Eine Internationale Herausforderung.* Interim Report of the 11th German Parliament. Bonn: Deutscher Bundestag, 583 pp.

Ginsburg, Norton (1989). Personal communication.

ESCAP (1988). *Coastal Environmental Management Plan for Bangladesh.* Two volumes. Bangkok: United Nations.

Institute of Energy Economies (1989). *Energy in Japan,* no. 95 (January 1989), pp. 48-51.

Ling Peihong (1989). "How to Reduce Carbon Dioxide Emissions in China." Paper presented at the International Workshop on "A Little Breathing Space: Carbon Dioxide Emission Reduction Strategies," held in Budapest, Hungary, on 14-15 April, 1989 (cited subsequently as "The Budapest Workshop").

Lovins, Amory B. (1989). "Energy, People, and Industrialization." Paper presented at the Hoover Institution conference on "Human Demography and Natural Resources," held at Stanford, California, 1-3 February, 1989.

Nitta, Yoshitaka, and Kenji Yamaji (1989). "An overview of CO_2 Emission in Japan, and Possible Countermeasures to the Greenhouse Effect." Paper presented at the Budapest Workshop.

Pachauri, R.K. (1989). "Stretching Our Breathing Space: A View from India." Paper presented at the Budapest Workshop.

Siddiqi, Toufiq A. (1979). *Environmental Dimensions of Energy Policies: An Initial Research Plan.* Honolulu: Environment and Policy Institute, East-West Center, June 1979, 72 pp.

Spiewak, Irving, and Alvin M. Weinberg (1985). "Inherently Safe Reactors," in *Annual Review of Energy,* edited by J.M. Hollander, H. Brooks, and D. Steinlingt, Vol. 10, pp. 431-62.

United Nations (1988). *1986 Energy Statistics Yearbook.* New York; United Nations, 435 pp.

World Bank (1987). *The World Bank Atlas, 1987.* Washington, D.C.: The World Bank, 29 pp.

World Resources Institute (1988). *World Resources 1988-89.* A Report by the World Resources Institute and the International Institute for Environment and Development, in collaboration with the United Nations Environment Programme. New York: Basic Books, 372 pp.

8

Consequences of Risk Management in Developing Countries

The present Chapter, which is about management of threat factor in climate change and their implication is a draft summary presented by Kirk R. Smith at a workshop title "Responding to the Threat of Global Warming: Options for the Pacific and Asia" held in June, 1989. It throws light on various aspects of climate change and its handling along with risks involved in the process.

"The potential in developing countries for large percentage increases in emissions of greenhouse gases (GHG) over the next decades has resulted in suggestions that control over such emissions should be considered as part of nearterm development planning. Sometimes the hope is expressed that such restrictions can be part of a win-win strategy, i.e., that concerns over global warming only lead us to take on programs such as reforestation, energy efficiency, and fuel switching, for which there are many other good reasons to undertake anyway. While undeniably true in many circumstances, this begs a crucial question: does the threat of climate change through GHG emissions justify efforts to alter the development pathway now being followed in poor countries?"

Many observers apparently believe that the implications of global warming are so grave that, in some fashion, restrictions on GHG emissions should be considered along with the other numerous and already burdensome restrictions on development, e.g., lack of capital, lack of skilled personnel, and lack of infrastructure.

This paper, although accepting that the threat is important enough to warrant changes in present development pathways, draws the opposite conclusion. Rather than impose new constraints it takes the position that the potential for global warming is actually one of the strongest arguments for *reducing constraints and accelerating development*. From the standpoint of the poorest two-thirds of the population in developing countries, concerns about climate change probably justify a policy response in which not only do GHG restrictions have no place, but GHG emissions rates may actually be stimulated locally.

I follow two lines of argument to reach this conclusion. Firstly, I argue that the best way to protect the poorest groups is to bring them as soon as possible to a minimum level of development at which they can be expected to adequately handle environmental stress. Secondly, I argue that, the extra GHG emissions necessary to accomplish this task are minuscule in the global GHG picture and thus will not be critical in determining climate change.

Environmental Stress Across the Development Spectrum

To a first approximation, the impact of climate change will be like having more and, perhaps, more severe natural disasters, for example, floods, droughts, tropical cyclones, and storm surges. Much evidence indicates that there is a marked difference in the impact of such events depending on the level of economic development. Cross-sectional evidence, for example, shows that the same size natural disaster will have vastly different consequences in different parts of the world, depending on the level of development. For illustration, a tropical cyclone of the size that may kill ten people in Florida might kill ten thousand people in Bangladesh. A similar ratio will be seen in the number left homeless. Only in the dollar amount of property damage do disasters appear larger in developed regions.

Longitudinal studies provide similar results. The same size hurricane that killed many people in the USA or Hong Kong in the early part of the century, e.g., kills few in either place today. This is true in spite of the great increase in population density that has occurred over the period.

The reasons for this effect are fairly obvious: better warning systems; more capable and organized fire, police, and medical protection; more and better roads; an educated and literate public; more substantial housing; a reduction in the number of people living at the margin with little savings or other means of security during periods of household or community disruption; and so on.

It is important here to distinguish the *stress* (analogous to the dose in toxicology) from the *consequence* (the response). Although the dose of natural disasters can be similar, the vulnerability of the population and thus the response is markedly higher in developing countries. In short, the poorest countries suffer greater loss of life, and the richer countries show more property loss (as measured by the usual indicators).

Although the analogy with natural disasters is not perfect, there is little reason to expect that the consequences of climate change will not have a similar distribution. All nations will experience stress, but few people will die of it in developed countries where the economic damage will be highest. Many, however, will die or become homeless and ill in the developing world. Climate change is an economic threat in developed areas but, in addition, a threat to life itself in poor areas.

This argues that the best approach for a developing-country planner worried about climate change may be to accelerate those aspects of development that will assist their poorest and most vulnerable populations in attaining the levels of health, flexibility, education, and resilience that will allow them to cope with environmental stress of all sorts, including climate change. This may offer a much more effective least-risk development pathway than would one attempting to rank development projects on the basis of greenhouse-gas emissions.

The marginal increase in resilience (reduction in vulnerability) to environmental stress, however, is not uniform across the development spectrum. At high levels of development the additional increase of resilience per unit development is much less than at low levels. The implication is that it may be possible to define some sort of minium resilience as a basic need. Development planning could then be designed to bring poor populations as rapidly as possible to this level, whatever the cost. Above this level, however, a range of other considerations such as GHG emissions might come into play.

The establishment of such a level would obviously require some careful investigation and will be geographically and perhaps culturally dependent. To illustrate the concept, however, it is instructive to examine the two most commonly available indicators, life expectancy and infant mortality. In a rough way, a cross-sectional analysis shows a slowing of the marginal increase in resilience when per capita energy use reaches one to one-and-a-half tons oil equivalent per year. In addition, such a minimum level of resilience is a necessary, if not sufficient, condition for achieving low birth rates. Parents who see many neighbour children fail to survive young childhood are not likely to wish to limit their own fertility.

No Blood from a Turnip

For illustration, let us take one ton per year per capita carbon emissions (mainly as CO_2) as the amount required to reach a minimum level of resilience. This level is somewhat less than the present global mean and lies in the gap between the rich and poor countries within which lie only a few countries such as South Korea. We can then examine the global GHG implications of policies designed to achieve this level in developing countries as fast as possible. For this purpose, consider a simple two-nation world consisting only of India and the USA. (These are actually the second largest developing nation and developed nation respectively, each with about 22 per cent of the population of its group.)

The important GHG parameters over time are analogous to those of taking an automobile trip: distance travelled, speed, and acceleration. For GHG emissions, these are: cumulative amount added to the atmosphere, annual rate of emissions, and annual rate of increase in emission rate. Table 1 lists these parameters at the present (1990) for India and the USA as well as projections at four points in the future given continuation of current conditions.

Table 1. Historical and projected carbon emissions: total accumulation, annual rate, and annual acceleration. This compares the carbon emissions for the United States and India starting in 1900. Pre-1990 values are based on historical data and projections are based on the assumption that 1987-1989 rates of growth continue in both countries, i.e., 4.6 per cent per year in India and 0.5 per cent per year in the United States. Only carbon dioxide emissions from fossil fuel use since 1900 are considered. All figures are given on a per capita basis.

Sl.No.	*Year*	*Acceleration (t/y)/y*		*Rate t/y*		*Accumulation tonnes*	
		India	*USA*	*India*	*USA*	*India*	*USA*
1.	1990	0.01	0.026	0.22	5.2	6	260
2.	2013	**0.029**	**0.029**	0.63	5.8	15	390
3.	2024	0.046	0.031	**1.0**	6.2	24	460
4.	2069	0.36	0.039	**7.7**	**7.7**	170	770
5.	2111	2.4	0.048	52	10	**1100**	**1100**

The most critical parameter for determining the extent of global warming is the cumulative amount of GHG in the atmosphere. As shown in Table 1, the amount placed into the atmosphere since 1900 as part of the US industialization process is equivalent to about 260 tons per person in 1990, more than forty times that of the average Indian. The present rate of emissions as well as the rate of increase in emission rate (acceleration) are also substantially higher in the US at present. Indeed, as shown, it will not be until 2013 or so until the acceleration becomes equal at about thirty (kg/year)/year. In addition, even if the present rapid rate of economic and energy growth continues in India, it will not be until nearly 2070 before the rate of emissions reaches that of the US, then at about 7.7 t/year.

Table 1 shows that under present conditions India would reach the emission rate of 1.0 t/capita-year, which is our arbitrary indicator of minimum resilience, in about 2024. At that point, however, India would still have been responsible for only a minor part of the total atmospheric accumulation, less than five per cent of that of the USA.

A question arises, therefore: is it really worthwhile to spend much effort to try to reduce the small addition that India will make in the next generation, which, even under these conditions of rapid growth in India and extremely small growth into he USA, will be less than ten per cent of the US additions during the same period (18 versus 190 tons, 1990 to 2024)? Rather, is it not likely that the huge benefit to be gained by bringing resilience up to a minimum standard far outweighs any GHG savings to be squeezed out of India's energy system during the same period?

Furthermore, if it were decided that the global community should limit GHG total emissions to their present level, it would still be possible to bring up the developing world to this minimum level without undue hardships in the presently developed world. All the countries in the world now below 1.0 t/capita-year, for example, could be brought up to that level and the total rate kept constant merely by reducing the average emissions of the developed countries to about 2.2 t/capita-year, the present level of Japan. This does not appear to be impossible, or, indeed, even difficult from a technical standpoint.

Conclusion: The Natural Debt

I follow the example of the climate modellers and emphasize that this (two-nation, one-pollutant) model is greatly oversimplified. It considers, for example, none of the other greenhouse gases, no sources other than fossil fuels, no distributional effects, and rigid growth rates. In addition, of course, energy use, income, health, and resilience are actually related in complicated ways. Efforts toward improving our understanding and ability to influence these relationships should have the highest priority.

Nevertheless, at least one conclusion seems fairly robust: large ratios of cumulative emissions between developed and developing countries will remain until far into the next century. Changing the scenarios would not likely significantly change this basic pattern.

It is these cumulative emissions that are the problem and it thus seems appropriate that the burden of slowing and reducing carbon emissions should be borne according to the amount emitted by each economy. In analogy to the national debt, this might be termed the *natural debt*. Over the years, just as economies take on a financial debt in order to grow faster, they take on a natural debt for the same reason. In this case, economies have borrowed the assimiliative capacity of the environment by releasing waste gases faster than they can be removed naturally. Just as there are economic disruptions if the national debt becomes too large, so too with the natural debt.

Developed countries are the holders of the largest natural debts (260 tonnes per capita for the US, for example, compared to six tonnes for India, in 1990) and are best able to devote some of their wealth to paying them off. They should not think of this as a sudden extra cost being imposed, but as the inevitable need to take responsibility to repay the loans that helped them achieve their present state of wealth.

References

British Petroleum Company, 1988, "Statistical Review of World Energy," London.

Energy Information Administration, 1989, "Annual Energy Outlook," U.S. Department of Energy, Washington, D.C.

Marland, G. et al., 1989, "Estimates of CO_2 Emissions from Fossil Fuel Burning and Cement Manufacturing," ORNL/CDIAC-25, Oak Ridge National Lab, Tennessee.

Mitchell, J.K., 1989, "Risk Assessment of Global Environmental Change," EAPI WP-13, East-West Center, Honolulu.

Smith, K.R., 1988, "The Risk Transition," EAPI WP-10, East-West Center, Honolulu.

Smith, K.R., 1989, "Have You Paid Your Natural Debt," East-West Environment and Policy Institute, East-West Center, Honolulu.

White, Gilbert F., ed., 1974, *Natural Hazards: Local, National, Global,* Oxford University Press, New York.

Wijkman, A. and L. Timberlake, 1988, *Natural Disasters: Acts of God or Acts of Man?* New Society Publishers, Philadelphia.

World Bank, 1988, *World Development Report,* Oxford University Press, New York.

9

Intersections Between Science and Politics with American Attitude

This chapter, looks into style and factors for American attitude and perception towards man-made deliberate atmospheric modifications. Here, we have also made an attempt to throw light on intersections and interactions between science and politics that currently bring to notice understanding of global warming. General public understanding of the environment rests on a complex and shifting blend of science and culture that fundamentally shapes both scientific practice and social policy. At present, for example, human modification of the atmosphere is seen by many as among the greatest threats to the earth's environment. This conception underpins worldwide efforts to understand and avoid anthropogenic environmental change.

Still, Americans have not always viewed modification of the atmosphere is such starkly negative terms. For much of the post-war era, in fact, Americans supported scientific research on ways of deliberately modifying weather in an effort to restrict the fury of nature. Indeed, the United States supported a vigorous research program into deliberate weather and climate modification for three decades, from the 1940s until well into the 1970s. By the late 1970s, in the wake of growing concerns about negative human impacts on the environment, much of this support had vanished.

Nevertheless, remnants of the promotion of deliberate intervention in atmospheric systems can be noticed as late as 1980, in a report by the US Department of Energy promoting efforts to control the climate through selective additions of carbon dioxide to the atmosphere, and even more recently, in a 1992 US National Academy of Sciences report recommending that "geoengineering" technologies be developed to counter the effects of global warming (US Department of Energy 1980; Committee on Science, Engineering, and general policy of the US National Academy of Sciences 1992, 433-464).

During the year January 1971, Robert M. White, the Acting Administrator of the newly formed National Oceanic and Atmospheric Administration (NOAA), expressed his faith that deliberate human modification of the weather should be regarded as a viable technology.[1] White said that "almost certainly" there were means to increase precipitation in a predictable way, that attempts to reduce the winds of Hurricane Debbie in 1969 had produced "encouraging results," and that "significant attempts" could be made to reduce lightning to aid in forest fire suppression. He declared that the World Meteorological Organization (WMO) had officially recognized the importance of weather modification, and he applauded the steps taken by the US federal government to advance the field (White 1971).

In retrospect, White's speech seems to have been the swan song of weather modification. Two year later, the secretary-general of the WMO said that "weather modification operations related to precipitation are a waste of money and effort" (Hart and Victor 1993, 676). And, while it took White and other meteorologists many years to arrive at a similar conclusion, their views became increasingly irrelevant as the US government progressively eliminated funding for weather modification research over the course of the following decade. Weather modification's proponents made so many grand promises about its future efficacy that it is tempting to believe that weather modification research ended simply as experiments showed that it did not work. This chapter argues otherwise. The field existed for most of its history with little clear evidence that rainmaking and hurricane abatement worked, but there was equally little clear fact that it did not. No convincing failures accompanied any of the seemingly distinct, random decisions that ultimately sealed the technology's fate. The field could conceivably have continued for several years. Meteorologists certainly argued that its potential had not been exhausted, and that it should continue to be funded. Why then did America abandon its efforts at checking the weather and climate?

A short answer, for which we will argue in this chapter, is that weather modification fell prey to large-scale changes in American attitudes toward technology, risk, society, and nature. These changes, embedded in broad patterns of societal change in the US (see Hays, 1989), turned what seemed, early in its history, as an uncertain but promising technology for mediating nature's violence into what appeared increasingly as a threat to the earth's fragile atmospheric environment.

Ironies of Research for Weather Modification

Amongst the ironies of weather modification research is that meteorologists, who became its strongest proponents later, were initially its largest skeptics. Vincent J. Schaefer is generally credited with having performed the first experiment in weather modification, in 1946. Although Schaefer's experiment was in fact by no means the first in American history (Spence, 1980), this experiment set activated a chain of events that led to scientific recognition of weather modification as a research field more than ten years later.

Schaefer with Langmuir

During World War II, Schaefer was the laboratory assistant of Irving Langmuir. Langmuir was working for General Electric on some chemical studies related to warfare, partly under Army contracts. Analysing the conditions under which aircraft icing occurs, they noticed that, occasionally, clouds at temperatures below freezing did not produce snow. This phenomenon had been familiar among meteorologists for more than twenty-five years, but Schaefer began experimenting with it with the help of a GE household freezer. Exhaling his breath, he readily produced supercooled clouds.

When one day he put little bit of dry ice in the freezer, he observed an instantaneous and spectacular change in the supercooled cloud. The same day, he also discovered that the best results were obtained with a minute amount of dry ice. Langmuir then managed for him to test this result on a real cloud in an experiment conducted near Schenectady, New York, in November 1946 (Schaefer, 1968a). The test successfully regenerated the laboratory observations of cloud physics.

In early 1947, a contract was signed between GE and the US Army Signal Corps for Project Cirrus. Until its termination in 1952, Cirrus involved 225 flights to test different cloud seeding techniques. These tests demostrated that like dry ice, silver iodide acted as a freezing agent. By burning silver iodide in acetone, it is possible to produce silver iodide smoke, enabling "cloud seeding" from the ground. Furthermore, silver iodide also proved effective at higher temperatures than dry ice. Langmuir, for his part, claimed to have discovered that applying water to warm clouds would create "a chain reaction mechanism" and create rain (Schaefer,

1968a). Project Cirrus also triggered a flurry of activities by small commercial firms. By the early 1950s, 10 per cent of the land area of America was under commercial seeding operations (Fleagle et al., 1974, 10).

On the other hand Langmuir was not a meteorologist and proud of it. He was perpetually at war with the meteorological profession (Byers, 1974). One example of how his claims enraged meteorologists involved an attempt to modify a hurricane by seeding it in 1947. The hurricane at question initially travelled in a north-east direction. After Langmuir seeded it, changed its course and, going westward, struck the coast of South Carolina and Georgia, GE's lawyers requested that Langmuir not demand that his seeding had caused the changed of direction as a result of the seeding.

The US Weather Bureau denied that there could be a causal connection between the seeding and the hurricane's change of direction. To advocate their views, Bureau experts pointed to meteorological records of an example of an earlier hurricane with a similarly erratic path.[2] Nevertheless, Langmuir did claim that his seeding had influenced the hurricane's change of course. Countering criticisms made by the chief of the Weather Bureau, Francis W. Reichelderfer, Langmuir argued:

> "I pointed out to him that the larger the storm, and the more energy that is stored in it, easier it should be at the proper stage in its development to get widespread effects. To assume that a hurricane could not be successfully modified by even a single pellet of dry ice is like assuming that a large forest could not be set on fire by such a small thing as a single match. (Langmuir in *Final Report of Project Cirrus,* quoted in Byers 1974)"

At some other platform, Langmuir claimed that a 1948 experiment in New Mexico produced 0.37 inches of rain over an area of 4,000 square miles. According to a Weather Bureau meteorologist, however, numerous natural reasons for the rain existed. Langmuir countered by asking, if the Bureau knew so much about it, why they had not forecast the rainstorm (Elliott, 1974, 70). Langmuir used the occasion to suggest that weather modification might be used to decrease the uncertainty created by unreliable weather forecasts by bringing the weather under human control. These kinds of problems with attributing causation have been endemic in disputes over the impact of weather modification ever since. For this, Langmuir used statistical methods to argue for the efficacy of cloud seeding, but again, his results were, severely criticized by the meteorological community. A 1950 evaluation released the American Meteorological Society concluded: "It is the considered opinion of this committee that the possibility of artificially producing any useful amounts of rain has not been demonstrated so far, if the available evidence is interpreted by any acceptable scientific standards" (Byres, 1974, 34). Yet Langmuir stepped up his claims, arguing in 1951 that he had been able to produce periodic large-scale weather modification effects over a large segment of the country (Elliott, 1974, 71).

In this connection, the professional community of meteorologists reacted with extreme skepticism. Primarily oriented toward forecasting, the idea of modifying the weather and the climate seemed far removed from meteorological concerns. A case in point is Jerome Namias who, unlike number of his colleagues at the Weather Bureau, remained on friendly terms with Langmuir. Despite their friendship, however, Namias sought to convince Langmuir that the periodic effects he claimed to have created could also be explained by the evolution of the general circulation of the atmosphere (Namias, 1986, 20).

In this context, the controversy around Langmuir raised important concerns in the US Congress. During the 1950s, Congress was generally supportive weather control efforts. However, Congress also wanted to halt excessive claims by several small private firms which dominated press coverage of weather modification activities. To do so, it sought to place weather modification research on sounder scientific footing (Byers, 1974), and to this effect Congress accepted and, in 1953, President Eisenhower signed a law creating the US Advisory Committee on Weather Control. Captain Howard T. Orville was appointed chair. Orville was a retired head of the Navy weather service, an ex-chair of the American Meteorological Society, and a former member of the steering committee of Project Cirrus, and was thus familiar to both meteorologists and weather control advocates. At first, Orville appeared to offer partisan support to the cause of weather modification.

However, the *Final Report* was rather cautions. In the course of its preparation, University of Chicago statistician K.A. Brownlee sharply criticized the statistical observations offered in support of weather modification, and the controversy this generated was widely reported in the professional press (McDonald 1956). This probably helped affect the conclusions of the Orville committee. The committee's most substantial conclusion was that under certain circumstances, cloud seeding demostrably increased precipitation by 10 to 15 per cent in mountainous regions of the Western United States. By the time the Orville committee had served its term, Congress had already achieved some of its aims. By 1956, commercial activity had dropped to about one-fourth of its 1952 top and it remained near that level for many years (Huschke, 1963). In 1957, Congressional passage of the Water, Cloud Modification Research Act designated the US National Science Foundation (NSF) as the coordinating institute for weather modification research, bringing weather modification under the umbrella of science.

NSF welcomed weather modification research, but it also changed it. Earl Droessler, then program director for atmospheric science at NSF, championed weather and climate modification throughout his career. However, his programs shifted the emphasis in weather modification research from the design and execution of experimental tests to investigations into the physical processes controlling cloud precipitation. NSF also merged weather modification research with theoretical study on the behaviour of the (global) atmosphere.

Among the tools used in both these research fields were computer models; in the latter field these models were similar to those used for forecasting the weather, particularly long-term forecasting (see next section). At NSF, weather modification grew to become a central program in meteorological research, with funding levels reaching close to those for the remaining of the atmospheric sciences combined by the early 1970s. Langmuir passed away in 1957, undaunted, at the age of seventy-six. Reichelderfer remained less than friendly toward weather modification until his retirement as chief of the Weather Bureau in 1963 (Langer, 1963). Vincent Schaefer would later move to an academic status at the State University of New York.

Charney with Von Neumann

In this early period of weather modification, one important exception existed to meteorologists' general skepticism toward altering the weather. Some time after Langmuir's beginnings, John von Neumann, announced his own interest in weather modification. Von Neumann, like Langmuir, was not a meteorologist.

But unlike Langmuir, who behaved defiantly toward the meteorological profession, von Neumann functioned closely with its establishment, and he was the architect of the wedding of meteorology and the computer. While Langmuir took a hands-on approach to weather modification, for von Neumann it lay still further away in the future, because it was linked in his mind to the yet to be developed long-range forecasting. In an interview with the *New York Times Magazine* in 1946, von Neumann declared his "intention of developing a very high speed electronic computing machine and of applying it to the prediction of natural weather and of calculating the effects of human intervention in the natural processes of the atmosphere."[3] For von Neumann, forecast and intervention were closely interlinked. Von Neumann's most important collaborator was Jule Charney, who joined the Meteorology group at Princeton in 1948. They worked together in 1949 on the design of a numerical forecast experiment and continued to collaborate through the 1950s on computer models of the atmosphere (for details, see Edwards, chapter 2, this volume). In 1955, von Neuman acted as one of the advisors on the Advisory Committee on Weather Control. During the preparation of its *Final Report;* von Neuman participated in panel on "possible effects of atomic and thermonuclear explosions in modifying weather." In the cause of this panel's deliberations, he mentioned an idea of Charney's, namely, that changing the albedo of the earth (a measure of the reflection of radiative energy) might be the most fruitful way to modify weather and climate. Although, in von Neumann's opinion, nuclear explosions did not have much effect on the weather, he thought that more theoretical and computer studies were needed (Heims, 1980, 283, 494), and he denied to temper his enthusiasm. He said at the time:

> "Our knowledge of the atmosphere is rapidly approaching a level that will make possible, in a few decades, intervention in atmospheic and climatic matters. It will probably unfold on a scale difficult to imagine at present. There is little doubt one could intervene on any desired scale, and ultimately achieve rather fantastic effects. (John von Neumann in 1956, quoted by Sen. Clinton Anderson in U.S. Senate 1964, 15)"

Amongst the two, Von Neumann also articulated one more reason to deveiop weather manipulation: he feared that the Soviet Union might develop it first, and he warned that this might ultimately be a more dangerous threat than ICBMs.

Expectations Peak in the Year 1966

Let's imagine, if the history of weather and climate modification were indexed to the degree of expectations it engendered about potential future successes, 1966 would be its apogee. Weather modification gained substantial support that year from major public and scientific institutions. The Weather Bureau issued report in which it announced its ambition to "undertake a major role in weather modification research." For this, the Bureau also recommended significantly increased support for microphysical studies of cloud dynamics and the processes controlling precipitation and microphysical research of the dynamics and thermodynamics of climate, both of which were central to weather modification as it was then conceived (Gilman, Hibbs, and Laskin, 1965). Two reports issued in 1966 by the National Academy of Sciences and NSF also weighed in a lot.

Both pleaded for a strong increase of funding to fundamental research in weather and climate modification. Both expressed optimism with regard to the principle of its feasibility (National Research Council, 1983; National Science Foundation, 1965). The climate in Congress and the Executive Branch was also favourably disposed toward weather modification in the later half of 1960s. Congress people such as Senators George McGovern of South Dakota, Clinton Anderson of New Mexico, and Alan Bible of Nevada made clear not only that they advocated weather modification but also that they had not forgotten about Irving Langmuir and John von Neumann, in whose scientific credentials they continued to put great trust (U.S. Senate, 1964).

Stewart Udall, then Secretary of the Interior, also favoured artificial rainmaking. It may have complemented nicely other water projects he cherished, such as the San Luis Dam and the Central Arizona Project (Worster, 1985). Udall announced notably:

> "What does appeal to me, because of its potential for all mankind, is the idea of enormous rivers of water flowing over us in the atmosphere; of huge pools of moisture poised above our heads; of enormous reservoirs in vaporous state sailing majestically over mountains, or bumping into them and dropping their precious burdens too soon." (Udall, 1966)

After 1966, Congress appropriated grown funding for both fundamental research at the Weather Bureau and NSF and also for operational research carried out under the supervision of the Interior Department's Bureau of Reclamation. Two technologies in total development were responsible for this optimism: satellites and computers. Statellites in particular, gave meteorologists hope that the central problem of insufficient amounts of data for prediction, forecasting, and weather and environmental modification would be solved (Malone, 1967). On April 1, 1960, the world's first weather satellite, TIROS I, was launched by NASA, In the next ten years, twenty-two satellites followed. The introduction of the Applications Technology Satellite (ATS I) in 1966 enabled meteorologists to continuously monitor weather conditions over a particular area of the earth's surface. Francis Reichelderfer and Harry Wexler at the Weather Bureau had favoured the use of satellites for meteorological purposes at least from the 1957 Soviet launch of Sputnik. Wexler saw to it that the design of the meteorological satellites was tailored to numerical forecasting, and at the time when data came pouring in, computers proved indispensable in managing it (Nebeker 1995, 175). Computers, of course, also served meteorology theoretically through the development of ever higher and more detailed data sets and numerical models of the global atmosphere (see Edwards, chapter 2, this volume).

Projects in the Context of Weather Modification

Excessive weather modification programs operated during this period to enumerate, but some stand out, either because of their size or because of their scientific or political importance (National Science Foundation 1965).[4] Project Climax, to enhance the snowpack in Colorado, was carried out at Colorado State University by Lewis Grant, from 1960 to 1970, supported by NSF. Early parts of the project were inconclusive.

By developing growingly complex models of the atmosphere, however, researchers were "finally able to identify a number of combinations of upper wind in the direction and temperature in the air stream that could be successfully exploited to produce additional snow," As per Edward Todd of the National Science Foundation (U.S. House of Representatives 1976b, 110; see also National Academy of Sciences 1973, 80-83, for detailed information on the Climax experiment). Begun relatively late, in 1972, the National Hail Research Experiment (NHRE) was the biggest NSF sponsored effort in the period, funded through NSF's Research Applied to National Needs program. NSF expected to bring it quickly to a point where a mission-oriented agency, such as the Department of Agriculture, could take it over and turn it into an operational program. NHRE was conducted in northeast Colorado by the National Center for Atmospheric Research (NCAR).

The research concept of NHRE had the peculiar feature that is was designed after hail suppression projects in the Soviet Union, which they say, had been very successful (U.S. House of Representatives 1976b, 144-159). Numerical cloud models were the outstanding feature of the Florida project through the guidance of Joanne Simpson at NOAA's Experimental Meteorological Laboratory (EML) in Miami.

This project's models of individual clouds and cloud systems appear to have been the first "operational" computer simulation models to be examined in weather modification experiments.[5] Simpson directed Project Stormfury (see below) between 1965 and 1967, and the approach she used, called *dynamic cloud seeding,* was evolved in part during these years. It was her stated aim to introduce the results of her work on cloud systems into large-scale global circulation models, this may, contributing to "man's eventual control of the atmosphere" (Simpson, Wiggert, and Mee, 1968). The dynamic cloud seeding approach was directed at the buoyancy forces and circulation that sustain the cloud, bringing about invigorated cloud dynamics with the experimentally induced releases of fusion heat. In a publication in *Science,* the project's initial results were described as "very encouraging," while those of an older approach, labelled "static," were dismissed out of hand as inconclusive and conflicting (Woodley, 1970).

EML based its evaluations of cloud seeding on a comparison between model simulation results and the observed behaviour of clouds. Moreover, the experiments were carried out using both statistical controls and randomization procedures. EML thus argued that its weather modification was science based in a way that previous cloud modification was not. Over time, reports from the project carried on to be positive, and this attracted scientific and political attention. In 1971, during a severe drought, the governor of Florida requested that EML seed clouds on an "operational" basis.

EML performed the seeding and their claimed to have produced an additional 100,000 acre-ft of water (Simpson, Woodley, and White, 1972).

Introduction of Project Stormfury's Work

He was one of the more successful of the several dozens of weather modification projects funded during this period. It is particularly notable for the historian, however, for its efforts to combine operational hurricane seeding with theoretical research of a highly advanced character than at most other weather modification projects. In 1955, the Weather Bureau established the National Hurricane Research Project, based in Miami. It was to look into the formation and dynamics of hurricanes, to improve hurricane forecasts, and to seek means for hurricane modification.

Then and later, huge damages from Atlantic hurricanes were frequently invoked to discuss for research funding into hurricane dynamics and control. (Hurricane Betsy, for example, was reported to have caused more than $1.4 billion (US) in damage in 1965.) The first hypothesis for how to modify hurricanes was evolved by R.H. Simpson and Joanne Malkus (later, Joanne Simpson). They based their idea on a relatively simple, qualitative understanding of the structure of a hurricane. Hurricanes owe their well-known vortex structures to an equilibrium between the centrifugal force of air particles travelling at high speeds around the hurricane and the centripetal force created by low pressure at the storm's centre.

Simpson and Malkus recommended that seeding near a hurricane's central eye would set in motion a chain of events, eventually reducing differences in the pressure gradient and, possibly dissipating the storm's strength (Simpson and Malkus, 1964). At this point, computer models of hurricanes were neither in existence nor was their need felt.

During the year 1961 a much-improved technique of producing silver iodide smoke was developed at the Naval Weapons Centre in California, which made it possible to bring large quantities of the freezing agent into the clouds within minutes. In this year only hurricane Esther was seeded with this new technique and the results were "encouraging if nonconclusive" (Gentry, 1974, 507).

Within a few months, the Navy and Weather Bureau took these uncertain results as a mark of future promise and together organized Project Stormfury. In 1963, Project Stormfury seeded the eye wall of hurricane Beulah, with what seemed to observers to be significant effect. Robert M. White, the new Chief of the US Weather Bureau, called the results of the experiment "encouraging," but noted that it was difficult to tell whether the observed results of seeding were the result of "man's action" or of natural fluctuations (White and Chandler, 1956). In 1964, Jule Charney and A. Eliassen published a model description of a hurricane that became the grounds for all subsequent hurricane models at Project Stormfury (Charney and Eliassen, 1964).

The model's (still qualitative) mechanism consisted of a feedback between cloud formation and atmospheric pressure. Cumulus clouds supplied the required heat to drive the pressure depression, while the depression vortex produced moisture, thereby maintaining the cloud system. According to Charney and Eliassen, this interaction causes large-scale self-amplification. In the assessment of meteorologists at the time, models based on this mechanism provided "realistic" results (Rosenthal, 1974). Charney and Eliassen's paper did not mention the probability of hurricane modification, but other models were constructed on the basis of it, notably by Stanley Rosenthal in 1967 and 1969. Rosenthal simulated the effects of seeding and helped work out strategies of where and where not to seed a hurricane (Rosenthal, 1974). But, according to its developers, the Rosenthal model did "not sufficiently simulate nature".

Confidence in the models won a boost in Project Stormfury's year of glory, 1969, when a series of project experiments appeared to show consistent evidence of the ability to affect Hurricane Debbie's dynamics. Gentry described it therefore:

> "If one considers the sequence of events in the Hurricane Debbie (1969) experiment, the results are quite impressive: seeded five times on August 18, and the wind speeds decreased 30 per cent; no seeding August 19 and the storm intensified; seeding on the inner wind maximum of the first four seedings on August 20 and it decreased, and seeding of the outer wind maximum on the fifth seeding and the winds decreased 15 per cent. (Gentry, 1974, 406)"

In this regard, computer simulation of the seeding of Debbie showed confirmation of wind speed reduction in the model of stanley Rosenthal, but not in another model. In following years, however, progress was not so easily achieved. In 1969, NSF commissioned the RAND Corporation to provide an overview of the field of weather modification. RAND's overview stated notably: "Three years have provided nothing substantial to the timorous optimism expressed in the National Sciences (1966) report on weather and climate modification. On the contrary, the trend of research seems to indicate a growing respect for uncertainties and desire to unravel them" (RAND Corporation, 1969). The RAND Corporation put the problem of hurricane modification succinctly: since there were too few hurricanes for any statistical evaluation to be meaningful, there remained only one alternative. It was absolutely importance to

> "be able to predict confidently what the behaviour of the storm would have been had we not interfered. And since today we cannot make the prediction, we cannot make the evaluation. . . The central problem in tropical storm modification lies in learning whether or not we have indeed effected the modification."

This report reads as a plea for greater coupling of weather modification experiments to the production of new simulation models of atmospheric processes on various scales. Project Stormfury, however, experienced hard luck. No more suitable hurricanes migrated into the seeding area (which had been severely restricted as a consequence of Langmuir's first hurricane seeding experiment).

There was one exception—hurricane Ginger in 1971—but it was such a poor hurricane that the failure of the seeding experiment could have been predicted beforehand.

Beginning of New Suspicions: 1970-73

In the year 1972, a cloud seeding operation near Rapid City, South Dakota, and the nearby Black Hills ended in misfortune. On the morning of June 9, 1972, the arrival of a moist band of clouds in this perennially dry area proved too enticing for weather modification experiment makers from the South Dakota School of Mines to ignore.[6] During two flights, the researchers seeded the clouds with 700 pounds of table salt (sodium chloride). What the cloud seeding team was not aware of, however, was that strong winds generated by a high-pressure area in the region of Hudson Bay had stopped the eastward march of the clouds just above the Black Hills.

The clouds, rendered stationary, were overhead for more than ten hours, releasing their water content and causing a devastating flood that took lives of over 200 people. A remarkable coincidence made Rapid City host town of the Third National Conference on Weather Modification only seventeen days later. In the margins of the conference, the flood was hotly discussed and it was heard many times that the risks posed by weather modification experiments were sufficient to justify restricting them to computer simulation experiments (Dennis, 1972). But this was not the view that prevailed. During the conference, a team of investigators commissioned by the South Dakota Weather Control Commission reported to the governor of South Dakota.

The conclusions, which the conference then endorsed, stated: (a) that the June 9 flood was a natural disaster, caused by meteorological conditions beyond human control; (b) that weather modification acts had not contributed materially to the flood; and (c) that weather modification operations should be resumed.

One year later, a scientist in Albuquerque, New Mexico, who had been a conference participant in Rapid City, published a "dissenting view" in a letter to the *Bulletin of the American Meteorological Society* (Reed, 1973). In it, asserted that cloud seeding had triggered the Black Hills storm, basing his conclusions on several possible scenarios presented at the conference.

He also mentioned the possibility that the seeding had produced "as yet unknown and unexpected dynamical effects." Based on statistical considerations, he also argued that experimenters had managed take too great a risk in Rapid City. In the same issue of the *Bulletin*, no less than six sharp rebuttals were published. The critic's use of statistics and "risk-benefit analysis" was badly disparaged, as was his reference to "unknown effects," which was declared to be speculative and unscientific. With in the rebuttals was one by the Weather Control Commissions's team of investigators. In it, the authors said that "the experience of those who have used salt has been that rainfall has been slightly increased from non-raining or lightly raining clouds."

They also presented a fairly precise estimate of the volume of rain that could have been deposited as a result of the salt seeding, basing their estimate on a linear ratio between the amount of salt and the volume of collected water. This estimate amounted to only a tiny fraction of the total water volume deposited during the flood (St.-Amand, Davis, and Elliott 1973; see Reed 1974 and following discussion). Two NCAR meteorologists were similarly unconvinced that a conclusive cause-effect relationship could be established between the seeding and the flood. Public opinion in South Dakota seemed at least initially, to accept the official findings. No organized opposition arose, and a study of public opinion, undertaken shortly after the event of the flood, showed that a majority of respondents (55 per cent) conceived that seeding had not produced the flood, while only 25 per cent thought that the seeding had been a determining factor (Farhar, 1974).

Two years later, however, the group Citizens Against Cloud Seeding started to oppose weather modification experiments in South Dakota, despite expert disavowal of any causal connection. After many public meetings, this group succeed in preventing state funds from being used to continue cloud sedding after June 30, 1976 (Dennis, 1980, 4).[7]

Reaction of Countrymen against Weather Modification

Following episodes also illustrate the contested view of weather modification activities that had arisen by the mid-1970s, with the Rapid City disaster quickly assuming an iconic status in public deliberations about weather control.

The first such episode we can describe here involved commercial weather modification; in the other two episodes here, we describe, public institutions carrying out weather modification research were implicated. The San Luis Valley of Southern Colorado is populated generally by ranchers and farmers. A high proportion of them are growers of Moravian barley, who under normal circumstances thrive well in the arid climate of the valley. But barely is highly vulnerable to hail, and, unfortunately, precipitation in summer quite often comes in the form of extremely large hailstones. In 1966, at the instigation of Coors Company, a commercial weather modification campaign was introduced to suppress hail and divert rainfall. During the first years, the project did not elicit much response, but this changed when 1970 turned out to be unusually dry.

That same year, some 400 farmers made a group called San Luis Citizens Concerned about Weather Modification. One of the allegations this group levelled against weather modification was that cloud seeding actually suppressed rain. In their opinion, silver iodide seeding would lead to the formation of small ice crystals that would be blown away by the wind before they could precipitate to the ground. The group raised popular favour, and their actions induced the Colorado legislature to grant the state greater regulatory authority. In early 1972, the Colorado legislature enacted a weather modification bill. Under this law, cloud seeding would need a permit and a public hearing.

The permit hearing for the San Luis valley experiment was held in July. Approximately 600 people attended, and the meeting lasted until 2:00 A.M. A clear majority opposed the granting of a permit. In the month of November 1972, an advisory referendum was held in the five counties of San Luis Valley. The vote was overwhelmingly negative (Carter, 1973).

Some time thereafter, W.K. Coors, president of the Coors Company, wrote to barley growers in the valley, attaching paramount importance to "weather management":

> "Unless we have good assurance of an adequate weather management program for the 1973 barley growing season by March, 1, 1973, the 1973 Moravian barley allotment for the San Luis Valley must be reduced 20 per cent. On each successive year, assuming no weather management program in that year, an additional 20 per cent cut in allotment must be made until the total Moravian barely production from the San Luis Valley has been reduced to 10 per cent of the Adolph Coors Company needs compared with the 60 per cent that it supplies now. 10 per cent is the maximum amount we are willing to place at the mercy of the natural elements which in our experience will give us a good quality crop once in twenty years. (Lansford, 1973, 659)"

With the completion of a new round of hearings, the permit was finally denied in 1973. The barley growers found another brewery to purchase their crop. Another episode occurred in Montana. In 1972, a public meeting ended a five-year practice of cloud seeding to increase snowpack over the watershed above Hungry Horse dam. The cloud seeding ostensibly raised the volume the water available for hydroelectric generation at the dam. The argument against the permit was grounded in ecological terms. Opponents argued that the Wilderness Act prohibited cloud seeding above a wilderness area in the urgent vicinity of the dam (Elliott, 1974, 84). In 1975, a citizens group in the Potomac basin similarly published a strong attack on weather modification activities in the region, implicating, in particular, Project Stormfury.

The group said that, since the initiation of weather modification research in the Washington area in 1957, the local climate had undergone a dramatic change, with rainfall consistently below average. The report blamed that a conspiracy of diverse interests supported clear weather, including recreation, airports, road builders, and the construction industry. According to the group, cloud seedings was responsible for 90 per cent of the air pollution troubles in the United States, and it specifically linked the use of silver iodide to a higher occurrence of lung diseases. Project Stormfury was credited with having stopped hurricanes from coming up the Eastern seaboard. Pointing out that hurricanes contribute 30 per cent of the precipitation in the area, the report also claimed that "if hurricanes are not allowed to go through their full life cycle, nature will find some other way to maintain heat balance, and this new method undoubtedly will be more disastrous than the hurricane." Hurricane Camille was a foretaste: "The most destructive tropical storm ever to transverse the east coast, [Camille was] without question due to the blunderings of the inept science"

These above mentioned events illustrate the growing opposition to weather modification, not because people believed it did not work, but because they believed uncertainties the method posed undesirable risks. Underlying this belief lay an increasing sense that human activities could substantially and destructively affect the natural environment. Messing with Mother Nature had come to be viewed as inherently problematic in American public consciousness. Stanley Changnon, a meteorologist in the job of the Illinois State Water Survey and a long-time supporter of weather modification research, noted that 1972, the year of the San Luis Valley controversy and the Rapid City disaster, can be considered the year when environmental concerns over weather modification began (Changnon, 1973). From the early 1970s on, new area of uncertainty was added to an already contested field.

Beginning of the Era of Inadvertent Weather and Climate Modification

The question arises is what is it that brought about the demise of weather and climate modification? It is tempting to think that at some point its practical and theoretical impossibility imposed itself so strongly on the meteorological community that the field was simply abandoned. This seems not to be so. Rather, the demise of deliberate weather and climate modification appears linked to the growth of environment concerns.

Within the field of weather modification, consistent with increasing American concerns about human impacts on the environment, a subfield emerged during the late 1960s and early 1970s concerned with "inadvertent climate modification" or the modification of long-term weather patterns with human activities that affect the atmosphere. From 1970 on, the possibility of inadvertent climate modification appears to have increasingly alarmed politicians and the public. Between the years 1973 and 1975, budget cuts virtually put an end to research on deliberate weather and climate modification. Notably, meteorologitists at the time strongly protested these cuts. The 1965 NSF report On *Weather and Climate Modification* did not address the chance of anthropogenic climate change under any label. This need not imply that the issue was not recognized by scientists at NSF.

However, it does suggest that it was not yet linked to deliberate modification of the atmosphere. The report did mention however, the possibility of adverse ecological consequences from planned weather and climate modification, for which a working group of the Ecological Society of America was called (National Science Foundation 1965, 61-70). The 1966 National Academy of Sciences report of the same title did discuss inadvertent modification of the atmosphere (National Research Council 1983, 82-108). The report identified many potential causes: (1) carbon dioxide, (2) urbanization, (3) forestation, deforestation, and agriculture, (4) supersonic transport aircraft, and (5) contamination of the very high atmosphere.

On the ground of "computations on sophisticated numerical models" at the Geophysical Fluid Dynamics Laboratory, the report downplayed the potential effects of increased carbon dioxide. Air pollution did generate substantial concerns linked to possible changes in precipitation patterns. The report described the effect of cities on regional climates as highly complex, and it recommended that research findings of this phenomenon be intensified. The effects of supersonic transport were constricted to their introduction of water vapour in the stratosphere, and again on the basis of the numerical models mentioned earlier, the report deemed them relatively benign. The obvious tenor of the National Research Council report *Weather and Climate Modification* was that inadvertent modification of the atmosphere was not a great cause for concern, though further research was heartily recommended (National Research Council, 1983).

Clearly this was the received view at the time. Roger Revelle, oceanographer and influential policy adviser to the House Science and Technology Committee, gave as his view that global warming as the result of a rise in atmospheric CO_2, or global cooling caused by air pollution, was at best a reason for "curiosity (rather) than apprehension".

Then, some change of stress occurred in 1968. In the "conference summary" of the First National Conference on Weather Modification, weather modification enthusiast Earl Droessler wrote:

> "Inadvertent weather modification is moving rapidly into the forefront of the truly big, urgent problems to be attacked by meteorology and allied science. There is an impending crisis regarding the volume of air pollution across the nation, and people are beginning to demand pure air to breathe. A variety of observations and ideas were presented to the Conference suggesting that man-made pollution may already be modifying precipitation patterns on local and regional scales at least, and may be affecting the global heat budget on even larger scales. (Droessler, 1968)"

Droessler was referring to a contribution by Vincent Schaefer (1968b) in which he announced his discovery that an atypical form of snowstorm was the result of badly polluted air, while ecologist Frederick Sargent (1968) was given the chance to issue a warning with respect to several "imponderable ecological risks" associated with weather modification.

Not mentioned in the summary report, but discussed at the conference, were the possibilities of climate modifications. Some years before, the President's Science Advisory Council, in a report linked with pollution abatement, had considered the use of reflective material in the atmosphere to counter a greenhouse effect (Hart and Victor, 1993). The deployment of such a technique would have been equal to full-scale climate modification.

Previously discussed 1969 RAND corporation report found that climate modification was technologically feasible. Various possibilities were considered. One of these sought to solution inadvertent climatic change:

> "The diversity of thermal processes that can be influenced in the atmosphere, and between the atmosphere and the ocean, offers promise that if global climate is adequately understood it can be influenced for the purpose of either maximizing climatic resources or avoiding unwanted changes. For example, to avoid undesired planetary warming, ways might be found to drain additional heat to space."

Anyway, that was the last of it. In the years to follow, no similar considerations were reiterated. It was for instance entirely lacking in a report by the President's Council of Environmental Quality (PCEQ) . The Council gave some suggestions with regard to the direction of research on weather and climate modification. Noting that only about 1 per cent of federal governmental research monies for weather modification went to programs examining inadvertent human modification of the climate, it recommended in particular a recognition of the significance of human-made atmospheric alterations and their significance for a possible impending change of the climate.

Not until 1991 would the National Academy resurrect its arguments that planetary-scale geoengineering could be used to counteract global warming. In 1970, concerns about environmental degradation went a temporary peak. The PCEQ was established through the signing into law of the National Environmental Policy Act by President Nixon, as the government's "policy arm" in environmental issues. It was the year of Earth Day (on April 22), and the year during which organizations such as Friends of the Earth, founded the year before, developed a widely acknowledged political impact.

At the time, two environmental dangers were considered to be of the highest importance: water pollution (mostly by pesticides) and air pollution by automobiles, smokestacks, and so on. The second one concerns us here.

Then the following PCEQ report noted that various forms of air pollution decreased the transparency of the atmosphere and that this might have a cooling effect: "If pollution were significantly responsible, then the world would face an important problem of manmade global climate modification." The inverse action of grown carbon dioxide content of the atmosphere was also noted, but the cooling problem received priority in the considerations of the report, the more so because it was linked with climate change that are already occuring.[8] Focussing on the annual average at the earth's surface, the report noted that while this average began a climb between 1890 and 1940 of 1.1 °F, it fell again between 1940 and 1970 with 0.5°F.

The report further said that ice coverage in the North Atlantic had been among the most extensive in over sixty years. The report showed prevailing opinions of climate researchers (see Hart and Victor 1993), including Reid Bryson at the University of Wisconsin, Madison. Bryson's theory of an impending cooling of the earth would receive greater attention in 1975.

Other concerns of the Council were also in step with the research agenda of the meteorologists. These include the issue of the climatological effects of urban heating and the pollution generated by jet aircraft. Missing among the council's concerns yet were the "polluting" effects of weather modification activities, because these did not become publicly contested for another few years.

Climate Change: The Genuine Experience

The PCEQ assessment that an actual cooling was already occurring and that it was linked to air pollution did not stand alone. Air pollution as a cause for climate cooling was given in the meteorological literature by several authors, but different were put forward as well, such as volcanic activity and solar variations. Against this variety of proposed external impacts on the climate, Namias held that the autonomous dynamics of air-sea interactions alone could be held responsible of what had been indeed the abnormally chilled decade of the 1960s. Namias invoked the amplification of the "long wave pattern," or Rossby waves, which affected the Northern Hemisphere, as the factor of the observed climatic fluctuations.

This regional phenomenon Namias saw in turn produced by the abnormally warms sea surface in the North Pacific. Namias's analysis no way stopped concerns about the perceived cooling of the climate. A 1974 report in Nature noted a "growing public awareness in North America that something is going wrong with the weather." Apparently, the "person in the street" was aware that frost was coming too early, and the local TV station's weather reporter commented on "three early cold waves" (Gribbin, 1974).

Similar observations were also made in scientific articles by Reid Bryson, who was the genuine subject of the *Nature* report. In an article on "The Lessons of Climatic History," in which Bryson included a section on "the present arctic expansion," he gave example of observations that "the growing season in England has diminished by two weeks," "midsummer frosts returned to the upper Midwestern United States," "the average temperature of Iceland has declined to its former [per-1945] level," and many others (Bryson 1975). Number of meteorologists noted in the same year a trend toward cooler temperatures, which could be the forerunner of a new ice age (Hammond, 1974). Two years later, however, two atmospheric scientists said to have found a warming trend on the Southen Hemisphere. They suggested that in the long run global warming as a result of the greenhouse effect might overtake cooling mechanisms in function on the Northern Hemisphere (Damon and Kunen, 1976). Between this years 1972 and 1976, climatic change had become a matter of serious concern, among various scientists, parts of the public, and some politicians. It has been noted that, compared to the previous decade, not very many new scientific findings had been experienced.

Yet global warming by rising CO_2 and global cooling by air pollution were taken considerably more seriously than in 1966. Recall also that proposals for deliberate modification of the climate to fight these possibilities, such as those put forward by PSAC in 1966 and by RAND Corporation in 1969, were no longer being put forward. Even toying with the idea of climate modification was irrelevant. Stephen Schneide, who in the hot summer of 1988 would become an important spokesperson in favour of the recognition of the greenhouse effect, expressed himself in definite terms against weather and climate modification. While his main argument was that "irreversible climate disasters" could result from attempts to stabilize the climate with technological means, he also noted that rainmaking had become a significant a tool of war in Vietnam, forfeiting its innocence (Schneider, 1976).

Weather Modification and Downfall

After this, the seeds had been planted for a development that eventually would be fatal for the prospect of weather and climate modification. After 1970, the issue of inadvertent climate modification contributed a lot to growing pressure from outside groups against weather and climate modification. The meteorologists sought to stem the damage from public criticism. "Inadvertent weather modification" was co-opted as a separate research activity, for which funds were allocated. Project METROMEX, a large-scale example of this research, tested the impact of St. Louis on precipitation patterns in its surrounding area (Berry and Beadle, 1974).

But this did not prevent an erosion of Congressional support for the total subject of weather modification, which declined steeply after

1973. The meteorologists blamed the public and finally accepted the inevitable. In 1975, the president of the American Meteorological Society admitted that too many uncertainties gathered weather and climate modification to sustain a claim for generous public support. Federal funding for weather modification had continuously increased from 1967 to 1972—it had in fact gone double during that period. Total funding had risen from $12.0 million in fiscal year 1972 to $15.2 million in FY 1973, to an awarded $25.2 million in calendar year 1973.

In the five-year period ending in FY 1973, the federal government had incurred $77 million, not including the Department of Defence expenditures of $21.6 million in Vietnam to make it rain on the Ho Chi Minh trail (Shapley, 1974). But in the month of January 1973, halfway through FY 1973, expenditures were cut back by $65 million at the direction of the Office of Management and Budget (OMB). In FY 1974, federal support fell down 21 per cent, when other research and development supported by the government increased. The losses were unevenly spread.

The Bureau of Reclamation's budget was nearly halved, NSF suffered a downfall of 30 per cent, while research on inadvertent modification almost doubled to total of $2.9 million. Stanley Changnon, by 1975 serving as president of the Weather Modification Association, charged the negative attitude of OMB to the "paradox" that the weather modifiers had created themselves: on the one hand, they claimed to have a working technology; on the other hand, they requested funds for more fundamental research into weather modification (Changnon, 1975). Changnon made it clear that the field still included quackery and was known for overstated claims. In hearings in front of the House Subcommittee on the Environment and the Atmosphere, he announced:

> "Thirty years of experimentation have provided a variety of scientific outcomes ranging from success to total failure with the outcomes too often dictated by the typical uncertainties associated with the vagaries of nature coupled with poorly conducted projects, that were often too brief in their duration."
>
> "...Weather modification, I believe, is still an immature basically uncertain technology unable yet to demonstrate sizable weather alterations and economic benefits in many areas of the United States." (U.S. House of Representatives, 1976b, 348-350)"

He also went on to make a plea for new and higher efforts in weather modification, and he expressed his expectation that since an actual "climate change in the sense of increased variability" had been underway since 1971, probably causing food shortages, the latter would place weather modification back on the national agenda again (U.S. House of Representatives, 1976b, 356).

From 1975 on, public concern about an impending climate change has in fact, grown considerably stronger. This has done little to help the cause of weather and climate modification, anyway. Joanne Simpson, by the early 1970s professor of environmental sciences at the University of Virginia, testified before the US House of Representatives in the course of hearings on the use of weather modification in Vietnam: "A paramount hard fact about weather modification is that there are today only about a half dozen programs over the whole world that have conclusively demostrated that the treatment works" (Simpson, 1975). She went on to claim that her own projects (in Florida, since 1968) fell in the category of the successful, and Changnon and other members of the scientific community were willing to grant her that. Same kind of statements were made by David Atlas, who in 1975 served a term as president of the American Meteorological Society. A year before he had become director of the National Hail Research Experiment, but now he urged his fellow meteorologists to be highly cautious.

Warning that the credibility of the entire science of meteorology might be injured by promising too much too early, he also concluded that "only a handful of experiments have demostratred beneficial effects to the general satisfaction of the scientific community".

Yet Robert M. White, Administrator of NOAA, still saw things from the other side when he testified to Congress in 1975:

> "Deliberate environmental modification is a growing issue. Man is developing a capability to modify atmospheric processes in a conscious and directed way. After three decades of controversial experimentation, this capability is still primitive. Nevertheless this is a field of research and development of great future promise. . . . Over the coming decades, this primitive capability will be transformed into a broader capability for affecting weather processes." (US House of Representatives, 1976a, 4)

Also, Earl Droessler tirelessly enumerated all the successes to date of weather modification. He called on Congress to establish a National Committee on Weather Modification, and he particularly addressed himself to the Department of Agriculture, in the hope of findings a new sponsor for weather modification research (Droessler, 1975).

As late as 1983, Droessler, by officiating president of the American Meteorological Association, continued to call for more weather modification research (Droessler, 1983). As if to illustrate their futility, Project Stormfury was formally terminated in the same year, twelve years later the last hurricane had been seeded. Between 1973 and 1976, the field of weather modification had managed to fix itself on the (lowered) 1973 level. But after 1976, publicly supported weather modification projects were abandoned one by one. During Congressional hearings in 1976 it was openly stated by NSF officials that the National Hail Research Experiment had been a failure. The technology of hail suppression was evaluated in 1975 by a research group that included social scientists.

Their assessment led to recommendations such as that made to the State of Illinois not to proceed with hail suppression experiments (Changnon 1977).[9] Funding for weather modification continued to decrease slowly and, by 1986, the NSF spent $1.5 million, while in 1972 it had been $5.4 million (not corrected for inflation; Changnon, 1986).

One of the last surviving weather modification research trials the 1982 Florida Area Cumulus Experiment-phase 2 (FACE-2), failed to stand up to a statistical test that was fashioned after double-blind clinical drug trials. It cannot be hoped that the Florida test is the definitive end of attempts to make rain. To begin with, the test results were contested within the research team itself. Hence, they likely mark only an end to this round of funding. Fresh projects can spring up anywhere in the world at any time. However, any new project proposal to make rain or in other ways affect the atmospheric environment will find a set of societal values very different from those in the 1960s, when belief in science and technology was naively innocent of the potential consequences of large-scale human activities. This is once more illustrated by the story of Project Stormfury.

Withdraw of Project Stormfury

In the year 1972, three years after the seeding of hurricanes Beulah and Debbie, the Navy unilaterally decided to withdraw from Project Stomfury. The Navy gave no reasons, but it was widely assumed that opposition raised against the military application of weather modification techniques in Indochina had led to the Navy's decision (US House of Representatives, 1976b).

The immediate consequence was that Stormfury was left for some time without airplanes to carry out seeding operations. The NOAA part of the Stormfury budget ($2 million annually) was also cut. An intentionally consented plan to move Stormfury's activities to the Pacific (instigated in part by the lack of aircraft) never materialized because of political opposition of some western Pacific nations, Mexico and Australia in particular. By 1973, the project's priorities had changed to improving the accuracy of hurricane forecasts, and more than ever before, it was felt that successful modification depended on advances in the predictive capabilities of numerical models. Apparently, strategies to inhibit the very development of a hurricane, or to deflect it back to the ocean, were completely ruled out, since it was now recognized that hurricanes were responsible for much of the rainfall in the Southeastern part of the United States.

This left reduction of wind speeds as the only acceptable aim. Yet a review panel of the National Academy of Sciences under the chairmanship of Thomas Malone declared hurricane modification a national goal and recommended greatly expanded costs.

Starting in 1977, Project Stormfury engaged in two new lines of inquiry, one on cloud physics, the other on "vortex evolution". Both led to the conclusion that modification of hurricanes was theoretically not feasible. In fact, Stomfury's internal advisory panel (on which Edward Lorenz served since 1965) had urged, every year between 1962 and 1973, for research in these areas, apparently because it was concerned that Stormfury's claims about hurricanes Beulah and Debbie might be unjustified.

At last, Project Stormfury was formally ended in 1983. Although that seems surprisingly late, one should remember that the last hurricane seeded was Ginger in 1971. The year 1983 will for even be foremost as a date marking theoretical conclusions indicating that hurricane modification was impossible. Looking back on its history, Stanley Rosenthal commented:

> "In retrospect . . . the changes in the hurricane [Debbie]'s intensity were the result of natural evolution rather than a consequence of seeding. . . . The goal of human control was captivating and seemed to be physically attainable in the beginning. . . . Stormfury . . . had two fatal flaws: it was neither microphysically nor statistically feasible." (Willoughby et al., 1985, 512-513)

In 1996, the Hurricane Research Division fed the following text on the Internet:

> "Perhaps the best solution is not to try to alter or destroy tropical cyclones, but just learn to co-exist better with them. Since we know that coastal regions are vulnerable to the storms, enforce building codes that can have houses stand up to the force of tropical cyclones.

Also the people that choose to live in these locations should be willing to shoulder a fair portion of the costs in terms of property insurance—not exorbitant rates, but ones which truly reflect the risk of living in a vulnerable region." (Landsea, 1996)

Multiple Use of Technology

Renowned experts Changnon and Droessler, each in their own different way, regarded the failure of weather modification research as bad luck and caused by a series of missed opportunities. If only the wonderful experiments by Joanne Simpson had not faced a equal in the sloppy experimental design in Oklahoma and Texas; if only a leading agency had taken firm direction in Oklahoma and Texas; if only a leading agency had taken firm direction of the research; if only nature had been a bit more cooperative and sent more hurricanes fit for seeding to the Atlantic coasts; if only a new drought had come that would have convinced people of the necessity of weather modification; if only the environmental tide would flow away again . . . But weather modification study had lost its credibility to make references of the form of "inconclusive but promising," and not simply because statistical evaluations remained difficult to carry out, even after thirty-five years.

To uncertainties about effectiveness, but also to competing economic interests and to legal constraints, uncertainties of a new type had been counted. Environmental concerns were clearly of prime importance in bringing down the field of weather and climate modification. The first important budget cut occurred in 1972, at the instigation of OMB. At the time, this decision hardly could have been disseminated by doubts about the effectiveness of weather modification. Mistrust of the technical potential of weather modification was not seriously voiced for many more years.

It is more plausible to assume that environmental worries were behind OMB's decision. By 1972, the Nixon presidency already had developed a strong policy profile on environmental matters. Moral considerations performed a substantial role in the discontinuation of weather modification research and activities. It is probably more apt to state that around 1973, moral considerations generating from the newly emergent environmental movement merged with a new sense of risk perception. Weather modification has always been approached through the dual concepts of benefit and risk. Prior to 1973, it was expected that the earlier outweighed the latter. One typical example is a suit by resort owners against the City of New York, reported in 1966 (Carter, 1966).

As per the New York court, the interest of the resort owners in good weather was outweighed by the public interest in ending a drought. After 1973, this reasoning no longer prevailed, and not simply as a consequence of a quantitative change in the balance of profits and losses. The very terms of the debate changed meaning. Potential benefits had always been indefinite but in the course of the 1970s, the concept of uncertainty changed from indicating lack of knowledge to denoting the intrinsic indeterminacy of atmospheric processes. A similar development befell the concept of "risk." One could say that, before 1971, "benefits and risks" were somehow equal to "gains and losses," and that there would be a net gain from weather modification.

Those at threat of loss could be helped by a proper insurance system that would protect them from "weather" damage. After 1973, people began to imagine the risks involved not in terms of discrete weather events but rather in terms of a change of climate. It was growingly feared that changing the weather could lead to an inadvertent change of the climate, rendering problematic the belief that insurance based on extreme weather events would properly keep risk at bay. In the course of three decades, American attitudes toward technology, nature, and society shifted dramatically.

From hopes in the 1950s for a technology triumphant that would check the fury of storms to fears in the 1970s for the environment in the face of the growing destructiveness of human society's technological excesses, Americans reevaluated their connection to nature and science. This, more than anything else, tipped the scales against weather modifications. We may note here that during the same time several more technologies designed to steer large natural and social systems underwent similar drawbacks. The field of urban planning faced a crisis of its rational planning methodology, while at the same time a large modernist housing project, Pruitt-Igoe in St. Louis, was literally blown to pieces because of its continued unmanageability.

The buildings were not even twenty years old. Ecology's first attempt to build comprehensive models to manage and steer large ecosystems was regarded as a failure (Boffey, 1976; Kwa, 1993). The 1973 oil crisis was a major cause that made American economists cease to believe in the existence of automatic stabilizers of the national economic system, and they left the kind of modeling through which they had hoped to identify them. And technocratic warfare in Vietnam was about to collapse (Gibson, 1986; Edwards, 1996a). The style of technoscientific reasoning that underlay all the examples enumerated here (cloud systems and hurricanes, ecosystems and cities, national economies and regional battlefields) conceived of wider systems as closed systems, amenable to steering in a manner that dealt with them comprehensively. With the benefit of hindsight, we could say that all these systems were at once too wide and not large enough. They could never really be closed, because there is always at least one variable changing behind the back of the analyst. Every attempt to force all the variables to behave adequately leads to unruliness within the system and unforeseen consequences outside it, blurring the very boundaries between system and environment that were supposed to remain closed.

The move to globalism, supported at the time by many environmentalists, was a way to acknowledge the latter aspect (Jasanoff, chapter 10, this volume). Weather modification's downfall occurred at the same time, and possibly for the same reasons, as when the other fields experienced their crises. The difference is that the weather modifiers had to be told, instead of discovering it by themselves. But the history of weather and climate modification did not stop entirely in tragedy.

Out of weather modification research emerged continuing concerns about anthropogenic climate change and an increasing demand for computer simulation models of the climate. In certain respects, meteorology has now become the glamour discipline for which so many early protagonists of weather modification had hoped. The atmospheric sciences are no longer the same, anyhow. Weather modification has become a marginal concern of the American Meteorological Society. The Society has given it up almost entirely, with the exception of rainmaking. The Bureau of Reclamation and several private firms till date seed clouds in America's West. Several of the latter, however, have transferred their activities to other nations of the world.

References

1. The NOAA was created July 9, 1970, at the same time as the Environmental Protection Agency. Like the EPA, the NOAA grouped several previously independent government agencies, among them the Weather Bureau (now called the National Weather Service). White had been chief of the Weather Bureau since 1963.
2. In 1974, the director of the National Hurricane Research Laboratory of the NOAA judged that "from results of seeding

experiments in recent years, and from increased knowledge of the behaviour of hurricanes, it seems very unlikely that the 1947 seeding could have had much effect on the hurricane except for the seeded clouds" (Gentry 1974, 506).

3. Recollection of Philip D. Thompson (1983). *The New York Times* article had appeared on January 11, 1946 (Aspray 1990, 351).
4. Twelve precipitation enhancement projects, of which two are mentioned in this chapter, are discussed in some detail in National Academy of Sciences 1973.
5. The laboratory belonged to the Environmental Science Service Administration, which after 1970 became NOAA.
6. The seeding was part of Project Cloud Catcher, a $675,000 experiment sponsored by the Bureau of Reclamation (Carter, 1973).
7. According to Dennis, it was primarily the two dry summers of 1973 and 1974 that had led to public discontent about the failure of weather modification to do something about it.
8. Interestingly, Helmut Landsberg, in a long review article on "Man-Made Climatic Changes" (Landsberg, 1970), also concluded that human-made aerosols constitute a more acute problems than CO_2.
9. Apparently, the NSF RANN program paid for the costs of the technology assessment project.

10

Coordination at International Platform and the Russian Standpoint

Institutionally Structured Cooperation for Policy Change

After the disintegration of the USSR in late 1991 Russia has become its legal success or in various international environmental agreements. Currently it is a member of nearly one hundred global accords on nature and resource protection and conservation. Approximately seventy of these are multilateral and the rest bilateral.

Russia participates in the environmental functions of international intergovernmental and non-governmental organizations, in their cooperative research programmes. Significant changes are under way at the policy and institutional framework of Russia's international environmental co-operation. However, the system of coperation is still away from its final form, and is of a transitional character. In large measure it reflects the serious political and economic changes initiated in Russia during 'transformation'—a shift from a totalitarian to a democratic state, from a command-based to a market economy. Environmental co-operation today represents a conglomeration of new latest and old approaches, of changing tenets, perceptions, and concepts. It involves both the inertia of older days and an impulse towards the new; disillusionment with the past and a desire to deviate from it.

A set of different factors defines the general framework of cooperation and shapes its structure, as well as new potentials for the development of co-operation and its constraints. *Perestroika* followed by 'transformation' in Russia marked a turning-point in the environmental co-operation system. Specifically, national and international environmental policies abandoned the ideological and institutional framework of a totalitarian regime. A new basis for world co-operation with the West was under formation. Progressive environmental policy started taking shape, with restructuring of environmental management, adoption of fresh legal and economic mechanisms, and an upsurge of the environmental movement and environmental *glasnost*.

Environmental policy became decentralized, with wider rights offered to the regional and local levels. New independent environmental institutions have now been created in Russia, destined to represent Russian interests in global environmental co-operation. However, there are also serious limits to the effectiveness of international environmental co-operation. The development of global environmental co-operation between Russia and the West has been defined largely by an inertia acquired back in Soviet totalitarian times, when the major factors behind for active participation in co-operation lay rather far from a true environmental involvement. These goals were mainly of a declarative character, highly politicized in their outcome, and tightly integrated into the foreign policy priorities of a communist state.

Numerous international environmental commitments were undertaken by the Soviets without any in-depth assessment of their effects on the national scale, of the possibilities for compliance, and the opportunities they might present—in balance, of real environmental interests. Some previous institutional characteristics and perceptions continue to have an impact on the system of international environmental co-operation, which is still, as said in a transitional phase. It is not only the legacy of communism that shapes Russia's major problems in the field of international environmental co-operation today, and the execution of international environmental obligations. The 'transformation' process has, in addition to its positive effects on environmental policy formation, had some negative implications for ecological stability in the national scale, as well as for international environmental security. It has imposed certain limits on environmental problem-solving in Soviet Republic and on the effectiveness of Russia's participation in international environmental co-operation.

Due to the general weakening of state authority during 'transformation', the situation has seen a sharp decrease in its potential for effective action in the field of environmental protection, and this in turn negatively influences the prospects of international environmental co-operation. Industrial production has plummeted (by as much as 50 per cent in 1994 compared to the 1990 level), thereby limiting the economic opportunities of the state for implementation of its national and international environmental policies. Investment has come to a standstill, largely as a result of severe inflation. Subsequently, the processes of structural changes in the economy, the introduction of clean technologies, and the installation of purification facilities have been liquefied.

Domestically there seems to be a widening gap between Russia's recent progressive intentions in international environmental co-operation in general and in dealing with world level environmental changes in particular, and their implementation under the current situation. During the 1990s Russia has also got involved in the UNCED (United Nations Conference on Environment and Development) process. This has had a considerable influence not only on its domestic environmental policy, including adoption of the concept of sustainable development among its priority goals, but also on strategies towards participation in international environmental co-operation towards resolving the major issues on the global environmental change agenda. How can we evaluate the recent modifications in the political, ideological, institutional, and financial framework of Russia's international environmental co-operation? It seems that in general environmental issues are beginning to rank higher on the national scale of preferences (despite some short-term fluctuations).

Environmental issues have been depoliticized, and are becoming more independent of other goals. We cannot yet declare that they are playing the major role in the political and public life of contemporary Russia, that they do in Western societies. However, the clear increase in the importance of environmental issues and of the international environmental agenda indicates that important systemic alterations are under way in this country. Currently, there have been institutional changes in the framework of international co-operation. Under the previous total supremacy of the state under communism, no social function (no matter how important) not accomplished by a special governmental institution had any chance for realization.

Throughout practically the whole Soviet era Russia's obvious endowment was not represented institutionally within the structure of power. It was considered that the industrial ministries that exploited natural resources and the environment were to safeguard them as well. In fact, within this system ministries were over-exploiting natural resources, polluting the environment—and regulating themselves in their own national activities. There was no specialized state institution to protect nature, nor any specialized institution dealing with issues of international environmental co-operation. As a net result of *perestroika,* major institutional changes were undertaken in this field. The State Committee on Environmental Protection was formed in 1988, and that meant that control functions about polluters and resource-users were withdrawn from the latter. The Committee became responsible for co-ordinating international environmental co-operation, as other ministries had changed their functions of regulating the implementation of international environmental agreements.

Thus, the environmental management function received its independence. Later on, during 'transformation', sectorial industrial ministries were dismantled in Russia, while the State Committee on Environmental Protection saw its status raised, and was turned into the then Minister of the Environmental and Natural Resources. A 1994 statute underlines its special institutional role in the regulation of international environmental co-operation. The ministry had to be in charge of the implementation of the country's environmental obligations as a result of Russia's participation in environmental conventions and accords, and thus in activities of international organizations; moreover, international activities of other governmental bodies in the sphere of the environment and resource use had to be co-ordinated with the ministry.

Currently a special inter-agency body is being established within the ministry with participation of other governmental units. It is to be responsible for the implementation of international environmental projects with participation of the World Bank and other international financial organizations. After the decentralization of environmental management in Russia, a considerable amount of environmental ministry competence was transferred to regional and local organs. This meant more opportunities for foreign partners to establish closer environmental co-operation at the local and regional level. The introduction of a new system of economic mechanisms of environmental management in Russia has also spread to the area of international co-operation. Charges and fines for pollution and resource use are being applied to solving not only domestic environmental problems, but global ones as well. Carbon dioxide emission charges are today being adopted in Russia, together with a system of fees for the production and consumption of ozone-depleting substances.

These are in order to induce to finance industrial restructuring and to switch over to alternatives to ozone-depleting substances. New actors—independent producers, NGOs, the mass media—that were previously totally controlled by the state, have appeared on the national arena. It is certain that the structure of interests that they represent and implement in the environmental sphere will change. This issue is of high importance, especially for the West trying to introduce new patterns of co-operation with Russia. Previously environmental interests were suppressed. With democratization, they are being gradually realized and revealed.

We may hope about them to take shape in the sphere of international environmental policy in the near future, associated with a return to the normal international practice of identifying and safeguarding national interests. Such a return to conventional practice would help to enhance the predictability of Russia's international environmental policies, making it dependent on environmental imperatives, not on exogenous pressures. That would have a positive effect on international environmental co-operation with Russian participation. On the other side, one should care not to view the future prospects associated with these changes through rose-coloured spectacles. Many obstacles exist till today. One of them lies in the deep-rooted habits of Russian bureaucracy, and in its aspirations to control completely the processes within its competence. Without constant assessment and pressures from the national public on the bureaucratic apparatus, serious failures are possible.

Targets and Methods of International Environmental Co-operation

First half of 1990s have been marked in Russia by the formation of new strategies of environmental co-operation, developed within the framework of significant modifications in environmental policies. Such strategies have been normatively fixed at the governmental level in a number of government documents. Basic among them is the Law on Environmental Protection (19 December, 1991), the first in the history of the country.

In envisages that in its environmental policies Russia will go further from the necessity to provide international environmental security and the development of international environmental co-operation. The following leading principles are to guide national approaches in this field:

1. Each state has the right to use its environment and its natural resources for the purposes of economic development and providing for the needs of its people;
2. The environmental welfare of one state cannot be provided at the cost of others;
3. The economic activities of a state should not damage the environment within and beyond its jurisdiction;
4. Any specific activity with unpredictable environmental consequences is inadmissible;

5. Global, regional, and local control should be provided over the state of the environmental and alterations in it;
6. Free international exchange of ecological information and environmentally safe technologies should be maintained;
7. States should provide mutual help in case of environmental emergencies;
8. Full environmental disputes are to be settled by peaceful means.[1]

In the Law, Article 92 in which these principles are set out, has a declarative character, announcing the state's obligations towards its public and to the global international community to work towards environmental security. The major principles of environmental co-operation stated there were already set up at the international level (the 1972 Stockholm Conference, the 1982 World Charter on Nature). Russia's environmental law was adopted in the midst of the most romantic period of reforms; as an outcome, some of its provisions, including those dealing with the issues of international co-operation, are chacterized by a certain detachment from hard reality. For example, if principles of environmental damage or of exclusion of environmental risk are to be executed in practice, then Russia will have to halt a greater share of its economic activities. As yet, no final concept for Russia's participation in international environmental co-operation has been shaped.

The Ministry of the Environment has indicated in the major federal program. 'Environmental Security of Russia', that it is necessary 'to work out a concept and prior directions' for Russian participation in international environmental co-operation during a time of transition to a market economy, as well as 'major measures to provide compliance with international obligations in support of international environmental security'. Though these targets were set by the ministry early in 1993,[2] as yet no results of its efforts on the issue have been announced. Today the UNCED process offers the framework for the elaboration of conceptual designs and strategies of Russia's international environmental co-operation.

Participations in UNCED preparations was begun by the Soviet Union, and Russia as its successor took part in the Rio Conference (in which seven states of the former USSR participated) and in the execution of its provisions. The UNCED process had a rather strong impact on Russia's environmental policies and strategies. During UNCED, Russia too signed the Convention on Biological Diversity and the Framework Convention on Climate Change, and supported *Agenda 21* as well as principles of rational use, conservation, and utilization of forestry. Russia is also a member of the Commission on Sustainable Development.

After the Conference, Russia held parliamentary hearings on the enforcement of the Rio provisions in 1993. Institutional structures—an inter-agency commission on the realization of UNCED provisions—were set up and mechanisms for control over their adherence are being instituted. Russia is one of few countries to adopt a national action plan on the subject— 'the National Plan of Action for Realization of the UNCED Decisions'. This serves as a basis for Russia's domestic efforts to provide sustainable development, and it incorporates leading items of strategies and concrete measures in environmental protection along the lines fixed in *Agenda 21*, with sections on environmental management, international co-operation, ecological education, priority measures to improve the state of the environment, and mechanisms for realization of the plan. The great impact of the Rio process would seem to be that the notion of sustainable development is becoming a foundation of Russia's environmental policy.

According to a recent presidential decree (No. 236 of 4 February, 1994), a national programme is to be elaborated on implementation of a policy of sustainable development. This strategy is to envisage concrete actions and principles of national policy realization both at the domestic and international levels. A huge range of provisions on international co-operation are conceived in Russia's national plan of action on UNCED implementation. First, it indicates the major directions for materializing the 1992 intergovernmental environmental agreement of the Commonwealth of Independent States (CIS) and for developing international co-operation between the former Soviet republics. Next, it notes that the international obligations of Russia within a framework of environmental accords, need close integration with other countries, especially European ones: the unique role of European ministerial conferences on the environment is stressed. Lastly, implementation of the UNCED national action plan requires an expansion of foreign financial and technical assistance at the bilateral level and within the limits of international financial organizations, especially the World Bank and the European Bank for Reconstruction and Development. In assessing the impact of the Rio process on Russia, V. Danilov-Danilian, Russia's minister of the environment, indicated that the major priorities of *Agenda 21* aimed at ensuing environmental policy formation in the developing countries, and expanding their environmental activities. Various actions had already been undertaken in Russia in this field, particularly regarding its scientific potential, development of environmental protection mechanisms, and environmental monitoring. The minister stressed that the true problem today lay in defining the mechanisms of international co-operation to provide financing for global environmental problem-solving, as well as the formation of national control mechanisms about the distribution and use of financial resources earmarked for this purpose.[3] At the Rio Conference, Russia, together with other countries of Eastern Europe, was inferred the special status of a state in transition to a market economy, with certain privileges granted in financing of environmental measures, in technology transfers, and in financial sanctions to international environmental funds.

Provisions for the transitional period were reflected in the Russian national plan of action which envisaged improvements in management mechanisms to adapt to a market economy, including a gradual shift from a centralized and strictly controlled system of management to a flexible decentralized one. In the course of the post-Rio process Russia took part in the 1993 Lucerne Conference on the environment in Central and Eastern Europe, where a progamme of action to resolve the most urgent problems in these countries with transformation economies was adopted. Russia has proposed a list of special sites and territories which require foreign aid in order to improve their environmental situation. The Rio process has affected and diversified the framework of Russia's environmental activities, particularly within the agenda for global environmental change. The process of formulating goals and strategies and undertaking actions is developing—some of these started earlier on certain aspects of global change management, and some of them to be shaped in the near future.

Together with more traditional issues (ozone-layer protection, climate change and trans-boundary air pollution), new fields of international co-operation for Russia have emerged. These include protection of biodiversity, conservation of forests, betterment of nature-protection areas and reserves, environmentally benign destruction of chemical and nuclear weapons, and solving transboundary environmental problems among the states of the former Soviet Union. The domestic implementation of international provisions on these issues requires serious restructuring and behaviour adaptation on the part of different actors. For instance, the domestic realization of the Rio principles on conservation of forests requires certain amendments to Russia's national forestry strategies. It is important to increase control over timber-cutting and export, to develop legislative norms for forest conservation, and to adopt a national programme for the preservation and reproduction of Russian's forests.

Indeed, these forests account for a quarter to the world's total forest resources and are important in ensuring ecological stability on a planetary scale. Domestic implementation of the provisions of the biodiversity convention necessitates the elaboration of a national plan for conservation and sustainable use of elements of biodiversity, including preservation of *in situ* and *ex situ* species, along with scientific research and specialist training. Particular attention should be paid to establishing mechanisms of access to information on genetic resources and technologies, and national steps to finance the implementation process. Assessing the first steps which Russia has taken in setting its national goals and strategies for international environmental co-operation, one might conclude that, despite the abundance of official government documents regulating the nation's international environmental co-operation, there is as yet no clear and comprehensive concept on this issue.

However, participation in international environmental co-operation is not engaged in for its own sake: it is encouraged by the necessity of solving environmental problems at the national and international levels. What major environmental concerns is Russia now bearing whose solutions will require such mechanisms as international co-operation? Unfortunately it is still rather difficult to get clear answers to this question. Various official documents published recently in the press and covering goals and strategies on international environmental co-operation share a common serious shortcoming. Fundamentally they seem to be mere summary lists of ministerial guidelines, composed with such remarkable bureaucratic skilfulness as to be reminiscent of the old adage 'a tongue is given to conceal one's thoughts'. In this nations, government documents on environmental issues ought to be expressed in the most democratic way, so that the public can hold their essence. Instead, they often follow the old bureaucratic traditions—in the form of a charade created for the purposes of internal bureaucratic games.

Agenda for Global Environmental Change

During the last years of its existence the Soviet Union, and thereafter Russia, became involved in the process of international regime formation dealing with global environmental difficulties—acid rain, ozone layer depletion, and global climate change. In connection with the management of these three environmental risks we may trace separate histories and patterns of domestic implementation, and varying results when in comes to fulfilling international obligations.

(*a*) *Transboundary Air Pollution With Acid Rain*

The expansion of the 1979 Convention of Long Range

Transboundary Air Pollution (LRTAP) coincided with the period of East-West detente in the late 1970s. The national approaches taken by the USSR and its preparedness for domestic implementation had their national specification. The major issue was that, due to westerly air currents, the import of air pollutants to the European part of the state was considerably higher than their export across the Soviet Union's western border. The USSR, and Russia state were victims of transboundary air pollution.

By the beginning of the 1990s about 1,730,000 tonnes of sulphur dioxide (SO_2) was carried annually across the western border of the USSR from Europe, while five times less was going in the opposite direction. Nitrous oxide (NO_x) imports accounted for about 930,000 tons, with their export being fifteen times less. The main flexes originated in Poland, Germany, Czechoslovakia, Hungary, and Finland. The exception was Scandinavia: SO_2 export from the USSR was higher than import, but the condition for NO_x flows was quite the opposite. Norway and Sweden were net-importers of SO_2. A provision envisaging regulation whether of air pollutant emissions or their transborder flows was introduced into the convention at the request of the Soviet Union. For the USSR this meant that in order to go with the Sulphur Protocol, major efforts to reduce air pollutant emissions would have to be concentrated mainly at enterprises situated along its western boundaries. Only the European part of the country was included in the area covered by the convention. Thus, measues to restructure polluting industries were not to be applied to the industrialized parts of non-European Siberia.

Domestic implementation of this international regime coincided with considerable structural changes in Soviet energy policy.

By the end of the 1970s and the beginning of the 1980s the energy sector of the European part of the USSR was in the process of shifting from coal to natural gas and to nuclear energy growth. These radical changes in the national energy balance that needed considerable governmental capital investments were not attributable to the Soviet entry into the international regime. Instead, these changes were the result of the impact of indigenous factors—the exhaustion of energy resources in the European USSR, the need of their transportation from the north and Siberia, and the shift to cheaper fuel—natural gas, and so on. All these factors served to facilitate for the USSR compliance with the Sulphur Protocol. From the start of the 1980s an active national policy for air protection was launched—with adoption of the law on air protection, elaboration of norms and standards, fixation of air purification facilities at industrial enterprises, and the compiling of a register of air pollution sources. Numerous efforts were undertaken to reduce emissions from industrial enterprises engaged in the production of energy, ferrous and non-ferrous metals, chemicals, and fertilizers that contributed to transboundary air pollution. As a consequence, SO_2 transborder flows were reduced, and national obligations were met. Sulphur dioxide emissions from the European USSR came down by 29 per cent during the years 1980-90.

In Russia today we can note a 41 per cent reduction from the base level of 1980.[4] However, these reductions are also attributable in part to the extreme decline in industrial production in Russia as a result of economic crisis. In June 1994 Russia became a party to the Protocol to the LRTAP Convention on more Reduction of Sulphur Emissions.

Problem of NO_x air pollution has not been solved in Russia. Discharges from transport have increased considerably during recent years. This problem is receiving considerable attention in Russia, because these emissions constitute about 41 per cent of the total NO_x emissions, and there is a stable upward trend. Envisaged for the near future in Russia are steps to control emissions from cars and to introduce new emission standards similar to those in the West, as well as to shift transport to natural gas and to use catalytic converters. It seem that it is much more difficult to control NO_x emissions than SO_2 discharges. But in the absence of innovations and of control and monitoring over car emissions, the situation might worsen in the future.

(*b*) *Safety of Ozone Layer*

During the two past decades the Soviet Union and then Russia have taken an active part in international research activities aimed at ozone layer protection. As a result of monitoring the dynamics of the stratosphere ozone layer, comprehensive data have been accumulated and analysed. At present a system of twenty-nine monitoring stations is functioning in Russia (forty-three in the USSR), caused at the end of the 1950s as a result of the International Geophysical Year. The national system is incorporated into an international one, and there is routine monitoring of the state of the ozone layer over Russian territory.

In line with international co-operative arrangements, data from German and Bulgarian stations are used in these evaluations. Functional data exchange on the state of the ozone layer over the Arctic was staged recently between Russia, Finland, and Canada, with Russia responsible for the reliable of maps on its dynamics. Regular ozone layer monitoring has been organized on the four stations in Antarctica, and in 1987 this programme was spread into a co-operative effort with German scientists.

Russia has also participated in several projects within the framework of the World Meteorological Organization and UNEP known as the United Nations Environment Programme. Russia is responsible for about 9-10 per cent of the world's production of ozone-depleting substances. According to official figures in 1990 total production and use of ozone-depleting substances including halons accounted for 124,652 tons (with halons alone at 4,242 tons).[5] Russia's Ministry of the Environment has said that in 1991 CFC (chlorofluorocarbans) production decreased from the previous year by 16 per cent, and halons by 40 per cent. The main production of ozone-depleting matter in the former Soviet Union is concentrated in Russia (80 per cent), and about 15 per cent in Tajikistan; other producers are placed in Ukraine, Belarus, Lithuania, and Latvia. From the mid-1980s the Soviet Union became involved in work on the creation of an international regime for the ozone layer.

After signing the international agreement, a process of domestic implementation was initiated, including institutional formation,[6] organizational steps and elaboration of responses to the risk of ozone layer depletion. Two national programmes were adopted on this issue: on research into the ozone layer (1990), and on expansion of technologies of ozone-benign halon production (1992). Attempts to shape national goals and strategies were undertaken at the completion of the 1980s. It was decided to approach the task of reducing and peventing the risk of ozone depletion by means of control over production and consumption of ozone-depleting substances, with the targets being first to reduce, and finally to phase them out completely by the year 2000; provision was also made for research and monitoring of the state of the ozone layer.[7]

The provision to decrease and then to cease production and consumption of ozone-depleting substances was introduced in Rússia's 1991 Law on Environmental safety.[8] Nevertheless, practical measures to implement the provisions of environmental law and environmental programmes have been implemented rather slowly and ineffectively. Adequate government financing has not been provided, and specific reduction goals have not yet been imposed on target groups. This has led to partial adherence to international treaty obligations. In 1992 obligations to decrease production and consumption of ozone-depleting substances were met, as well as the Protocol's provisions on information exchange and scientific research. Anyway, due to the critical economic situation in Russia, the remaining obligations were not fulfilled, it was reported in 1992 at the fourth meeting of the parties to the Montreal Protocol.[9]

An other set of serious obligations has been imposed on Russia after it signed the 1992 amendment the Montreal Protocol. Starting from 1996 Russia is to his completely the production and use of refrigerants containing CFCs, as well as exclude all trade in them (at present about 50 per cent of the refrigerators produced in Russia are exported). Experts have said that it may be difficult to restructure the industrial production completely during the remaining period and to meet international obligations.[10] Russia is presently in the process of elaborating a national programme: "Production of ozone-benign refrigerants and compliance with international obligations of Russia to protect the ozone layer.

This programme seeks continuing ozone layer research, including the construction of a model of interactions between the ozone layer, man, and the biosphere, to provide continuous monitoring of ozone layer dynamics. It presupposes elaboration of concrete actions to convert Russian enterprises to ozone-benign technologies,[11] collecting and recycling present ozone-layer depleting substances. However, given the prevailing economic crisis in the country, the prospects of programme implementation would seem uncertain, and a gap might exist between the programme as it has been elaborated and its actual implementation.

(*c*) *Safety Measures for the Global Climate*

Scientists have been involved in international scientific co-operation on the global climate (Global Atmosphere Research Programme, World Climate Programme, as well as in global climate conferences, and activities of the International Panel on Climate Change, etc.). Since the 1950s M. Buidyko and his school have been busy in research on global climate change; and their work, especially the scientific results of analogue palaeoclimatic reconstructions, has become famous in the world scientific community. Predictions of global warming were presented internationally in the early 1970s: The results of analysis of data compiled in Russia for over a century, joined with the results of palaeoclimatic reconstructions, served as a basis for evaluations of global climate change and its impact on a national scale, as well as for the creation of national responses.[12] Until recently, the management of global climate-change risk was not a priority item on Russia's national environmental agenda.

The specifics of national notions of the effects of climate change have defined Russia's approaches towards the problems, as well as towards the formulation of aims and strategies, and participation in the international regime under formation. Russia's attitudes to this issue have been quite similar to those of the USA. According to Russian scientists, there still exists great uncertainty in perceptions on the comparative role of anthropogenic and natural factors in global warming. There are as yet no well-defined replies concerning the consequences of global warming for man and nature on a national scale.

For instance, according to the work of M. Buidyko and other scientific analysis, most of the former Soviet territory, and especially areas north of 50ºN latitude might benefit from global warming. On a national scale, a 5 per cent increase in grain production is feasible due to a predicted increase in the duration of the growing season by ten to fifteen days by the year 2005, and due to the positive agricultural effect of grown carbon dioxide content on crop production. The boundary of agricultural zones might expand northwards because of permafrost zone reductions.[13] On the other side, there might also be negative impacts of global warming. Due to changes in precipitation patterns droughts might increase, especially in the southern areas, as well as the feasibility of crop failure. Changes in the permafrost areas might negatively affect engineering constructions.

Great potential for lowering greenhouse gas emissions appears to lie in the restructuring of national energy production and consumption patterns. The current energy intensity of Russia's GNP (gross national product) is twice times higher than in the countries of Western Europe, and about one-third of the energy resources are wasted.[14] Compliance with Russia's international obligations to decrease greenhouse gas emissions requires considerable investments in restructuring the energy balance. Despite the availability of different modern technologies in the energy, transport, and industrial sectors which might enable a downward trend in greenhouse gas emissions, during the past five years no policy of struetural changes in Russia has been enforced nor have new technologies been installed, due to the lack of financial resources for industrial investment.

However, Russia has been granted some flexibility in terms of time-scales and emission-level reductions, by classifying it as one in a group of states with economies under transition. In recent years, a 7-10 per cent downfall in carbon-dioxide emissions in comparison with the 1990 level has been noted in Russia as a result of lower industrial production. Russia would seem to have sufficient prospects in international co-operation on the global warming issue connected with enhancing its greenhouse gas sinks, and especially through conservation and reproduction of its wide forest resources. According to figures from the Russian federal forestry service about one-third of the national anthropogenic carbon dioxide emissions are taken in by the Russian forests.

Conclusion: Fresh Possibilities

While Russia has undertaken a progressive reshaping of its environmental policies, serious difficulties still remain. It will not be easy to solve the problems not only of getting along well with international obligations, but also of the national implementation of international environmental agreements. The situation is defined by a vast range of political, socio-economic factors deeply rooted in the specifics of the transitional period in Russia. The recent weakening of state authority has had severely negative consequences for Russia's adherence to its international obligations. Due to the lack of adequate administrative control, environmental standards and values adopted in compliance with international provisions are being violated.

Weaker border controls, and higher levels of poaching in the country result, for example, in increased non-compliance with the obligations undertaken under the Convention on International Trade in Endangered Species of Forest Fauna and Flora (CITES). A certain shift can be noted towards giving priority to solving urgent environmental problems on the national and local scales, instead of problems of a global character. According to data from the early 1990s, practically none of the 750 non-governmental environmental groups registered in the previous Soviet Union indicated global environmental protection among their established goals. Their activities were focused instead on regional and local environmental issues.[15] A crucial limiting factor is the absence of financial resources for domestic implementation of international obligations. Russia's 1994 federal budget allocates for environmental purposed about 0.6 per cent of its expenditure or about 0.15 per cent of GNP. Moreover, its seems that this downward trend in state financing of environmental activities will continue.

Presently about one-tenth of the environmental programmes of the Ministry of the Environment receive funding. Only 37 per cent of the envisaged financial resources were in fact, allotted in 1993 to the major federal environmental programme 'Ecological Security of Russia'.[16] This deficit of federal resources for environmental purposes is accompanied by a difficult situation concerning capital investments in the environmental sphere. As a result, the installation of purification facilities and modern resource-saving technologies has been decreased considerably during recent years. Financial shortages are a major factor in Russia's non-compliance with some provisions of international environmental commitments. This was exemplified in connection with the violation of the international ozone layer regime, and with restructuring the non-ferrous industries of the Kola Peninsula to cut down SO_2 emissions as agreed under the international Long-Range Transboundary Air Pollution regime.

Despite the fact that financial assistance from the West is of great significance, Russian experts doubt that it can solve entirely the environmental problems of Russia, as well as the problems related to adherence to its international obligations. It might definitely help in reducing the time-limits of environmental restructuring and *perestroika*, and contribute to success in this area. The transitional period in Russia necessarily involves greater instability in the major prerequisites for international environmental co-operation.

Strong implementation of international environmental obligations would seem to be closely linked with the success of this transitional period, and whether a way out can be found to Russia's internal political, economic, and social problems. Success in the domestic implementation of international agreements relies on progress in systemic transformation—on the rapid creation of market-based and democratic institutions and culture.

Realization of an environmental strategy in Russia is dependent on handling the economic recession. Thus, for a relatively long period of time, solving the most urgent environmental problems in Russia, as well as domestic execution of international environmental commitments and compliance with international obligations, will remain intertwined with the prospects of general economic normalization, and with stability of the state. Solving the environmental problems of Russia and increasing the effectiveness of international environmental co-operation are closely linked with democatization, a necessary prerequisite for exposing and defending environmental interests.

This is especially important in the case of Russia, since the environmental consciousness and political will of political leaders on this issue still tend to be rather weak. Political pressures from the green movement and the public are of great important. Indeed, this field might be regarded as one of the important directions for international co-operation. Co-ordination of actions between NGOs in Russia and in the West is unavoidable. Pressures from foreign NGOs exerted in Russia can be even more effective than the desperate efforts of local NGOs and the local public to solve environmental difficulties and blocks.

References

1. 'Zakon Rossiiskoy Federacii ob Ohane Okuizhauishei Prirodnoy Sredy' (Law of the Russian Federation on Environmental Protection) (1992). *Verhovnogo Soveta Rossiikoy Federacii,* 10: 629.
2. 'Federalnaya Celevaya Kompleksnaya Nauchno-Tehnicheskaya Programme "Ekologicheskaya Bezopasnost Rossii" (1993-5)' (Federal Complex Science and Technology Programme "Environmental Secuirty of Russia') (1993). *Zelenyi Mir* (special issue), 9.
3. V. Danilov-Danilian (1993), 'Tochki nad i', *Zeklenyi Mir,* 14: 7.
4. 'Obzor Zagrriazenia Okruizhauishei Prirodnoi Stredy v SSSR' (Oveview of the Environmental Pollution in the USSR) (1991), (Moscow: Hydrometeoizdat), 9; *Gosuidarstvennyi Doklad* (n. 5 above), 92.
5. Data presented to the UN Environmental Programme.
6. After signing the Vienna Convention in 1985 according to a resolution of the Council of Ministers of the USSR, an Interdepartmental Commission was set up to implement the provisions of the regime. The State Committee on Hydrometeorolgoy was nominated at the head of it to co-ordinate activities of other ministries. In 1987 the Ministry of Chemical Industry became responsible for the elaboration of measures aimed at reducing the production and consumption of ozone-depeleting substances.
7. *Eknomicheskaya Gazeta* (1988), (July), 1.
8. 'Zakon Rossiiskoy Federacii ob Ohrane Okruizhauishei Prirodonoy Sredy' (n. 2 above), 616-17.
9. *Gosuidarstvennyi Dokland* (n. 5 above), 92.
10. *Segodnya* (1994), 18 June.
11. Such measures include: introduction of ozone-benign halons for refrigerators, components of foam plastics, aerosol cans unsing ozone-benign propellants or on a non-propellant basis. Producers of ozone-depleting substances are to be reconstructed and shifted to hydrocarbon propellants, fluorine-containing solvents should be substituted, and the creation of alternatives to CFCs and halons is foreseen.
12. M. Buidyko (1989), 'Introduction', Greenhouse Effect. Climate Change, and Ecosystems (Leningrad: Gidrometeoizdat), 10-16.
13. *Nacionlny Dokland SSS k Konferencii OON 1992 goda po Okruizhayushei Srede i Razvitiy* (USSR National Report for the 1992 UNCED Conference) (1991) (Moscow: Mineco), 168.
14. *Izvestia* (1992), 14 July.

15. *Sprravochnik Ekologicheskyh Obshestvennych Ob' dinenyi na Territorii SSSR* (Compendium of the Environmental Public Organizations on the Territory of the USSR) (1991) (Moscow: VNIIC Ekologia), 245.
16. *Rossisky Vesti* (1994), 17 June.

11

Strategies to Handle Greenhouse Warming: Chinese Stand

Contents of this chapter are views/opinious and findings of Prof. Qu Geping who is an administrator with the National Environment Protection Agency of China.

Global warming has become an issue of great concern and focus of discussions among scientists and the general public the world over in recent years. It is the theme of this year's World Environment Day, which is not accidental. Environmental problems such as greenhouse effect and the depletion of ozone layer have become a major potential threat to the existence and development of the mankind on the earth. This has awakened people and they have become to understand that strategies must be sought and common efforts must be made to deal with these problems.

Facing global warming, what environmental changes will take place in China? What impact will it exert on the economic development and the people's livelihood? What strategies will China take? These are questions the general public of China and all these who are interested in global environmental problems are concerned about.

I

Data show that in the last hundred years, the global climate has experienced a tendency of gradual warming. 1920s saw the first warming period. In 1930s and 1940s, the global average temperature was 0.3-0.4 °C higher than that at the end of last century. This was then followed by a period with lower temperatures. With the world entering 1980s, the globae began to experience the second warming period which is the hottest decade of the century. The years with the highest temperatures since 1900 are all within this decade. The global average temperature in 1980s is 0.6 °C higher than at the end of the last century. It can be said that since 1920s, the global climate has been obviously getting warmer.

Various different predictions are available on the tendency of the future'global climate change. However, most of the scientists are of the view that the world will continuously getting warmer.

The general tendency of the climate change in China in the past is basically in correspondence with that of the world: It was comparatively cool before 1920s, warmer in 1940s and cooler in 1960s and 1970s, and rises again in 1980s. However, there are also some differences: First, the temperature came down a little in 1930s; secondly, the recent temperature rise began in the middle of 1970s, which was earlier than the other parts of the world, but the warming in 1980s is not so radical as that of the world. There are two characteristics in China's warming in the last decade: (a) The warming in the North (mainly north of Huai River and Qinling Mountain, particularly in the North-east and North of China) is more obvious than in the South: (b) The warming in winter is more pronounced than in the other seasons. Take the last winter (December 1988-February 1989) for example, the temperature in most parts of China was higher to various degrees than the average temperature of the precious years with the North-east and North being most obvious.

What future climate change will take place in China? According to the predications by China's meteorologists, the surface temperature in China will tend to rise under continuous fluctuations. The scale of warming will not be smaller than that in the northern hemisphere, and the north will have a higher rise than the south. According to the study by the late meteorologist M. Zhu Kezhen, in the 5,000 years of civilization in China, there have been several warm periods and cool periods. The difference in the annual mean temperature between warm periods and cool periods is no more than 3 °C. It can be seen if the annual mean temperature in 2030s is 1.5-4.5 °C higher than today, it will mean a temperature rise higher than what has happened in the past several thousand years. To put it specifically, if the annual mean temperature rises by 2 °C, the temperature in Beijing then will be similar to today's temperature in Yellow River watershed: if it rises by 3 °C. Beijing's temperature will be similar to today's temperature in Huai River watershed: if it rise by 4 °C, Beijing's temperature will be similar to today's temperature in Changjiang (Yangze) River Valley.

II

Climate change will extent a profound impact on China's economic development and people's livelihood. Though some of the impact is only an assumption, reasons are solid for being on the alert.

Climate change will move the northern border of China's subtropics from Qinling Mountain and Huai River. The temperature in winter in Xuzhou and Zhengzhou then will be similar to the present temperature in Hangzhou and Wunan. The temperature zone will move to the north by 4-5 degrees of latitude. Most of the frozen soil in the Qinghai-Tibet Plateau and small glaciers in Qilian Mountain and Tai Mountain will disappear. At the same time, the raining belts will also move. There will be move rain in summer in Hainan Island of the Tropics. While in other areas, there will be less rain, especially in the north-west which is a dry area and will get even drier in the next century.

Such climatic change will have an obvious impact on China's agriculture. On the one hard, the warming will help to raise the agricultural output in some areas, and on the other hand, it will lead to less rain in summer and higher temperature and more rain in winter. This will increase the capital cost of agricultural production. Since China's population accounts for 1/5 of the world population, we should attach great importance to food production. Because China is a developing country with comparatively backward farming methods and low ability to combat natural disasters and climatic change, the warning will have a serious impact on China.

The rise of the sea level caused by global warming as an other threat to China. China has a long coastal line. Owing to the historical reasons, most of China's economic, forces are located in the coastal areas with dense population. The delta areas near the river estuaries are mostly rich areas with fairly developed economy. If the sea level rises, apart from flooding part of coastal areas, the area of alkaline and saline soil will increase, erosion and sedimentation in the coastal areas and the downstream of big rivers will become more serious, water way transportation will be affected, difficulties in drainage will increase and the work land of sea dykes and ports will also increase.

As a country with the largest population in the world. China is very much concerned about the trends of global warming because the possibility that global environmental problems will have impacts on China's industrial and agricultural production and people's health is the greatest.

III

Factors causing global warming are complex: There are man-made as well as natural factors. The climate change of 100 years ago was mainly caused by natural factors while human activities are the main cause for the climate change in the recent hundred years.

Now most of the scientists believe that the built-up of carbon dioxide and other greenhouse gases in the atmosphere is the main cause of the greenhouse effect. These gases mainly come from the combustion of fossil fuels. At present, the whole world consumes seven billion TDE of fossil fuels a year, or 90 per cent of the total energy consumption. The carbon dioxide released from the combustion of fossil fuels accounts for 70 per cent of the total amount of the newly released carbon dioxide. The past century saw the sharp increase in the release of carbon dioxide. The annual release of carbon dioxide was about 90 million tons in the 1960s, but soared to 5 billion tons in 1985. The same period, however, saw the sharp decrease of forest—the "sanitation worker" and the "storage" for the atmosphere—at an annual average rate of 9-24 million hectares. This is evident that the greenhouse effect is closely related to the production and subsistence activities of the human beings. To solve the problem of the greenhouse effect and prevent the climate from getting further warm therefore requires efforts to adjust the productive activities and the lifestyle of the human beings. This obviously is an ardous task. Its fulfilment requires various countries in the world to gain a common understanding of the seriousness of the problem and shoulder their international bounden duty.

China's energy consumption amounted to 800 million tons standard coal, which is similar to that of Japan. As a major energy consuming power, China fully understands its duty in adjusting energy strategies and in controlling greenhouse effect.

China has two problems to solve in the way the energy is utilized: First, fossil fuels make up 95 per cent of the primary energy consumed, most of which are relatively "dirty" energy source—coal. In 1986, in China, coal accounted for 72.4 per cent of the total primary energy production and 76.0 per cent of the total primary energy consumption while it was 23.3 per cent in the United States. 24.8 per cent in the Soviet Union. 18.8 per cent in Japan, 10.0 per cent in France. The world average was 30.0 per cent (see Table 1). Second, the energy efficiency remains low, averaging about 30 per cent which is 50-100 per cent lower than some advanced countries (see Table 2).

Table 1. Composition of Primary Energy Consumption in 1986 (%)

	World	*China*	*US*	*USSR*	*Japan*	*FRG*	*France*	*UK*	*Italy*
Oil	38.0	17.1	43.2	34.3	55.8	42.6	43.0	36.2	60.9
Gas	20.0	2.3	22.4	37.4	10.2	15.5	12.5	23.5	21.7
Coal	30.0	76.0	23.3	24.8	18.8	30.1	10.0	32.4	9.8
Nuclear power	5.0	/	6.1	/	10.3	10.9	32.8	7.5	1.8
Hydro-power and others	7.0	4.6	5.0	3.5	4.9	1.0	1.7	0.4	5.8
amount of consumption (100 million tons of standard coal)	108.4	8.08	26.59	19.36	5.66	3.78	2.81	2.93	1.90

Table 2. A Comparison of Energy Efficiency of China and Other Countries (%)

	China (1985)	*US (1973)*	*US (1970)*	*Japan (1980)*	*USSR (1980)*
Energy efficiency	32.3	40	50	58	43

Therefore, China has great potential to tap in improving the energy utilization ways. This is a starting for point our participation in the global effort to improve the global environment.

The endeavour to control the spread of the greenhouse effect will exert enormous pressure on various countries, but will also provide them with chances to effect changes and make progress. For China, it is a new challenge which will inevitably trigger deep-going reforms to the orientation, scale composition and efficiency of energy consumption. After the decade-long reform and development, China's economy is at the crucial stage of the readjustment of the industrial structure. If we can have a good grasp of this opportunity to take an active part in the joint effort to improve the economic development, our effort will pay off to promote the economic readjustment and development.

In participating in the joint action to improve the global environment and prevent the global climate from getting further warm. China will mainly do two things: improving the way the energy is used and strengthening the protection of forest and vegetation.

Improving the Way the Energy Utilization

(a) Striving to control the scale of energy consumption. China is the most populous country in the world. Its huge population has posed a heavy burden on China's subsistence and development. It is predictable that the scale of future energy consumption will widen with each passing day. The countermeasures that could be taken include: *First*, developing the production of non-fossil fuels whose combustion will not release carbon dioxide and other greenhouse gases, which will be discussed later; *second,* controlling the growth speed of energy consumption, and advocating and developing the energy-saving production processes and lifestyle. In this regard, we think in this way: although China's per capita share of energy consumption is low, the total amount of energy consumption is considerably huge. For example, in 1987, China consumed 830 million tons of crude coal as energy. And the consumption of coal is expected to hit 1.1 billion tons by 1992. This increase in energy consumption brings pressure on both the production and the shipment of crude coal. It also exerts great impact on the environment. Judging from the angle of the long-term development of economy, the way out lies in the development of new industries which consume less energy. However, potential must be tapped in improving the energy utilization efficiency of those energy-guzzling traditional industries. If the thermal efficiency of coal can be raised from 30 per cent at present to 45 per cent. China would be able to save about 300 million tons of crude coal, and reduce the pollutants in the atmosphere by 40 per cent. Financially speaking, this will also save China 150 billion yuan in the production of coal.

(b) Improving the utilization rate of energy. China's energy utilization rate is about 30 per cent on the average compared to 57 per cent in Japan. 51 per cent in the United States and 40 per cent in Britain. As far as the average thermal efficiency of the energy consuming equipment is concerned, it is 35-40 per cent for ordinary thermal power stations. 80 per cent for industrial boilers and 50-60 per cent for industrials furnaces and civilians stoves in the developed countries, compared to less than 30 per cent. about 60 per cent and 15-20 per cent respectively in China. Generally speaking, China lags far behind the advanced countries, which shows China has great potential to tap in seeking improvement and enhancement. During the economic development in the last few years.

China has always attached great importance to saving energy. In 1988, the amount of energy and electricity consumed for the generation of every 10,000 yuan worth of industrial output value dropped by 5.63 per cent and 5.75 per cent respectively from the previous year. This is a proof of good result. Of course, it is impossible for China to keep the energy saving at such a high rate for a long period of time. There will be more tough difficulties ahead of us. Nonetheless, we'll take energy saving as the orientation of our work for a long period of time to come. Our target is: by 2000 the energy consumption for every 1000 yuan of GNP will be 7.2 tons of standard coal (it was 23.73 in 1985), per capita energy consumption will be 1 ton and energy saving rate will be 50 per cent. China is currently extremely in short of energy. About one-third of its material production capacity often suffers from power failure and short supply of coal, causing enormous economic loss. Saving energy is therefore the need of the environmental protection and is also of great significant to the economic development.

To save energy, breakthrough must be made in the following two aspects: (a) Technical renovation must be made on a large scale instead of minor changes and modifications to the existing equipments and processes. If China's industrial technologies and energy utilization technologies still remain at present levels, we will achieve no obvious progress in energy conservation. It means that technological progress is the key link; (b) Economic mechanisms for energy conservation should be formulated in energy conservation, general calls and administrative orders will yield little results while economic levers with price mechanisms as the chief tool can achieve doubled success.

(c) Actively developing and using new energy sources: Nuclear energy, solar energy, wind energy, biological energy and other kinds of new energy are accepted as the clean energy which does not engender greenhouse gases and other atmospheric pollutants. Although new energy sources have their own weak points in technology and cost, they represent the orientation for the world's development of energy: hence they have a bright future. China is making effort to develop and use the new energy.

China has always been attaching importance to the development of hydropower stations in energy production. China is rich in hydropower sources with a theoretical potential of 680 million Kw of which 370 million Kw can be tapped. 1900 billion Kw hr of electricity can be generated per year. China has built not only the world famous large hydropower works such as the Gezhouba Hydropower Station but also numerous small hydropower stations. These small hydropower stations numbered more than 76,000 in 1984, generating a total of 8.5 million Kw of electricity, it reached 10.06 million Kw in 1986. Construction of the small hydropower stations gained further ground in the last few years. Electricity generated by these small power stations in the countryside has helped reduce coal consumption and, moreover, improve the conditions of farmers in daily life and the conditions for the improvement of the ecological balance.

Under strict safety measures, nuclear energy is a new kind of clean, safe and highly efficient energy. China began to build its nuclear power production bases in the early years of the 1980s. Projects with a total generating capacity of 2.1 million Kw of nuclear power a year will go into production soon. By the end of this century, China's nuclear power production will hit 6 million Kw. Undoubtedly, the development of nuclear power will help reduce consumption of fossil fuels, contributing to the decrease in the release of greenhouse gases.

In China, the development and use of solar energy have always received encouragement. In cities in north China, many buildings have been installed with solar energy equipment. And efforts are being made to increase the use of solar energy in industrial production. In the rural areas, besides encouraging the development of small hydropower stations, China has also made effort to develop methane-generating pits and solar energy stoves to help solve the shortage of fuel in daily life. As a result, energy consumed in the rural areas is diversified, including bioges firewood electricity generated by small hydropower stations, coal, solar energy, wind energy and plant stalks.

Strengthening Protection of Forest and Vegetation

Forests are the 'lung' of the earth. Through photosynthesis, forests inhale carbon dioxide and exhale oxygen, thus playing an important regulatory role to the global climate. China is poor in forestry resources. Due to the incessant wars in history and the wanton falling to trees in the ensuing years, China's forest areas had further decreased. In order to save the forest resources and expand the areas covered with trees. The Chinese government has promulgated many regulations including the Forest Law and the Regulations Concerning the Water and Soil Conservation. In the meantime, China introduced the system geared to encourage people to plant trees on a voluntary basis. This system has been followed for ten years. Each year, there were 100 million Chinese citizens who took part in the tree-planting activities. They have planted altogether close to 10 billion trees averaging 1 billion trees, each year. This has increased the greened areas both in cities and their suburbs.

In the countryside, the reform to the forestry management system and the introduction of the contracted forestry responsibility system have aroused the enthusiasm of the farmers for planting trees. Many barren hills have been greened now. It is China's target to raise her forest cover from 12 per cent at present to 18-20 per cent by the end of this century. So long as we can persist in following the correct policy on forestry and strengthen protection of forest resources in accordance with the law, this target should be able to be attained.

In addition, China attaches importance to the protection of grasslands and prevents them from being reclaimed in a blind way. For lands which are not suitable for reclamation but have already been reclaimed for farming, efforts have been made to turn them back into grassland. In the meantime, efforts have also been made to avoid overgrazing. The degradation of the grassland eco-system is being reversed.

Efforts made by China to protect the environment have contributed to improved conditions for a better environment and resources, stimulating the development of the economy. Of course, much remains to be done in this regard, and the task is arduous. We have taken note of the long-term impact of the global environmental problems on the economic and social development. I am convinced that this international workshop will help promote the dissemination of needed knowledge, the exchange of experiences and co-operation among various countries.

12

Impact on Economic Growth of Austria

In the light of proposed restrictions a nation is supposed to oberve to protect environments, it is inevitable that economic development will receive a setback. Otherwise, it is difficult to realise assumed (ideal) future with the environmental changes taking place to quickly. This problem has found place on priority list of almost all nations.

I

Sustainable Development Through World Commission on Environment and Development

The minute, we start, the most important topic on the agendas of international conferences is the issue of climate change. Among climatologists there is unanimous agreement that the emissions of greenhouse gases, such as carbon dioxide, methane, nitrous oxide, chlorofluorocarbons and tropospheric ozone, contribute to the change of the earth's climate in necessary way.

In particular the emissions of the trace gas CO_2 causes such a change with far-reaching consequences for all life on Earth.[1] This danger had led to a renaissance of discussion, which has its roots in the study of the World Commission on Environment and Development.

This Commission argues in its final report for sustainable development. It defines: 'Sustainable development is development that meets the needs of the day without compromising the ability of future generations to meet their own needs.' (WCED, 1987:43). Today sustainable development, or sustainability, is a key notion in the discussion about a re-orientation of our economy in the light of various environment problems, in particular in view of the possibility of global climate change.[2] As quoted above, the Commission draws our attention to two different types of distribution conflicts. Both significant for sustainable development, and both are characteristic for the greenhouse effect: on the one hand we have a conflict.

On the other hand we can identify a distribution conflict between present generations, that is, an inter-generational conflict. The main source of carbon dioxide emissions is the burning of coal, oil and gas. The growing production of energy with these fossil fuels had led to a remarkable increase in atmospheric CO_2 concentration. However, this increasing fuel use has allowed the improvement of production and consumption likelihood in the industrialised countries since the beginning of the industrial revolution.

Even today the extensive use of energy produced from non-renewable fossil fuels is a fundamental prerequisite for ensuring better supply of goods. In particular, the development of the less developed regions depends on the expansion of their energy use in various economic and social activities. In this connection they have to use fossil fuels, since alternatives are not available in an adequate amount. This indicates the above mentioned distributional conflicts. One prerequisite of the improving use possibilities in industrialised countries has been the increasing use of energy.

This energy has been produced by the burning of fossil fuels. Because of this the concentration of CO_2 in the atmosphere is still going up. A future development in this way will lead to a CO_2 concentration which is followed by a climate change with probably catastrophic and irreversible impacts for future generations. If this is to be stopped, the industrialised countries have to reduce their energy consumption in favour of future generations.

This demand for energy reduction reflects the intergenerational distribution conflict. At the same time, the possibilities for the development of the less developed regions are restricted by the high level of emissions and the corresponding resource use in developed countries. An industrialisation of the less developed nations which has the use of fossil fuels as its prerequisite, will strengthen the resource and environmental problems. If the less developed countries are to have the opportunity to use fossil fuels, the industrialised countries have to start reducing their energy consumption.

This demand reflects the intra-generational distribution conflict.

Both types of distribution conflict are generated by the use of non-renewable fossil fuels. The greenhouse gas emissions which are related to the use of fossil fuels will compromise the ability of future generations to meet their own needs. But we have to be conscious that environmental policy to solve the distribution conflict between present and future generations (i.e., to solve the environmental problems) might be compromising the ability of the less developed areas to improve their production of consumption goods.

In this manner, contributions to a concept of sustainable development have to bring out these distribution conflicts. This is necessary to understand the problems of formulating strategies for sustainability. This paper will offer a model permit for that. With this model we will make some simulations to illustrate our thesis and to draw some conclusions for an international environmental policy.

II

Production Structure of Two Regions: An Outline

Here, we use a neo-Austrian approach to intertemporal production to analyse the relationship between climate change, resource scarcity and economic development (Faber et al., 1987; Faber and Proops, 1993) and the distributional impacts of environmental policy. We begin by outlining the production structure of two regions: a developed region (DR) and a less developed region (LDR). Then we use an input-output approach to study the macroeconomic and distributional impact of climate change, natural resource and a resource tax to avoid climate change.

The Developed Region and Production Structure

Let us assume that the developed region can produce the consumption good with two linear-limitational production techniques. Technique T_1 consists of one process R_1. This uses l_1 units of labour to generate the consumption good. If the amount of labour used in R_1 in period t is denoted by $L_1(t)$ and the amount of the consumption good generated in the first process is $x_1(t)$, then we get:

$$x_1(t)=L_1(t)/l_1. \qquad \ldots (12.1)$$

Technique T_2 involves two production processes: R_2 uses l_2 units of labour, k_2 units of capital and n_2 units of resources to produce one unit of the consumption good. Denoting by $L_2(t)$ the amount of labour and by $K(t)$ the amount of capital granted to the production process 2, and supposing that $N_2(t)$ is the total amount of resources used in R_2 in period

t, the amount of consumption produced is then described by:

$$x_2(t)=K(t)/k_2=L_2(t)/l_2=N_2(t)/n_2. \qquad \text{...(12.2)}$$

For purpose of efficiency l_1 has to be greather than l_2 (cf. Faber and Proops, 1993). We again assume that the capital good deteriorates at a constant rate c $(0 < c < 1)$.

The capital good is produced in process R_3, where l_3 units of labour are joined with n_3 units of resources to produce one unit of the capital good. If $L_3(t)$ units of labour and $N_3(t)$ units of resources are supplied to R_3 in period t, gross investment equals:

$$I(t)= N_3(t)/n_3=L_3(t)/l_3. \qquad \text{...(12.3)}$$

The intertemporal relationship of gross investment and the stock of capital can be calculated by the following equation:

$$K(t+1) = (1-c)K(t) + I(t). \qquad \text{...(12.4)}$$

In order to integrate emissions into our model we assume that the level of emissions depends only on the amount of the homogeneous resource used in production. This is similar to the CO_2 problem, where we have a proportional relationship within resource use and emissions, and no 'end of the pipe' technology for CO_2 emissions. Thus, the emission coefficient e, which gives the amount of emissions resulting from the use of one unit of resource, is constant in all times. This resource could also be interpreted as a composite resource consisting of the fossil fuels coal, oil and gas. For such a constant composite commodity a constant and peculiar emission coefficient can be calculated. Hence the total emissions E of the economy can be calculated by the following equation:

$$E(t) = e\{N_2(t) + N_3(t)\}. \qquad \text{...(12.5)}$$

The developed region contains no non-renewable resource. It is therefore necessary to import the resource from the less developed region, if technique T_2 is to innovated. New capital goods can be used in the later duration and consumption goods cannot be stored. We assume further that we have no capital saturation, i.e., we have insufficient capital to produce only with T_2. We further assume that the total amount of labour $L(t)$ is regular over time, i.e., there is no population growth and $L(t) = L$.

The Less Developed Parts: The Production Structure

Here, in the less developed region (LDR) two production processes are available. To distinguish the two regions we mark the variables of the less developed region with ^ ('hat'). $\hat{R}_1$ uses $\hat{l}_1$ units of labour to generate one unit consumption goods. If the total labour supplied to $\hat{R}_1$ is denoted by $\hat{L}_1$ (t) and the intensity of the process is $\hat{x}_1$ (t), we get:

$$\hat{x}_1(\mathrm{t}) = \hat{L}_1(t)/\hat{l}_1. \qquad \ldots (12.6)$$

Process $\hat{R}_2$ is the resource extraetion process. We assume that $\hat{l}_2(t)$ units of labour are necessary to extract one unit of resource. Because of a decreasing concentration of the resource, and absence of technical progress, $\hat{l}_2(t)$ is increasing over time:[3] This provides the production function for process $\hat{R}_2$:

$$\hat{N}(t) = \hat{L}_2(t)/\hat{l}_2(t). \qquad \ldots (12.7)$$

We assume further that we do not have any population growth. Therefore the total amount of labour $\hat{L}(t)$ is constant, i.e., $\hat{L}(t) = \hat{L}$. We also assume that consumption goods cannot be stored.

Operationalisation of Technique T_2 and Inter-regional Trade

For the purpose of above model, we derive conditions for the innovation of technique T_2 in the DR. Because the DR requires resources for such an innovation, which are only available in the LDR, the innovation of technique T_2 in DR is owing to the introduction of inter-regional trade in the model. Necessary and sufficient conditions for the innovations are derived in the appendix in Jöst (1994).

To grasp these conditions look at the scenario below. The innovation of technique T_2 in DR takes three periods. In the first period the resources have to be imported; in the second period the capital goods are produced and in the third and last period the consumption goods is manufactured in process R_2. This provides the time structure of the innovation of technique T_2.

If the LDR extracts resources, it is important to reduce the production of the consumption goods in $\hat{R}_1$, because total labour supply is exogenously given and constant. Thus, the LDR is only extracting resources if the cut in consumption is compensated for by the DR. The total labour necessary to extract $\hat{N}(t)$ units of resources is $\hat{L}_2(t) = \hat{N}(t)\hat{l}_2(t)$.

Therefore, the labour remaining for production in $\hat{R}_1$ is $\hat{L}_1 = \hat{L} - \hat{L}_2$. Together with equation 12.6 we see that consumption production in LDR is decreased by:

$$\hat{N}(t)\{\hat{l}_2(t)/\hat{l}_1\} \qquad \ldots (12.8)$$

if $\hat{N}(t)$ units of resources are extracted. This is equal to the minimum import of consumption goods. On the other hand this is equal to the least export of consumption goods by the DR to import $N(t)$ units of resources. If we further introduce a parameter μ with $\mu \geq 1$ we obtain the following equation for the import of consumption goods by LDR:

$$I\hat{m}(t) = \mu\,\hat{N}(t)\{\hat{l}_2(t)/\hat{l}_1\cdot\} \qquad \ldots (12.9)$$

This parameter has a significant interpretation: if μ is equal to one, the imports of the LDR are equal to the opportunity costs of extracting $\hat{N}(t)$ units of resources and the LDR will realise a stationary consumption path in all periods. If μ is greater than 1, the LDR can feel a consumption path above the stationary path.

This scenario shows that the LDR is only willing to extract the resource if it is compensated for the lower consumption production. But this is only the case if the consumption production in the DR is increasing by the innovation of the fresh technique.

Without the resource, the DR uses T_1 to produce a stationary consumption path. If the amount of consumption goods produced with technique T_2 in the DR is higher than the amount of consumption goods generated with the stationary programme, this additional production can be used to compensate the LDR. If these additional consumption goods exceed the opportunity costs of resource extraction in the LDR, the DR is capable to compensate the LDR, and the level of consumption in the DR is higher than in the stationary programme.

Hence the innovation of technique T_2,and therefore the development of inter-regional trade, relies first on the degree of superiority of technique T_2. It depends secondly on the time preference of the DR, because we have seen above that it takes time to import the resource and form the capital goods necessary for production. And it depends thirdly on the resource scarcity, because the amount of labour necessary to extract the resource depends on the scarcity of the resource (modelled as a function of cumulated resource consumption).

In this scenario we can now interpret the parameter μ. It provides a measure for the distribution of the additional consumption goods produced by the innovation to technique T_2 in the DR.

III
Technical Formulation of the Input-Output Model

In order to describe the development of our model economy over time we present the technology of our model in an input-output framework. This approach is similar to Faber and Proops (1993), who analyse resource problems in this framework. Here we use the input-output approach to study the impact of a resource tax on greenhouse gas emissions. Then we discuss the distributional effects of this tax.

Every production process in the DR and LDR corresponds to a production sector of the economy. If we denote the prices of the goods with P and the corresponding subscript, we derive the value input-output table for the DR and LDR (see Tables 12.1 and 12.2).[4] We are this way able to derive prices for all goods by equating the total costs to the total revenues for each sector, assuming perfect competition.

As Faber and Proops (1993) have shown for the neo-Austrian model, these equations have to be valid for a market economy, when all production factors are completely used.

If we assume that DR imports resources at price $P_{Im} = \hat{P}_N$ we get the following equation: $P_l L_1 = P_x x_1$. Together with (12.3) we get:

$$P_l l_1 x_1 = P_x x_1, \text{ i.e., } P_x = P_l l_1. \qquad \ldots (12.10)$$

The use cost of the capital goods P_k is calculated using (12.2) ...(12.11)

$$P_l L_2 + P_k K + \hat{P}_N \hat{N}_2 = P_x x_2 - cP_1 K$$

i.e.,

$$P_k = 1/k_2 \,[p_x - P_l l_2 - \hat{P}_N n_2] - cP_1.$$

And at last, we derive the price for new capital goods P_I together with (12.3):

Table 12.1 Value Input-Output Table for DR and Period t

	1	*2*	*3*	*Consumption*	*Investment*
1				$P_x x_1$	
2				$P_x x_2$	$P_I(\text{-}cK)$
3					$P_I I$
L	$P_l L_1$	$P_l L_2$	$P_l L_3$		
K		$P_K K$			
Im		$P_{Im} \hat{N}_2$	$P_{Im} \hat{N}_3$		

$$P_l L_3 + \hat{P}_N N_3 = P_I I, \text{ i.e., } P_I = P_l l_3 + \hat{P}_R n_3. \quad \ldots (12.12)$$

In the similar manner we derive the price equations for the LDR.[5]

Table 12.2 Value Input-Output Table for LDR and Period t

	1	*onsumption*	*Resource*	
1			$\hat{P}_x \hat{x}_1$	
2				$\hat{P}_N \hat{N}$
L	$\hat{P}_l \hat{L}_1$	$\hat{P}_l \hat{L}_2$		
K				
R		$\hat{P}_n \hat{N}$		

From consideration of (12.6) and (12.7) we have the equations to derive the prices as below:

$$\hat{P}_l \hat{l}_1 \hat{x}_1 = \hat{P}_x \hat{x}_1, \text{ i.e., } \hat{P}_x = \hat{p}_l \hat{l}_l \quad \ldots (12.13)$$

$$\hat{P}_l \hat{l}_2(t) \hat{N} + \hat{P}_n \hat{N}, \text{ i.e., } \hat{P}_N = \hat{P}_l \hat{l}_2(t) + \hat{P}_n. \quad \ldots (12.14)$$

In the equation for sector two there are two different prices for the resources: $\hat{P}_N$ is the price of the extracted resource, which is exported in the DR, while $\hat{P}_n$ is the price of one unit resource before it is extracted.

Further, we have to think the value of exports equals the values of imports, and we assume that consumption goods are traded with price P_x and resources are traded at price $\hat{P}_N$. Therefore, we get from the point of view of the LDR the trade balance equation as below:

$$\hat{P}_N \hat{N} - P_x Im\hat{} = 0. \qquad \ldots (12.15)$$

Together with (12.9):

$$\hat{P}_N \hat{N} - \mu P_x \hat{N} \{\hat{l}_2(t)/\hat{l}_1\} = 0 \qquad \ldots (12.16)$$

and after rearrangement we get:

$$\hat{P}_N - \mu P_x \{\hat{l}_2(t)/\hat{l}_1\} = 0. \qquad \ldots (12.17)$$

If labour in DR is the numeraire and the price of the consumption goods is equal in both regions, and equal to the price in the DR, we can draw from (11.17) an equation for the distribution parameter μ by using (12.14). Thus, we obtain for μ:

$$\mu = 1 + \hat{P}_n \{\hat{l}_1 / P_x \hat{l}_2(t)\} \qquad \ldots (12.18)$$

To resolve the price system $P_x, P_k, P_l, \hat{P}_l, \hat{P}_x, \hat{P}_l, \hat{P}_n, \hat{P}_N$, and to find a value for μ we can now use the non-profit conditions for the five sectors, the equation for the distribution parameter μ, and our assumptions that labour in the LDR is numeraire ($P_l = 1$) and $P_x = \hat{P}_X$. In this setup, we cannot solve the prices in units of the numeraire, because we have two prices for the resource: the price $\hat{P}_N$ for the resource as an input in production and $\hat{P}_n$ as a price for the resource before it has been extracted.

This price is known from resource economic literature as the resource rent, and it is an indicator of the scarcity of natural resources. This element cannot be determined within the above mentioned formulated static Leontief model. Therefore, we need intertemporal considerations about future consumption, and hence future resource use.

Net Investment to Net Production

In order to describe explicitly the dynamics of our model, we use the savings ratio, which we define to be the ratio of Net Investment (NI) to Net National Product (NNP).[6] We expect in our model a falling rate of return on capital, due to a long-run increase in resource rents. Therefore, the savings and investments are expected to be reduced in the long run. To capture this effect we use a savings ratio which is an increasing linear performance of the rate of return on capital, r; i.e.,

$s(r) = a + br \ (a,b > 0)$.

With this assumption we can end up with our model and we use as a definition of the savings ratio the following equation.

$$s = NI^{DR}/NNP^{DR} = P_I\ (I - cK)/\ P_x(x_1 + x_2) + P_I(I - cK) - \hat{P}_N Im \quad \ldots (12.19)$$

Natural Resource Rents of The Dynamics

For the purpose to describe the dynamics of the resource rents we use the simple Hotelling rule.[7] Neglecting extraction costs for simplicity, the rate of increase of resource rent is equal to the rate of return on capital:

$$\hat{P}_n(t) - \hat{P}_n(t-1)\ /\ \hat{P}_n(t-1) = r(t-1). \quad \ldots (12.20)$$

Ecological Impacts of Emissions in the Atmosphere Change

With the objective to analyse the ecological impact of trace gas emissions, we have to know the concentration of these gases in the atmosphere. Because CO_2 is the most important greenhouse gas, causing 60 per cent of the anthropogenic greenhouse effect, we limit ourselves to CO_2. The development of the concentration of anthropogenic CO_2 emissions in the atmosphere can be described in analogy with the accumulation of capital (for more details cf. Nordhaus, 1993).

$$M(t) = \beta E(t) + (1 - \delta_M) M(t-1). \quad \ldots (12.21)$$

In this equation $M(t)$ is the collection of emissions in the atmosphere, $E(t)$ are emissions; the parameter β gives the part of emissions remaining in the atmosphere and δ_M is the deterioration rate of CO_2 molecules in the atmosphere. This equation permits us to simulate climate change. In a similar way to climate models we assume that doubling the concentration in the atmosphere is a critical threshold.

If this border is reached, we assume that present capital goods cannot be used in the same way as before. We integrate this into our model by assuming that the rate of deterioration of the capital goods is increased if atmospheric concentration exceeds two times of the initial concentration.

IV

Distributional Impact of Climate Policy

To illustrate this, we make some simulations with the above described model. We stress that this model is formulated to explore the interdependencies between resource scarcity, climate change, and financial growth to illustrate the intergenerational and intra-generational distribution conflicts of environmental policy.

Our model does not represent real economies. Thus, it is not suitable for forecasting ģenuine economic development.

In order to avoid climate change in our model economy, we introduce a resource tax. This resource tax is, in the case of CO_2, equivalent to an emission tax. The cause behind this is that the emissions are proportional to resource use and that we have no 'end of the pipe' technology for CO_2 emissions. Therefore, we use in our model a resource tax to reduce emissions. If we introduce the resource tax, we receive a new price for the resources $\hat{P}_N^\tau$ in the DR: $\hat{P}_N^\tau = \hat{P}_N + \tau$.

The above resource tax in our simulation model is a price for the use of the atmosphere as a depository for CO_2 emissions. We know from natural science that the carrying capacity of the atmosphere is limited, if we want to avoid climate change. In climate models it is felt that doubling the atmospheric concentration is a critical threshold and it is assumed that there are no adverse environmental effects until we have reached this threshold. If we further consider that CO_2 is a stock pollutant, the price for this cumulative pollutant should rise over time (cf. Stroebele, 1993).

From this point of view, the atmosphere can be interpreted as a non-renewable resource and we have a scarcity rent for the limited capacity of the atmosphere. Thus, we apply the Hotelling rule to describe the development of the scarcity rent for the use of the atmosphere as a depository for CO_2 emissions, which in our model is the resource tax. We assume that τ is increasing over time proportionally to the rate of return on capital. For the following simulations we have used different initial values for the resource rent.

This allows us to analyse the distributional effects of the initiation of a resource tax in the DR. Therefore, we compare a scenario with $\hat{P}_n = 0.04$ and a tax $\tau = 0.21$ with a higher initial resource rent $\hat{P}_n = 0.25$. These assumptions ensure that the initial prices $\hat{P}_n$ and $\hat{P}_N^\tau$ for the resources are same in both scenarios.

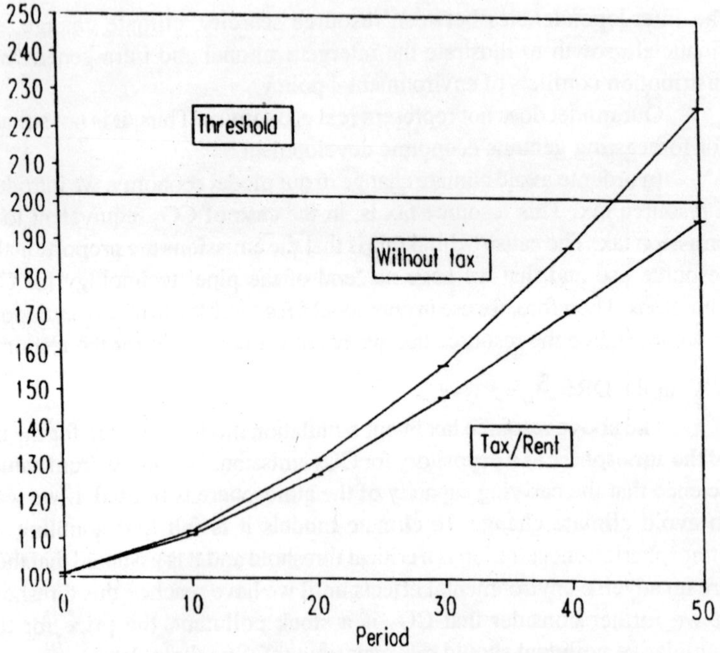

Fig. 12.1. CO_2 Concentration in the Atmosphere.

At first we look at the scenarios with resource taxes and without resource taxes. Fig. 12.1 shows that we can reach the environmental aim, since concentration does not reach the threshold. We further see that the consumption possibilities in the developed region have changed for better, although the resource price in the tax scenario is higher.

But we get different pictures of the consumption possibilities if we compare the tax scenario with the rent scenario. In both scenarios we can achieve the environmental goal. The curves for the concentration are identical in the tax and the rent scenario. But Fig. 12.3 shows that consumption in the LDR is lower in the tax scenario, compared to the scenario with the larger initial resource rent.

Thus, we can conclude that the resource tax in the DR is equal to a redistribution of consumption from the LDR to the DR. The sources of this distribution effect will be analysed below.

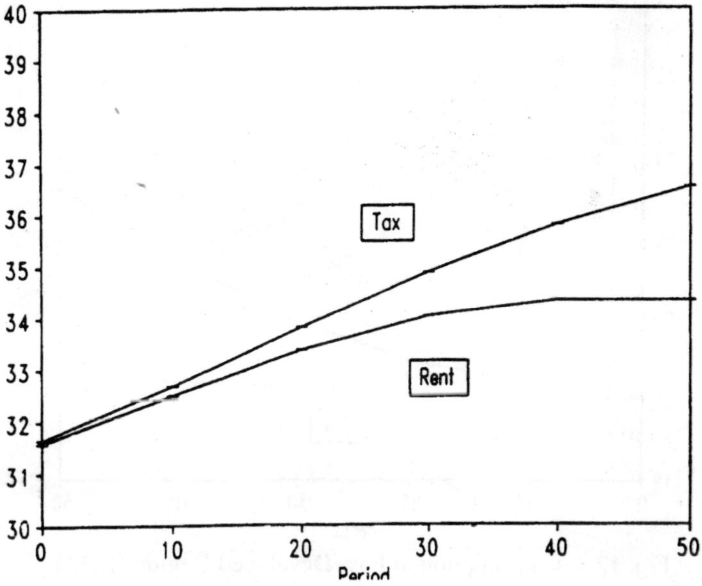

Fig. 12. 2. Comsumption in Developed Region (DR).

The positive resource rent is a prerequisite for the LDR to use more than in the stationary consumption path. This is documented in equation (12.18):

$$\mu = 1 + \hat{P}_n(\hat{l}_1 / P_x \hat{l}_{2(t)})$$

where μ gives the part of consumption produced by the superior technique T_2 in the DR, which needs to be exported to the LDR. The level of the initial resource rent is different in both scenarios at time $t = 0$. Thus, the LDR can import fewer consumption goods per unit of resource exported. Fig. 12.3 shows that the consumption possibilities are greater in the rent scenario than in the tax scenario.

Thus, to sum up, we can say that the introduction of the resource tax leads to a twofold improvement in the situation of the DR: On the one side, the DR is better off in terms of consumption goods. On the other hand, the higher resource price avoids climate change.

But this improvement makes the LDR worse off. The lower initial resource rent has caused a lower consumption in the LDR over time. An other solution of the environmental problem is that the LDR sets a higher

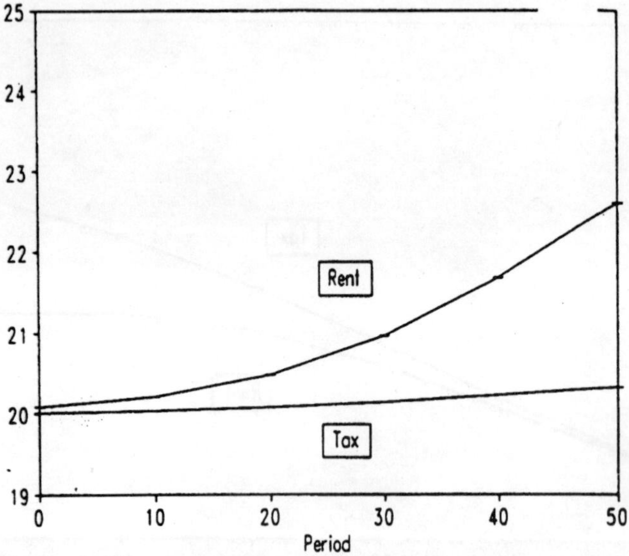

Fig. 12.3. Consumption in Less Developed Region (LDR).

initial resource rent. If this is the case, we can also avoid climate change. In this case the curves for the tax scenario and the rent scenario in Fig. 12.1 are identical. At the same time, in this scenario the LDR is better off in terms of consumption than in the tax scenario and the DR is worse off in terms of consumption (cf. Figs. 12.2 and 12.3).

V

Conclusions

Above simulations with our model show that the dynamics of economic development depend on the possibility of using resources: the DR requires resources to innovate the superior technique T_2. With this technique the DR is able to improve its consumption production over time. The LDR is capable of improving its consumption possibilities by exporting the resource to the DR.

But this holds only if the amount of consumption goods imported for one unit of resource exceeds their extration costs, i.e., if resource scarcity is taken into account. But resources are not only a prerequisite for economic growth and the distribution of the surplus production in the DR. The use of these resources causes greenhouse gas emissions, which accumulate in the atmosphere.

In analogy to capital accumulation, which reflects the improving consumption possibilities, the accumulation of greenhouse gases reflects the environmental results of production. This lets us reach the conclusion that the stock of capital in the economy and the stock of trace gases in the atmosphere restrict future economic development. If we compare the concentration of emissions in the given scenarios we see the time lag in the effect of environmental policy. Even after 10 periods we observe significant differences in the development of the emission concentration. Thus, a resource tax has to be introduced early, and the tax has to increase over time, as discussed above. Any way it is difficult to implement such a preventive environmental policy.

Our analysis has shown the underlying distributional conflicts of environmental policy: the introduction of a resource tax reduces the increase of atmospheric concentration, but we notice a redistribution of consumption from the LDR to the DR compared to a scenario without tax. This distributional conflict is important for the implementation of an effective environmental policy. To keep the analysis as simple as possible, we supposed that emissions occur only in the DR. In this model the implementation of an effective climate policy relies only on the decisions of the DR. But in real economies the production in the LDR also leads to greenhouse gas emissions. Thus, an effective climate policy depends in addition on the policy of LDR. If the LDR does not execute an adequate climate policy, it is possible that (1) the DR shifts production processes to the LDR, or (2) that the LDR makes better its economic growth by an extensive use of fossil fuels. In this way, an effective climate policy requires an international agreement, and therefore a consensus among all countries is necessary. An obstacle for such a consensus are the above mentioned distributional effects.[8]

However, our scenarios reflects that the implementation of a resource tax by the industrialised countries will lead to a redistribution of resource rents from resource owners to resource users. This redistribution makes it more troublesome to design an international agreement. If such an agreement is designed and becomes effective, its nature and outcome relies on the strength of the negotiating positions of the participants.

Our analysis shows that a resource tax, or a carbon tax, which reduces the increase of CO_2 concentration in the atmosphere will improve the consumption possibilities of the DR. Still, the changes in relative prices by this policy are disadvantageous for the resource exporting LDR. A different result is possible, if the LDR realises a higher resource rent. This ensures the same result concerning the CO_2 concentration. However, the LDR can improve their consumption possibilities. The improvement of the economic situation of the less developed countries is important in the light of global environmental problems. Without such a compensation, there is a danger that environmental policy will not have the desired effect. This can be shown by the greenhouse gas problem. Around 80 per cent of world-wide emissions are caused by the industrialised countries. Because of their role in this problem, the industrialised nations should play an essential part in its solution. Therefore, they should compensate the negative distribution impact by transfers to the less developed regions. This is, not least, necessary to prevent the emergence of CO_2 intensive production in the less developed countries. While our model is very simple, and reproduces the complex real structures in a rather stylised manner, it shows that the global environmental problems, environmental policy and development policy are related very closely. To realise this, as already said in our introduction, is one of the central theses in the sustainability debate. Our simple two region model shows the underlying distributional conflicts which have to be solved if environmental policy is to make sure that the present generations can meet their needs without compromising the ability of future generations to meet their needs.

Notes

1. For an encompassing discussion of the natural science side of the problem cf. IPCC (1990).
2. For a discussion of the concept of sustainability cf. Solow (1992). The difficulties of such a concept are analysed in Farber, Jöst and Manstetten (1994).
3. For the foundations of this relationship cf. Faber, Niemes and Stephan (1987, in particular chapter 4).
4. For the sake of clarity we neglect the time variables.
5. In the LDR, the variable $\hat{N}$ in the input row should be distinguished from the $\hat{N}$ in the output column. For the former, it represents raw mwterial 'in the gound'. For the latter it is extracted raw material, ready for use. In this model we assume that raw material can be used as resource in production without further treatment (cf. Faber and Proops, 1993).
6. This is usual assumption in growth theory. Cf. Solow (1970).
7. A detailed discussion of this is given by Farber and Proops (1993) and Dasgupta and Heal (1979, in particular in chapter 6).
8. For a discussion of the significance of a consensus in environmental policy cf. Binswanger, Faber and Manstetten (1990).

References

Binswanger, H.C., Faber, M. and Manstetten, R. (1990) The dilemma of modern man and nature: an exploration of the Faustian imperative, *Ecological Economics* 2:197-223.

Dasgupta, P.G. and Heal, G.M. (1979) *Economic Theory and Exhaustible Resources,* Cambridge University Press, Cambridge.

Faber, M. Jöst, F. and Manstetten, R. (1994) *Limits and Perspectives of the Concept of a Sustainable Development,* Economics Discussion Paper No. 204, University of Heidelberg.

Faber, M., Niemes, H. and Stephan, G. (1987) *Entropy, Environment and Resources. An Essay in Physico-Economics,* Springer-Verlag, Heidelberg.

Faber, M. and J.L.R. Proops (1993) Natural resources rents, economic dynamics and structural change: a capital theoretic approach, *Ecological Economics* 8:17-44.

Falk, I. and Mendelson, R. (1993) The economics of controlling stock pollutants: an efficient strategy for greenhouse gases, *Journal of Environmental Economics and Management* 25:76-88.

IPCC (1990) *Climate Change. The IPCC Scientific Assessment,* Cambridge University Press, Cambridge.

Jöst, F. (1994) *Klimaänderungen, Rohstoffknappheit und wirtschaftliche Entwicklung. Ein neo-Österreichisches Zwei-Regionen Modell,* Physika-Verlag, Heidelberg.

Nordhaus, W.D. (1993) Rolling the DICE: An optimal transition path for controlling greenhouse gases, *Energy Economics* 15:27-50.

Solow, R.M. (1970) *Growth Theory: An Exposition,* Oxford University Press, Oxford.

Solow, R.M. (1992) *An Almost Practical Step Toward Sustainability.* Invited Lecture on the Occasion of the Fortieth Anniversary of Resource for the Future, 8 October, 1992.

13

Reply of Malaysia to Global Climate Change

This chapter is originally a paper by Peter Y.C. Ho (Deparment of Environment, Kuala Lumpur) titled "Malaysia's Response to Global Climate Change." This was presented at the workshop on "Responding to the Threat of Global Warming: Options for the Pacific and Asia" dated 21-27 June, 1989 at Honolulu, Hawaii. This chapter contains Malaysia's concerns and response to global climate change and international reactions on Malaysian response.

Introduction

Concern in Malaysia over global climate change has, over the last two-three years, been given greater attention as evidence from various studies confirmed the threat to the global environment due to effect of various "greenhouse" gases. Evidence presented by various national and international organizations obtained through systematic monitoring and research, and presented at various forums have been the catalyst for creating awareness of the problem.

Concern on the subject has increasingly become a topic of discussion not only among scientists and environmentalists but also among the public. This awareness has no doubt been created through the media including local and foreign newspapers and magazines, local radio and television, non-governmental group forums as well as the education efforts of the Department of Environment. This year, the Department of Environment, in conjunction with World Environment Day, is organising an exhibition on the theme which was adopted by the United Nations Environment Programme, entitled "Global Warming: Global Warning."

Concerns of Climate Change

Although no clear consensus has been made on the magnitude of environmental changes due to global climate change, Malaysia, nonetheless, is concerned even if the changes are smaller than predicted. This concern is due to some of the following factors:

(a) Malaysia is the largest producer of rubber and palm oil in the world and any significant shift in weather conditions is likely to affect crop production. Reduction in yields due to climate change will reduce earnings from these two commodities which contribute significantly to the economy of the country. Similarly, other crops such as cocoa (of which Malaysia is the world's fifth largest producer) will similarly be affected.

(b) Malaysia is a coastal state with a coastline stretching more than 2000 km. Much of the coastline consists of low-lying mangrove areas which play an important role in coastal fisheries and aquaculture, mangrove timber supply as well as coastal protection. Inundation, due to sea level rise, of the coastal mangroves and induced changes affecting coastal ecology and stability will have serious implications to coastal fisheries; timber supply (particularly for the piling and charcoal industry), as well as coastal protection works along the coast. Coastal aquaculture, especially those using pond aquaculture systems, will likely be eliminated or moved inland. Coastal funds constructed along most of the mangrove areas and normally protected by a mangrove buffer, will have to be strengthened at great cost.

(c) The two largest rice growing areas in Malaysia, the MADA in Kedah and the Tanjung Karang area in Selangor, are located on flat coastal plains. Erratic rainfall distribution and low rainfall in recent years have affected water supply for wet rice irrigation. In addition, sea level rise would raise the spectre of salt water intrusion and salinization of soils which will affect crop production. Engineering measures to strengthen coastal protection works will have to be undertaken.

(d) Major stretches of coastal areas are presently experiencing severe coastal erosion. The effect of sea level rise which is likely to increase coastal erosion is an area of concern since many of these areas support growing tourism and associated tourism related activities and facilities. In addition, major coastal towns, (almost all state capitals are coastal) will likely face inundation or increased frequency of flooding.

(e) Climate changes resulting in higher rainfalls and increased intensity of rain have implications not only to soil erosion particularly in the cultivated hilly areas where major agricultural cash and food crops are grown, but will increase the intensity and frequency of floods. Current flood protection works are based essentially on past records of rainfall and do not include those projected due to climate change. With regards to soil erosion, originating from land disturbances due to logging, agriculture, urbanization and others, is difficult to control even presently, given the high rainfall and intensity of rains in Malaysia.

Responses of Malaysia

Several actions are being taken by Malaysia to address the issue of global climate change. These actions, initiated over the past two years, are aimed at:

(a) Improving an understanding of global climate change such as the causes, the process, and the likely affects. Information based on findings by local, other national and international organizations will be used;

(b) Participating and supporting international meetings and forums on global climate change; and

(c) Developing local policy responses initially and action subsequently to address problems due to climate change.

International Response

Malaysia has participated actively in international meetings related to global climate change. Malaysia has been represented in all recent meetings such as the "Montreal Protocol on Substances that Deplete the Ozone Layer" and the "Vienna Convention for the Protection of the Ozone Layer." As a measure of Malaysia's commitment to the problem the First Meeting of the Parties to the Montreal Protocol and the First Meeting of the Conference of the Parties to the Vienna Convention were attended by the Malaysian Minister of Science, Technology and the Environment in which the following commitments were made:

that the Malaysian Government agreed to subscribe to the Vienna Convention and to ratify the Montreal Protocol.

Malaysia is presently collaborating with Thailand and Indonesia on a UNEP sponsored project on "Socio-Economic Impacts and Policy Responses Resulting from Climate Change." The study which was initiated in 1988 will examine climate impacts for each of the three countries and consists of three main stages:

(a) Estimation of the direct impacts of climate change, at selected locations, on agriculture water resources and coastal resources;
(b) Aggregation of these direct impacts to the "national" level; and
(c) Formation and testing of policy scenario alternatives.

The project is assisted by three consultants appointed by UNEP. Results of the study will be used to guide the government on policy responses that may be taken in anticipation of global climate changes.

National Response

The above UNEP project, while it is regional in intent, is also applicable as a national study on the problems due to global climate change. The studies being undertaken or to be undertaken include the following:

(a) Climate change effects on the productivity of major agricultural crops. Specific study on the major rice growing area of MADA in Kedah will be carried out;
(b) Change to water resources availability and related flood implications using the Kelanten River Basin as a model;
(c) Costal changes affecting coastal protection works, mangroves, urban centres, tourism and recreational beaches, and coral reefs are to be studied in different areas.

For the purposes of the above studies a National Steering Committee and various technical committees have been set up with participation from no less than 15 government agencies, research institutions and universities.

In relation to issues on the use of ozone depleting substances the Ministry of Science, Technology and the Environment has:

(a) Initiated dialogue with industry and other government agencies on the implications of the Montreal Protocol to discuss various strategies to reduce consumption of CFCs and to seek alternatives;

(b) Collect official statistics on the import and export of CFCs and halons through scheduling these chemicals as controlled substances under the Customs Act.

Other actions taken, though not primarily directed towards the problem of global climate change, include the development and adoption of a National Forest Policy directed at conservation of remaining forest resources to ensure sustainable supply of timber and other forest products, use of forest for various beneficial uses, and a reafforestation programme for logged over forest areas with poor regeneration capacity.

Conclusion

In summary, awareness of the potential impacts due to climate change is growing though the need for greater awareness of the issue by politicians and policy makers needs to be enhanced.

14

Reply of New Zealand to Global Climate Change

This chapter is an edited version of the paper titled "New Zealand's is Response to Global climate change prepared by Judy Lawrence, the then Manager at Global Environmental issues Project, New Zealand Ministry of Environment the same was presented by the author at the Climate change workshop at Hawaii held from 20th to 27th June, 1989.

New Zealand identifies culturally and politically with the Pacific Basin. Its policy response to the climate change issue has two main foci.

The international community by representing the Pacific context, and domestically by focusing on the peculiarities of an isolated island nation which is economically developed, but dependent on its primary production—agriculture, forestry and fishing—sectors for two-thirds of its export earnings.

Small nations like New Zealand in association with other small nations can play a very effective role internationally by keeping global issues on the international agenda and by raising the peculiar vulnerabilities of island nations in such fora as UN, UNEP/WMO, IPCC, SPREP, OECD, IUCN.

On 9 May in Geneva the Secretary for the Environment, Dr. Roger Blakeley, represented New Zealand as cochair of the Coastal Zone Management Subgroup of the Intergovernmental Panel on Climate Change (IPCC), Response Strategies Working Group. He sought their leave for me to report to this meeting about the work of the Coastal Zone Management Subgroup. I will also outline New Zealand's domestic response to Global Climate Change.

New Zealand's International Response

New Zealand is taking a very active role in the international activities on global climate change at Ministerial and official representative levels.

New Zealand was an active participant and signatory to the Hague Declaration seeking global institutional means which provide legally binding solutions to the global climate issue subject to the control of the International Court of Justice. New Zealand supports further work on a global climate Convention through existing institutions in the UN system such as UNEP/WMO and the IPCC. It is important that the work of Pacific based agencies link into the international work of existing institutions.

New Zealand supports the SPREP work on climate change and ways in which the Pacific input to this work can be strengthened. The SPREP Intergovernmental meeting in July will further address this issue.

The WMO/UNEP Intergovernmental Panel on Climate Change (IPCC) will provide an integrated assessment of climate change scientific findings, impacts and response strategies by mid-1990. Work will follow on a global climate convention and protocols.

IPCC Response Strategies Working Group Coastal Zone Management Subgroup

The Coastal Zone Management Subgroup goal is:

"To provide information and recommendations to national and international policy centres, enabling decision making on:

(a) Coastal zone management strategies for the next 10-20 years;

(b) long term policies dealing with limitation and/or adaptation with respect to climate change/sea-level rise."

The Subgroup will take into account technical, economic, social, cultural, environmental, legal, and institutional aspects.

For the purpose of the Coastal Zone Management Subgroup, the "coastal zone" has been defined as:

"The area of sea-land interface extending seaward as far as land-based anthropogenic activity directly affects the sea, and extending landward as far as the marine environment affects the land in a physical, environmental, social, cultural or economic sense."

A report is being prepared for June 1990 addressing:

(A) the extent and timing of sea level rise and associated climate change effects including regional changes in climate, changes in variability and extremes, transient predictions and uncertainties.

(B) the impacts of sea level rise and associated cliamte change effects on land use, ecosystems, water resources, and human activities.

(C) the context within which the problems arise, for example, the relationship with existing problems, timing and national (site specific), regional and global aspects such as acceptable levels of risk, costs and benefits associated with preventative responses and the relationship with other natural disasters.

(D) available adaptive options and costs for coastal areas and activities at risk. Land loss and flood risk have been identified as critical factors. National and cultural differences were recognised as important when identifying appropriate response strategies.

(E) social, economic, legal, institutional, environmental and cultural implications of adaptive options. The NZ delegation considered that the following issues needed to be addressed by countries when responding to sea level rise and coastal zone problems associated with cliamte change.

(a) a consensus needs to be developed on the expected range of rates of sea-level rise
(b) institutional means need to be established to make this information widely available
(c) persuasive means need to be developed, as well as legislation and regulations, including fiscal measures
(d) areas prone to inundation through a rising sea level need to be identified and mapped
(e) contingency measures need to be generated to cope with extreme events
(f) planning needs to be developed and/or improved to cope with social implications of sea-level rise
(g) future development of the coastal zone needs to be controlled, including land-uses
(h) technical options available need to be inventoried
(i) financial, social, cultural, environmental, and legal implications need to be identified
(j) geographical considerations need to be taken into account (tropical or temperate coasts, continental coasts or island systems)
(k) international implications (forced migration) need to be consideed.

(F) possible funding for adaptive options, in particular mechanisms to assist developing countries to implement adaptive options.

The Netherlands as cochair identified the following criteria to be considered when identifying problems:

1. vulnerability
2. people at risk
3. economic values
4. environment
5. Percentage of Gross National Product

It was suggested that scenarios need to be developed covering the periods between the present and 1990 (existing problems), the present and the year 2050 and the present and the year 2100.

In addition, the following categories of responses were suggested for the analysis:

(a) technical measures leading to a lessening of risk for lives, economy, environment

(b) non-technical measures, leading to adandonment of regions at risk (resettlement, landuse planning).

Long term costs in terms of lives, economy and environment need to be weighed, in particular the financial implications in coastal zone management for developing nations where neither the technological nor the financial ability to cope with the threat of sea level rise and associated coastal effects exists.

The work plan is ambitious with a mid-April 1990 draft reporting date.

The facilitate a comprehensive input to the programme by as many different geographical situations and nations, two workshops are planned:

(A) Workshop 1 in November 1989 to be held in USA (sponsored by USA) on Adaptive Options and Policy Implications for Coastal States in the Temperate Zone.

(B) Workshop 2 in late 1989 or early 1990, to be held in Australia (sponsored by Australia, New Zealand and the Netherlands) on adaptive Options and Policy Implications for Coastal States including island nations in the tropical zone.

The focus in Workshop 2 will be on possible severe problems for Pacific and Indian Ocean countries. Liaison with SPREP will ensure maximum country participation.

The Response Strategies Working Group Steering Committee met from 10-12 May in Geneva and identified the following key issues to be addressed:

(a) policy options to limit global warming
(b) legal initiatives towards a global convention on climate
(c) ways of increasing involvement of developing countries in the work of IPCC.

Several key conclusions were drawn from the scientific evaluations:

(A) revolutionary changes will be required in energy consumption patterns and technological development if CO_2 levels in the atmosphere are to be stabilised by the end of the century at twice pre-industrial levels or lower.
(B) changes required would be radical improvement in energy conservation and energy efficiency in domestic, manufacturing and transport sectors, savings in energy conversion, a shift from fossil fuels to renewable energy resources such as solar and wind power and photovoltaics, use of less carbonated fuels, e.g. natural gas and biomass from plantations, a rapid phaseout of CFCs and a halt to tropical rainforest destruction and increased afforestation.
(c) the steering group decided to initiate work on a global climate convention in accordance with the UN General Assembly resolution to so do. The elements of a convention will be reported by June 1990 as part of the IPCC report to UNEP/WMO and the 45th UN General Assembly. It is anticipated that UNEP would take up the negotiation of a global convention and the necessary protocols.

Preparatory work will begin shortly on

(1) legal measures and processes
(2) technology transfer and development issues
(3) financial resources
(4) public education and implementation measures
(5) economic (market measures).

(D) directions were given to all subgroups of RSWG to make special efforts to encourage participation by developing countries including funding assistance of attend workshops and meetings.

New Zealand Climate Change Programme

The Government agreed in June 1988 that a coordinated climate change programme was required by New Zealand to respond effectively to the climate change issue which has potential widespread implications for New Zealand society. Three working groups on climate change have been set up under a Steering Group chaired by the Secretary for the Environment, Dr Roger Blakeley.

The establishment of the New Zealand programme followed the Ministry for the Environment seminar "Climate Change—The New Zealand Response": held on 29-30 March 1988 which addressed what the New Zealand response should be, including:

(a) the need for further refinement of the climate change predictions;
(b) the need for planning to take into account the predictions of climate and sea level changes;
(c) the development of reviewable planning guidelines for local authorities to work from;
(d) the need to inform and educate the public on the issues;
(e) the need to initiate a programme to reduce greenhouse gas emission and to recognise the links with energy policy.

The following working groups were set up in June 1988 to:

(A) produce a report on the scientific basis for the predictions of climate change. This was completed in December 1988 (Facts Working Group convened by the Royal Society of New Zealand).
(B) develop an interim data base of all New Zealand climate change information and assess the impacts of climate change using the Facts Working Group predictions in order to produce an interim impact assessment report to be completed by March 1990 (Impacts Working Group convened by Ministry for the Environment).
(C) develop policy on how New Zealand can respond to climate change (including mitigation and adaptation strategies) for presentation to Government by mid-1990 (Policy Working Group convened by Ministry for the Environment).

The Ministry for the Environment provides overall coordination for this programme and there is significant involvement by many other departments. These include the New Zealand Meteorological Service, Department of Scientific and Industrial Research, Department of Conservation, Ministry of Agriculture and Fisheries, Ministry of Forestry, Department of Survey and Land Information, Ministry of Energy, Department of Maori Affairs and Ministry of Womens Affairs.

In addition it was agreed that the working groups should consult with a wide range of interests outside government from other institutions and agencies and from the community including tangata whenua.

The Facts Working Group has published an abridged version of its report. The following conclusions were reached:

(A) The most likely prospect is an accelerated warming trend, so that global temperatures average 0.5-1.0 °C higher than present by 2025, and perhaps 1.0-2.0 °C higher than present by 2050. In New Zealand latitudes the annual average warming should be in the same range as the global average values. There is some possibility that winter temperatures will rise faster than summer temperatures in more southernly parts of the country.

(B) No meaningful predictions can, at present, be made about wind changes although on average the prevailing westernly winds could decrease, particularly in the winter period.

(C) The snowline is expected to retreat by about 100-150 metres for every 1°C rise in temperature. However, whilst New Zealand temperatures have increased by 0.5 °C since the 1940s no retreat of snowline or advance of treeline has yet been measures.

(D) An urgent need exists to improve regional computer models to help determine possible future variations to the dominant westernly wind over New Zealand, and to further explore atmospheric circulation patterns during past analogous climates.

(E) The most likely mean sea level change in the New Zealand region, consistent with the expected temperature changes, is estimated to be a rise of 10-20 cm by 2025 and a rise to 20-40 cm above present levels by 2050. This does not take account of any vertical movements of the land due to tectonic forces. No significant mean sea level change is expected to result from changes in large scale atmospheric circulation patterns.

New Zealand scientists at the Meteorological Service and Department of Scientific and Industrial Research especially are taking an active role in the climate modelling work being done in the Southern Hemisphere in collaboration especially with Australia and also in the measurement of trace gases at clean air sites.

The agricultural, forestry and conservation agencies are actively involved in impacts research with respect to their sectors.

The Steering Group of the New Zealand Climate Change Programme and the Royal Society of New Zealand have a coordinating role over climate change research to ensure continued support and its focusing on the key political issues.

The Impacts Working Group includes a comprehensive network of New Zealand's leading experts on the broad range of physical, biological, economic and social issues likely to be affected by climate change. Currently, first order impact scenarios are being prepared for workshop in July at which time the social and economic impacts will be considered. The Impacts Working Group are reporting to a core group that has been charged with preparing impact scenarios from the information the experts provide. The core group will also consult widely with special interest and community groups throughout New Zealand.

The Policy Working Group is currently scoping the key policy issues to enable the impacts work to be focused on most likely effects requiring policy responses. A wide range of natural and physical resource based departments and service sectors are addressing the issues along with sectors based on cultural, social and external relations and trade interests. Work to data is of a preliminary nature as the policy group awaits the impact scenarios.

Several preliminary themes have already emerged:

(a) institutional/legal issues
(b) research/data/monitoring issues as they relate to limitation and adaptive responses
(c) operational policy issues, for example, health, energy, agriculture, transport
(d) information/education issues
(e) transboundary/migration/Pacific issues
(f) cultural issues (tangata whenua)
(g) economic issues
(h) social issues.

The key focus that the New Zealand policy programme will have prior to the impacts scenarios completion, will be to address the range of limitation responses as they relate to CO_2 and other greenhouse gas emissions.

With international initiatives developing on a global climate convention, New Zealand needs to be in a position to address how a convention and protocols might affect its emissions policy and in particular its energy management.

In the meantime the preliminary indications from the impacts group are:

(A) largely negative impacts could be experienced by freshwater fisheries due to water temperature over current changes.
(B) positive impacts would be experienced by the agricultural sector with opportunities to respond to a change being presented.

(C) increased vigilance at New Zealand's borders could be necessary to avert possible importation of unwanted pests.

(D) changes in soils could be subtle, increased erosion and soil fertility changes could be associated with climate extremes being amplified.

(E) coastal, high altitude, "island" ecosystems, could be at greatest risk.

International fora have emphasised the need for national and regional scale assessments of the effects of global warming and atmospheric deterioration.

New Zealand and other Pacific island nations have unique problems and national programmes such as New Zealand's will help shape the international responses and focus attention on the urgency for action considering a range of effects and responses appropriate to geographic location and cultural circumstances.

15

Greenhouse Gases Environment Versus Economy in Indian Subcontinent

When, in India, we talk of global environment, the most important for us, as Indians, is to include our country in this connection. Only then, we can relate the findings of international level to our subcontinents. In the recent years, we have witnessed a growing concern regarding the accumulation of greenhouse gases (GHGs) in the earth's atmosphere. This concern has led to many in-depth studies of the phenomenon. Individual country studies have included all ranged from simple (albeit data-intensive), inventories of GHGs to evaluation of policy options to stabilize or reduce emissions in some future year. Impact studies have focused on better understanding the effects of gases on atmospheric temperature, monsoon patterns and rise in sea level.

IPCC estimates that the global temperature would increase up to 3.5°C by 2100 under the most likely scenarios.[1] The results of these models and other studies prompted calls for an international treaty which nations could adopt to limit the growth of emissions. Such a treaty was put forward at the 1992 UNCED meeting in Rio de Janeiro.

The text of the treaty was debated for many months prior to the convention. One of the critical divisive issues was the distribution of burden among the various parties. This issue lies at the heart of the debate among nations on climate change. Burden sharing is difficult to resolve since the emissions burden that each nation shoulders is distinct for each gas. And, it depends on the historical cumulative emissions that a country may have emitted through its use of various fuels. The burden varies by the type and extent of impact that a nation may have to endure as well. The cumulative share of carbon dioxide emissions from the developing countries between 1870 and 1986 is estimated to be only 15 per cent but, with 76 per cent of the world's population, their part of energy-related carbon dioxide emissions in 1986 was about 27 per cent. This share is increasing since their modern energy growth is more speedy than for other countries. IPCC scenarios of future emissions indicate that worldwide emissions of carbon and other gases would continue to increase even if the developed countries were to reduce emissions from their present levels.[2]

These shares suggest that the developed countries should shoulder a greater responsibility for historical emissions but the opportunities for reducing incremental emissions may be more abundant in the developing nations.

Unlike other airborne pollutants, such as SO_x and NO_x, which are emitted in trace amounts, are very reactive and can be scavenged at the source, GHGs are emitted in far more diluted and much higher amounts, which poses a problem in attempting to physically remove the gases. The main alternatives consist of eliminating or reducing the emissions of these gases, or growing biomass to sequester carbon dioxide.[3] Much of the present deforestation occurs in developing countries, and reversing or slowing this process would aid in reducing future emissions. Due to the above background, developed countries have insisted that reducing GHG emissions from the developing countries is vital. If necessary, such emissions reduction could be accomplished with assistance from the Global Environment Facility (GEF). On the other hand, the third world countries have argued that the growth of emissions is an unavoidable consequence of economic growth, as was the case with the industrialized countries during their past. Therefore, global environmental protection should not be allowed to penalize development. Is this difference reconcilable? For a signatory to the Climate Convention, the adoption of policies and strategies to limit emissions growth is an important goal to pursue. A nation would find it easier to follow such options to the extent that these are adoptable without hindering its current or anticipated development trends. Many studies have pleaded that alteration of growth patterns will lower social welfare and add to the cost of future socio-economic development. We will cite several studies for India to illustrate the opposite view that the adoption of such policies need not affect social welfare.

Indeed, accelerated adoption of certain energy and forestry policies, some of which are already being promoted and implemented, will lead to reduced carbon emissions and/or increased carbon sequestration at no extra cost to the nation. The pursuit of such policies will shift the business-as-usual growth to basic-needs-oriented development. Adoption of such policies may be expressed or thwarted by many barriers in developing economies. In the case of India, scarcity of capital and of hard currency are twin dilemmas which often limit adoption of the most efficient policies. Lack of institutions to ensure the adoption of high energy-efficiency technologies is another barrier. Reddy (1991) lists the many barriers to improving energy efficiency.[4] If adoption of such policies were to enhance social welfare and achieve reduction of GHG emissions at no extra cost, then is a nation justified in seeking international support for implementation of these options? As we illustrate for India, even if the life cycle cost of abatement projects is smaller, the up-front costs of these projects may make them prohibitively expensive to pursue. As provided for in the Convention, India could justifiably seek support for projects meriting such aid through the Global Environment Facility.

In this chapter we have addressed three main issues dealing with these topics: emissions inventory and the uncertainty of estimates; energy efficiency, fuel substitution and the economics of GHG abatement; and emissions and sequestration from biomass growth.

Uncertainty of Estimates in Emissions Inventory

As has been said a number of times, the Climate Change Convention calls for each Party to prepare an emissions inventory. GHGs included in the inventory are carbon dioxide, methane, carbon monoxide, nitrous oxide and also CFCs. Carbon dioxide and methane are emitted in large amounts than the other GHGs, and CFCs are regulated under the Montreal Protocol. Several other different inventories have been prepared for India by experts both national and international. Emission estimates of CO_2 from energy sources are in relatively close agreement. Estimates of CO_2 from non-energy sources, and of methane from all sources, vary widely and have been debated in many forums. In Table 15.1, we show the estimates of annual greenhouse gas emissions from anthropogenic activities in India for 1986. Carbon, emitted as carbon dioxide, emissions total 164 teragrams. Of all, these, emissions from forestry and land use changes amount to 20 teragrams. A more recent estimate places carbon emissions (as CO_2) from fossil fuel sue at 133 teragrams in 1988 compared to 139 in 1986, as reflected in Table 15.1.[5]

Methane emissions are estimated at 55 teragrams in Table 15.1. Boden et al.[6] estimate emissions of this gas from livestock and rice paddies to be 10 teragrams, compared to 48.2 in Table 15.1. The smaller figure is the result of new emissions measurements which reflect smaller rice biomass from Indian paddy fields and the fact that areas emitting high methane flux are a fraction of full paddy area; and above-surface biomass weight is reportedly smaller than elsewhere.

Table 15.1. Estimates of annual GHG emissions from anthropogenic activities in India, 1986 (teragrams of gas)

	CO_2	CO	CH_4	N_2O	CFCs
I. Energy					
1. Coal production	-	-	1.7	-	-
2. Coal combustion	378 (103)	6.6	0.04	0.03	-
3. Oil combustion	114 (31)	3.9	0.01	0.01	-
4. Gas combustion, flaring	18 (4.9)	0.01	0.002	0.002	-
5. Gas venting, leakages	-	-	-	-	-
II. Industry					
1. Cement manufacture	18 (4.9)	-	-	-	-
2. CFCs (CFC-11 Equiv.)	-	-	-	-	0.01
3. Landfills	-	-	1.7	-	-
III. Agriculture and forestry					
1. Animal husbandry	-	-	10.4	-	-
2. Rice cultivation	-	-	37.8	-	-
3. Fertilizer use	-	-	-	0.04	-
4. Biomass combustion	-	55.6	3.5	0.09	-
5. Deforestation, landuse changes	73 (20)	-	-	0.03	-
Total	601 (164)	66	55	0.2	0.01

Amount of carbon in the CO_2 shown in brackets

Source: Ahuja, D (1990), *Climate Change Technical Series: Estimating Regional Anthropogenic Emissions of Greenhouse Gases,* US EPA Report No. 20P-2006.

This emissions inventory is for a single year and does not provide guidance on trends or future growth of these emissions. Oak Ridge

National Laboratory has tracked historical emissions for several countries, including for India (Fig. 15.1. Carbon dioxide emissions from India have come up at 5.7 per cent annually since 1950 as India climbed from thirteenth to fifth place in the world as a national contributor. With increased shares of oil and gas, the share of CO_2 emissions from coal has come down from 87 per cent in 1950 to 71 per cent in 1989. We have selected future scenarios from two authoritative reports for carbon dioxide emissions from energy (power) and forestry sources. In Table 15.2, we show

Table 15.2. Situation for India of future carbon dioxide emissions (million tons of carbon)

			Annual growth rate (%)
(1) Modern energy sources[a]	*1985*	*2025*	
High	115	703	4.5
Low	115	615	4.2
(2) Biomass sources[b]	*1986*	*2011*	
High	64	99	1.7
Low	64	70	0.4

Sources: (a) Pachauri, R. K., Suri, V. and Gupta, S. (1991). *CO_2 Emissions from Developing Countries: Better Understanding the Role of Energy in the Long Term. Volume 3: China, India, Indonesia and South Korea.* July. LBL Report 30060.
(b) Ravindranath, N. H., Samashekhar, B. S. and Gadgil, M. (1992). *Forests: Case Studies from Seven Developing Countries, Volume 3: India and China.* August. LBL Report 32759.

emissions estimates for commercial energy sources for 1985 and 2025, and for biomass sources for 1986 and 2011. Emissions from modern energy sources increase at a fast pace in these scenarios but those from biomass increase much more slowly in either scenario.

Economics of GHG Abatement Through Energy Efficiency and Fuel Substitution

As evident, the production and use of modern energy in India generated 115 million tonnes of carbon in 1985, or 10 per cent of all carbon emissions emanating from the developing world. From a global

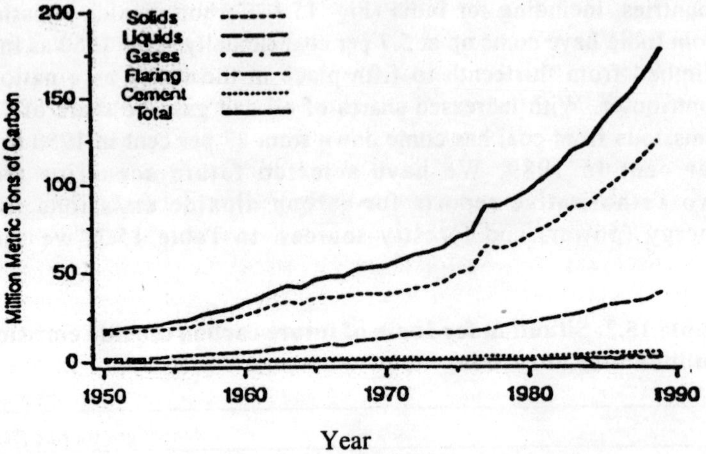

Fig. 15.1. CO_2 emissions from Indian Subcontinent 1950-1989

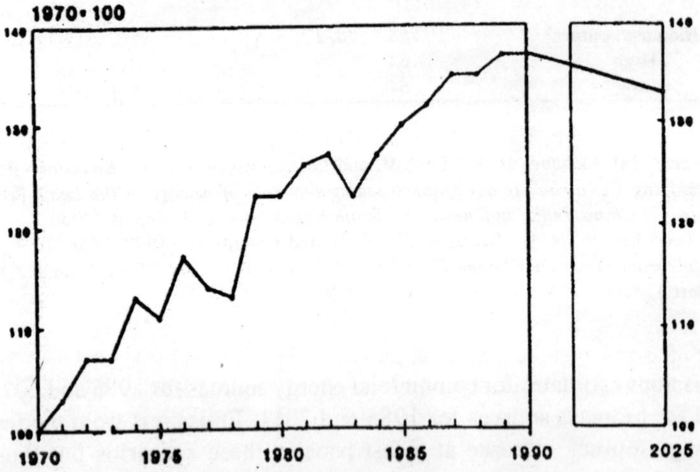

Source: J. Sathaye and A. Ketoff, *CO_2 Emissions from Developing Countries: Better Understanding the Role of Energy in the Long Term,* Vol. 7 (LBL Report 29607 Rev., Feb. 1991)

Fig. 15.2. Primary energy per GDP, India, 1970-2025 (HE scenario excluding biomass)

perspective, India will account for 21 per cent of the *increase* in carbon emissions generated from energy use in developing countries between

1985 and 2025.[7] Between 1970 and 1990, the intensity of India's primary modern energy use increased by 38 per cent (Fig. 15.2). In numerous sectors of the Indian economy, the intensity of energy use per unit of value added exceeds that found in most industrialized and many developing nations.

The increasing intensity in India shows replacement of human and animal draught power by mechanical and electrical devices. In particular, agricultural electricity use is increasing much faster (at almost 20 per cent annually) than the value added draws from this sector. The high intensities also reflect the underlying inefficiency of energy use in industry, transport and power generation. For example, energy intensities of cement production for wet, dry and the wet-dry processes were as much as 20 per cent and, in certain cases, 50 per cent, above international norms.[8] Similar figures have been documented for steel, aluminium and other major energy intensive industries.

One latest study has shown that direct and indirect carbon emissions may be higher from construction activity than any other component of India's final demand.[9] Energy-intensive materials like glass, cement, bricks, steel, aluminium, and asphalt constitute the bulk of the components of a buildings or any other type of structure.

Thus, emissions associated with construction are large. Reducing construction activity to reduce emissions is not a viable solution since a growing infrastructure is necessary to maintain the pace of economic development in India. Using materials more productively through better designs of buildings and other infrastructure would be the better approach. India's opportunities for curtailing emissions of carbon include rectifying its currently uneconomic distribution of fuels and inefficient energy-use patterns. Abundant but carbon-intensive coal resources satisfy almost 50 per cent of India's modern energy demand. In recent years, the costs of coal production and transportation have risen primarily due to changes in technology and low productivity. Arguably, more efficient fuel options (primarily oil, natural gas and renewables) could serve economically viable substitutes for coal in the coming times.[10,11]

Making sure which alternatives provides the most cost-effective means for India to restrain the growth of CO_2 entails a thorough economic evaluation of the available options. In the industrialized countries, economic evaluations of reducing carbon emissions have concentrated on taxation policies. However, in most developing countries where fiscal and technological resources are scarce, any effective emissions abatement strategy must go beyond evaluating the impact of changes in national taxes on levels of carbon emissions.

Carbon conservation efforts much identify the types of energy-supply and energy-use technologies needed to restrain the growth of carbon. They must also assess the capital investment and foreign exchange needs needed to acquire less carbon-intensive technologies and fuels. Through the 1980s imports of crude oil and petroleum products constituted the biggest single commodity group in India's import bill. In Table 15.3 we show the share of oil imports in total imports in each year between 1980-81 and 1990-91. It also relates oil imports in this period to export earnings. While we find no secular trend in Table 15.3 we can discern a clear pattern in which oil imports were linked to the growth in consumption of petroleum products and the trends in the domestic production of crude oil. The higher international oil rates in 1980-81 boosted India's oil import bill. In response, India accelerated the exploitation of the offshore Bombay High Reserves. Thus, production of Indian crude tripled to 28.9 million tons in 1984-85. The consumption rate accelerated in the latter half of the 1980s. Consumption increased at an annual average rate of 5.5 per cent during the Sixth Plan (1980-85), but it increased at 6.8 per cent per year during the Seventh Five-Year Plan. As Bombay High was exploited completely in the mid-1980s and no new discoveries on the same scale as in the mid-1970s were made, oil imports rose inexorably.

Table 15.3. Petroleum imports (products and crude) as proportions of all imports and of export earnings

Year	*Oil imports (net)* *As % of all imports*	*As % of export earnings*
1980-81	42	78
1981-82	37	64
1982-83	30	48
1983-84	20	33
1984-85	21	31
1985-86	22	40
1987-88	15	22
1988-89	14	19
1989-90	16	20
1990-91	23	30
Average	21	31

Source: Reddy, C. R., D'Sa, A. and Reddy, A.K.N. (1992). 'The Debt-Energy Nexus: A Case Study of India', *Economic and Political Weekly,* July 4.

Crude oil imports, thus increased in 1985-86, and petroleum product imports followed suit in 1987-88. As we show later, the nexus between oil demand and import payments has an important bearing on India's capacity to decrease emissions. Generation, transmission and distribution of electricity are the most capital intensive of all energy activities. In the growing Indian economy, demand for electricity has gone up faster than that for other forms of energy. Driven by this growth, demand for capital to finance the supply of electricity has also increased commensurately. Much of the capital to finance the energy sector is drawn from the government budget.

In the past, the government devoted an ever-increasing share of its budget to the energy sector. During the Sixth (1980-85) Five-Year Plan, for example, the government allocated 27.2 per cent of its plan outlay to the specific energy sector. This share increased share was insufficient to provide adequate power to the growing Indian economy. Power shortages are now common throughout the economy and 'brown-outs' in various cities during peak periods are the norm. The government is pursuing private sector power generation to alleviate power shortages. But the government has not yet set priorities in selection of technologies. Further, the management and operation of the power sector itself must be improved prior to seeking additional financing. A recent analysis of the growth of carbon emissions and the economics of abating emissions from modern energy use in our highlights the relationship between abatement strategy on the one hand and capital investment and foreign exchange or hand currency requirements on the other (Table 15.4).[12]

Table 15.4. Economic implications of reducing carbon emissions

	1985	2005
GDP (billion US$)	193	512
GDP / capita (US$)	256	428
1. *Scenario 1*		
Emissions (million tons)	*110 mt*	*390 mt*
Cost	$38 billion	$107 billion
Investment	$8 billion	$29 billion
Investment / GDP (%)	4.1 %	7.0 %
Foreign exchange	$3.6 billion	$22.4 billion
FE / GDP (%)	1.9 %	4.4 %

2. *Scenario 2*		
Emissions (million tons)	*110 mt*	*340 mt*
Cost	$38 billion	$94 billion
Investment	$8 billion	$26 billion
Investment / GDP (%)	4.1 %	5.1 %
Foreign exchange (FE)	$3.6 billion	$22 billion
FE / GDP (%)	1.9 %	4.2 %
3. *Scenario 3*		
Case 1		
Emissions (million tons)	*110 mt*	*280 mt*
Cost	$38 billion	$95 billion
Investment	$8 billion	$23 billion
Investment / GDP (%)	4.1 %	4.5 %
Foreign exchange (FE)	$3.6 billion	$25 billion
FE / GDP (%)	1.9 %	4.8 %
Case 2		
Emissions (million tons)	*100 mt*	*280 mt*
Cost	$38 billion	$105 billion
Investment	$8 billion	$32 billion
Investment / GDP (%)	4.1 %	6.2 %
Foreign exchange (FE)	$3.6 billion	$23 billion
FE / GDP (%)	1.9 %	4.5 %

Scen. 1: Efficiency frozen at 1985 levels
Scen. 2: Includes efficiency improvements
Scen 3: Lowest carbon emissions
Case 1: Lowest carbon emissions through greater fuel switching and fuel efficiency
Case 2: Lowest carbon emissions through increased reliance on renewables, e.g., solar, wind, hydro and biomass

Source: Mongia, N, et al. (1991), endnote 12.

For the proceeding table, the analysis assumes annual average rate for GDP and population growth. A linear programming model couples these rates to energy demand growth by sector and end-use. The model reduces the cost of providing energy services to the Indian enconomy. Energy service may be provided by new energy supply or higher efficiency of supply and/or use. The model computes the investment and foreign exchange need for meeting the estimated demand for energy. Table 15.4 shows the foreign exchange requirement for fuel imports only.

As shown above in Scenario 1, energy intensity is frozen at 1985 levels. Energy sector investment as a proportion of GDP increases to 7.0 per cent by 2005. Foreign exchange requirements go up from 1.9 per cent in 1985 to 4.4 per cent by 2005. In each case, the sharp increase will require that financial resources be transferred to the energy sector from other sectors which will also ask for more capital and foreign exchange. Reducing the intensity of energy use a illustrated in Scenario 2, restrains the growth of carbon emissions to 340 million tonnes. As this reduction is achieved primarily through cost-effective efficiency improvement, the cost of abatement is negative.

The Indian economy benefits from restraining carbon emissions growth. The scenario takes hold of the many opportunities available to use electricity more efficiently, which reduces investment requirement.[13,14] However, the opportunities for reducing petroleum products demand are limited, and more troublesome to implement, and this is reflected in the 4.2 per cent foreign exchange to GDP ratio, which changes little from Scenario 1.

Initiating less carbon-intensive fuels (Scenario 3) can reduce emissions further than in Scenario 2. This result is achieved through either the import of natural gas as illustrated in Case 1 or with the help of use of renewables as illustrated in Case 2. Renewables include the use of wind, solar, hydro and biomass resources.

Natural gas imports increase the ratio of foreign exchange to GDP to 4.8 per cent while slowing down the investment needs. Increased use of renewables drives up the investment requirement sharply to 6.2 per cent of GDP. Restraining emissions beyond what might be achieved through efficient fuel allocation and consumption would increase either capital investment or hard currency requirements. The unit cost of conserved carbon rises from Scenario 1 to Scenario 3 as more expensive approaches are followed to curtail carbon emissions (Table 15.5). By conducting alternate runs of Scenario 2 and placing progressively tighter constraints on carbon emissions, the cost of conserving carbon at levels between those in Scenarios 2 and 3 were fixed. For example, the cost of conserved carbon is US$0.02 per kilogram when emissions are reduced from 340 million to 300 million tonnes.

Table 15.5. Unit cost of conserved carbon, India

Carbon emissions (million tonnes)	*Unit cost of conserved carbon (1985 US$ / kg)*
390-340	–0.27
340-300	0.02
300-280	0.05

In this analysis, the Scenario 3 costs of restraining carbon emissions are lower than those for Scenario 1. This implies that India can reduce carbon emissions at a net benefit to the economy, and the energy sector would thus, not require any new resources to reduce emissions. Scenario 3 costs compared to Scenario 2 are between 1 and 11 billion dollars higher. Many energy efficiency improvements are embedded in Scenario 2. This way, if India energy sector were to become more efficient, this analysis implies that it would need additional resources to reduce emissions.

Which of the two paths (Scenarios 1 or 2) India takes to provide energy services will ensure whether resources need to be transferred to or away from the energy sector, and consequently whether the nation would be justified in seeking resources from the universe. Restraining emissions from energy use in India will require that fuel allocation and energy efficiency be improved to their maximum potential. The scenario analysis done in Table 15.4 includes many opportunities for improving efficiency of electricity use and supply. Additional measures to improve oil use efficiency would have further reduced the FE/GDP ratios shown in Table 15.4. What approaches might have yielded a better efficient use of oil in India? Four important shifts in strategy could be implemented:

(a) a shift in long-haul freight movement from road to rail with the purpose to reflect the economic cost of transportation for each mode;
(b) a shift in cooking fuel from kerosene to LPG to push the use of more efficient stoves;
(c) electrification of non-electrified households which would decrease kerosene consumed for lighting;
(d) replacement of diesel pumpsets with electric pumpsets.[15]

Above mentioned four strategies would have reduced demand for oil in the scenarios between 1980 and 1990 by 14.4 per cent. More importantly these steps would have decreased by 5 million tons the demand for kerosene and diesel, the two critical middle-distillates which are imported. The result of four strategies would be a reduction of the 1985 FE/GDP ratio of 1.9 per cent in Table 15.4 to 1.3 per cent. If we assume that this kind of improvement may be achieved by 2005, then the ratio for Scenario 2 would fall to 2.9 per cent from 4.2 per cent. A lower share of GDP allocated to importing oil would make the fuel significant payment more manageable. Strategies 3 and 4 would enhance demand for electricity which would add to investment requirements shown in Table 15.4 for 2005. As we pointed out above, there are many options to improve efficiency of electricity use that are easily implementable.

The options for improving efficiency of oil consumption involve a diverse set of actors which make them difficult to implement. For some end uses, such as lighting, electricity use is more efficient than oil use. Shifting to electricity in such selected end-uses would make a nations's energy efficiency. Further, since improving system efficiency for electricity may be easier than for oil, increased electricity demand from strategies 3 and 4 could be better restricted. In light of the cost, capital investment and foreign exchange parameters, to what extent can India restrain carbon emissions from modern energy use? Stabilization of emissions or limiting their rise to 20 per cent over a 20-year period has been discussed for the industrialized countries. Analyses show that this goal could be achieved without a net loss of GDP in some of the countries. The Energy Modelling Forum-12 in its deliberations on scenarios assumed that restraining emissions growth to a 50 per cent increase over a 20-year period was plausible for the developing nations.

On the other hand, Scenario 3 in Table 15.4 shows that, at best, emissions for 2005 could be held to 155 per cent (280 compared to 110 million tonnes) above the 1985 level.

Further reduction in emissions would reduce annual GDP growth from the 4.9 per cent assumed in Table 15.4. In fact, we estimate that to achieve the 50 per cent limit suggested by EMF-12 would require that the current pattern of unsatisfied energy demand continue in the future and that India's annual GDP growth be limited to 3 per cent.[16] Most possibly, these requirements would be unacceptable to India.

State of Emissions and Sequestration from Biomass Growth

Here, forests, defined as woodlands with more than 10 per cent crown cover, occupy about 20 per cent of the Indian land area. This proportion may be compared with 57 per cent for heavily forested nations like Indonesia and Malaysia. Deforestation has led to a major decline in forest area in most countries; India is no exception.

About one-fifth of the forests standing today are extremely degraded. Half a million hectares or 0.8 per cent of total forest area was deforested in 1986. The primary conversion activity in our country is agriculture followed by pasture and harvesting. The primary conversion activities vary by region. In the state of Karnataka, conversion to agricultural land accounts for 33 per cent, but submergence and resettlement because of power and irrigation projects account for 42 per cent, and mining for 21 per cent of the lost forest area between 1956 and 1984.[17] Table 15.6 reveals the carbon emissions from India associated with deforestation. These are divided into three categories: inherited, prompt and delayed. Inherited emissions are caused by past forest activities and occur in the base year. Prompt emissions are those that are produced immediately as a result of a forest conversion activity. Delayed are cumulative emissions that take place over time as decomposition of biomass occurs.

Releases of carbon dioxide because of changes in soil organic carbon, both from forest conversion activities and areas under harvesting and afforestation programmes, are also included here. The committed emissions displayed in Table 15.6 have been much discussed. An earlier World Resources Institute estimate placed these emissions at 140 million tons.[18] More recent estimates from other sources place the committed emissions closer to the figure given in Table 15.6.[19] In the section above on energy, we discussed the potential and economics of restraining emissions from that sector.

Growing biomass offers an opportunity to sequester carbon which would decrease net emissions from India. What is the potential for such offsets and to what extent might it be achieved while simultaneously pursuing or accelerating currently planned socio-economic betterment? The development of agro-forestry and tree plantations on previously unforested lands can provide India with options to reduce its net emissions. The biomass density and carbon accumulation of new forests can go beyond those of the initial natural vegetation depending on the silvicultural practices. In addition, afforestation projects can provide gainful employment to rural peasants who formerly earned their living with the help of activities resulting in deforestation.

Our country has a strong, rapidlly growing afforestation programme. India's afforestation process was accelerated by the enactment of the Forest Conservation Act of 1980 which aimed at stopping forest clearing and degradation through a strict, centralized control of land-use rights. The afforestation activities resulted in a total of 11.5 million hectares as of 1986.

Another 5.6 million more hectares were cut down between 1986 and 1989, raising the total planted area to 17.1 million hectares. In Table 8.6, we show the carbon uptake, the annual carbon balance and the net committed emissions from India. The committed carbon uptake is almost two times as large as India's committed emissions.

Table 15.6. India's forestry related carbon emissions and uptake, 1986

Carbon emissions (MtC)				*Carbon uptake (MtC)*				*Annual carbon balance (MtC/year)*[a]	*Net committed emissions (MtC)*
Inherited[a] (1)	Prompt (2)	Delayed (3)	Committed (4) = (2) + (3)	Inherited (5)	Prompt (6)	Delayed (7)	Committed (8) = (6) + (7)	(9) = (1) + (2) – (5) – (6)	(10) = (4) – (8)
26	38	26	64	68.8	n.a.	120.0	120.0	–5	–56

(a) Inherited emissions for India were calculated following historic average deforestation rates for the past ten years.

Source: Makundi, W. Sathaye, Jand Masera, O. 1992. *Carbon Emissions and Sequestration in Forests: Case Studies from Seven Developing Countries,* Volume 7: Sunmary, August, LBL Draft Report LBL-32119.

Over the years, the country would sequester 56 million tonnes of carbon from past afforestation activities. This figure is sufficiently large to make a dent in the emissions from the energy sector.

The yearly carbon balance in Table 15.6 shows a net uptake of 5 million tonnes from forestry activities. Combining this figure with emissions from energy shown in Table 15.4 would reduce emissions from latest energy and forestry to 105 million tonnes of net carbon emissions.

The above figures have important implications for future carbon emissions from India. The carbon sequestration occurred and is occurring through programmes with the main goal of promoting sustainable rural socio-economic development. Carbon sequestration is an unintended result of these actions. Given the potential for reducing net carbon emissions from India, the various factors that have contributed to this sequestration are worth taking note of. They also include:

(a) Setting up of the Forest Conservation Act of 1980;
(b) Preparation of an environmental impact statement needed with the beginning of the Fifth Five-Year Plan of 1975-80;
(c) Reduction of subsidies to forest-based industries beginning in the second half of 1970s;
(d) More industry- farmer links which have encouraged production of tree crops;
(e) decentralized political decision making—village and district level authorities have been set up in West Bengal and Karnataka, for example, that are far more motivated to ensure the prudent use of local resources;
(f) Introduction of strong environmental movements in different parts of the country;
(g) biomass fuel conservation programmes in all the states.

There is no doubt that strengthening these programmes would enhance carbon sequestration and accelerate rural development. As Saxena points out in a recent article, implementation of programmes will benefit some groups at the cast of others within India.[20] Most of the programmes proposed in the article, such as welfare forestry on forest lands, social security plantation, farm forestry for the poor, etc. will benefit the rural poor and the rich at the cost of lower level officials.

However, not pursuing such programmes will make everyone lose in the long run. Favourable scenarios have shown a net carbon uptake from forests in 2011 to be 121 million tons. Interpolating between the base year, 1986, and 2011 provides a net uptake of 57 million tons in 2005.[21] Thus, forests could offset India's modern energy related carbon emissions shown in Scenario 2, Table 15.4 by 17 per cent in 2005. India's net emissions from these two sources would be decreased to 28.3 million tons in 2005. This outcome would be achieved at no additional cost to those shown in Scenario 2. Further, given the exponentially higher sequestration potential for 2011, forests could offset as much as 25 per cent of the energy emissions in the year 2011.

Consumption of Biomass

As we all know, carbon is stored away or released when the biomass from a tree is utilized. The type of use and its duration determine the net carbon emissions. A tree burnt for the target of land clearing will release most of its biomass immediately. A tree providing lumber used to make buildings will store carbon away for decades. What is the best use of trees in order to sequester carbon? Hall, Mynick and Williams disclosed that while sequestering carbon in forests is a relatively low-cost strategy for offsetting carbon dioxide emissions from fossil fuel combustion, substantially greater benefits can be obtained by replacing fossil fuel with biomass grown sustainably and transformed into useful energy using modern energy conversion technologies.[22]

Biomass substituted for coal can be as effective as carbon sequestration, per ton of biomass, in decreasing carbon emissions. However, fuel substitution can be carried out indefinitely, while carbon sequestration can be effective only until the forest reaches maturity. Also, greater biomass resources can be committed to fossil fuel substitution at any particular time than to carbon sequestration because biomass (such as sugarcane bagasse) can play a much larger role in reducing greenhouse warming by replacing fossil fuel than by sequestering carbon. Moreover, biomass energy is potentially less costly than the displaced fuel energy in a wide range of circumstances, so that the net cost of displacing carbon dioxide emissions would generally be negative.

Findings

On the basis of this above, we can say that India's carbon emissions are likly to grow in the future because of the increasing energy and food consumption needed to support a growing economy. However, strengthening the present afforestation programmes, increasing energy efficiency, and prudent use of renewable options in selected applications have the potential to offset a significant part of the GHG emissions. Implementing the three types of options will not be that easy. Energy and forest products consumption and supply patterns, and forest landuse are shaped by a large number of actors at various levels. Improving resource allocation and use patterns will necessitate action at the national and international levels.

Reddy has outlined many barriers to energy efficiency improvement. Similar barriers exist to increased afforestation and renewable energy use. Energy consumers are mostly uninformed, first-cost sensitive, indifferent and helpless to improve efficiency.[23] National institutions are supply-biased, with little incentive to innovate. The government is uninterested, is short of capital and skills, has insufficient training facilities and limited access to hardware and software.

Energy efficiency agencies are relatively powerless compared to their supply counterparts or they are part of the supply agency and therefore have no incentive to cut down demand for their product. Further, bilateral and multilateral aid agencies target the supply aspects of energy systems with inadequate attention to demand-side measures. Other issues, such as an anti-innovation bent, the large-is-convenient funder and the project-mode sponsor contribute to the lack of attention to the three options. Number of the barriers listed above arise because there is no incentive for the various actors to behave differently. Concern about climate change can provide this incentive. The establishment of the GEF and the growing attention being paid to environmental matters at the World Bank is a positive sign which will alter future lending practices of multi-lateral institutions.[24] Increased attention to environmental issues holds out the hope that these and other similar institutions will start to address the concerns of the poor, and not just those of the elite, in the developing countries. For example, dislocation of rural populations caused by building the Sardar Sarovar dam, coal mines and afforestation schemes are being studied and addressed.

Concern about climate change can imporve on this dimension by explicitly developing projects which provide sustainable solutions to meet the energy, food, water and other requirement of the poor. These projects will halt deforestation and/or lead to increased greening of rural areas in India. Our analysis suggests that in India pursues basic-needs oriented development with stress on end-use efficiency, decentralized renewables and afforestation programmes, then its carbon emissions growth will slow and its economy will improve more rapidly. Simultaneously, it is in the interest of the developed countries to fund India's incremental expenses of switching to less carbon-intensive technologies. Such technologies represent the most cost-effective path to economic development. For perhaps the first time in history, the interests of the developing nations are aligned with those of the industrialized countries creating an unprecedented paradigm for future human development.

More importantly, many of the measures to implement the three options have the potential to make better the condition of the poor in the developing countries. Efficient energy use and selected renewable options have been successully demonstrated as necessary means to provide improved water supply, lighting and fertilizer, which has fostered rural development.[25] Afforestation in India, through natural regeneration programmes, directly aids rural villagers.

In the end, concern about the shared global problem of climate change offers a unique opportunity to align the interests of the developed and developing countries, rich and poor. While competition and dissimilar targets have often frustrated and defeated cooperative ventures, climate change offers a common incentive for collective action. Pursuing the socio-economic development goals of the South is consistent with the environmental targets of the North, and provides joint benefits to economy and ecology that are in the shared interests of all of us.

References

1. IPCC (1992). *1992 IPCC Supplement,* February.
2. *Ibid.*
3. Hall, D., Mynick, H. and Williams, R. (1991). 'Cooling the Greenhouse with Biomass Energy'. *Nature,* September 5; Hall, D., Mynick, H. and Williams, R. (1991). 'Alternative Roles for Biomass in Coping with Greenhouse Warming'. *Science and Global Security,* Volume 2, pp. 1-39.
4. Reddy, A. (1991). 'Barriers to Improvements in Energy Efficiency'. *Energy Policy,* December, pp. 953-61.
5. Mitra, A.P. (eds.) *Global Change: Greenhouse Gas Emissions in India, A Preliminary Report,* Scientific Report No. 1. Prepared under the auspices of Council of Scientific and Industrial Research, New Delhi, June 1991.
6. Boden, T., Sepanski, R. and Stoss, F. (Eds). *Trends 91: A Compendium of Data on Global Change.* ORNL Pub. No. ORNL/CDIAC-46, pp. 442-45.
7. Sathaye, J and Ketoff, A. (1991). *CO_2 Emissions from Developing Countries: Better Understanding the Role of Energy in the Long Term. Volume 1: Summary,* February, LBL-29507.
8. Bureau of Costs and Prices (1986). *Energy Audit of the Cement Industry.* Ministry of Industry, Government of India, New Delhi.

9. Parikh, J., Gokarn, S. and Barua, A. (1992). *Climate Change and India's Energy Policy Options.* Indira Gandhi Institute of Development Research, February. Report prepared for the Rockefeller Foundation.
10. Government of India, Bueau of Costs and Prices (1988). *Towards a New Energy Policy,* Delhi.
11. Reddy, A. Sumithra, G. Balachandra, P. and D'Sa, A. (1991). 'A Development-Focused End-Use-Oriented Electricity Scenario for Karnataka'. *Economic and Political Weekly,* April 6 and April 13.
12. Mongia, N., Bhatia, R., Sathaye, J. and Mongia, P. (1991). Cost of Reducing CO_2 Emissions from India. *Energy Policy,* pp. 978-86, December.
13. Nadel, S., Kothari, V. and Gopinath, S. (1991). *Opportunities for Improving End-Use Electricity Efficiency in India.* Report prepared by American Council for an Energy Efficient Economy for the World Bank and US Agency for International Development, November.
14. Reddy, *et al.* (1991), *op. cit.* (Reference 11).
15. Reddy, A. (1981). 'A Strategy of Resolving India's Oil Crisis'. *Current Science,* Vol. 50, No. 2, pp. 50-53.
16. Sathaye, J. (1992). *Carbon Emissions from Brazil, India and China.* Presentation to the EMF-12 meeting in Washington, DC, May.
17. Reddy, A. (1987). *On the Loss and Degradation of Karnataka's Forests.* Paper presented at the International Conference on Tropical Forestry, 1-2 July, Bellagio.
18. World Resources Institute 1990. *World Resources 1990-91.* New York, Oxford University Press.
19. Kaul, O.L. (1991). *Forest Biomass Burning in India.* TERI Information Service on Global Warming, New Delhi, 2 (2): 2-17.
20. Saxena, N.C (1989). 'Forestry and Rural Development'. *South Asia Journal,* Vol. 3, Nos. 1 and 2, pp. 70-89.
21. Ravindranath, N.H, Somashekhar, B.S and Gadgil, M. (1992). *Forests: Case Studies from Seven Developing Countries, Volume 3: India and China,* August. LBL Report 32759.
22. Hall, et.al. (1991 a,b) *op. cit.* (Reference 3).
23. Reddy (1991) *op. cit.* (Reference 4).
24. Reddy, A.K.N. (1992). *Has the World Bank Greened?* Paper prepared for the Second Edition of the Green Globe Yearbook, Fridtjof Nansen Institute, Norway, September.
25. Rajabapaiah, P., Jayakumar, S. and Reddy., A (1993). 'Biogas Electricity—The Pura Village Case Study', Chapter 18, pp 787-816 in Johanson, T., Kelly, H., Reddy, A. and Williams, R., (eds.) *Renewable Energy: Sources for Fuels and Electricity,* Island Press, Washington DC.

16

Alternatives for Energy Policy in India

The present chapter is an edited version of a paper presented at ECOTECH Seminar during the Rio de Janerio's Earth Summit and at a number of other environmental meets of national and international level by Jyoti Parikh and Subir Gokarn. In this chapter has been presented analytical description of carbon dioxide emissions in India and also possibilities of alternative policies have been explored. Special focus has been made on 60-sector point input-output model, newly evolved model for flow of energy and its examination. Global negotiations on climate change have generated considerable interest among environment policy-makers, economists, atmospheric scientists and numerous other interested parties. There are four major greenhouse gases (GHGs): carbon dioxide (CO_2), methane (CH_4), chlorofluorocarbons (CFCs), and nitrous oxides (N_2O). Among these, CO_2 attracts the most attention, because:

1. CO_2 emissions can be confidently estimated from the energy balances of each country because they are directly related to energy consumption and cement manufacturing.
2. CO_2 is the most significant greenhouse gas emitted by the developed countries in terms of magnitude (as well as radiative forcing).
3. Hikes in CO_2 emissions are measured regularly and global emission levels for CO_2 are increasing more rapidly than, say, methane.

Due to the above reasons, various authors have carried out analyses of the possibilities of reducing CO_2 emissions at global and national levels.

Though global approaches highlight the policy direction and the magnitude of the efforts required, Blitzer *et al* have pointed out that the possibilities of GHG emission reduction needs to be discussed using *country-level* models with sufficient structural explanation. Their model for Egypt shows that if Egypt curtailed GHG emissions in 20 years by 20 per cent over base year CO_2 production levels, it would reduce the GDP growth rate by 3.13 per cent. A decrease of 40 per cent would slow GDP growth by 32.4 per cent. Alternatives at country-level depend *inter alia* on:

1. Various energy resources and technologies used (i.e., coal, oil, gas, hydro or nuclear).
2. Patterns of development (whether agrarian, industrial or service-oriented economy).

Two nations, India and China are considered to be major players in global climate change because of their possible increase of CO_2 emissions due to increases in income and level of population. Moreover, both depend on coal. Several authors, for example Mathur and Sathaye and Ketoff, have carried out CO_2 accounting exercises by keeping in view energy supply and energy end-use activities such as manufacturing steel, fertilizers, cement, and so on.

While this simple and fast method could show that India's emissions in 1985-86 were 115 million tonnes and will rise to 615 million tonnes by 2025, it is not adequate to give policy guidance or to assess the effects on the economy of alternative emission reduction policies, which may depend not only on alternative emission reduction policies, which may depend not only on technologies but also on fuel substitution, fuel consumption, patterns of development, etc. Indirect CO_2 emissions can also affect substantially. Thus, an overall economy wide exercise can provide additional insights and policy guidance. This article reports on such an exercise, using the input-output table for the year 1983-84 that was taken account of during the Seventh Plan, 1985-90.

Global Negotiations for Climatic Change with India

Case study of India is of particular interest, because India may be the most populated country in the world by 2025 and its GHG emissions may rise substantially. Despite the truth that in 1986 it emitted only 0.2 tonnes per capita of fossil CO_2 (compared to 5.4 tonnes per capita in the USA), it is the sixth largest CO_2 emitter in the world. Parikh *et al* have shown that, to accommodate even a modest increase of emissions by only India and China, the developed countries would have to reduce their GHG emissions by 30 per cent by 2025, to keep global emissions in

2025 at the same level as in 1986. India's emissions are projected to increase fourfold compared to 1986, but even then would be only 0.36 tonnes per capita less than the world average of 1.2 tonnes per capita in 1986. There is yet another concern about India's future fossil CO_2 emissions Table 1.

Table 1. Fossil-fuel consumption and carbon emissions in India.

		Oil	
	Coal (tonnes)	*HSD/LDO*	*FO/LSHS*
GJ/tonne[a]	21	44	38
TC/GJ[b]	0.026	0.020	0.021
TC/tonne	0.546	0.88	0.79
Consumption (1983-84), 10^6 tonnes	121.3	14.125	5.6
Resources, 10^6 tonnes	186.000	756[c]	

India's major energy source is coal, with resources of more than 186 billion tonnes, against production of 221 million tonnes in 1990-91. Proven coal resources are estimated at 56 billion tonnes, while oil and gas resources are only 756 million tonnes and 686 billion cubic metres respectively. Therefore, coal will continue to provide more than 60 per cent of India's energy needs. Coal has the highest CO_2 emission coefficient per primary Giga Joule (GJ).

Coal in India has nearly 35 per cent ash content. Standard Indian coal is calibrated to generate 20.9 GJ per tonne as compared to the United Nations standard coal at 29.7 GJ/tonne. This difference in the Indian energy data system has not been kept in view and has caused confusion in international data systems. Thus, the combination of high population, coal predominance in energy-use and high potential growth due to currently low income levels causes concern about India's carbon emissions in global circles. On the other hand, India's viewpoint is different. From its perspective, India's fossil-based carbon emissions were only 115 million tonnes in 1985 against 5.4 billion tonnes for the world and 1.3 billion tonnes for the USA.

Even in 2025, its total emissions are likely to be only 0.6 billion tonnes—a per capita emission of 0.36 tonnes compared to a total world average of 1.2 tonnes per capita. These emissions would not be a problem if the developed countries' present and past use of fossil fuels had not resulted in an excessive build-up of CO_2 in the atmosphere. India has to tackle basic problems of health and nutrition and needs to work on basic environmental problems such as increasing access to safe drinking water and sanitation and reducing the use of bio-fuels which affect the

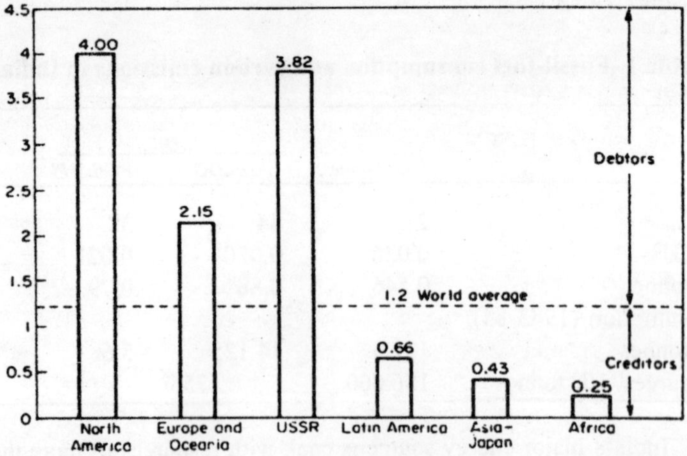

Fig. 16.1. Per capita CO_2 emissions by world regions (from fossil fuels and cement). *Source: Trends 90: A Compendium of Data on Global Change,* Oak Ridge National Laboratories, Nashville, TN, 1990.

health of women and children. Under the 'Polluter pays principle', those above the world average should pay money to those below the world average see Fig. 16.1. Under certain conditions, a tradeable emission quotas system is regarded as economically efficient in allocating resources to the reduction of CO_2 emissions will transfer resources to 'cerditor' countries by buying emission rights. Creditors can then use these resources according to their own priorities.

This is the best option in international negotiations. However, until such an international system is in place, there are feasibilities for other countries to invest in India to reduce CO_2 emissions in those projects which are of interest to India while others can claim credit for the reductions in CO_2 emissions. These are undertood as 'offsets' in other countries. This may be second-best solution from the viewpoint of the creditor countries. Offsets lack the flexibility of the tradeable quota system since the transfer of resources from debtors to creditors is restricted to emission-reducing investment, and funds may not be directed towards the environmental priority of their choice (e.g., drinking water).

However, such steps may be negotiated even bilaterally by, say, one of the EC countries in response to the CO_2 emissions-reduction policy of the EC. Regardless of these negotiation matters the structure of India's CO_2 emissions is of interest to policy analysts in India and elsewhere. We try to quantify emissions here by economic sector, using the input-output approach explained in the next section.

The Base Case Input-output Act

In this context, transformed commodity flow matrix for the Indian economy generates a technology coefficient matrix simply by dividing each column, representing all inputs into a given activity divided by the level of output of that move. These coefficients are conventionally expressed in value of input/unit value of output. In the present exercise, for coal and petroleum refining activities, all inputs other than coal and petroleum products are described as value of input/tonne of carbon equivalent. In the case of coal and petroleum product inputs into these activities, the coefficients are interpreted as tonnes of carbon equivalent/ tonne. Same way, coal and petroleum product inputs into all other activities are interpreted as tonnes of carbon equivalent/unit value of output. The conventional solution of the input-output system is represented by:

$$X = [I - A]^{-1}F \qquad \text{. . . (1)}$$

Where X is a (60×1) vector representing levels of outputs of each activity; A is a (60×60) matrix containing input usage coefficients for each activity; and F is a (60×1) vector representing the ultimate demand for each commodity. F is the sum of vectors C, I, G and E-M, representing private consumption, gross investment (gross fixed capital formation + changes in stocks), government use and net exports (exports - imports) respectively.

For any row i (i = 1–60) of the $(I - A)^{-1}$ matrix, the jth element represents the combined direct and indirect requirement of commodity i to satisfy one unit of last demand for commodity j. We have two rows in the $(I - A)^{-1}$ matrix (i = 8, 26) denominated in terms of tonnes of carbon emissions. Representing these rows as CE^c and CE^p (carbon emissions from coal and petroleum made goods repectively), we derive the following measure of total (direct + indirect) carbon emissions arising from the satisfaction of each component of the final demand vector F:

$$TCE_i \equiv TCE^c_i + TCE^P_i = \Sigma_i\,(CE^c_i\, F_i) + (CE^P_i\, F_i) \qquad \text{. . . (2)}$$

where TCE_i is total carbon emissions attributed to the ith element of the ultimate demand vector from direct + indirect coal usage; TCE^P_i is total carbon emissions attributed to the ith element of F from direct + indirect petroleum product usage; CE^c_i is the ith element of the coal queue of the $(I - A)^{-1}$ matrix; CE^P_i is the ith element of the petroleum products row of the $(I - A)^{-1}$ matrix; and F_i is the ith element of the final demand vector F.

$\sum_i CE^c_i F_i = X^c$ = total carbon emissions from coal.

$\sum_i CE^p_i F_i = X^p$ = total carbon emissions from petroleum

Further,

$$PCE_i = TCE_i / \sum_i TCE_i \quad \ldots (3)$$

where PCE_i is the part of the ith sector in total carbon emission. Note that this exercise is carried out for carbon generated from production activities only. Carbon emitted from direct consumption of fuels (e.g., private transportation) is not considered. These, however, constitute a relatively small proportion of total carbon emissions.

Following section analyses the picture for unit carbon emissions by sector, and percentage distributions of carbon emissions across sectors for the 1983-84 technology coefficient matrix and final demand vector.

Pondering over Consequences: base case 1983-84

(a) *Sectoral Direct Carbon Emissions*

As can be seen in Fig. 16.2 that electricity is the largest sector, and is responsible for 28 million tonnes, or 33 per cent of all carbon

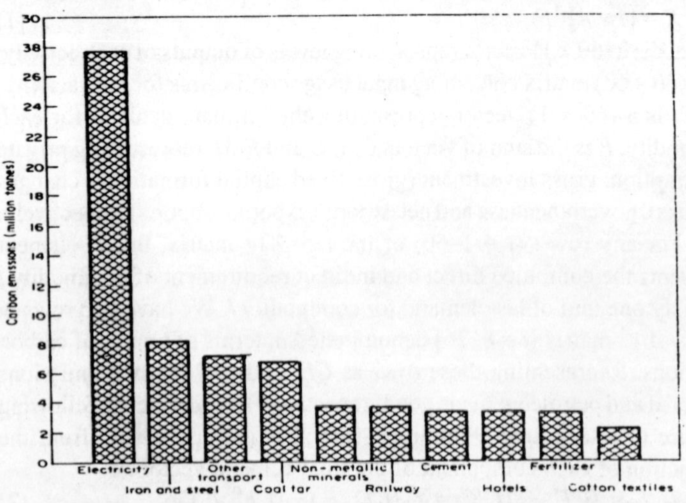

Fig. 16.2. Direct carbon emissions in India by sector, 1983-84.

Source: Model results by J. Parikh and S. Gokarn.

emissions from fossil fuels. The second largest sector is iron and steel, with a 9.8 per cent share of the total. Other transport, counting out railways, accounts for only 8.6 per cent of emissions. This is in contrast to the developed countries, where emissions from power and transport are comparable. Coal tar used in road buildings is the next highest (8.1 per cent. Non-metallic materials (4.5 per cent) which include glass, pottery, asbestos and so on, railways, cement, hotels and fertilizers all contribute similar amounts (roughly 4-5 per cent each).

Hotels and restaurants also include a huge variety of informal units, such as tea shops and sweet shops. Fertilizer production excludes fuel for feedstock because its use for feedstock does not contribute to carbon emissions. Emissions from cement also carry fuel-use as well as CO_2 emitted by the process of cement manufacturing. Together with cotton textiles (2.5 per cent these ten sectors account for 82 per cent of total emissions.

(b) Coefficients of Direct and Indirect Carbon Emission

Till now, our results have been similar to those which could have been obtained from some of the conventional methods. However, it is here that the input-output approach gives considerable further insights by tracing fuel flows in all sectors through all the elements of the $[I-A]^{-1}$ matrix. For example, to produce and transport coal, further fuel is needed. Similarly, fuel may also be needed to produce output of other sectors of the economy, used as inputs in the power/energy plants. These indirect requirements change the original patterns considerably. One has to be careful in interpreting the indirect requirements to avoid double (or multiple) counting.

However, what this stresses is that the associated carbon emissions are an essential part of a sector's activity, and need to be considered as an integral part of performing that activity. Here the direct and indirect carbon emission coefficients for all 60 sectors. It can be seen in Fig. 16.3 that electricity coefficient hike from 3.47 tonnes per Rs 1000 (from matrix A) to 4.89 tonnes to 2.95 tonnes. Due to its large transport requirements, the iron and stell sector move from fifth to third place and its coefficient increases from 0.92 to 2.22 tonnes. Once indirect emissions are accounted for, many sectors in Fig. 16.4 significantly increase the emission of carbon—paper (0.94 to 1.89); fertilizers (0.6 to 1.8); and inorganic chemicals (0.26 to 1.82). Again, non-metallic minerals increase from 1.2 to 1.8 tonnes. This above analysis stresses the importance of indirect emissions. However, to estimate emissions in the economy, these coefficients should be multiplied only by the final demand and not by the gross output vector. Otherwise in that situation there would be double counting. It must be stressed that the direct coefficients described above

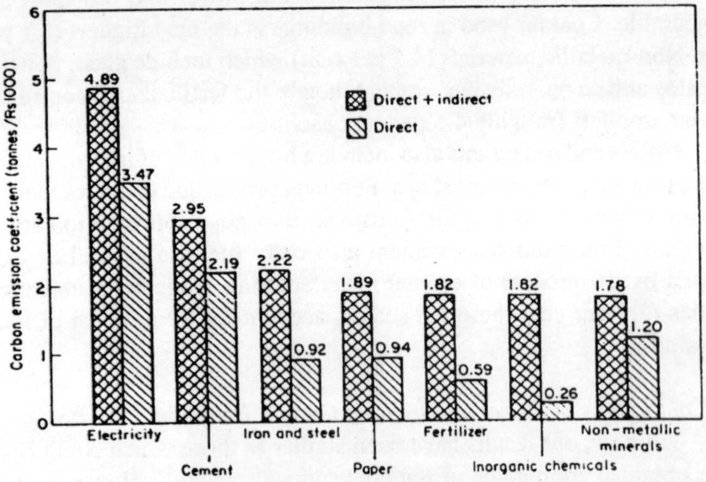

Fig. 16.3. Carbon emission coefficients, India, 1983-84.
Source: Model results by J. Parikh and S. Gokarn.

refer to the production of goods or services by each sector (tonnes of carbon/unit of output), whereas the indirect coefficients refer to the final (as opposed to the intermediate) demand fulfilled by the product of each sector (tonnes of carbon/unit of final demand satisfied). As the denominators are separate, the two are not comparable.

The comparisons made in this discussion are intended to highlight the different perspective that one gets about carbon emissions when the indirect coefficient becomes the ground of analysis. These sectors, along with their ratios of total of direct emissions, which shows values for all 60 sectors of the input—output table. Excessively high ratios of total to direct emissions can be seen in cash crops, animal husbandry, wool and synthetics, printing and publishing, petroleum products, machinery for food, textiles and electronics and other numerous transport equipment.

Most of all, construction has a very large indirect component. Some of the service-oriented activities which will increase in volume in future are communication, trade, medical and education, each one of which has not insignificant indirect emissions. Thus, the conventional approaches in the literature could gain substantial additional peeps if the indirect emissions are studied in detail. As is shown in the next section, a very different picture emerges when we obtain emissions by final demand.

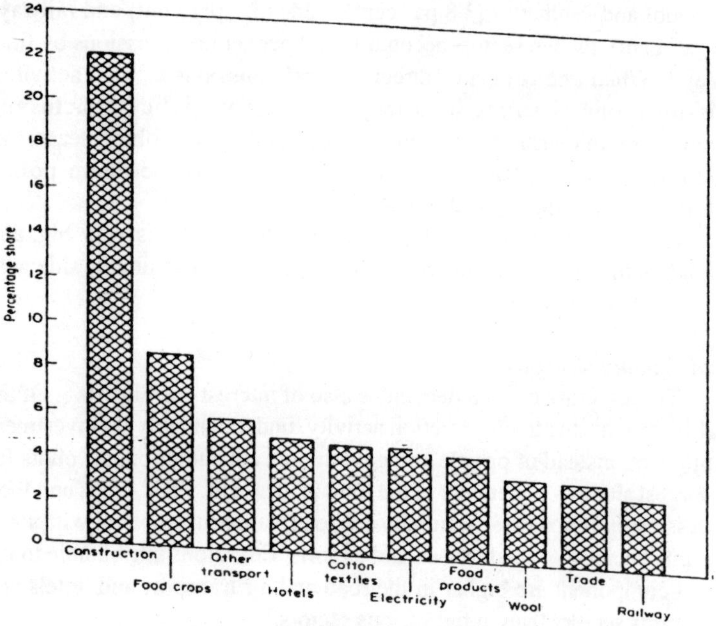

Fig. 16. 4. Percentage share in total carbon emissions, India, 1983-84.
Source: Model results by J. Parikh and S. Gokarn.

(*c*) *Utimate demand and then Emissions*

Insights given by emissions by final demand (the vector *F*) lead to interesting policy conclusions.

Sectoral Shares. Fig. 16.4 reveals that as much as 22 per cent of the emissions in the economy are attributable to the construction sector, which is the destination of energy-intensive materials such as iron and steel, cement, bricks, non-metallic minerals including glass, concrete and asbestos and wood. Much electricity goes into energy-intensive materials for construction to provide infrastructure for a growing economy.

The next most carbon-emitting basic need is in the food crop sector (8.6 per cent). As yet, agriculture in India is not energy-intensive. Moreover, food processing is listed as a separate final demand. 'Other transport', adding personal and public transport, is the third largest (6 per cent). (Goods and materials transported for construction or food production or processing are already included in those activities.) Sectors like hotels, cotton textiles, electricity and food processing account for roughly 5 per cent each. Together with wool and synthetics (3.8 per cent), trade (3.7 per cent) and railways (3.1 per cent), the ten sectors account for 67 per cent of emissions by final demand. When one compares direct sectoral emissions to final activities emissions, one is struck by a major alternative policy conclusion. Optimization of construction methods is as significant a policy measure as improving energy efficiencies, which is the most common policy prescription for reducing CO_2 emissions.

In a growing economy, the need for infrastucture is very big, and alternative methods of construction should be considered side by side with energy-efficiency measures for CO_2 reduction.

Final demand structure

The structure of final demand is also of interest see Fig. 16.5. Of the total emissions due to construction activity, understandably its investment component, instead of private and government consumption, accounts for the largest share—19 per cent of the total 22 per cent. Food crops and food processing emissions are essentially due to private consumption, with some amounts because of seeds, stock and exports. Emissions attributable to the export component are higher in the road and air transport and hotels and restaurants sectors than in the various sectors.

Scenarios of Policy for Energy/Power

Till now, we have seen the relationships between the structure of Indian economy and CO_2 emissions as they are captured in the input-output matrix of 1983-84. We have seen which are the largest emitting sectors. After inverting the matrix, we also found which final demand sectors are the most CO_2 emitting. How do these structural details help to formulate policy for CO_2 reduction? That is, given the structure of the system, how will it reply external policies such as reducing CO_2 emissions? We consider two types of policies for reducing CO_2 emissions:

1. Decreasing use of either coal or oil by conservation of the same amount of useful energy, so as to highlight the difference between these two conservation alternatives.
2. Substituting oil for coal, a fuel with more CO_2 emissions than oil, keeping the same energy use in the economy.

It is guessed that these policies can be effected without affecting the levels of production. Undoubtedly, it will take some time before the changes

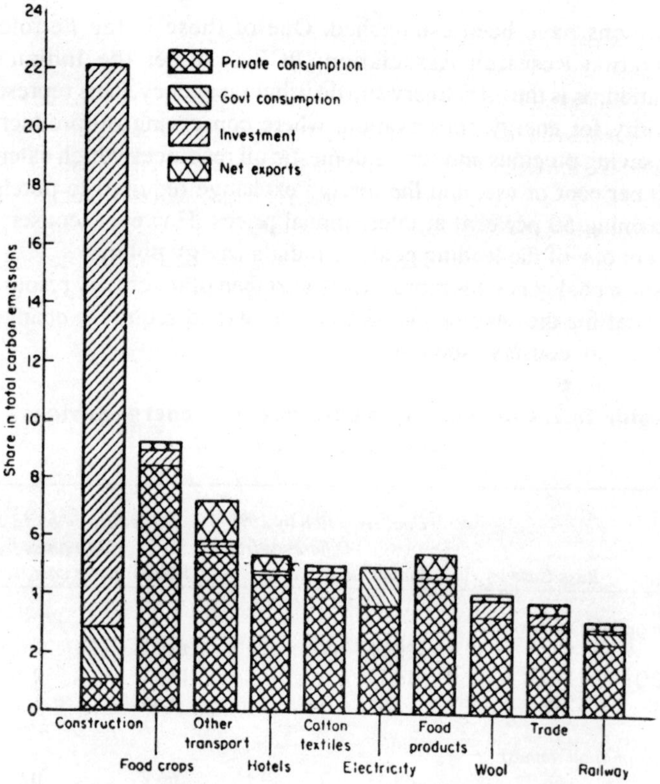

Fig. 16.5. Carbon shares from final demand, India, 1983-84.
Source: Model results by J. Parikh and S. Gokarn.

are made, and some feel that, for this reason, a simulation of scenarios for, say, the year 2000 or beyond is necessary. However, this compounds two uncertainties—the accuracy with which the scenario for 2000 can be prepared and the accuracy with which the effects of policies can be captured. To avoid being diverted into another exercise of generating scenarios for the future, we consider the following problems in the base year itself, 1983-84, thinking these policies work instantly.

What can we learn about the effects of CO_2 reduction policies? This question is addressed for two separate policies—energy conservation of coal and oil and energy substitution of coal with oil.

(a) *With energy conservation CO_2 reduction*

It has been a goal of India's energy policy for some time. Several organizations have been established. One of these is the Petroleum Conservation Research Association (PCRA) under the Indian Oil Corporation, as is the oil refinery and distribution agency. This represents the priority for energy conservation, where conserving oil/products is seen as saving precious and scarce domestic oil resources which cater for only 50 per cent of use, and the foreign exchange required to purchase the remaining 50 per cent at international prices. However, conserving coal is not one of the leading goals of India's energy policy.

Since coal generates more CO_2 per GJ than other energy resources, saving coal for the sake of global warming would require a change in India's energy conservation policy.

Table 16.2. Comparison of base case with energy savings from coal and oil.

		Coal reduction by 10%		*Oil reduction by 13.5%*	
	Base Case	*Values*	*Difference from base case*	*Values*	*Difference from base case*
Tonnage (million tonnes)					
Coal	121.3	109.17	12	121.3	0
HSD/LDO	14.13	14.13	0	12.22	2
FO/LSHS	5.6	5.6	0	4.84	1
Emissions (million tonnes)					
Coal	66.2	59.58	7	66.2	0
HSD/LDO	12.43	12.43	0	10.75	2
FO/LSHS	4.43	4.43	0	3.83	1
Total	83.06	76.44	7	80.78	2
Value (million Rs)					
Coal	24.260	21.834	2.426	24.260	0
HSD/LDO	41.431	41.431	0	53.838	5593
FO/LSHS	15.120	15.120	0	13.003	2117
Total	80.811	78.735	2.076	73.101	7710

To evaluate the implications of this shift, we compare two scenarios, both of which save the same amount of useful GJ (107 million GJ). To save this energy from coal, we would require a 10 per cent reduction of coal use (i.e., 10 per cent of 121 million tonnes of coal). To protect this energy from oil, a 13.5 per cent reduction in oil use would be necessary. We compare saving 250 million GJ from coal with saving the same amount from oil. Table 16.2 gives this comparison, along with base case outcome with no such policy.

Table 16.2 highlights two scenarious in which 107 million useful GJ are saved from coal and oil respectively, assuming that the relative efficiency of oil to coal is 2.35. Since the economy consumers much more coal than oil, despite the lower heat value, only 10 per cent coal savings are required to save the same useful GJ as a 13.5 per cent reduction in oil consumption.

In actual amounts, this changes into 12.1 million tonnes of coal and 2.7 million tonnes of oil. It will be assumed that it is possible to do this without incurring capital costs, or that they have similar capital costs. Both results are against the base case (i.e., no energy savings). It can be seen that 6.6 million tonnes of carbon will be saved if this energy is saved from coal, but only 2.18 million tonnes of carbon are saved if it is saved from oil. Both keep safe the same amounts of GJ, and values of fuel used are much lower compared to the base case for both the cases.

However, more valuable fuel in the oil-saving scenario is saved—Rs 7.7 billion compared to the base case. On the other side, only Rs 2.4 billion would be saved if this much energy were saved from coal. Clearly, it is in India's interest to save oil rather than coal. The marginal cost of the additional carbon savings from coal against oil is Rs 1150 per tonne of carbon (US$1 = Rs10 in 1983-84).

Table 16.3. Sectoral emissions under alterrnative scenarios of savings from coal and oil

Sector	*Base case Values (10^6 tonnes of carbon)*	*Coal reduction by 10% (Values 10^6 tonnes of carbon)*	*Difference from base case*	*Oil reduction by 13.5% Values (10^6 tonnes of carbon)*	*Difference from base case*
Electricity	27.73	25.00	2.73	27.67	0.06
Iron and steel	8.18	7.43	0.75	8.1	0.08
Other transport	7.18	7.16	0.02	6.25	0.93
Coal tar	6.75	6.08	0.67	6.75	0.00
Non-metallic minerals	3.75	3.42	0.33	3.68	0.07
Railways	3.64	3.36	0.28	3.52	0.12
Cement	3.37	3.04	0.33	3.36	0.01
Hotels	3.33	3.12	0.21	3.32	0.01
Fertilizers	3.2	3.08	0.12	3.00	0.20
Cotton textiles	2.13	1.95	2.13	2.08	0.05

However, in any case, one should look beyond the amount of carbon savings and at the details. Table 16.3 indicates which sectors require more attention. For example, in the case of saving coal, it would be necessary to save carbon from the sector of power (2.7 million tonnes of carbon), iron and steel (0.8 million tonnes), coal tar (0.7 millionl tonnes) and 0.2 to 0.3 million tonnes each from non-metallic minerals, railways and cement. On the other side if one has to save this carbon from oil, a completely different sectoral strategy is required. Most attention will be required for the transport sector (0.9 million tonnes), iron and steel (0.7 million tonnes), and fertilizers (0.2 million tonnes). This shift of attention to different sectors will also translate into diversion of efforts— manpower, fuels, technology development etc. Thus the GHG reduction savings policy would be at variance with India's energy conservation policy, which has emphasized saving oil.

(*b*) *Scenarios for Fuel Substitution*

Presently, India follows the policy of substituting coal for oil because of an abundance of coal resources and inadequate oil production, resulting in large imports. When oil cannot be substituted by coal directly, it is done through electricity production like diesel pumps have been systematically replaced by electric pumps over the last 15 years, oil-fired boilers by coal-fired boilers, and so on. Even diesel in transport is substituted by electricity by electrification of railways and by encouraging suburban electric railways when possible. The need for massive investment has limited the progress of these substitutions, but they are a component of strategic planning.

These measures are not only for the limited purpose of fuel substitution, but also to speed up transport and reduce congestion. Therefore, we construct two fuel substitution scenarios as explained above along with the assumption of relative efficiency of a factor of 2 between oil and coal. Unlike in the previous case, where energy was reduced (conservation), here only substitution takes places, i.e., energy in the economy in terms of GJ does not come down. There are two equivalent scanarios: 10 per cent of coal consumption substituted by oil and 13.5 per cent of oil or gas consumption substituted by coal.

The difference between the two can be explained as the implications of changing the fuel substitution policy from its current policy. It should be pointed out that currently much more gas is available to make it possible to carry out gas substitution. In fact, gas-based power generation is already picking up rapidly.

But gas is also priced as an oil-equivalent fuel. Therefore, the results discussed below are likely to be of same kind for gas substitution for coal.

We can well see in Table 16.4 that the current policy of substitution will lead to 12 million tonnes of additional coal and would cut nearly 3 million tonnes of oil, leading to 4.3 million tonnes and 8.7 million tonnes of additional carbon emissions against base case and oil substitution, respectively. However, it saves fuel worth Rs. 10.600 million over the alternative policy of coal substitution by oil (or gas).

Thus, the alternative substitution policy will cost Rs10.5 billion in fuel only, but will save 8.7 million tonnes of carbon. The magnitude of the trade-off is, in this framework, purely an act of the relative price (per unit of useful energy) of the two energy sources. This cost measure captures only the variable cost implications of fuel substitution, and ignores the differences in capital requirements of substitutions in various sectors of the economy.

Table 16.4. Comparison of alternative substitution scenarios.

	Base case	*Substitution of coal for oil*	*Substitution of oil for coal*	*Difference between (2) and (3)*
Fuel tonnage (million tonnes)				
Coal	121.30	133.43	109.17	24.26
HSD/LDO	14.10	12.52	16.07	–3.55
FO/LSHS	5.60	4.84	6.36	–1.52
Emissions (million tonnes of carbon)				
Coal	66.20	72.82	59.58	13.24
HSD/LDO	12.43	10.75	14.10	–3.35
FO/LSHS	4.43	3.83	5.02	–1.19
Total	83.06	87.40	78.71	8.69
Value (million Rs)				
Coal	24.260	26.686	21.834	4.852
HSD/LDO	41.431	35.838	47.024	–11.186
FO/LSHS	15.120	13.079	17.161	–4.082
Total	80.811	75.603	86.019	–10.416

HSD=high-speed diesel; FO=fuel oil; LDO=light diesel oil; LSHS=low-sulphur heavy stock.
Model results by J. Parikh and S. Gokarn.

If we see in a wider sense, the costs of fuel substitution should also consider (i) the opportunity costs of increased foreign exchange outlays on petroleum products and capital goods; (ii) the prices of diminished output of coal in terms of regional income and employment effects; and (iii) the costs (or benefits) of the change in the nature of local pollutants resulting from the substitution. It is protemetic to assess a *priori* which of these various components will eventually dominate the cost of substitution.

If the variable energy costs are the most significant element, then the trade-offs quantified here may be right approximations of the true costs of carbon savings achieved through fuel substitution.

Conclusion

Energy policy planners of India need to take note of the current debate on global warming. This concern has devalued India's coal resources. There will be pressures from international aid agencies to substitute gas and oil instead of coal. India needs to study its options carefully. We have estimated CO_2 emissions for 60 sectors for India from the input-output matrix for 1983-84. The highest emissions are from the electricity sector (33 per cent) followed by iron and steel (9.8 per cent), and, road and air transport (8.6 per cent), coal tar (8.1per cent), non-metallic minerals (4.5 per cent), railways (4.3 per cent), cement (4.0 percent), hotels and restaurants (4.0 per cent). While comparing direct and indirect emission coefficients from every sector, it can be seen that total emission coefficients could be much larger than direct emission coefficients for many sectors, such as electricity, iron and steel, cement, and the others.

The Indira Gandhi Institute of Development Research (IGIDR) has carried out a detailed exercise concerning the possibilities of reducing carbon emissions by the power system in India. It may be feasible to do that with modest investment.

When one inverts the matrix and multiplies it with the final demand vector, an entirely different picture emerges. We get emissions by demand, where all indirect and embodied emissions are noticed. The order of emissions for final demand are: construction (22%), food crops (8.6%), road and air transport (6%), and so on. Construction by itself is not a very CO_2-intensive activity, but that picture varies when one considers the coal and oil *embodied* in construction materials such as iron and steel, metals and alloys, glass, cement and bricks. When multiplied by the final demand vector, it is the biggest largest CO_2-emitting sector.

Understandably, the construction needs of a growing developing nation which needs to build factories, offices, roads, schools, hospitals and houses, are considerable. On the other hand, food crops production, which is the first basic need, is not as energy-intensive because it is handled with labour-intensive technologies. Electricity, which is more an intermediate good, moves to sixth from first place. This exercise brings out the important policy conclusion that *increasing construction efficiency* by optimizing the usefulness of construction materials, as well as by implementing construction technologies that use less energy-intensive materials, could be as important as improving energy efficiency for decreasing carbon emissions.

While the latter is well known, not enough attention is given to the former to reduce CO_2 emissions. Much of the construction is needed for infrastructure and production purposes. Carbon is used in exports in transport and hotels, and it is embedded in imports, in iron and steel and electricity. Policy scenarios of energy conservation for fossil fuels are also carried out. Two scenarios are formed, both of which save 250 PJ (PJ = 10^6 GJ) of primary energy: one saves it from coal and the other saves it from oil. They show that while both coal and oil reduction lead to reduced CO_2 emissions, to decrease energy from oil is more attractive for India due to savings in imported oil. India's preferred energy policy would be to save oil rather than coal. For example, saving 250 PJ from coal saves only Rs 2706 million.

Similar amount of useful energy savings (about 107 PJ) could be obtained from primary energy reduction from oil and would save Rs 7710 million. This difference of Rs 5634 million could be interpreted as incremental prices to India to follow coal-conserving policies. It is necessary to take such wide interpretations of *incremental costs* where two development strategies are compared and not just to apply a cost-benefit analysis of coal conservation projects different from other alternatives. Also at stake are the totally different sectoral approaches necessary to achieve this reduction. For example, to reduce CO_2 from coal would need efforts for power (2.7 million tons), iron and steel (0.8 million tonnes), coal tar (0.7 million tonnes), and so on. On the other hand, reducing CO_2 from oil would require efforts in models of road and air transport (0.9 million tonnes), iron and steel (0.7 million tonnes), fertilizers (0.2 million tonnes), and so on.

This diversion of attention to various sectors will also translate into diversion of manpower, fuels, technology development, etc. Thus, a GHG reduction policy which would emphasize coal conservation would be at variance with India's energy conservation policy, which has stressed saving oil rather than coal. When coal substitution by oil and gas is promoted, the incremental costs of following such a strategy are even more because precious resources are substituted in place of cheap and abundant coal. Substitution of 10 per cent coal in energy terms leads to additional coals of Rs 10.416 billion. This would also be a difference with India's current substitution policy which promotes the substitution of coal for oil in this situation.

17

Indian Reactions towards FCCC Implementation

This Chapter is an extract of Inaugural address by Sh. Kamal Nath. Then Minister for Environment and Forests at the International workshop titled "Joint Implementation of Abatemeat Commitments Under the Framework Convention and Climate Change." The Indian effort was organised by Tata Energy Research Institute (TERI) at 10-00 hrs at IIC, New Delhi dated 21st January 1994. The chapter, i.e., inaugural address contains India's standpoint on the International FCCC.

The matter came up for discussion for the first time at the 8th INC in August last year and generated a plethora of views, from the legalistic to the practical. It is a controversy that we can well do without, because it should not be allowed side-track the real challenges that confront us and the core of what we set out to achieve at Rio.

The concept of Joint Implementation is new and seems to represent different views to different people. Our understanding has been more in the nature of appreciating the various aspects as to what is really meant by it, and its applicability in the overall context of the Convention itself.

Before we actually go on to assign a definition to Joint Implementation it is necessary that we assess its implications. Humankind is today in an unprecedented—and, may I add, unenviable position, and climate change is one of the challenges facing humanity. For millions of years the greenhouse effect has maintained the earth's climate at a stable average temperature, permitting life to flourish. However, human activities on land, water and soil have gradually grown unsustainably, and have experienced a quantum leap during the last century or so. In the span of a single human generation the earth's life-sustaining environment is now expected to change more rapidly than it has in any comparable period of human history. Much of this change will be of our own making, and we have it in our power to control it to some extent.

Climate Change itself was virtually an unknown issue 15 years ago, but even small changes in our gaseous environment have big effects. The impact of climate change measured in terms of increase in an average global temperature would result in sea level rise, extreme weather patterns, regional disruption of water supply, declining food production, damaged forests, wildlife and biodiversity, and harmful, unpredictable effects on public health. A UN report says that the world faces a 3 °C rise in average temperature within the next century, and if this is to be contained, we would have to go in for at least a 70 per cent cut in human generated carbon dioxide and other greenhouse gases urgently.

The bulk of the earlier CO_2 build-up is on account of industrial countries, which are even today the largest sources of gaseous emissions. In spite of this, in a spirit of global cooperation, the developing countries, who have done little or nothing to create the problem, entered into negotiations and a large number of them, including India, signed the Framework Convention on Climate Change at the Earth Summit in 1992. It has now received the required number of ratifications and the Convention is expected to come into force on the 21st March 1994, (coincidentally but appropriately on the day of the Spring Equinox, regarded since pre-historic times the world over as a day of natural regeneration).

The Convention acknowledges that the change in the earth's climate and its adverse effects are a common concern of humankind: it at the same time recognises that all Parties, taking into account their common but *differentiated* responsibilities, and their specific national and regional development priorities will formulate, promote and cooperate in the implementation of the objectives of the Convention. The objectives deal with reduction and sequestration of greenhouse gas concentrations in a manner that would prevent danger to our ecosystems and reduce interference with the climate system, while ensuring that food production is not threatened, and enabling economic development to proceed in a sustainable manner.

These goals have to be achieved by reducing emissions through control of emission sources and sequestering harmful gases by enhancing carbon sinks. Perhaps the mechanism of Joint Implementation has been flagged in this context. Ever since the concept of Joint Implementation was mooted, divergent views have been voiced. But whatever interpretation is ultimately agreed upon, I am sure that all of you would agree that there can be no mechanism which encourages the needless growth of emissions, on the one hand, and creates hurdles in the path of swift development of economically poor societies on the other.

We cannot allow legalistic wrangling to side-track the fundamental issue of international equity. We have to recognise that sustainable development globally is unachievable without the removal of obstructions to equitable relations between and within nations. Central to this discussion is an absolute need for a thorough socio-economic assessment of 'global benefit', *what* it is and *who* provides it; and equally important an assessment of 'global disbenefit', *what* it is and *who* provides it. In making this assessment, we would have to accept the fact that people who live sustainably (and have been doing so for centuries) in terms of globally equitable and efficient use of energy per capita, provide global benefit, whilst people with unsustainable lifestyles, in terms of globally equitable resource use per capita, create global disbenefit. The real tension in this debate is that between 'costs' and 'benefits'. Cost/Benefit Analysis is being used to distract attention from the kernel of the debate. We cannot allow Joint Implementation to be given an interpretation which would result in an attempt to 'pass on the abatement parcel' to the *wrong* address, without even putting on the proper postage!

I would like to draw the attention of this Workshop to the fact that while change in the earth's climate and its adverse effects are admittedly the common concern of humankind, the Convention envisages that the actions to meet the challenge are to be based on *differentiated responsibilities* and are *dependent* on the *capabilities* of the countries. While all States are responsible for preventing further damage to the atmosphere, it is inescapable that this responsibility is in direct proportion to the contribution of each to the harmful gases, and to the technological and financial means at their disposal. The 'precautionary principle', supplements the traditional imperative of 'react and correct' with 'forecast and prevent': activities are to be permitted only if it is certain that they do not cause serious damage to the atmosphere. But this cannot be interpreted to mean that the socio-economic development of the South can be thwarted, while the prodigious lifestyles of the North can remain untouched, by juggling around with averages and semantics.

Conspicuous lifestyles have harmed our environment irreparably. Deprivation and poverty, are not going to help the environment in any way, either. Everyone is vulnerable to the unmitigated continuation of stark inequalities in living standards. If disaster strikes our planet we all suffer. A cocoon of luxury will not cushion us from the reverberations of unjust and skewed patterns of development. There are a host of areas which revolve around this question, and which would be resolved only with fundamental structural change in the international economic order.

I would not like to prejudice the deliberations of this international workshop with a strait-jacketted view in the inaugural session itself, but I would certainly like to underscore the need for standing on its head any presumption about the utility or otherwise of any interpretation of Joint Implementation. We would have to address a variety of questions:

(a) To what extent would Joint Implementation facilitate the transfer of technology to developing countries?

(b) To what extent would the overall objectives of emission reduction be achieved?

(c) Do we have reliable methodologies to determine the base scenario of emissions which could be used to calculate the amount of emissions actually avoided through Joint Implementation?

(d) What are the financial and economic implications of Joint Implementation?

(e) What are the political implications in terms of sovereignity over natural resources?

(f) Will Joint Implementation adequately facilitate the quantum reductions envisioned by scientists, or would it result in side-stepping core issues?

It would be too optimistic to hope that all these questions will be answered in this workshop; but poised as we are at the eve of the 9th INC, and gathered as we have here some of the finest international experts on the subject, I am sure that your deliberations will help clarify the implications of, and the concerns regarding, this crucial issue.

18

Conclusion

There are numerous ways in which human activity can affect the environmental changes. One method is through changing the characteristics of earth's surface, e.g., turning a large forest into a parsture, agriculture or urban land, which changes the amount of sunlight that is absorbed or reflected at earth's surface, the roughness of the surface of earth or/and its hydrological characteristics. One more method, which is of particular interest to the researches, is by adding gases and particles to the atmosphere, referred to as the increased 'greenhouse effect.' Both the methods have been found treatment in this volume to some extent thus more factor has been made on the global warming through greenhouse effect. A number of other industrial and agricultural practices, apart from the ones mentioned above also make significant contributions.

Time and again, it is being reproduced in the study that main greenhouse gas that is emitted in the atmosphere is CO_2 which is produced through burning of fuels like coal, oil and natural gases in order to generate energy used of transportation, heating, manufacturing and numerous other applications. Next significant gas is methane which is added to atmosphere through cultivations of rice, etc. Then came CFCs due to their role in depletion of ozone layer.

Climate change caused through various factors is likely to have wide ranging impacts on human health with a noted grant in mortality because of heat stress and increases in potential transmission of many infections diseases, including malaria, dengue and yellow fever. The IPCC has estimated that while it may be possible for global agricultural production to keep pace with increasing demand over the next fifty years to a century if appropriate adaptations are made, there is possibility for difficulties in certain regions.

In dealing with the climate at national levels, numerous analysis, reports and seminars, etc., in recent years have been devoted to how the governments can best exert influence on large and small decision-makers in order to avoid a continuations of trends that might lead to uncontrollable manmade environmental change. In spite of the remaining gaps in scientific knowledge, we know well which direction we should go if IPCC agreement is not completely off the mark. We, which includes, well aware governments and citizens—know very well what kind of action to avoid at both macro and micro level. The problem is about the methodology to avoid it.

Domestic and regional level formulation of climate policy started in many countries and continents with the well-established instruments of environmental policy or evolved in 1970s and 1980s, along with stress on command and control. To varying amount's supported by informations campaigns and public research funding. In the previous pages of the book, we have discussed national level approaches and attempts towards proposed disasters of environmental changes which include the United States of America, Soviet Union and China among big powers. Apart from these, environmental policies of New Zealand, Malaysia, Austria also find mention in different chapters. As a follow up of consensus at various platforms of international level, environmental efforts and policies of Indian subcontinent has received special treatment. Last but not the least. Asian continental understanding of changing environment concern up through a special chapter on this subject.

In all this chapters, we have seen that either global agreements only or domestic efforts alone cannot solve the problem. Both national and international steps need to be coordinated in order to have a fruitful solution to difficulties stemming from the climatic changes. Most important behind there is political will to fight the problems which should start at unilateral, i.e., national level. It is also said that success of political initiatives is not that easy to realise. But the hard fact is that if political intervention is ineffective at domestic level, what can we expect beyond that. In this state of affairs, meaningful action at international level will become almost inconceivable. That would, in fact, be self-defeating, as national measures, even for the developed countries can be meaningful only if other Government also take appropriate action. Therefore, the dual difficulty: fragile indifferent steps at national level must somehow be coordinated globally if they are to make any sense in relation to the assumed collective problems.

While talking of inter-governmental organisation in their context, it can have a number of functions vis-a-vis the participating states. In the simplest interpretation, an inter-governmental organisation, i.e., an IGO is just a forum for discussion among State representatives but even this apparently technical act can have the effect of setting an environmental issue on the agenda of governments, compelling them to consider the subject matter. With an international regime going up the track of IGO functions, the potential for feedback to domestic level changes miraculously. As evident, fundamental driving forces behind environmental policy are hidden primarily within the national boundaries.

Thus, the significance of connections to the domestic politics, the very first concerns the science element in the national context. As much research findings about the environment are international. The connection to the outside world will often be seeable from the first discussion on an issue. On the other hand, international assessment like IPCC will support the scientific capability participating nations. In the same manners, fixing objectives standards and targets at international level will improve the readability and status of domestication like environmental NGOs.

If this becomes operational anyhow, if some governments of atleast developing countries can be sufficiently attracted to produce and execute some plans for national efforts, the first steps towards global monitoring system will be acknowledged as initiative from the south almost inevitably. And if others follow the practice, this could slowly develop into a comprehensive reviews. And on both sides, NGOs and other national interests can use the information given and evaluation done to influence the governments at home. If such a systems of mechanism can be ensured, both the national and international actors will be satisfied and in wider interest, problems of environment (change) can be tackled to a large extent.

Index

F

G

H

I

ENVIRONMENT AND ITS GLOBAL IMPLICATIONS

ENVIRONMENT AND ITS GLOBAL IMPLICATIONS

THEORY AND PRACTICE—VOL. I

Edited by
Gopal Bhargava

PUBLICATIONS

KALPAZ PUBLICATIONS

DELHI - 110052

ENVIRONMENT AND ITS GLOBAL IMPLICATIONS
(Environment)

Rs. 1800 (Set)
Rs. 900 each volume

ISBN : 81-7835-113-7 (Set)

ISBN : 81-7835-130-7 (Vol. I)

Published in 2002 in India by
Kalpaz Publications
C-30, Satyawati Nagar
Delhi 110 052

Laser Typesetting: Graphic Print, Delhi
Printed at: Chawla Offset Press, Delhi

Contents

Preface

Talking about environment has become fashion of the day. But the issue is not so simple as it appears to be. If we do not pay serious attention to the problems associated with it right now, our future generation will not be passed on a safe and healthy environment to live. But our scientists, academicians, politicians and social workers are not ignorant of this fear of environmental sword hanging on their heads. They all are engaged in their own way in finding solution to the present and more disastrous future hazards that might occur due to the rapid changes that are taking place either globally and locally.

Since efforts in this regard are highly significant a global level, so a number of attempts have been made and are being at international level in the form of various agreements, treaties, conventions and formation of agencies and panels. IPCC is the most important amongst these which along with other finds mention in the various chapters. There have also been regional associations more specifically of third world countries.

It is a well proven fact that Environmental change is the bigger hurdle in the development of developing nations as are still in the process of setting foot and coping with the problems arising out of these changes are even more troublesome which involves both cost and technology. This way, they are more vulnerable than the developed world.

Issues like global warming, air pollution, water shortage, forestation and natural disasters like floods, droughts, volcanos etc. are generating equal tension among both developed, and developing world. Though the process of looking for solutions and alternatives to environmental hazard, has brought them closer to one another on international platform, still, a lot needs to be done to ensure sustainability of environment and stabilisation of changes.

This book, an effort in this regard, makes an attempt to document various theoretical and practical aspects of environmental change at one place and thus serves as a good source of information for environmentalists, researchers as well as social workers Its suggestion and recommendation in the chapter "Environmental Concerns" can be of use to implementing agencies also.

The book has been divided into six sections. It contains 19 chapters in total.

Section I is general about technical and human aspect of environment and the regular changes with it.

Section II discusses the impacts of environmental change in sources and human activities. Specific impacts on Agriculture and food supply, electric energy and mineral energy are also discussed.

Section III is about efforts made/ being made/ to be made at global level and for that matter formations of various global and regional bodies.

Section IV presents solutions and alternatives to tackle the problems arising out of continuous changes in environment.

Section V is miscellaneous section which talks about economy and computer models.

Section VI, i.e., the last section is conclusion of the whole book in the form of summary of hurdles and recommendations.

Gopal Bhargava

Introduction

Problem related to environment is one of the burning issues of the day and for that matter environmental change is a topic of endless fascination. Day to day variations in environment are a staple of conversation in many countries. The developed world has experienced the increasing volume of foreign travel in recent years which has given more and more people direct experience of climates different from those in their native countries. It is normal to compare present environmental conditions with those of past years. On longer time scales older people often contrast present day weather with that of their youth. There is also widespread realisation that climate conditions in remote past were different from the present ones.

This is well-known to all of us that past human societies, with less developed technologies were more vulnerable than ourselves to short-term disasters like drought, flood and storms leading to harvest failure and famine. We know that there have been periods in the past for colder than today, when ice sheets covered extensive areas of the northern land masses as well as warmer eras such as those when the huge animals like dinosaurs appeared and flourished.

In an over populated world the impact of environmental disasters is brought into our homes by the media. Natural disasters are often exacerbated by political instability or economic mis-management. These disasters frequently affect underdeveloped countries but some latest experiences in Britain and USA demonstrate that these can also have a substantial effect on the developed world.

Assumptions of future changes having a serious impact on humanity used to be the sole preserve of science fiction writers who have entertained, and some times scared us with their tales of returning glacier conditions, global warming and a rising sea level. Within last two decades however, environmental change has stepped outside the realm of science fiction to become a real worry for all of us. In recent years there has been an explosion of awareness and concern over environmental issues among the masses within the industrialised world. Some worries are local, such as landscape changes caused by the construction of a new motorway. Other issues are significant on regional scale like the problem of acid rain. Some more issues are truly global and of these, change is probably the most important in that it is likely to affect everyone to a certain extent in future. Therefore, coming to terms with the problem by trying to adapt to environmental changes or attempting to reduce their impact by cutting greenhouse gas emissions also requires a truly global approach.

In the late 80's and early 90's, the term 'greenhouse effect', and 'global warming' came into everyday use and there was a great upsurge of interest in the subject. At a time when green issues were receiving unprecedented attention, worry about global warming was highlighted by the media in a spate of popular books, articles, TV documentaries and news items. It was difficult to open any current affairs magazine without finding a reference to global warming and its possible consequences. Such media often made dire predictions about floods, droughts and famines, etc.

Efforts of global level also began to be made in this direction. In 1988 the world meteorological organisation and the UN environmental programme—inter-governmental panel on climate change (IPCC) are the important ones to be mentioned here. The group of almost 400 scientists was given the task of assessing and summarising current knowledge on environmental change specifically the possibilities of global warming. In 1989, at the Toronto Conference on the changing Atmosphere with the benefit of improved computer models, there was a call to initiate practical measures to cut emissions of carbon dioxide. There was general agreement at the conference that the effects of global warming were likely to prove second only to global nuclear war if man did not start cutting back greenhouse gas emissions on a substantial scale. Many politicians were reluctant to take any action until the IPCC report appeared even though it was only intended to summarise existing knowledge rather than present new findings.

The first IPCC scientific report came out in 1990 with a follow-up in 1992. Though it was criticised for brushing aside controversies and failing to highlight uncertainties, it has become an important yardstick against which new research findings can be assessed. The scientific assessment called for a start on discussions about political action. In 1992, the second UN Conference on Environment and Development was held at Rio-De-Janerio. One of the major results was signing of a Framework Convention on climate change which represented a more towards concerted action on reduction of greenhouse gas emissions.

As a resuIt of these notable developments, global warming appeared increasingly on political agendas, though the real progress has been slow. There has been an inevitable difficulty in presentation of future state of environment due to media. Much media coverage of issues about environmental change and global warming has been alarmist and sensationalist, taking extreme scenario and presenting them as near-certainty with the little discussion of possibilities of their happening or the possible time scale involved. Media reporting has often overlooked areas of consensus and focussed on extreme position on a way more appropriate to political debates. This has also led to misguidance of scientist busy with conducting research on the subject.

More attention has been given to management options that would reduce the emissions of CO_2 associated with energy use. Studies have looked at the potential emissions reductions as a result of measures affecting both demand and supply of energy (IPCC report, 1996). After the 1996 IPCC assessment of the impacts of change, the need for more regionally based approaches was recognised. This led to the IPCC (1998) report on The Regional Impacts of Climate Change. An Assessment of Vulnerability and a variety of national of regional impact assessments. Many more efforts in the direction and Environmental change have been made at international platform in the form of various conventions, panels, treaties and agreements etc. which will find mention in various chapters of the book. Since it is important to understand the significance of environment on society in general and humanity in particular, the book incorporates both the impacts as well as recommendations for sustainability of change in the Ecosystem.

1

Some Basics about World Environmental Change

World Weather: Global and Regional

If we look into the past one century, we see that a new chapter has opened in the history of the atmosphere's chemical composition—a chapter written by the man. Atmospheric carbon dioxide (CO_2) concentrations measured at the summit of the volcano Mauna Loa in Hawaii gave the first intimations of an anthropogenic effects on the climate system (Keeling *et al.* 1976). Data from numerous other sources later approved these intimations, which finally connected to data on earlier climates extracted from ice cores given in graph 1.1. Though today we are not sure of all the ramifications these changes may have for the climate in the next few centuries, still the data accumulating indicate that climate has become warmer during the last hundred years.

Furthermore, there is growing evidence that changes in the atmosphere's chemical composition can affect global climate to an extent comparable to or exceeding that associated with natural climate variability. This effect is due to the increase in the atmospheric greenhouse gases.

Some of these GHGs are purely of anthropogenic origin whereas the emission of others—especially CO_2 has rose significantly during the last hundred years. Compared to the loading of the atmosphere with relatively short-lived pollutants that have a merely local impact, the changes in the atmosphere brought about by the fairly stable GHGs are cumulative and have a global influence. Potential consequences and appropriate response strategies therefore involve our planet as a whole. These inferences have led to the concept of global environmental change.

Box 1.1. Global Climate during the Last Hundred Years.

In July 1955, the General Assembly of IUGG (the International Union of Geodesy and Geophysics) in Boulder, Colorado, evidence from various observational techniques, model calculations and analyses of natural archives were brought together give the message that our present climate is anomalously warm. Observations on land and in the ocean show a global warming of 0.3 to 0.6 Kelvin[3] over the past one century. This warming trend's causes are not yet fully known, but evidence for the importance of the role played by anthropogenic greenhouse gases and sulphate areosols is becoming more powerful. Some uncertainty regarding the cause of global warming is linked to the fact that data from the last one Millennium demonstrate that significant climate fluctuations have occurred as a result of natural phenomena such as volcanic eruptions, fluctuations in solar irradiance, changes in the earth's orbit around the sun, and internal fluctuations of the combined ocean/atmosphere system (e.g., the EI Nino/ Southern Oscillation phenomenon).

Model calculations of growing complexity show that the superposition of natural and anthropogenic factors can explain why the global temperature trend may have a different sign in some parts of the world (e.g., cooling in the North Atlantic and in some parts of China and North America), but that natural factors alone cannot readily explain the observations made during the last century.

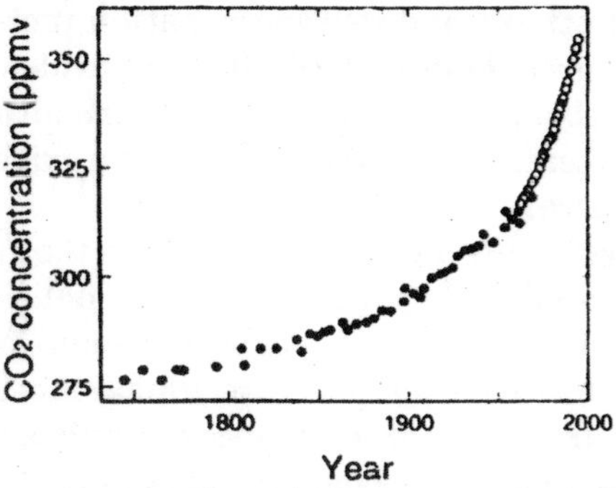

Fig. 1.1. Above are given the variation in atmospheric CO_2 concentration from 1750 to the present. Black dots show values between 1750 and 1989 found in air bubbles enclosed in an ice core from Siple Station (Antarctica); open circles give values measured in air at Mauna Loa station (hawaii). ppmv=parts per million by volume. From Friedli and others (1986).

Environment and Greenhouse Gases

It is well clear that the earth's climate system is driven primarily by the influx of (shortwave) solar radiation. Although thermal energy can be gathered in the ocean, on the continents, and in the atmosphere (mainly as water vapour), on a long-term basis the earth's heat account is in a state of quasibalance, so that the outgoing radiation (both shortwave and infrared) is in equilibrium with the incoming solar isolation. The atmosphere's chemical composition affects the outgoing infrared radiation. The greenhouse gases (GHGs) absorb part of the infrared radiation the earth emits to space and remit it earthward.

As a result low-level atmospheric temperatures are maintained at 15^0 Celsius, that is, at a level 33 Kelvin more than would be the case were the earth without GHGs. The most important natural GHGs are water vapour and carbon dioxide (CO_2). The term "manmade GHGs" (mGHGs) indicates the increase in natural GHGs brought about by human activities and to new GHGs of purely anthropogenic origin.

Atmospheric concentrations of CO_2 have increased by more 25 per cent from pre-industrial values. This addition accounts for 53 per cent of the anthropogenic greenhouse effect. Although absolute concentrations of other mGHGs are still much smaller, they contribute significantly to the greenhouse effect because they have a stronger effect on atmospheric radiation. Instances of such mGHGs are methane and its concentration increase causes 15 per cent of the greenhouse effect, nitrogen oxides 6 per cent and chlorofluorocarbons, CFCs 24 per cent. Agriculture is the great cause of the concentration increase of nitrogen oxides and methane in the atmosphere.

Though the experts analysts acknowledge the global dimension of climate dynamics, they also admit that neither individuals, families, communities, nations, nor ecosystems experience either global mean surface air temperature, global mean precipitation or the average frequency of occurrence of hurricanes, instead the local manifestations of the global climate system: Although climate is controlled globally, it is endured locally. In one of its original meanings, the word climate explains a property of the local and regional environment, something that matters for the plants, animals, and people living at a specific place.

As against this, global climate, a relatively recent scientific concept, has remained for most people an abstract idea that is not easily accepted as a motivation for drastic changes in behaviour. The word "global" establishes a new kind of understanding of the interrelationships among different phenomena observed at different locations on the globe. One of best known instances of this is the relationship between the occurrence of so-called EI Nino events and a shift in the major atmospheric pressure systems in the South Pacific popularly known as the Southern Oscillation (SO).

On climatic changes, Bjerknes was one of the first to show that the occurrences of EI Nino events are closely related to an unusually small SO index. He used the word "teleconnection" to describe the seemingly simultaneous appearance of these anomalies at locations numerous kilometres apart (Bjerknes 1969). Today, the EI Nino[1] Southern Oscillation (ENSO) phenomenon is just one of many known examples of teleconnection.

Climatic Phenomena Classified

The classification of climate phenomena as per their spatial dimension and coherence helps the scientist to analyze and understand the underlying causes of climate changes and to prepare mathematical models of the global climate. Beyond the realm of scientific interest, however, the perception of the global dimension of climate and its relation to human activities is also of noteworthy relevance of human society. Like on other human activities is

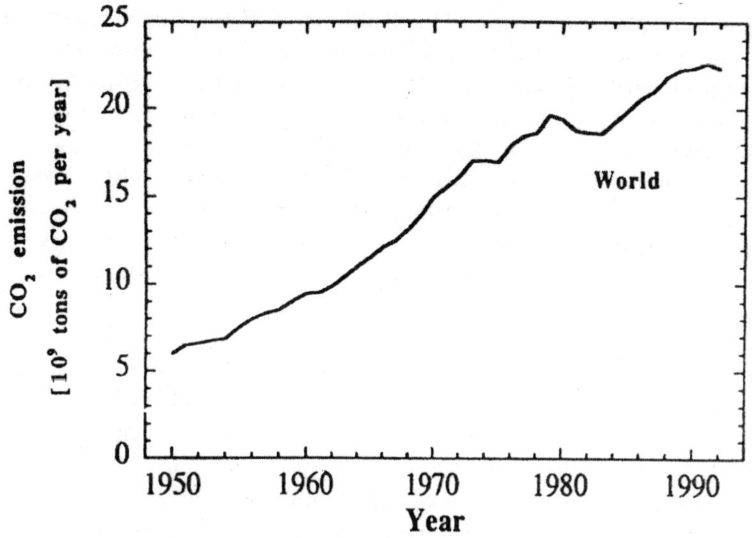

Fig. 1.2. Global anthropogenic emission of carbon dioxide (CO_2) due to the burning of fossile fuels increased about fourfold betweenn 1950 and 1991. Note the influence of the oil price crises in 1973 and in the early 1980s.

also of noteworthy relevance of human society. Like on other human activity, the input into the atmosphere of long-lived substances such as GHGs or the radionuclides produced during nuclear bomb tests in the 1960s has created the perception that certain (local) environmental occurrences can have an impact far from the local source. In April 1986, when a nuclear reactor was burning at Chernobyl, people in Europe were shocked when they got to know that a catastrophe in an unknown, distant city could affect their well-being within a few days.

Similar lessons from the global climate are usually less spectacular and thus equally less effective, although some cases, such as the problem of skin cancer due to the ozone hole over the southern hemisphere or the 1992 hurricane Andrew, have started to make their presence felt in the international media.

Any focusing on the regional perspective of global climate change document faces several challenges. There is only one climate system on earth, the global one, and every attempt to separate it into independent regional pieces appears bound ultimately to fail. Thus, when dealing with climate, it seems reasonable to adopt a top-down approach; that is, an approach in which an understanding of local climate follows as a by-product of looking at global climate. Climate first of all depends on the composition and dynamics of the atmosphere, which neither knows regional limits nor respects national borders. In fact, during the last twenty years we have learned from studies of various environmental archives—ice cores, tree rings, and the like— that on geological time scales, climate has always differed, and that most changes, especially the major ones, have been of global nature.

On the bases of reviews of various previous studies, it has been said that though the processes causing climate changes are still only poorly understood, we realize that the dynamics of the atmosphere alone are insufficient to explain them and that other components of the climate system, such as the oceans, the biosphere, and the polar ice caps (the so-called cryosphere) must be included in the analysis of climate variability.

The question now arises is, why then we look at local or regional climate only? What are the advantages and the limitations of such an approach? What motivates scientists to undertake a research project on climate change focused on the European Alpine region? What is so special about this part of central Europe that it needs the attention of scientist, politician, or concerned citizen? Why should global change be of special importance for mountain areas, especially the Alps? Does not the very concept global point to the fact that climate change is a problem that spans the whole earth and requires a global perspective for both scientific analysis and action? Three different aspects to the approach adopted here render the study special and meaningful: the regional perspective, the specific choice of the Alpine region, and the research's interdisciplinary focus.

Box 1.2 Weather and Climate System

Though the two are used interchangeably, weather and climate are different from each other. Weather refers to the atmosphere's current state as people feel it. With the invention of more and more sophisticated instrumentation, a more objective, quantitative description founded on the once measurement of solar radiation, precipitation, air pressure, wind speed and other variables replaced the one rather qualitative characterization of weather (sunshine, cloudiness, rain, storms, etc.). With growing understanding of the basic principles that determine the atmosphere's physics, it became feasible to predict the weather for the next one or two days. One important condition for this was the establishment of a worldwide observational network (including weather ships on the ocean) and efficient dissemination of the data obtained.

In spite of the significant increase in data availability over the last twenty years, correct weather forecasts are still not normally possible for longer than about a week to ten days. Responsible for this limit is the unstable and chaotic nature of the solution to the atmosphere's important physical equations.

Difference Between the Weather and Climate

Climate is different from weather. According to the *Oxford English Dictionary,* the English word climate was borrowed from the French *climat,* which in turn is drawn from the ancient Greek word *klima* with the root *klinein,* "to slope." The word was adopted in late Latin, where it was used in the sense of region, district or neighbourhood. This meaning has survived in the more poetic term *clime.* In the sixteenth century and later climate became more and more associated with phenomena related to the weather. For example, it was used to describe a belt of the earth's surface contained between two given parallels of latitude or, closer to its present meaning, to characterize a region with respect to its atmospheric conditions and its weather as they influence animal or vegetable life. *Climate* in its original meaning described a local or regional property of the environment, a set of conditions difficult to define accurately and completely but considered to be of paramount importance for life. Later the word was also used to describe the system causing these conditions. Finally, the word *climate* also became popular beyond its scientific context to explain the imponderable factors that make up people's cultural, economical and social environment.

Local Understanding of World Climate

We all know, in environment, climate is a central factor for plants, animals and humans. Together with the soil's physical and chemical properties, it is one of the important nonbiological conditions that determine the evolution of life at any particular location on earth. At a time when humankind's capability to shape its own environment appears unlimited, we tend to forget that the amount of rain that falls on a given piece of land, the humidity and temperature of the air, and the force of the wind can make the difference between paradise and hell, between life and death. In fact, these factors fix up the stage for the spreading out of the human race and for the evolution of agriculture, on which all human cultures are based.

In brief, for the history of the species *Homo sapiens*. Recently, Richard Potts, and archaeologist at the Smithsonian Institution in Washington, D.C., suggested that the variability of climate, and thus of the physical and ecological environment, has been a great contributor to the significant brain evolution of the genus *Homo* over the past two million years.

Previous Notions

In spite of climate's vital importance, for quite some time we had little hope of reaching a deep understanding of its dynamics. The development of the weather seemed to obey a different kind of law from that governing, for instance, the strong, tough and thus predictable motion of the sun, moon and planets. Certain patterns in weather, such as seasonal variability or the arrival of the monsoon, must have caught the attention of early man, especially the farmer. Yet these phenomena could vary strongly from year to year, perhaps causing famines and leading ultimately to the downfall of whole cultures. Climate catastrophes could be neither prevented nor predicted. Humankind could only prepare for the unexpected and observe the weather closely to evolve a certain "statistical experience" of the local or regional climate. Since in most cases supernatural powers like some deity or deities were made responsible for the weather and related phenomena, the observation of important factors such as the onset of the monsoon or the height of the annual flood of the Nile in ancient Egypt was regarded a religious or royal act. It was unthinkable to the ancient Egyptians that the Nile flood could have such a solid reason as the amount of precipitation falling in eastern Africa during the preceding few months (which in turn seems to be related to the ENSO phenomenon even further away) and could thus be predictable.

Latest inventions and studies have greatly changed our understanding of how the weather functions. Most societies have discharged their super natural Gods from their climatic responsibilities, although divine weather makers have not yet retired completely—especially during droughts. Today we know the principal laws that govern the atmosphere's physics. We can reproduce them as mathematical equations and solve these equations on computers.

There was even a time when scientists extrapolated their achievements so far as to dream of total control of the environment. Some time later, the ability to master weather and climate seemed just on the horizon. But before this could happen, hope turned to irritation or even fear when it became clear that not only is climate more difficult to understand than assumed, let alone to control, but humankind may already have inadvertently triggered climate changes, and not necessarily to our usefulness. Recognition of the possibility of inadvertent climate change gave climate research both a tremendous boost and unprecedented significance. In the last twenty years, atmospheric scientists have developed a series of climate models of increasing complexity, the General Circulation Models (GCMs). These have gone up progressively in the complexity of their representations of the climate system by modeling more dimensions, resolving smaller spatial scales, describing more physical processes, and treating interfaces and boundary conditions in a better and more sophisticated manner.

Because the ocean carries a long-term climate memory by storing heat, advanced GCMs also include ocean models.

(A) Definitely, models of climate are forms of weather models. Weather models generally fail for a time span of more than five to ten days because of the atmospheric system's nonlinear nature. Since atmospheric flow is mostly unstable or even mess, flow patterns that develop from slightly different initial states often evolve into very different states over a time period on the order of ten days. This is the ground for the often cited metaphor that a tiny event such as the flap of a butterfly's wings might at last be responsible for engendering a hurricane.

(B) Another consequence of the nonlinearity of the governing equations is that no time and space scales are available that would allow a natural separation of small-from large-scale phenomena. In other words, for weather and climate, everything ultimately depends on everything else. The regional climate in the Alps, for example, depends on the global state of the ocean and atmosphere, which weather events in the Alpine region, in turn, partly influence. In nutshell, this is why science emphasizes the global aspects of climate dynamics.

(C) The last important factor that makes climate forecasting difficult is that the earth's climate system is not autonomous, that is, not independent of changes occurring external to the earth. The sun is obviously the engine driving the weather, but only recently was it learnt that changes in this engine's setup may be the main cause of past climate changes and even of part of the changes in climate that we have been experiencing this century. These climate changes may be directly linked to the sun's properties, such as variations in the solar constant, or to the geometry of the earth-sun setup. Milutin Milankovic, the father of climate modeling and of the astronomical theory of paleoclimates, used the astronomical parameters of the earth's orbit to explain the periods of almost 22,000,40,000, and 100,000 years found in long-term climate records extending over the past period of changing glaciation. However, only some of these external factors are known and are predictable, whereas others, such as the short-term fluctuation in solar radiation and the accompanying variation of sunspot abundance, are still only half understood.

Because of the above three factors, calculating climatic averages rather than examining specific daily forecasts is the generally accepted method of assessing climate changes still, this has intrinsic and endemic problems, as Wigley (1995) has recently discussed. Our computers are still too slow to allow calculations to be performed with the spatial resolution necessary to resolve regional features. For instance, a small country like Switzerland would be represented by only about, say, four points in the spatial grid used to calculate the atmosphere's physical state. There are air temperature, humidity, cloud cover, wind speed, etc. Similarly, in a conventional GCM, the altitude of only four points would represent the country's complex topography. In such a representation, the majestic Alpine peaks shrink to harmless round hills of less than a thousand meters in altitude.

This has two key impacts: (1) First, by shortening and smoothing the tops, we may well be introducing modeling distortions that affect vast regions of the earth, if not the entire model. (2) Alpine climate can vary drastically from one locality or valley to another. Global models do not show this fine structure.

This way, some important questions such as the mean frequency of heavy rain events at a specific Alpine locality or the anticipated mean snow cover cannot be answered with the global models presently in use. Flood conditions in Alpine rivers do not result from the yearly mean precipitation over the Alps but from the rainfall's temporal and local distribution. It is this latter information that people living in the Alpine region should learn how to know to prepare for possible climate changes. It is often be argued that as larger and faster computers continue to develop, the above-mentioned limitation due to computer capacity will rapidly disappear. In fact, this is not the case. If we assume that computers will continue to double in speed at their historical rate of once every third year, it will still be several decades before we have machines fast enough to run GCMs with spatial resolutions of a few kilometres. Moreover, for any finite representation of the climate system, the need would remain to represent the effect of unresolved processes.

Right now, we simply lack an adequate data set to be able to calibrate and run a high-resolution global model and we have no immediate expectation that this situation will change in the near future. As a complement to global climate model-based analysis, regional analysis follows a different path and can show results fundamentally different from those yielded by GCMs. Global and regional approaches are like the two sides of a coin; although they produce independent pictures, they cannot be separated. With respect to physical climate modeling, Giorgi and Mearns (1991) distinguish between three different categories of regional analysis:

(i) Purely empirical approach: In this, regional climate scenarios are constructed using instrumental data records or paleoclimatic analogues. One factor why the European Alpine region turns out to be ideal for analyzing regional climate change is the rather large number of available data sets (both instrumental data and paleodata).

(ii) Semi-empirical approach: This uses GCMs to describe the atmospheric response to large-scale forcing (e.g., GHGs, solar forcing, etc.) and employs empirical techniques to observe the so-called mesoscale forcing (i.e., local topography, the presence of a large inland water body, etc.), which can modify the local circulation. Moreover, such local features are expected to be important in the Alps.

(iii) Modeling approach: This describes mesoscale features by increasing the model resolution only over the area of interest, either by using a grid of variable resolution or by nesting techniques, where a higher-resolution region is imbedded in a lower-resolution world model.

Analysis

In analysis, we find that undoubtedly modeling approach is purely hierarchical (top-down) if information from the high-resolution subregion does not feed back into the low-resolution domain. To benefit completely from the global and regional approaches complemen-tarity, two-way nested models are needed, where information flows in both directions between the global and regional sub-models, that is, both top-down and bottom-up. The second gives a fundamentally different role to regional studies: Instead of merely being a blown-up regional view of the global problem, regional studies may capture aspects that trigger a global phenomenon in almost similar way as a local disturbance in atmospheric flow, such as that a mountain generates, may develop into a much larger atmospheric structure.

Upto here, we have gone through the interrelation-ship between global and regional features by using examples from atmospheric physics. In fact, as exemplified in other chapters, a similar dualism also exists for biological as well as for socio-economic factors of the climate change problem. However, because causal processes are to radically different in physical, biological, and social systems, we don't expect exactly the same relationships between global and regional phenomena.

It has been seen that the top-down/bottom-up dualism is even more relevant for socio-economic aspects. As explained above, it is not easy to make people act on such general statements as "The global mean temperature will rise by 1.5-4.5° C by the end of next century." We argue that the complex interaction between technology and society asks for the emergence of new socio-economic patterns to achieve the policy goals stated in global treaties such as the Framework Convention on Climate Change (FCCC) prepared at the 1992 Rio de Janeiro conference, which has now been signed and accepted by more than 150 nations. For the necessary processes of social learning to be successful, social contact networks are essential for the creation and diffusion of radical innovations. More often than not, these contact networks have a regional dimension.

Thus, the regional analysis of sociotechnical transformation processes in combination with regional climate scenarios provides an approach to the problem of climate change that cannot easily be extrapolated from a global approach.

Regional and Global Factors are Identical

The fact that the regional and the global are complements and not substitutes means that it is impossible to evolve a unique coherent view of climate change in a region. That the various scientific disciplines are far from distinct strongly reinforces this perception. Just as the global and the local must be seen as complements, so must the contributions from different scientific fields. As such, there is no such thing as one single regional "view" of climate change in environment.

In short, it can be said that investigations on global climate change are a vital complement to global studies because they enable us to take hold of local and complementary aspects of the phenomenon that would otherwise be missed. Notwithstanding, a regional approach will not evolve a singular view of the climate change phenomenon. The best we can hope for is a set of complementary (but often contradictory) views that when juxtaposed presents before us a relatively comprehensive picture which will help better to resolve the problems of climate which we are unable to handle today.

Significance of Alps in Global Research

Alps is considered a key region in the study for climatic changes at global level. The term "regional" remains somewhere between the terms "global" and "local". A region is more than a single city or mountain valley but less than a continent or the whole globe. A region may be defined by some special geomorphologic characteristics or by a common sociocultural frame. Since the former often determines the development of the latter, a region exactly exhibits both physical and social identities. This certainly applies to the Alpine region, where, in spite of obvious dissimilarities such as the various dialects spoken, the special topographic conditions have triggered the evolution of rather similar socioeconomic structures. By the Alpine region, we understand an area bordered roughly by the cities of Stuttgart (Germany), Vienna (Austria), Milan (Italy), and Marseilles (France).

The Alps are a big mountain range extending along on 800-kilometer arc from the Mediterranean in the south-west to the edge of the central European plain on the north-east. This mountain range has a mean width of about 200 km, an average ridge height of about 2,500 m a.s.l. and a maximum elevation of more than 4,800 m a.s.l. (Mont Blanc).

Historical Background

If we look into the pages of past, the Alpine region has had a very dynamic history. Continual confrontation with the vagaries of an unpredictable climate together with the vulnerability of both man and animals in an area where natural catastrophes are frequent and often severe has traditionally stimulated innovative action. Seven hundred years ago, one of the first democratic systems came to existence in the mountainous central cantons of Switzerland, triggered by the need for wise self-organization by people living under extreme conditions and granted by the then-powerful European ruler kings to guarantee free access to the important transit routes across the Alps. Alpine streams and rivers, fed during the whole year by snow and ice in the high mountains, provided an important source of mechanical power. In those valleys, following the instance of Great Britain, the industrial revolution first took hold on the European continent. Even today, the Alpine region is still responsible for many technical innovations. Its relative wealth and independence serves as a lifestyle model for much of the less developed nations on the globe. The Alps are also of great interest for a researcher.

Importance for Climatology: Meteorological stations, several at high altitude, have accumulated long time series of weather data that have proved very valuable in the present debate on climate change. These data reflect that the Alpine weather and climate is influenced not only by large-scale global forcing, but also by local topographical details. This demonstrates the importance of a regional approach to the problem of global climate fluctuation. The Alpine trends in mean air temperature during the last hundred years are qualitatively similar to those observed globally.

For the paleoscientist, the Alps are an extremely interesting source of data. Because of the existence of long weather records and the bulk of traces the weather has left on natural objects (glaciers and moraines, lakes, permafrost and block flow, the altitude of the tree line, etc.) paleoecological studies in this region are among the most sophisticated in the world. In this connection we should not forget that the many observations of fossils in the Alps helped lay the foundation for the development of the theory of evolution. In the same manner, paleo-observations made scientists in the last century realize that climate has not been constant in the past but has a spectacular history, with a famous event (the last Ice Age) having occurred about 10,000 years ago. In fact, the Swiss scientist Louis Agassiz was among the first to postulate the existence of the Ice Ages.

Help in Examining Impact on Ecology

Apart from considering its direct impact on society, climate change's possible consequences on ecosystems are also examined. According to our present understanding of ecosystem adaptation mechanisms, the speed of change rather than its magnitude determines ecosystem survival. From paleo-studies we know that not all climate changes must result in high rates of extinction and a drastic downfall of biodiversity.

On the contrary, climate changes have often triggered a new evolutionary thrust. In principle, ecosystems are capable of moving geographically, provided that the driving force, climate change, does not go beyond a certain critical speed. The global climate policy debate would benefit if a specific upper limit for a noncatastrophic ecological adaptation to warming could be defined. In most cases ecosystems response to change results in a spatial redistribution of various types of ecosystems. Commonly these shifts occur horizontally, that is from north to south or vice versa. For example, the transition zone from forest to tundra has moved back and forth considerably during the last million years.

In the Alps such movements take place mainly along the vertical axis, that is, between low and high altitudes. Thus, the dislocation of habitats found over several hundreds or thousands of kilometers along the horizontal axis may be studied and observed in the Alps within a range of some hundreds of meters in altitude. During this process, the form of the local topography can result in isolated vegetational islands or even in the local disappearance of a given plant community, despite the fact that at some distance, higher mountains might yield the right conditions for the community.

Till now, we have mentioned the intimate relationship between the geographical and social characteristics typical of the Alpine region. There are some socio-economic case studies those are example of social learning processes and potentially useful for a reduction of greenhouse emissions both in the Alpine region and globally. The first case deals with the problem of tans-Alpine freight traffic, an issue that, ironically, was of central significance when the first Swiss cantons became independent about 700 years ago. This example, demonstrates how conventional policy can run into serious problems if the process of social learning is ignored. The second case focusses on the problems related to energy-efficient individual transport using light weight vehicles. Here the different stages mof the innovation process and the role of the regional contact networks are observed and analyzed. Both examples are typical for the Alpine region, where there is a long history of finding collective solutions to key problems, and where problems related to economic restructuring, environmental policy and climate change are becoming more severe. Above all, the case studies can also serve as examples for the mechanisms of innovative change in other regions.

Current Methods of Research on Global Climatic Changes

Till some years back, global climatic research was conducted in the classical scientific paradigm, according to which physical observations like measurement of air temperature, humidity, solar radiation and wind speed can be explained in terms of natural laws. The emergence of ever larger climate models is based on the conviction that these laws will eventually be able to depict the essential aspects of future climate, that is, that computers will take over the role of the previous weather gods. Tacitly, this approach also implies that, given a "correct" scientific forecast of climate change, society will accept the new gods' verdict and respond rationally to the given recommendations. This may sound simple, but it is not in fact so. The consequences of the few basic physical laws that are relevant for describing the energy balance and water mass balance in the atmosphere are highly complex and far from being completely understood in all their ramifications. It is by no means clear whether they will ever be helpful to answer such basic questions such as, how much snow will fall in the Alps next century. However, most climate researchers would agree that the best strategy for shifting the present limits of understanding consists of two approaches: (a) more and better observations and (b) better and larger models.

Usefulness of Natural Science Approach

The natural science approach has been highly successful in the last 200 years. In a simplified manner, scientific progress can be described as a regular process of hypothesis building, followed by hypothesis testing by well-defined experiments until the hypothesis eventually takes on some kind of final form and becomes a fixed rule or even a law, in the sense of Newton's Laws. Because such rules and laws must be consistent with each other, (meaning they should not lead to contradictions), mathematics offers itself as the ideal language for constructing these rules and deriving new rules by combining old ones. A set of rules–or a set of mathematical equations—is the basis of what today is called a mathematical model.

Limits of Physical Paradigm

It is well clear that the paradigm of the mathematical description of the world (the physics paradigm)—like every concept—has certain limits. With respect to the problem of climate change, two different kinds of possible limits have to be kept in mind : (a) the technical limitations of the physics paradigm applied to a specific aspect of climate, e.g., to climate change in the Alpine region; and (b) the restricted role scientific information (even if it is of the most complete kind imaginable) performs within the context of society's view of climate change and the design of a possible strategy for action. Regarding the first limit, the great success the scientific method has achieved tends to conceal the fact that its power unfolds mainly when tackling a rather special category of queries related either to the very small (molecular level) or to the purely physical (nonliving matter, astrophysics, etc). Problems related to the environment usually do not belong to this category.

For example, it is difficult, if not impossible, to plan and design experiments related to environmental problems that affect the dynamics of the globe as a whole. In the case of climate, only one atmosphere exists, in which humankind has already inadvertently started many simultaneous experiments, the outcomes of which are difficult to interpret. Thus, it is often almost impossible to test hypotheses through well-defined experiments, a procedure that according to Popper (1959) separates science from metaphysics. In this regard, mathematical models can take on a new role. Remember that climate models mathematical structure is extremely complex. Their solutions may become unstable and chaotic, and thus the consequences of all model calculations are subject to uncertainty. Individual model runs *predictive* power may be small. However, in combination with the modern computers, enormous capacity, the models can substitute for genuine climate experiments. By repeating model calculations with slightly different assumptions as well as by comparing the results from differently structured models, a feeling can be evolved for the models overall behaviour. For example, more robust features can be separated from more arbitrary ones. We call this the *exploratory* use of models.

The Difference Between the Predictive and Exploratory Use of Models

This can be illustrated by using the metaphor of a popular computer game, the Flight Simulator (FS). The game's two important components are one, a mathematical model of a given airplane that describes the plane's reaction to the manipulation of the control stick and other elements of the keyboard and a selected landscape of mountains, rivers, and shorelines as well as cities, townships, roads and airfields. In our metaphor, the airplane represents the weather/climate system (or rather, a mathematical model of it, e.g., a GCM).

The control stick for the rudder, elevator, engine thrust and much more like this stands for the forces external to the climate system such as the sun, but also for anthropogenic factors such as the concentration of GHGs. Compared to this, the landscape represents the potential global climatic states; flying over it is like passing through a series of weather and climate situations. Using the FS predictively, the operator wants to fly from A to B on a preselected route. The pilot anticipates, for a well-defined operation of the control stick, the plane's course and the series of landscape segments that have to appear on the screen. However, the FS's real strength is that is can be used to perform experiments that it the real world are either too expensive, too dangerous, or not at all possible. For instance, the simulator pilot can explore the plane's limits before it crashes. She or he can also explore new components of the unknown landscape and thus acquire a certain familiarity with its geography.

As in the case of weather forecasts, the plane's response or the landscape that is going to appear on the screen are almost well determined in the short-term but open if the pilot is trying out new maneuvers or flying far into new territory.

As in real life, in game also, it is important to be prepared to make decisions based on premises whose validity is uncertain. For this, exploratory models are of great help. They can produce alternative scenarios that can then be analyzed for their impact on the plane's course (i.e., on climate). Doing so may reveal strategies for the future that are robust where to details still unknown. Let us take example, if one must fly from A to B and knows neither the exact location of B's airport nor the direction from which the runway must be approached, a first robust decision would be to direct the plane in B's general direction. To bring this metaphor again to the problem of climate change: whatever the value of the global mean temperature in the year 2050 may be, we know that reducing our energy dependence must be a flow in the correct direction, since it improves our flexibility with respect to future energy strategies.

Despite all this, the above discussion on mathematical models, strengths and limitations misses the essential role such tools play for social processes. In fact, the real issue is neither the FS nor the climate model alone, it is in fact the interaction of model and operator (pilot or humankind). The peculiar combination of a mathematical tool and human beings represents a system able to learn by gathering virtual experience. Mathematical models are learning tools that can be important in overcoming the physics paradigm's second limitation, which refers to the role scientific information can really play in determining society's understanding of climate change and in promoting societal changes.

Even if precise climate forecasting is relevant, people also have other gods. Perhaps they are more concerned with health, wealth, or prestige, or they struggle with short-term problems like seeking a job or-even more basically—getting enough food and water to satisfy their immediate survival needs. In addition, the climate modelers' message may not be as straightforward and unequivocal as one could expect. As discussed before there are clearly doubts concerning the scientific community's assertion that a mathematical model can ultimately be built that will be capable of forecasting future climate, at last with the spatial resolution many politicians require to justify action. However, this would ignore the need to implement short and medium-term remedial action to forestall irreversible long-term changes.

In this regard, we note that the Intergovernmental Panel on Climate Change (IPCC) has linked the scientific community directly with the policy debate, and the IPCC's activities have put climate change high on the agenda of national governments and international organizations. However, it is imperative that scientists acknowledge the intrinsic limitations of their often quite mechanistic approach and allow the debate to be initiated to encompass the panoply of wider issues. Taking no action while waiting for better models should not become the tacit policy either of the scientists, who may be attracted by financial support for their work, or of the politicians, who could postpone implementing costly and infamous measures. Betting everything on the one card of better climate prediction may have other impacts for the socio-economic and socio-political system. Let us make the unrealistic assumption for a second that we are able to predict the future climate and its impact on the hydrological cycle to any desired degree of precision. Would political decisions be simpler and easier to make under such circumstances? Such predictions would make known not only the losers of climate change, but also the winners. Is is realistic to assume that solidarity for a global reduction of CO_2 emissions would then be able to survive? We believe that the present situation, in which anthropogenic climate change becomes more probable every day, but uncertainty remains concerning the further growth of these changes, could be used fruitfully to trigger a process of social discourse and learning.

There is no doubt that a successful climate policy must communicate an uncertain message to a society that may still have other priorities. Due to this problem, the old idea of "speaking truth to power" no longer works. As an alternative, *integrated assessment* (IA) is an attempt to combine scientific and social expertise in an exploratory method to find new political and technical strategies for the future. Those strategies are aimed simultaneously at decreasing the potential for global change (for instance, by reducing the emission of GHGs) as well as at increasing society's capability of dealing with anticipated changes.

The Clear Process and Science for Policymakers

Last decade of 20th century saw a great revolution in the field of environment. In 1992, a group of scientists of various disciplines submitted a set of proposals to the then-new Swiss Priority Programme Environment, a programme financed by the Swiss National Science Foundation. They had coordinated their projects within the CLEAR umbrella project. Ultimate objective of CLEAR's was to use climate models less for forecasting purpose and more in an exploratory manner, trying to enhance our understanding of key processes, stressing levels of uncertainty and studying processes of risk communication referring to environmental changes.

Funds for the project were offered by the priority programme and viewed as an ongoing process of learning and cross-fertilization among different disciplines. Thus, the book does not primarily concentrate on issues of global change, and provides a final recipe for dealing with global change in the Alpine region. In effect, the book also attempts to carry the debate on global change from the scientific into the political community. It is meant as science for policymakers, but not according to the outdated recipe of hierarchical knowledge transfer, i.e., "We scientists tell you politicians the right solution to the problem." There is no "right" solution, there are just options for the next couple of steps, and these can only be found if science, politics, and economy get together cooperate.

2

Environmental Change: An Issue of Human Concern

Global Temperature

Temperature differs greatly from place to place and from time to time, yet when surface temperatures are averaged globally they differ from year to year by only fractions of a degree. The near-constancy of the Earth's temperature discloses the presence of homeostatic controls; and an analogy is often drawn between the Earth and the human body, which has a consistent temperature of 37°C. But the scientific community, and indeed many political leaders, have become increasingly concerned since the Stockholm Conference (1972) that the Earth's temperature is expected to rise to 'fever' levels within 50 to 100 years unless remedial actions are taken quickly. The rising concern about these issues led directly to a series of national and global conferences and reports. World Climate Conferences were held in 1979 (organized by WMO and ICSU) and 1990 (organized by WMO, ICSU) and UNEP in co-operation with UNESCO and FAO) (WMO, 1979, 1991).

The Intergovernmental Panel on Climate Change (IPCC), with three Working Groups dealing respectively with likely climate change and reasons for this environmental impacts, and possible responses was established in 1989 by UNEP and WMO, and reported to the Second World Climate Conference.

Four causes have been accounted for the current widespread concern:

1. Atmospheric concentrations of greenhouse gases have gone up significantly in the last three decades. As has been studied since the last century, this could lead to global warming.

2. Making use of computer models that simulate current climate, it is calculated that for an equivalent doubling of greenhouse gas concentrations, the Earth's climate should warm significantly.

3. Analogues received from other planetary atmospheres, particularly that of Venus, support the results of the simulations for Earth.

4. There has been a global warming trend over the last quarter of the century. Six of the seven warmest years in this century occurred in the years 1981, 1983, 1987, 1988, 1989 and 1990.

A Background

But not a single of these arguments above, taken individually, is convincing evidence of climate warming: taken together, however, they are a *yellow alert.* Undoubtedly, changes in other factors might counteract at least some of the global warming.

Desertification and deforestation, for instance, increase the reflection of solar radiation back into space, as do sulphate aerosols from volcanic eruptions and fossil-fuel combustion.

1. At the time of the Stockholm Conference, the relative importance of these various factors was not sure, and some scientists believed that net cooling was likely.

2. However, by the late 1970s most climatologists thought that tropospheric aerosols would not have a great effect on the Earth's temperature, and that in some situations, for example, over snow-covered surfaces, aerosols might even result in warming, because part of the incoming solar radiation would be last in the atmosphere, thus decreasing the amount lost by reflection from the surface.

3. At the Villach meeting of 1985 there was a general consensus that the greenhouse warming threat was indeed real, although even today a few scientists challenge this approach. In this connection, as has been pointed out by Wigley (1991), even if tropospheric aerosols were to reduce climate warming significantly, this would be largely a Northern Hemisphere effect because most fossil-fuel emissions occur in that hemisphere. This would increase interhemispheric differences in the atmospheric general circulation, which could be just as disruptive to the climate system.

There is no doubt that climate is already a limiting factor for development in many parts of the world, and in some areas water consumption, e.g., for agricultural, industrial and domestic purposes is already beyond the capacity for natural replenishment and restoration. Let us see an example, the Aral Sea has dropped 14 metres in the last 30 years (Precoda 1991), and many sub-Saharan cities, California and other areas are experiencing risingly severe shortages of drinking water. If climate change leads to further desiccation of those parts of the world, the consequences would be serious.

Impact on Environment Through Greenhouse Gases

There generally are, water vapour, ozone, carbon dioxide, methane, the chloroflurocarbons (CFCs) and nitrous oxide.

Effects of Natural Gases: The natural greenhouse gases have exercised a powerful influence on the Earth's climate since the formation of the planetary atmosphere. In pre-industrial period, this natural effect maintained a global mean surface temperature 33°C warmer than would be the case without it. Due to the short turn-round time of water in the atmosphere, water vapour concentrations are in global equilibrium for current climatic conditions. Of course, global warming would cause atmospheric water vapour concentrations to rise, thus enhancing the greenhouse effect. However, both the amounts and the distribution of clouds would then change, thus modifying the global radiation budget in as yet unknown ways. Lack of precise knowledge of such atmospheric readjustments is a major source of uncertainty in the predicted response of climate to increased concentrations of greenhouse gases (IPCC 1990a).

Impact on Other Gases

The other greenhouse gases are relatively long-lived, and their upward trends are a matter of record. Recent findings (IPCC 1992) indicate that the increase in atmospheric concentration of methane has slowed down. There are also indications that emissions of methane from rice paddies are less than previously estimated.

The Main Sources of Greenhouse Gases are:

(a) CO_2, i.e., Fossil fuel consumption, deforestation.

(b) CFCs, i.e., Aerosol propellants, solvents, refrigerants, foam-blowing matters etc.

(c) Nitrous Oxide
(1) Microbial processes in soil and water.
(2) Biomass burning and fossil fuel usage.
(d) Methane, i.e., Anaerobic bacteria from natural wetlands, rice paddies, rumen of cattle and other mammals, and guts of termites and other wood-consuming objects.

Source : UNEP Environmental Data Report 1991/1992.

Table below gives a look at carbon emissions of various countries.

Table 2.1

1988 Carbon Emissions for Selected Countries

Sl No.	*Country*	*Amount (million tonnes)*	*Per capita amount (tonnes)*
1.	Brazil	55	0.4
2.	Canada	119	4.6
3.	China	610	0.6
4.	France	87	1.6
5.	India	164	0.2
6.	Japan	270	2.2
7.	Mexico	84	1.0
8.	Poland	125	3.3
9.	UK	152	2.7
10.	USA	1310	5.3
11.	USSR	1086	3.8

Source : Marland *et al.* (1989) and Trends 90 (1990).

Guessing the Increase in Warmth

Since the greenhouse gases differ in their effectiveness in absorbing the Earth's radiation, and in their atmospheric lifetimes, they vary in their *global warming potentials* (GWP). GWP is defined as the time-integrated warming effect due to the release of one kilogram of a given greenhouse gas into the present atmosphere, relative to that of carbon dioxide.

The IPCC Reports (1990a,b) provide detailed comparisons which show that over the long-term, carbon dioxide, methane and the CFCs are the important concerns amongst the gases originating from human activities. However, the IPCC Scientific Assessment Working Group concluded recently (IPCC, 1992) that 'although the GWP a meaningful concept, there is increasing uncertainty in its calculation, especially regarding the indirect effect. Whilst this is likely to be significant for some gases, previous estimates of indirect GWPs are likely to be in substantial mistake. While the elimination of CFCs under the Vienna Convention on the protection of the Ozone Layer and the Montreal Protocol will contribute directly to mitigating climate change, the consequential estimated reduction in the amount of global warming may not be as great as was believed several years ago.

The latest findings of the IPCC Scientific Assessment Working Group (IPCC 1992) and Ozone Assessment Panels indicate that the depletion of ozone in the lower stratosphere in middle and high latitudes is thought to have approximately offset the radiative forcing contribution of CFCs over the last decade or so. Furthermore, the cooling effect of sulphur emissions, recognized in the IPCC 1990 report, may have offset an important part of the greenhouse warming in the Northern Hemisphere during the past several decades (IPCC, 1992). It is to be noted that because of the large warming capacity of water, the oceans currently absorb a substantial proportion of the extra energy input due to the already existing increase in concentrations of greenhouse gases. As a result, the current 'realized' rise in surface temperature is only a fraction of the 'warming commitment' which will eventually occur. The present commitment implies a hike of about 1°C.

If we want to evaluate the effectiveness of various strategies for 'managing' climate warming, it is necessary first to have quantitative estimates of the source and sink strengths of the various gases involved. Much attempts has been spent over the last 20 years on this task, but there are still gaps, particularly in the case of methane whose concentrations are increasing more rapidly than models predict.

Findings of Climate Models of Earth-Atmosphere

These findings indicate that for a doubling of carbon dioxide from its pre-industrial level, of any combination of greenhouse gases with an equal warming potential the atmosphere would warm on average by between 1.5 and 4.5°C Celsius. Furthermore, the warming would be the maximum in the polar regions and least in the tropics.

As a consequence, the decrease in the equator-to-pole temperature gradient would slow the atmospheric heat engine (i.e., the general circulation) which shifts heat from tropical to polar regions. At the same time the continents would warm more than the oceans, so that the summer monsoons would intensify as well as change their seasonal characteristics.

Therefore, the world's future weather patterns could be quite different from those of recent years. Unfortunately, the simulations give very unclear and uncertain estimates of even globally averaged precipitation, wind and other weather elements, although it can generally be argued that warmer temperatures are likely to generate an increase in evaporation as well as rainfall. Also, the *timing* of climate change is very uncertain, even be given greenhouse gas scenarios. The Earth system contains lags and many feedback processes, making the level of climate change difficult to estimate. Intermediate 'transient' climates cannot yet be predicted with any confidence, especially on the regional scale.

For instance, Watts and Worantine (1991) have recently suggested that the atmospheric cooling between 1940 and 1970 could be explained by changes in upwelling patterns in the world ocean circulation during that period, and may of course, have been a first response to greenhouse warming. Understanding of some climate feedbacks and their incorporation into the models has improved, particularly about the role of upper tropospheric water vapour. Coupled ocean-atmosphere models are capable of reproducing many features of atmospheric variability on intra-decadal time scales (IPCC 1992). Last but not the least, volcanic eruptions such as the recent one at Mount Pinatubo in the Philippines might spread aerosols through the stratosphere, partially masking a long-term warming trend for a certain duration.

Regional Concerns for the Global Environment

There can be nothing more tragic than the fact that individuals and governments worry more about the environmental changes to be expected in their own regions than they do about global averages. Also, they are less concerned about future temperatures, which can probably be estimated with least uncertainty of all the weather components, than they are with other meteorological phenomena such as the frequencies of droughts and tropical storms.

It is so fateful that global climate models are still too coarse to provide this kind of local information, particularly in areas where there are topographic features (e.g., major lake systems and mountain ranges) not represented in the models. At the present time, much attention is being paid to this problem with the help of the below:

1. Small-scale models that cover only one grid square of a global model.

2. Analogues of the past (the examination of climate and climate impacts in seasons or years that were abnormally warm, either regionally or globally).

3. Palaeo-analogues, i.e., the examination of biospheric regimes during warm geological periods.

There is still need for massive work as these approaches currently provide a very uncertain basis for assessing future climate conditions, and it is even difficult to quantify the degree of uncertainty. A substitute therefore is to begin with some assumed future climate in a region, and to examine what it would mean for the biosphere and society. The same approach was followed by the IPCC Working Group 2.

Given below is the list of some of the potential impacts of climate change that are causing concern are IPCC, 1990c; WMO, 1991.

A Sampling of some of the Potential Climate Change Impacts of Current Concern

(a) Environmental: Effect on especially vulnerable populations (sea level rise, desertification, thawing of the permafrost) leading to millions of environmental refugees.

(b) Health of Human beings: Human health (increasing heat stress and frequencies of air pollution episodes; shifts in ranges of vector-borne diseases).

(c) Forestry: Shifts in ranges of species: grown frequencies of forest fires: economic disruptions.

(d) Agriculture: Shifts in ranges of crops, agricultural pests and livestock diseases; shifts in demands for irrigation and watering.

(e) Electricity: Effects on hydro-electric generation through declining water levels in reservoirs and other inland water systems in some regions, and possible increases elsewhere.

(f) Infrastructure: Roads and runways built on permafrost in the Arctic and sub-Arctic.

Source : IPCC (1990c); WMO (1191).

Regarding this, the idea of tallying up the winners' and 'losers' from climate change has to be rejected. As was pointed out at the Second World Climate Conference, and by Parry and others (1988) in the agricultural context, the biosphere and society are adapted to current climatic conditions to such an extent that climate change would provide few immediate benefits—even to regions with, for example, improved rainfall or longer frost-free periods (the soil might be unsuitable or the land might already be committed to other purposes).

One more argument sometimes heard (e.g., NAS, 1991) is that because agriculture accounts for only a small part of the economy of an industrialized country such as the United States, a decline in crop yields would have not much impact. However, Daly (1991) emphasizes that the demand for food is inelastic, and that a permanent downfall in food supplies would be very serious, both nationally and globally. Unfortunately, developing countries would be least able to cope. Of the numerous areas of concern, there is no doubt that some of the most serious impacts would occur if climate warming were sufficient to cause a significant rise in sea level. The extent of the rise can be assumed from models given the emissions of greenhouse gases to be expected over the next century.

Some Assumptions for Environmental Changes by 2030 (IPCC Business-as-Usual Scenario: Changes from Pre-industrial)

Here are some estimates upto year 2030. The numbers given below are based on high-resolution models, scaled to be consistent with our best estimate of global mean warming of 1.8°C by 2030. For values consistent with other estimates of world temperature rise, the numbers below should be decreased by 30 per cent for the low estimate or increased by 50 per cent for the high estimate. Precipitation estimates are also scaled in a similar manner.

(a) Central North America (35°-50°N 85° - 105°W)

The warming differs from 2 to 4°C in winter and 2 to 3°C in summer. Precipitation increases range from 0 to 15 per cent in winter whereas there are decreases of 5 to 10 per cent in summer. Soil moisture decreases in summer by 15 to 20 per cent

(b) Southern Asia (5° - 30°N 70° - 105°E).

The warming varies from 1 to 2°C throughout the year. Precipitation changes little in winter and generally increases throughout the region by 5 to 15 per cent in summer. Summer soil moisture increases by 5 to 10 per cent.

(c) Sahel (10°-20°N 20°N 20°W-40°E)

The warming ranges from 1 to 3°C. Area mean precipitation increases and area mean soil moisture decreases marginally in summer. However, throughout the region, there are areas of both increase and decrease in both parameters throughout the region.

After conducting research on the issue, in the IPCC estimates of regional climate change by the year 2030 for the business-as-usual scenario, i.e., the one in which energy policies are not modified), the levels of confidence in these estimates are not high. Another consideration of great importance is that in addition to climate many other physical and socio-economic conditions are also expected to change to a great extent in the next 40 years. Climate change impacts have generally been studied one by one, assuming that all other factors remain constant. Within the last decade.

However, there has been a growing recognition of the linkages between impacts and of the necessity to undertake integrated regional assessments, involving both the physical and the socio-economic sciences. In view of the great uncertainty involved, new methods of policy analysis are being developed and tested: Efforts are now being made to construct scenarios particularly within IPCC, for the development of more comprehensive analyses of the dependence of future greenhouse gas emissions on socio-economic assumptions and projections (IPCC, 1992).

Alternatives to Fight the Problems under Assumption

As it is obvious by now that the climate change is a risk management issue, but unlike the situation with flood and earthquakes, for which are back hundreds of years old, there is no historical experience to guide the assessor. Nevertheless, many political leaders now accept the need for strong national and international responses to meet the threat: greenhouse gases and their impact have become a major public policy issue—particularly in developed countries, island states and low-lying regions of the developing world. In the not too dissimilar case of CFCs, the detection of an *ozone* hole in the Antarctic stratosphere gave direct evidence of an impact, and led to rapid public policy responses.

In the case of climate change, on the other hand, where global warming cannot be found out with certainty, most political leaders have been persuaded to act as a result of technical arguments put forward by their senior scientific advisors, largely on the basis of computer simulations. As already said, there has been a sustained large-scale scientific effort aimed at improved monitoring of climate change, better understanding of the complex processes involved, and the development of appropriate strategies for coping with possible problems arising out of the proposed changes.

Prominent Efforts Received in this Direction

Owing to various assessments of the likely impacts of climate changes especially those of IPCC Working Group 3 on Response Strategies (IPCC, 1990d), it is well evident that the principal actions that should be taken to address the problems are:

1. Decrease in emissions of greenhouse gases;
2. Analyses of the vulnerability to climate change of present and proposed patterns of land use and development;
3. Evaluation of the capacity of both the biosphere and society to adapt to climate change;
4. Engineering studies and research to reduce uncertainties and to design more efficient energy systems;
5. Ensuring of improved early warning monitoring systems.

All the steps mentioned above need to be taken at both global and national levels. With respect to emission reductions, a wide range of industrial and other activities contribute to greenhouse warming, multiplying the control problem. However, many nations have accepted that at least a start should be made, and a policy of 'no regrets' is being promoted, i.e., a policy under which the reduction of greenhouse gas emissions is also justified on other bases. Grubb *et al* (1991) further suggest that a comprehensive approach be adopted in which, in principle at least, all the major greenhouse gases, and their risks and sources would be considered in the development of control strategies and approaches.

In the table that follows are given some examples of 'no-regrets' climate-warming policies

Policy	*Effect on greenhouse gases*	*Other beneficial effects*
Policy of Tree planting	Grown biosphere sink strength	Better microclimate Less soil erosion Decreased seasonal peak river flows
Policy for Energy conservation	Decreased CO_2 emissions	Sustainability of non-renewable resources for current and future generations
Policy for Energy efficiency	Decreased CO_2 emissions	Regulation of non-renewable resources for current and future generations
Policy for CFC emission control	Decreased CFC emissions	Less stratospheric ozone-layer depletion Less surface UV-B and skin cancer and blindness

There are some more questions to which answers are required. There remain, however, the questions of:

1. What will be the expenses (of taking action, of delaying action, and of not taking action at all)?

2. How should this expenditure be shared (within countries and amongst countries)?

3. List of special arrangements to be made in the case of developing countries who need to develop, and consequently to increase their greenhouse gas emissions?

Stress was land in the Second World Climate Conference that despite the remaining scientific uncertainties, 'nations should now take steps towards lessening sources and increasing sinks of greenhouse gases through national and regional actions' (WMO, 1991). The Conference emphasized that "The long-term goal should be to stop the build-up of greenhouse gases at a level that minimizes risks to society and natural ecosystems', and that 'technically feasible and cost-effective avenues exist to reduce carbon dioxide emissions in all countries', these being the major culprits in global warming. Actions needed include steps to improve the efficiency of energy use, and parameters to develop renewable sources of energy.

Since the Conference, a number of countries and the European Community as a whole have announced actions aimed at stabilizing their emissions of carbòn dioxide, generally at 1990 levels by or close to the year 2000. The latest findings concerning the cooling effects of CFCs and sulphur emissions are examples of the complexities that have to be dealt with in understanding the environment, and the contradictions and trade-offs that have to be kept in mind in formulating appropriate strategies. The latest thinking is that the major culprit in global warming is CO_2 and that urgent action is essential in this area.

At its 44th Session, the United Nations General Assembly agreed on the need to prepare, as a matter of urgency, a framework Convention on Climate Change. This suggestion was supported by the Ministerial Declaration of the Second World Climate Conference. Negotiating sessions of the Intergovernmental Negotiating Committee established for the purpose were held in 1991, and will go on till 1992, with the target of having a framework Convention ready for signature in June 1992 at the UN Conference on Environment and Development in Rio de Janeiro, Brazil.

Thus, to sum up the chapter, one can say that the climate change issue raises important questions of international equity. At present, the major proportion of greenhouse gases comes from the industrialized countries which contain only about one-fourth of the world population. Agarwal and Narain (1991) have suggested that each person on Earth is entitled to an equal share of the capacity of the world's oceans and biosphere to absorb carbon dioxide. Others, alongwith spokesmen from the developing world, insist that the developed countries must reduce their emissions so that more of the planet's capacity for assimilation of greenhouse gases will become available for the developing and recently industrializing countries—and that the latter must be assisted through the transfer of adequate new and additional financial means through various forms of technical assistance, and through transferring to them environmentally-sound technologies in the broad sense of the term in order to pursue sustainable development treks. This will be a major challenge in future. To support actions and policy analyses, a strong programme of studies, applications, research and monitoring is needed. High priority items in addition to the above should incorporate:

—More understanding of the global cycles of the greenhouse gases;
—Better capability to produce climate change scenarios at the regional scale;
—Improvement of the Global Climate Observing System and the Global Oceanic Observing System;
—Evaluation of the underlying ethical questions of inter-regional and inter-generational equities;
—Evaluation setting up the real costs of action and inaction in the area of climate change;
—Introduction and/or application of economic incentives and disincentives for achieving stabilization and reduction of CO_2 and other greenhouse gases not controlled by the Montreal Protocol;
—Comprehensive and firm application of the 'Polluter Pays Principle' and the 'Precautionary Principle'.

By ensuring the efficacy of steps mentioned above, there is no doubt that assumed disasters due to changes in the environment can be minimised.

3

Expected Disasters for Resources and Activities of Humanity

After having discussed the basics of technical and human aspects of environmental changes, it is required to evaluate expected disaster and its impact. The questions to which need answers are: how much will sea level rise and what effect will that have; how much will water resources be affected; what will be the result for agriculture and food supply; will human health be affected? This chapter deals with these basic issues.

Everyone knows that the answers to these questions are far from simple. It is relatively easy to consider the effects of a given change (in say sea level or water resources) supposing nothing else experiences changes. But other factors will change. Ecosystems have great potential to adapt, and man has even more ability to respond and adapt to change.

In determining how serious the effects of global warming can be, allowance must be made for response and adaptation. The likely costs of adaptation also need to be taken into account. The assessment of the impact of global warming is also made more complex because global warming is not the sole human induced environmental problem. The loss of soil and its impoverishment (through poor agricultural practice), the excessive extraction of ground water and the damage due to acid rain instance of environmental degradations on local or regional scales which are having a substantial impact now. If they are not set right, they will tend to exacerbate the negative impacts likely to arise from global warming.

Due to the reasons, the various effects of climate change so far as they concern human communities and their activities will be seen the context of other factors which might alleviate or exacerbate their impact.

The following paragraphs will look at various impacts in turn and then bring them together in a consideration of the overall impact.

Expected Increase of Sea Level

Lot of evidence for large changes in sea level during the Earth's past history can be given. For instance, during the warm period before the onset of the last ice age, about some 120,000 years ago, the global average temperature was a little warmer than today. Average sea level at that time was about 5 or 6 metres higher than it is today. When ice cover was at its maximum by the end of the ice age, some 18,000 years ago, sea level was over 100 m lower than today, sufficient, for example, for Britain to be joined to the continent of Europe. It is often thought that the main reason for these sea-level changes was the melting or growth of the large ice-sheets that cover the polar regions. It is no doubt true that the main reason for the drop in sea level 18,000 years ago was the amount of water locked up in the big extension of the polar ice-sheets. In the Northern hemisphere these extended in Europe as far South as Southern England and in North America to south of the Great Lakes.

It must also be true that the main cause for the 5 or 6 m higher sea level during the last warm interglacial period was a reduction in the Antarctic or Greenland ice-sheets. But changes over less periods are largely governed by other factors which combine to produce a significant effect on the average sea level.

Different Factors for the Likely Sea-level Rise

1. The largest of these comes from thermal expansion of water in the oceans; as the oceans warm the water expands and the sea-level rises.

2. The other main contribution comes from the melting of glaciers. If all glaciers outside Antarctica and Greenland would melt, the rise in sea-level would be about 50 cm (between 30 and 50 cm)[2]. Substantial glacier retreat has occurred during the gone years scientists estimate that glacier melting may have contributed about 5 cm to the observed global sea-level rise of 10-15 cm within this period. Modelling the effect of climate change on the behaviour of glaciers is, anyway, complex. The growth or decay of a glacier

depends on the balance between the level of snowfall on it, especially in winter and the amount of melting in the summer. Both winter snowfall and average hot temperature are important, and both must be taken into account in future projections of the rate of glacier melting.

3. Prefably it is surprising that the net contribution expected from changes in the Antarctic and Greenland ice-sheets is low. For both ice-sheets there are two competing effects. In a warmer world, there is more water vapour in the atmosphere which causes to more snowfall. But there is also more ablation (erosion by melting) of the ice around the boundaries of the ice-sheets where melting of the ice and calving of icebergs take place during the summer months.

For Antarctica, the estimates are that accumulation is more than ablation, leading to a small net growth. For Greenland, ablation is greater than accumulation. For the two taken together the net effect is almost nil, although there is considerable uncertainty in that estimate.

One portion of the Antarctic ice-sheet in the west of Antarctica is often mentioned as of special concern. A big part of it is grounded well below sea level. There have been suggestions that it could disintegrate fast, in which case its melting would cause sea level to rise by about 5m. It is not clear whether melting of the West Antarctic ice-sheet contributed to the rise in sea level during the last interglacial period, 120,000 years ago.

Although scientists are not still very confident in their ability to model the dynamic behaviour of large ice-sheets, there is no reason to suppose there is fear in the short term (for instance, during the next century) of the collapse of any of the major ice-sheets. Much more understanding of the behaviour of large ice-sheets must be obtained before the amount of warming which might induce such collapse can be estimated. As per the estimates for the business-as-usual scenario the total average sea-level rise is predicted to be almost 15 cm by 2030 and about 50 cm by the year 2100. Because of the slow rate of rise in temperature of much of the oceans, sea-level rise due to global warming will lag behind temperature change at the surface. One when does what would happen if the temperature rose as in the business-as-usual scenario until the year 2030, at which time greenhouse gas concentrations were still so that no further change in radiative forcing of the climate would occur after that date. By 2030, sea level would have gone up about 15 cm. In the remaining 70 years of the next century a further 20 cm or so of sea-level rise would be expected, the rise continuing through the following century too.

Regional Variations of Impacts

All the estimates of average sea-level rise provide a general guide as to what can be expected. Sea-level rise, however, will not be uniform over the world. The effects of thermal expansion in the oceans will vary considerably with location. Moreover, movements of the land occurring for natural reasons or because of human activities (for example, the removal of groundwater), can have comparable effects to the rate of sea-level rise arising from global warming. At any given region, all these factors have to be taken into account in determining the likely value of future sea-level rise.

The Consequences

Impact of climate change can be dangerous:

1. Rise in Sea Level— A rise in average sea level of 15cm by 2030 and about half a metre by the end of the next century may not seem a big deal. Many people live sufficiently above the level of high water not to be directly hurt. However, half of humanity inhabits the coastal zones around the world. Within these, the lowest lying are some of the most fertile and thickly populated. To people living in these areas, even a fraction of a metre increase in sea level can multiply enormously their problems.

Some of the areas which are especially vulnerable are Bangladesh and similar delta areas, the Netherlands and the small low-lying islands in the Pacific and other oceans. Bangladesh is a densely populated country of about 120 million people located in the complex delta region of the Ganges, Brahmaputra and Meghna Rivers. (About 7 per cent of the country's habitable land with about six million population) is less than 1 metre above sea level and about 25 per cent (with about 30 million population) is below the 3 metre contour. Estimates of the sea-level rise next century are of about 1 metre by 2050 (compounded of 70 cm due to subsidence because of land movements and removal of groundwater and 30 cm from the effects of global warming) and nearly 2 m by 2100

(1.2 m due to subsidence and 70 cm from global warming)[6]—although there is a large uncertainty in these estimates.

2. Agricultural land will be affected— It is quite impractical to think of full protection of the long and complicated coastline of Bangladesh from sea-level rise. Its most obvious effect, therefore, is that great amounts of good agricultural land will be lost. This is serious: half the country's economy is drawn from agriculture. 85 per cent of the nation's population depends on agriculture for its livelihood, and many of these people are at the very edge of subsistence.

3. Natural disasters— This is not the only effect of sea-level rise. Bangladesh is extremely prone to damage from storm surges. Every year, on average, at least one serious cyclone attacks Bangladesh. During the past twenty-five years there have been two very large disasters with extensive flooding and loss of life. This disaster in November 1970 is probably the largest of the world's natural disasters in recent times; it is assumed to have claimed the lives of over a quarter of a million people. Well over a hundred thousand are thought to have lost their lives in another storm in April 1991. Even small rises in sea level add to the vulnerability of the region to such storms.

4. Agricultural production affected— Another effect of sea-level rise is the productivity of agricultural land: the intrusion of saltwater into fresh groundwater resources. Right now, it is estimated that in some parts of Bangladesh saltwater extends seasonally inland over 150 km. With a one metre rise in sea level, the area affected by saline intrusion could go up, with a large effect on the supply of fresh water.

Now the question arises is, what possible responses can Bangladesh make to these likely future problems? Over the time-scale of change which is currently envisaged it can be assumed that the fishing industry can relocate and respond with flexibility to changing fishing areas and changing conditions. It is not much easy to see what the population of the affected agricultural areas can do to relocate or to adapt. No significant areas of agricultural land are available elsewhere in Bangladesh to make up that lost of the sea, nor is there anywhere else in Bangladesh where the population of the delta region can easily be located. It is evident that very careful study and management of all aspects of the problem is required. The sediment reduced by the rivers into the delta region is of particular importance. The amount of sediment and how it is used can have a great effect on the level of the land affected by sea-level rise. Careful management is therefore required upstream as well as in the delta itself; groundwater as well as sea defences must also be maintained carefully if some alleviation of the effects of sea-level rise is to be achieved.

This kind of situation exists in the Nile delta region of Egypt. The likely rise in sea level next century is made up from local subsidence and from global warming in much the same way as for Bangladesh—almost 1 metre by 2050 and 2 metres by 2100. About 12 per cent of the country's arable land with a population of over 7 million people would be affected by a 1 metre rise of sea level. Some safety from the sea is afforded by the extensive sand dunes but only up to half a metre or so of sea-level rise.

More examples of vulnerable delta regions, especially in south-east Asia and Africa, can be given where the problems would be similar to those in Bangladesh and in Egypt. For example, several large and low-lying alluvial plains are distributed along the eastern coastline of China. A sea-level rise of just half a metre would inundate an area of about 40,000 square kilometres where over 30 million people currently live. One particular delta which has been extensively studied is that of the Mississippi in North America. These studies underline the point that human activities and industry are already exacerbating the serious problems of sea-level rise due to global warming. Because of river management little sediment is delivered by the river to the delta to counter the subsidence taking place because of long-term movements of the Earth's crust. Also, the building of canals and dykes has inhibited the input of sediments from the ocean. Studies of this kind stress the importance of careful management of all activities influencing such regions, and the necessity of making maximum benefit of natural processes in ensuring their continued viability.

Let us now turn to the Netherlands, a country more than half consisting of coastal lowlands, mainly below present sea-level. It is one of the most densely populated regions in the world; 8 of the 14 million inhabitants of the region live in large cities like Rotterdam, The Hague and Amsterdam. Large system of about 400 km of dykes and coastal dunes, built up over many years, protects it from the sea. Latest methods of protection, rather than creating solid bulwarks, make use of the effects of various forces (tides, currents, waves, wind and gravity) on the sands and sediments so as to create a stable obstacle, against the sea—similar policies are advocated for the protection of the Norfolk coast in eastern England. Protection against sea-level rise next century will need no new technology.

Another type of area of especial vulnerability is the low-lying small island. Half a million people live in archipelagos of small islands and coral atolls, such as the Maldives in the Indian Ocean, consisting of 1190 singular islands, and the Marshall Islands in the Pacific, which lie almost entirely within three metres of sea-level. Half a metre or more of sea-level rise would decrease their areas and remove up to 50 per cent of their groundwater. The cost of protection from the sea is far beyond the resources of these islands' populations. For coral atolls, however, there is sufficient hope that coral growth, providing it is undisturbed, will match sea-level rise up to the rate of about half a metre a century.

Given above here are some examples of areas particularly vulnerable to sea-level rise. Many other areas in the world will be affected in similar, although perhaps less dramatic, ways. A number of the world's cities are close to sea-level and are being increasingly affected by subsidence because of withdrawal of groundwater. The rise of sea-level due to global warming will multiply this problem. There is no technical difficulty for most cities in taking care of these problems, but the cost of doing so must be included when calculating the overall results of global warming. So far, in considering the impact of sea-level rise, places of dense population where there is a large effect on people have been considered. There are also areas of significance where few people live.

The world's wetlands and mangrove swamps currently occupy an area of about a million square kilometres (the figure is not known very accurately), equal approximately to twice the area of France. Their bilogical productivity equals or exceeds that of any other natural or agricultural system. Over 2/3rd of the fish caught for human consumption, as well as many birds and animals, depend on coastal marshes and swamps for part of their life cycles, so they are of importance to the total world ecology. Such areas can adjust to slow levels of sea-level rise, but there is no proof that they could keep pace with a rate of rise of greater than about 2mm per year—20cm per century. What will tend to occur, thus, is that the area of wetlands will extend inland, often with a loss of good cultivable land. Sea defences could be erected to prevent this, but a considerable cost and with a net loss of wetland area.

5. Other problem related to Environment— Global warming is not the only reason for sea-level rise but it is likely to exacerbate the impacts of other environmental problems. Well-thought management of human activities in the affected areas can do a lot to alleviate the likely effects, but substantial adverse impacts will continue.

In delta regions, which are particularly vulnerable, sea-level rise will lead to substantial loss of agricultural land and salt intrusion into drinking water resources. In Bangladesh, for instance, over 10 million people are likely to be affected by such loss. A further problem in Bangladesh and other low-lying tropical regions will be the increased intensity of disasters because of storm surges. Low-lying small islands will also prove to bear loss of land and fresh water supplies. Countries like the Netherlands and many cities in coastal regions will have to spend substantial amount on protection against the sea. Sufficient amounts of land will also be lost near the important wetland areas of the world. Attempts to put costs against these effects, in both money and human terms, will be considered later in the chapter.

Consequences for Fresh Water

In the environmental system, the global water cycle is a fundamental component of the climate system. Water is surrounded between the oceans, the atmosphere and the land surface. Through evaporation and condensation it provides the primary means whereby energy is transferred to the atmosphere and within it. Water is essential to all forms of life; the main cause for the wide range of life forms, both plant and animal, on the Earth is the wide range of variation in the availability of water.

In wet tropical forests, the jungle teems with life of enormous variety. In drier regions sparse vegetation exists, of a kind which can survive for long periods with the minimum of water; animals there are also well adapted to reverse conditions. Water is also a key substance for humankind; we need to drink it, we need it for the production of eatables, for health and hygiene, for industry and transport. Humans have learnt that the ways of providing for livelihood can be adapted to a large variety of circumstances regarding water supply except, perhaps, for the completely dry desert.

1. Water Hideout— Water availability averaged per capita in different countries differs from 1,000 cubic metres (220,000 imperial gallons) per year to over 50,000 cubic metres (11 million imperial gallons)—although quoting average numbers of that kind hides the enormous disparity between those in very poor areas who may walk many hours each day to fetch a few gallons and many in the developed world who have access to virtually unlimited supplies at the turn of a tap.

2. Changed Living Standards and Scarcity of Water— The demands of increased populations and the desire for higher standards of living have brought with them much more requirements for fresh water. During the last 50 years water use worldwide has grown four times, it now amounts to about 10 per cent of the estimated global total of the river and groundwater flow from land to sea areas. Two-thirds of human water use is currently for agriculture, much of it for irrigation; about one-fourths of it is used by industry; only 10 per cent or so is used domestically. Increasingly, water stored over hundreds or thousands of years in underground aquifers is being tried for current use. With this rapid growth of demand comes greatly increased vulnerability regarding water supplies.

3. Water Sharing— More vulnerability arises because many of the world's major sources of water are shared. About half the land area of the world is within water basins which fall between two or more countries. There are 44 countries for which at least 80 per cent of their land areas came such international basins. The Danube, for example, passes through 12 countries which use its water, the Nile through 9, the Ganges-Bramaputra through 5. Other countries where water is low are critically dependent on sharing the resources of rivers such as the Euphrates and the Jordan. The achievements of agreements to share water often bring with them demands for better use of the water and better management. Failure to agree brings increased possibility of tension and conflict. The UN Secretary-General, Boutros Boutros-Ghali has said that 'The next war in the Middle East will be fought over water, not politics."

4. Water Evaporation— The availability of fresh water will be substantially changed in a world affected by global warming.

The increase of temperature will mean that a larger proportion of the water falling on the Earth's surface will evaporate. This would not matter if there were more rainfall to make up for the evaporation.

The joint effect of less rainfall and more evaporation in these places would mean less run-off. Other parts of the world would have increased precipitation, for example, the monsoon regions of south-east Asia, where studies indicate substantially greater run-off in the hot weather. The run-off in rivers and streams is what is left from the precipitation which falls on the land after some has been taken by evaporation and by transpiration from vegetation, it is the major part of what is available for human use. The amount of run-off is highly sensitive to changes in climate; even minor changes in the amount of precipitation or in the temperature (affecting the amount of evaporation) can have a big influence on it.

Watersheds in arid or semi-arid regions are especially sensitive because the yearly run-off is in any case highly variable. Some watersheds in mid latitudes in the northern hemisphere, where snowmelt is great source of run-off, can also be severely affected. For these places, as temperatures rise, winter run-off will increase substantially and spring high water will be much decreased.

But, as has been constantly stressed, the severity of climate impacts depends to a great degree on extreme conditions. This is well illustrated by looking at the scale of natural disasters about water—either too much water in floods or too little in droughts. In the list of natural disasters, floods were third (after tropical cyclones and Earthquakes) in order of severity leading to loss of life. A UNESCO study in 1973 found that each year, in Asia alone, river floods damage or destroy about 40,000 square kilometres of land and crops, and affect the lives and wellbeing of over 17 million people. During the period 1980-85, more than 160 big serious floods were recorded, killing or injuring more than 120,000 people, destroying the homes of nearly 20 million and causing damage estimated at over 20 thousand million US dollars—a very large amount indeed for the economies of the countries involved. Droughts do not occur high up on the table of natural disasters, not because they are unimportant, but because, unlike most other calamities, their effects tend to felt over a long period of time.

The 'dust bowl' years in the 1930s in the United States are still within living memory, as are the droughts and famines in India in 1965-67 which, it is estimated, approx imately. Claimed one and a half million lives. We have all been made very aware of the disastrous consequences of drought in the Sahel region and in other parts of Africa in the 1980s—which are still happening only too frequently on that continent. Any temperature or rainfall record shows a large variability. The inevitable consequence of variability added to higher average temperatures (meaning higher evaporation) and higher average rainfall will be a higher number and greater intensity of both droughts and floods. Some of the areas likely to be affected are just those areas which are specifically vulnerable to floods and droughts at the moment. But droughts and floods are also likely to occur in locations where, at present, such disasters are uncommon.

One can identify watersheds that are particularly vulnerable to climate change by asking certain questions about them. These are:-

1. How much water storage is there in the watershed relative to the yearly flow? In Colorado, in the United States, for instance, the storage is four times the yearly flow, whereas in the Atlantic States it is only one-tenth of the yearly flow.

2. What is the extent of a demand as a percentage of the potential supply? Again in the United States, for the Missouri river basin it is 30 per cent, for the Rio Grande it is 64 per cent and for the lower Colorado 96 per cent. Almost no water in the Colorado river reaches the sea. Therefore, though the Colorado has substantial storage and is thus not very sensitive to annual variations.

3. What is the quantity of groundwater being used? There are many places in the world where groundwater is being used faster than it is being replenished. To give two instances, for more than half the land area of the United States over a quarter of the groundwater withdrawn is not being replenished, so every year the water has to be taken out from deeper levels; and in Beijing in China the water table is falling by two metres a year as its groundwater is pumped out.

4. How different are the stream and river flows? This question is particularly relevant to arid and semi-arid areas. Detailed

studies considering these criteria have been carried out for a number of areas.

Changes in Rainfall

There is another reason, not unconnected with global warming, for the vulnerability of water supplies: the link between rainfall and changes in land use. Large deforestation can lead to large changes in rainfall. A similar tendency to reduced rainfall can be expected if there is a decrease in vegetation over large areas of semi-arid regions. Such changes can have a devastating and major effect and assist in the process of desertification. This is a potential threat to the drylands covering about one quarter of the land area of the world.

Now the question everyone would ask is what sort of action can be taken to decrease the vulnerability of human communities to water supplies? Irrigation absorbs about two-thirds of world water use, and is of great importance to world agriculture. Irrigation is due on about one-sixth of the world's farmland which produces about one-third of the world's crops. In some areas the ratio is much higher; for example, over 80 per cent of the agricultural land in California is irrigated. Most irrigation is through open ditches, which is very wasteful of water; more than half is lost through evaporation and seepage. Microirrigation techniques, in which perforated pipes deliver water directly to the plants, provide large opportunities for water conservation, making it feasible to expand irrigated fields without building new dams. Management of the existing infrastructure can be made better, for instance by arranging for the integration of different supplies, and conservation in the household and industrial sectors can be encouraged. Most of these actions will cost money, although they may be much more cost-effective ways of coping with future change in water resources than attempting to develop major new facilities.

One can thus say that the likely effects of global warming on water supplies are: (a) First, the current vulnerability of many communities to water shortage should be noted. This is especially true of arid and semi-arid regions where the growing demands of human communities mean that droughts, even for short periods, are more disastrous than in the past. Vulnerability is well demonstrated in many areas of the world where the amounts of groundwater extraction greatly exceed its replenishment—a condition which can not continue for very long into the future. Because of population growth these vulnerabilities will increase and will exacerbate the negative effects of global warming.

(b) Two, climate change because of global warming will result in large changes in water supplies in many places. Although the present state of information regarding regional and local climate change does not allow scientists to identify clearly the most vulnerable areas, they are able to indicate the sort of area which will be the most affected. Such areas are those arid and semi-arid areas with less rainfall leading to greater aridity and even desertification; continental areas where decreased summer rainfall and increased temperature result in a substantial fall in soil moisture and much increased vulnerability to drought; and areas such as those served by the Asian monsoon, where increased rainfall will cause a greater incidence of floods. The changing pattern of climate extremes, especially droughts and floods, will be the cause of most of the problems.

Consequences for Farming

1. After fresh water, agriculture and food supply are great problems to be faced because of changes in the climate.

2. Every farmer understands the need to grow crops or rear animals which are suited to the local climate. The distribution of temperature and rainfall throughout the year are key factors in making decisions regarding what crops to be sowed. These will change in the world influenced by global warming. The patterns of what crops are grown and where will therefore also change. But these changes will not be simple; economic and other factors will take their place alongside climate change in the decision-making process.

1. Adaptability of Crops: There is enormous capacity for adaptation in the growth of crops for food. We have seen some of this with what was called the Green Revolution of the 1960s when the evolution of new strains of many species of crops resulted in large increases in productivity.

Between the mid-1960s and the mid-1980s global food production went up by an average annual rate of 2.4 per cent—faster than global population—more than doubling during that thirty-year period. Grain production grew even faster, at an annual rate of 2.9 per cent. With the detailed knowledge of the conditions required by different species and the expertise in genetic manipulation available today, there should not be much difficulty in matching crops to new climatic conditions over large parts of the world. At least, that is the case for crops that mature over a year or two. Forests attain maturity over much longer periods, from decades up to a century or even more. The projected rate of climate change is such that, during this time, trees may find themselves in a climate to which they are not comfortable. The temperature regime or the rainfall may be substantially changed, resulting in stunted growth or a larger susceptibility to disease and pests. One instance of adaptation to changing climate is the way in which farmers in Peru adjust the crops they grow depending on the climate forecast for the year. It is a country whose climate is strongly influenced by the cycle of El Nino events. Two of the major crops grown in Peru, rice and cotton, are very sensitive to the amount and the timing of rainfall. Rice requires large amounts of water, cotton has longer roots and is capable of yielding greater production during years of low rainfall. In 1983, following the 1982-1983 El Nino event, agricultural production went down by 14 per cent. By 1987 forecasts of the onset of El Nino events had become sufficiently good for Peruvian farmers to take them into account in their planning. In 1987, due to the 1986-1987 El Nino, production actually increased by 3 per cent, thanks to a useful forecast.

2. Prevalence of Water: The availability of water is the most important of the factors affecting agriculture and food production. The deficiency of water supplies to climate change carries over into a vulnerability in the growing of crops and the production of food. Therefore, the arid or semi-arid areas, mostly in developing countries, are most at risk.

3. Growth Boosting: A further factor, which can actually lead to increased production as a result of climate change, is the boost to growth which is made, particularly to some crops, by increased atmospheric carbon dioxide. Detailed studies have been carried out of the sensitivity to climate change of the prominent crops which make up a large proportion of the world's food supply. They have used the result of models to observe and calculate the changes in temperature arid precipitation which might be expected when the atmosphere has a doubled carbon dioxide concentration. They too include the possible effects of economic factors and the possibility of modest levels of adaptation. Such models are yet at an early stage of development and cannot be employed as detailed predictions. They tend to show that, with appropriate adaptation, the impact of the average climate change which would occur with doubled carbon dioxide on the supply of food for the world as a whole is not likely to be very high. What has not been studied to any extent is the likely effect of climate extremes (especially of the incidence of drought) on world food supply. Nor have the studies considered the integrity of the world's soils, which are presently being lost by erosion at an alarming rate.

Keeping in mind, future needs, two activities which can be pursued now are particularly important. One, there is large room for technical advances in agriculture in developing countries where much is still very primitive. In other words, there needs to be continued development of programmes for crop breeding and management, particularly in conditions of heat and drought. These can be immediately useful in the improvement of productivity in present marginal environments.

Secondly, when considering fresh water supplies, improvements need to be made in the availability and management of water for irrigation, especially in arid or semi-arid areas of the world. A detailed chapter has been included to discuss the problems in a thorough manner.

The Consequences on Ecology

As we all know well, a little over 10 per cent of world's land area is under cultivation. The rest is to a greater or lesser extent unmanaged by humans. Out of this about 30 per cent is natural forest. The variety of plants and animals which form a local ecosystem is sensitive to the climate, the type of soil and the availability of water. Scientists in this fields, i.e, Ecologists divide the world into biomes—regions characterized by their distinctive vegetation. This is well illustrated by knowledge about the distribution of vegetation over the world during past climates, which indicates what species and what ecosystems are most likely to grow under different climatic regimes. The information gleaned from paleo sources could be utilised to produce maps of the optimum distribution of natural vegetation within the climate scenarios expected to occur with global warming, since climate is the major factor determining the distribution of biomes–changes in climate alter the suitability of a region for different species, and change the competitiveness of different species under an ecosystem, so that even relatively small changes in climate will lead, over time, to large changes in the composition of an ecosystem.

1. Frequent Changes: Various kind of changes took place over thousands of years. With global warming similar changes in climate occur over a few decades. Most ecosystems cannot respond or accommodate that fast. Natural ecosystems will therefore become increasingly unmatched to their environment. How much this matters will vary greatly from species to species; some are much more vulnerable to changes in average climate or climate extremes than others. But all will become more prone to disease and attack by pests. Any positive consequence from added fertilization due to increased carbon dioxide is likely to be more than outweighed by negative effects from other factors.

2. Effect on Forests: Trees are long-lived and take a long time to reproduce. Because it is not easy for them to respond fast to climate change, the world's forests are likely to be the most affected. The decline in the health of many forests in recent years has received much attention, particularly in Europe and North America where much of it is thought to be due to acid rain and other pollution originating from heavy industry, power stations and motor vehicles. Not all damage to trees, however, is thought to have this origin.

Studies in several regions of Canada, for instance, indicate that the dieback of trees there is due to changes in climatic conditions, especially to successions of warmer winters and drier summers. In some cases it may be the double effect of pollution and climate stress creating the problem; trees already weakened by the effects of pollution fail to cope with climate stress when it comes. The assessment of the impact of climate change studied for the MINK region of United States concluded that under the warmer, drier conditions of the analogue climate they studied, decline and dieback of the forested part of the region would go down the mass of timber in the forest by 10 per cent over twenty years. The results of these studies disclose more serious levels of forest dieback which are likely to occur with the rapid rate of climate change expected with global warming.

3. Threat to Biodiversity: A further concern about natural ecosystems, especially forests, relates to the diversity of species which they have. Much concern is being expressed at the moment because of the threat to biodiversity from extensive cutting of forests. There is a danger that the rapid climate change expected as a result of global warming will also lead to great loss of species in some ecosystems although the likely effect is difficult to quantify.

Now about ecosystem in oceans although we know much less about ocean ecosystems, there is considerable evidence that biological activity in the oceans has changed from time to time during the cycle of ice ages. The changes in ocean water temperature and the possible changes in some of the patterns of ocean circulation might result in changes in the regions where upwelling occurs and where fish congregate. Some fisheries could collapse and others expand. Presently, the fishing industry is not well adapted to address major change.

The Consequences for Health of Individuals

Our health is dependent on a good environment. Many of the factors that lead to a deteriorated environment also lead to poor health. Pollution of the atmosphere, polluted or improper water supplies, and poor soil (leading to poor crops and inadequate nutrition) all present dangers to human health and well-being and help in spreading of disease. In considering the impacts of global warming, many of these factors will tend to be exacerbated through the climate change which will take place in the warmer world.

1. Direct Effects on Human Health— Humans can live comfortably in very varying conditions and have great ability to adapt to a wide range of climates. However, certain extreme conditions are not very tolerable and can encourage the transmission of some diseases. The main difficulty in evaluating the impact of climate change on health is that of unravelling the effect of climate from the large number of other factors (including other environment factors) that affect health.

2. Frequent Heat Stress— It will be that of heat stress in the extreme high temperatures that will become more frequent and more widespread. Studies using information from large cities where heat waves commonly occur show deaths rates which can be doubled or tripled during days of unusually high temperatures. While such an episode may be followed by a period when fewer deaths occur, showing that some of the death would in any case have occurred about that time, most of the grown mortality seems to be directly associated with the excessive temperatures. It might be thought that compensation for the periods of excessive heat would be offered by fewer occasions of severe cold. Studies tend to show, however, that increased mortality due to periods of excessive heat will considerably be more than any reduction in the periods of cold, especially amongst aged people who find it particularly difficult to cope with high temperatures.

3. Fear of more Diseases— A further likely impact of climate change on health is the increased spreading of diseases in a warmer world. Many insect occupants of disease thrive better in warmer and wetter conditions. For example, epidemics of diseases such as viral encephalitides carried by mosquitoes are known to be linked with the unusually wet conditions which occur in the Australian, American and African continents associated with different phases of El Nino cycle. Some diseases, presently largely confined to tropical regions, with warmer conditions could spread into mid-latitudes. Malaria is an example of such a disease which is caused by mosquitoes under conditions which are optimum in temperature range of 15-32°C with humidities of 50-60 per cent. More diseases which are likely to spread for the same reason are yellow fever, dengue fever and lymphatic filariasis.

Planning the Expenditure

Undoubtedly, planning and estimating the likely cost community of the various impacts listed above is a difficult task. For a costing to be at all realistic, especially when it is to apply to periods of decades into the future, it must account not only for direct damage but for the possibilities of adaptation too. However, even crude attempts at costing help to provide an idea of the size of the problem. The most detailed studies of impacts have been carried out for the United States and have been summarized by William Cline. For those impacts against which some value of loss can be placed, the total figure is about 60 thousand million dollars per annum or about one per cent of the US Gross Domestic Product (GDP) in 1990. For other countries in the developed world, estimates of the cost of effects in terms of percentage of GDP are similar, for the developing world, figures of annual cost of 2 per cent or more of GDP have been estimated.

As some have explained, their estimates are crude, are based on very broad assumptions and should not be considered as accurate values. They offer a first indication of the scale of the problem in economic terms.

An introductory enquiry might suggest that the costs of global warming, although large, at a percent or two of Gross World Product (GWP) are not impossibly high and that we could probably buy our way out of the problems of its impact. There are, however, as Cline points out, two factors. One is that the studies have only been concerned with the impacts of global warming up to about the middle of the coming century. The longer-term impacts, if the growth of greenhouse gases continues along a business-as-usual scenario, are likely to be much higher.

The second is that not all impacts can be quantified in terms of economic costs. The loss of human amenity, natural amenity or the loss of species cannot be easily counted in money terms. This can be emphasized by focusing on those who are likely to be especially disadvantaged by global warming. Most of them will be in the developing world at around the subsistence level. They will find their land not any more able to sustain them because it has been lost either to sea-level rise or to extended drought. They will thus wish to migrate and will become environmental refugees. It has been estimated that, under a business-as-usual scenario, the total number of persons displaced by the results of global warming could total in the order of 150 million by the year 2050 (or about 3 million per year on average) about 100 million due to sea-level rise and coastal flooding and about 50 million due to the impact on of agricultural production mainly due to the incidence and location of areas of drought. The cost of resettling 3 million displaced person per year has been estimated at between $1,000 and $5,000 per head, giving a total about 4,000 million per year. What the estimated cost for resettlement counts out however, is the human cost associated with displacement. Nor does it include the social and political instabilities which will show heads when substantial populations are seriously disrupted because their means of livelihood has disappeared. The effects of these could be very large indeed.

It is thus well clear that there is no single factor that is affecting the environment and obviously, there is no sole impact/ consequence of environmental change. Global warming is the main, we leading to many others we have seen yet. In the coming chapter we shall see in detail the impacts of environmental and climatic changes in different fields and possible layout.

4

Consequences on Global Food Production

This chapter has been based on observation of a research conducted by Oxford's Environmental Change Unit in collaboration with Columbia University, USA in 1994. Initially, in 1989, potential changes in national grain crop yields were estimated using crop models and a decision support system evolved by the US Agency for International Development's International Benchmark Sites Network for Agrotechnology Transfer (IBSNAT 1989). The crops modelled were wheat, rice, maize, and soyabeans. These crops form more than 85 per cent of the world's traded grains and legumes. The estimated yield changes for the 18 countries were interpolated to provide estimates of yield changes for all regions of the world and for all the leading crops, by reference to all available published and unpublished information. These yield changes were used as inputs for a world food trade model, the Basic Linked System (BLS), developed at the International Institute for Applied Systems Analysis (IIASA) (Fischer *et al.* 1988). Outputs from simulations by the BLS disclosed facts and information on food production, food prices, and on the number of people at risk from hunger occuring out of food shortage.

Situation with Environmental Change

Platform for climate change developed in order to estimate its effects on crop yields and food trade. It is called climate change scenario. A climate change scenario is defined as a physically consistent set of changes in meteorological variables, based on generally accepted projections of levels of CO_2 (and other trace gases). The range of scenarios used aims to capture the range of possible effects and to set limits on the associated uncertainty.

The scenarios for this study were created by changing obtained data on current climate (1951-80) according to doubled CO_2 simulations of three general circulation models (GCMs). The GCMs used are those derived from the Goddard Institute for Space Studies (GISS), Geophysical Fluid Dynamics Laboratory (GFDL), and United Kingdom Meteorological Office (UKMO). Mean monthly changes in climate variables from the accurate gridbox were applied to observed daily climate records to create climate change scenarios for each site.

1. Significance of GCMs: They currently provide the most advanced means of predicting the potential future climatic consequences of increasing radiatively active trace gases. They have been shown to simulate current temperatures reasonably well, but do not reproduce present precipitation as accurately, and their ability to reproduce current climate varies considerably from region to region (Houghton *et al.* 1990). They have not been validated till date to project changes in climate variability, such as changes in the frequencies of drought and storms, even though these could affect crop yields significantly.

2. Trace Gases: Levels of future emissions of trace gases, as well as when the full magnitude of their effects will be realized, are not certain. Since other greenhouse gases besides CO_2 (e.g., methane (CH_4), nitrous oxide (N_2O), and the chlorofluorocarbons (CFCs), are also increasing, and 'effective CO_2 doubling' has been defined as the joint radiative forcing of all greenhouse gases having the same forcing as doubled CO_2 (usually defined as 600 ppm). For this study, CO_2 concentrations in 2060 are estimated at around 555ppm (based on Hansen *et al.* 1988). The effective CO_2 doubling will occur around the year 2030, if current emission trends do not change. The climate change caused by an effective doubling of CO_2 may be delayed by 30-40 years or longer, hence the projections for 2060 in this study.

Yield Simulations in Crop Models

The IBSNAT (Crop) Models

These were used to estimate how climate change and increasing levels of carbon dioxide may alter yields of world crops at 112 sites, representing both main production areas and vulnerable regions at low, mid, and high latitudes. The IBSNAT models employ simplified functions to forecast the growth of crops as influenced by the major factors that affect yields, that is genetics, climate (daily solar radiation, maximum and minimum temperatures, and precipitation), soils, along with management practices. Models used were for crops like wheat (Ritchie and Otter 1985; Godwin *et al.* 1989); maize (Jones and Kiniry 1986; Ritchie *et al.* 1989), paddy and upland rice (Godwin *et al.* 1992), and soyabean (Jones *et al.* 1989). These models were selected for use in this study because they have been validated over a wide range of environments (see Otter-Nacke *et al.* 1986) and are not particularly limited to any location or soil type. They are thus suitable for use in large-area studies in which crop growing conditions differ greatly. The validation of the crop models over various environments also improves the ability to estimate effects of changes in climate. Furthermore, because management practices such as the choice of varieties, the planting date, fertilizer application, and irrigation may be different in the models, they permit experiments that simulate adjustments by farmers and agricultural systems to climate change.

Better Efficiency Ratio of Yield

Most plants growing in experimental environments with increased levels of atmospheric CO_2 exhibit higher rates of net photosynthesis (i.e., total photosynthesis minus respiration) and reduced stomatal openings. (Experimental effects of CO_2 on crops have been studied by Acock and Allen (1985) and Cure (1985).) By so doing, CO_2 reduces transpiration per unit leaf area while enhancing photosynthesis. Thus, it generally improves water-use efficiency (the ratio of crop biomass accumulation or yield and the amount of water used in evapotranspiration). The crop models followed in this study also account for the beneficial physiological effects of increased atmospheric CO_2 concentrations on crop growth and water use (Peart *et al.* 1989). Ratios were calculated in measured daily photosynthesis and evapotranspiration rates for a canopy exposed to high CO_2 values, based on published experimental findings (Kimball 1983; Cure and Acock 1986; Allen *et al.* 1987), and the ratios were applied to the appropriate variables in the crop models on a daily basis. The photosynthesis ratios (555 ppm CO_2/330 ppm CO_2) for crops like soyabean, wheat and rice, and maize were 1.21, 1.17, and 1.06, respectively. These effects are based on experimental results that may overstate the positive effects of CO_2, because uncertainty exists about the extent to which the beneficial effects of increasing CO_2 will be seen in crops growing in variable, windy, and pest-infected (weeds, insects, and diseases) fields under the situation of climate change.

Deficiencies of these Models

Crop growth require a number of simplification. For example, weeds, diseases, and insect pests are assumed to be controlled; there are no problem soil conditions (e.g., high salinity or acidity); and also there are no extreme weather events, such as heavy storms. The crop models simulate the current range of agricultural technologies available around the globe. They do not include induced improvements in such technology, but may be used to test the effects of some potential improvements, such as the introduction of varieties with more thermal requirements and installation of irrigation systems.

Experiments for Crop Modelling Simulation

These were performed at the 112 sites in 18 countries for baseline climate (1951-80) and GCM doubled CO_2 climate change scenarios, with and without the physiological effects of CO_2. This involved the following task :

(a) Area boundaries were defined for the major production regions in the country studies. and the current production of major crops in those areas was estimated.

(b) Studied climate data for representative sites within these regions were provided for the baseline period (1951-80), or for as many years of daily data as were available, and the soil, crop variety, and management inputs important to run the crop models at the selected sites were specified.

(c) These models were validated with experimental data from field trials.

(d) Baseline data and climate change scenarios were used the crop models with and without the direct effects of CO_2 on crop growth.

(e) Changes in agricultural practices that would lessen any adverse consequences of climate change, by simulation irrigated production and other adaptation responses (e.g., shifts in planting data and crop varieties) were identifield and evaluated.

Drawing Estimates of Potential Yield Changes

1. Totalling of Field Findings: Findings crop model for wheat,, rice, maize and soyabean from the 112 sites in the 18 countries were aggregated by weighting regional yield changes (based on current production) to estimate changes in national level yields. The regional yield estimates represent the current mix of rainfed and irrigated production, the current crop varieties, nitrogen management, and soils. The study simulated almost 70-75 per cent of the world production of wheat and maize. Even though only two countries (Brazil and USA) simulated soyabean production, their joint output accounts for 76 per cent of world total. Less of the total world rice production was simulated than total production of the other crops.

This is because India, Indonesia, and Vietnam have lot of rice production not included in the study. Production data were put together by scientists participating in the project and from the FAO (1988), the USDA Crop Production Statistical Division, and the USDA International Service.

2. Yield Change Estimates for Crops and Regions not Simulated: Variations in national yields of other crops and commodity groups and regions which were not simulated were estimated on the basis of similarities to modelled crops and growing conditions, last published and unpublished climate change impact studies, and GCM climate change scenarios, Estimates were made of yield changes for the three GCM scenarios with and without the direct effects of CO_2. The yield changes with the direct effects of CO_2 were grounded on the mean responses to CO_2 for the different crops in the crop model simulations.

Main source of uncertainty in the estimates lies in the sparseness of the crop modelling sites. They may not correctly represent the variability of agricultural regions within countries, the variability of agricultural systems within similar agro-ecological zones, or dissimilar agricultural regions. However, because the site results relate to regions that account for about 70 per cent of total world grain production, the results concerning world totals of production contained in this report are believed to be adequately substantiated.

Food Trade

The estimates of climate-induced changes in yields were used as inputs to a dynamic model of the world food system (the Basic Linked System) in order to assess expected impacts on future levels of food production, on food prices, and on the number of people at risk from hunger. Impacts were assessed for the year 2060, with population growth, technology trends, and monetary growth projected to that year. Assessments were first made assuming no climate change, and subsequently with the climate change scenarios described above. The difference between these two assessments is the climate-induced effect. A further set of assessments examined the efficacy of a number of adatations at the farm level in mitigating the impacts and the effect on expected future production of liberalizing the world food trade system, and of different rates of growth of economy and population.

Basic Linked System (BLS)

It consists of linked national models. The BLS was designed at the International Institute for Applied Systems Analysis for food policy studies, but it can also be used to assess the effect of climate-induced changes in yield on world food supply and agricultural prices. It consists of 20 national and/or regional models which cover about 80 per cent of the world food system. The rest 20 per cent is covered by 14 regional models for the countries which have broadly similar attributes (e.g., African oil-exporting countries, Latin American high-income exporting countries, Asian low-income countries, etc.).

The categorisation is base on country characteristics such as geographical location, income per capita, and the country's position with regard to net food trade. The BLS is a general equilibrium model system, with representation of all economic sectors, empirically estimated parameters and no unaccounted supply sources or demand sinks for details, Fischer *et al.* 1988 for a complete description of the model. In the BLS, countries are linked through trade, world market prices, and money flows. It is a recursively dynamic system: a first round of exports from all countries is calculated for an assumed set of world prices, and international market clearance is checked for each commodity. Global prices are then revised, using an optimizing algorithm and again transmitted to the national model.

After this, these generate new domestic equilibria and adjust net exports. This process is repeated until the world markets are cleared in all commodities. At each stage of the reiteration domestic markets are in equilibrium. This whole process yields international prices as influenced by governmental and inter-governmental agreements. The system is solved in annual increments, simultaneously for all countries, Summary indicators of the sensitivity of the world system include world cereal production, world cereal prices, and proportion of world population at risk from lack of fond (this is defined as the population with an income insufficient to either produce or procure their food requirements).

This system does not incorporate any climate relationships *per se*. Effects of changes in climate were introduced to the model as changes in the average national or local yield per commodity, as estimated above. Ten commodities are included in the model: wheat, rice, coarse grains (maize, millet, sorghum, barley, etc.) bovine and ovine meat, milk and dairy products, other animal products, protein feeds, other food, non-food agriculture, non-agriculture. In this report, however, consideration is limited to the main grain food crops.

Experimentation Models

Finding given in this chapter are for the following scenarios:

1. The Reference Scenarios: This involved projection of the agricultural system to the year 2060 with no effects of climate change on yields and with no great changes in the political or financial context of the world food trade. It assumes:

(a) United Nations medium population estimates, which are 10.2 billion by 2060 (UN 1989; IBRD/World Bank 1990);

(b) Almost half trade liberalization in agriculture introduced gradually by 2020;

(c) Liberalised economic growth (ranging from 3.0 per cent per annum in 1980-2000 to 1.1 per cent per annum in 2040-60);

(d) Know-how is projected to increase yield over time (cereal yields of world total, developing countries, and developed nations are assumed to increase annually by 0.7 per cent, 0.9 per cent, and 0.6 per cent, respectively);

(e) Agricultural productivity not changed due to climate change.

2. The Climate Change Scenarios: These are projections of the world food system including effects on agricultural yields under various climate scenarios (the '2 x CO_2 scenarios' for the GISS, GFDL, and UKMO GCMs. The food trade simulations for these three scenarios were started in 1990 and assumed a linear alteration in yields until the doubled CO_2 changes are reached in 2060. Simulations, were made both with and without the mental effects of 555 ppm CO_2 on crop growth and yield for the equilibrium yield estimates.

In these scenarios internal adjustments in the model occur, such as increased agricultural investment, reallocation of agricultural resources as per economic returns, and reclamation of additional arable land as an adjustment to higher cereal prices, based on shifts in comparative advantage among countries and regions.

3. Scenarios with the Impact of Farm-level Adaptations: The Model called Food Trade Model was first run with yield changes assuming no external adaptation to climate change and was then re-run with different climate specific changes in yield assuming a range of farm level adaptations. These include such measures as switching planting dates, changing crop varieties, and the use of various amounts of irrigation and fertilizer. Two adaptation levels to handle potential effects on yield and agriculture were considered. Adaptation level 1 includes those adaptations at the farm level that would not involve any specific changes in agricultural practices. It thus included changes in planting date, in amounts of irrigation, and in choice of crop varieties that are presently available.

Adaptation level 2 includes, in addition to the former, major changes in agricultural practices, for example, large shift of planting date, the availability of new cultivars, wide expansion of irrigation, and increased fertilizer application. This level of adaptation would possibly involve policy changes at the national and international level and would be likely to involve significant costs. However, policy, expenditure and water resource availability were not studied explicitly.

4. Future Economy: Last group of scenarios assumed changes to the world tariff structure and different rates of growth of economy and population. As with the previous experiments, these were made both with and without climate changes impacts. These scenarios had:

(a) Complete trade liberalization in agriculture introduced gradually by 2020:

(b) Slow economic growth, ranging from 2.7 per cent per annum in 1980-2000, to 1.0 per cent in 2040-60 (global gross domestic product (GDP) in 2060 is 10.3 per cent less than the reference scenario, 11.2 per cent lower in developing countries, and 9.8 per cent lower in developed countries);

c. Slow population growth, UN low population estimates (c. 8.6 billion by 2060).

Without Adaptation—Yields

Proceeding table shows wheat yield changes by GCM 2 × CO_2 climate change scenario for the countries where crop model simulations were conducted. Findings show that climate changes scenarios without the direct physiological effect of CO_2 cause decreases in simulated crop yields in many cases, while the direct effects of CO_2 mitigate the negative effects mainly in mid and high latitudes. The magnitudes of the estimated yield changes vary by crop. Maize production is most negatively affected, perhaps due to its lower response to the physiological effects of CO_2 on crop growth.

Protein feed is least affected because soyabean responds significantly to grown CO_2, at least under the scenarios of smaller increases in temperature (e.g., the GISS and GFDL scenarios). The differences between countries in yield responses to climate change are related to differences in present growing conditions. At low latitudes, crops are grown nearer the limits of temperature tolerances and global warming may subject crops to increased stress. In many mid- and high-latitude areas increased temperatures can prove useful to crops otherwise limited by cold temperatures and short growing seasons in the present climate. The primary causes of decreases in yield are:

—Reducing the growing period (especially grain-filling stage) of the crop. This occurred at some sites in all countries.

—Reduction of water availability. This is increased by evapotranspiration and loss of soil moisture and in some cases a decrease in precipitation in the climate change scenarios. This happened in Argentina, Brazil, Canada, France, Japan, Mexico, and the USA.

Table: Present Level of Production and Changes in Simulated wheat Yields under GCM 2 × CO_2 Climate Change Scenarios, with and without the direct Effect of CO_2[a].

	Current production			Change in simulated yields					
Nation	Yield (t/ha)	Area (ha × 1000)	Production (t × 1000)	GISS[b] (%)	GFDL[b] (%)	UKMO[b] (%)	GISS[c] (%)	GFDL[c] (%)	UKMO[c] (%)
1. USA	2.72	26595	64390	—21	—23	—33	—2	—2	—14
2. Brazil	1.31	2788	3625	—51	—38	—53	—33	—17	—34
3. Australia	1.38	11546	15574	—18	—16	—14	—8	11	9
4. Canada	1.88	11365	21412	—12	—10	—38	27	27	—7
5. Egypt	3.79	572	2166	—36	—28	—54	—31	—26	—51
6. China	2.53	29092	73527	—5	—12	—17	16	8	0
7. France	5.93	4636	27485	—12	—28	—23	4	—15	—9
8. India	1.74	22876	39703	—32	—38	—56	3	—9	—33
9. Japan	3.25	237	772	—18	—21	—40	—1	—5	—27
10. Former USSR									
a) winter	2.46	18988	46959	—3	—17	—22	29	9	0
b) spring	1.14	36647	41959	—12	—25	—48	21	3	—25

	Current production			Change in simulated yields					
Nation	*Yield (t/ha)*	*Area (ha × 1000)*	*Production (t × 1000)*	*GISS*[b] (%)	*GFDL*[b] (%)	*UKMO*[b] (%)	*GISS*[c] (%)	*GFDL*[c] (%)	*UKMO*[c] (%)
11. Uruguay	2.15	91	195	—41	—48	—50	—23	—31	—35
12. Pakistan	1.73	7478	12918	—57	—29	—73	—19	31	—55
Average World yield	2.09	231	482	—16	—22	—33	—11	—4	—13

1. Results for each country represent the site results weighted according to regional production. The world estimates represent the country results evaluated
2. by national production. Source: Resenzweig and Parry, 1994.
   [b] GCS 2 × CO_2 climate change scenario only.
3. [c] GCM 2 × CO_2 climate change scenario with direct effects of CO_2.
4. [d] World area and production × 1000 000

—Low standard of vernalization. Some temperate cereal crops require a period of low temperature in winter to initiate or accelerate the flowering process. Poor vernalization results in low flower bud initiation and ultimately less yields. This caused decreases in winter wheat yields at some sites in Canada and the former USSR.

With adaptation-yields

Observations of the research tested the efficacy of two levels of adaptation. Level 1 implies little change to existing agricultural systems, reflecting farmer response to a changing climate. Level 2 implies more substantial change in the area of agriculture, possibly requiring resources beyond the farmer's means. It also represents an optimistic assessment of world agriculture's response to changed climate conditions as predicated by the GCMs tested in this study. In each case, the adaptations were checked as possible responses to the worst climate change scenario (this was usually, but not always, the UKMO scenario). Changes in economic or domestic agricultural policies were beyond the scope of this study; the expenses of adaptation and future water availability under the climate change scenarios were also not considered.

First level, i.e., level 1 has:-

(a) Change in planting date that do not imply major changes in crop calendar;

(b) Extra application of irrigation water to crops already under irrigation; and

(c) Shifts in crop variety to currently available varieties better adapted to the projected climate.

Second one, that is, Level 2 adaptation includes.

(a) Major shifts in planting date;

(b) More fertilizer application;

(c) Introduction of new varieties; and

(d) Setting up of irrigation systems.

Alternation in yield occur for both adaptation levels were based on crop model simulations where available, and were extended to other crops and regions using the estimation methods mentioned above. The adaptation estimates were developed only for the scenarios with the direct effects of CO_2 as these were judged to be most realistic.

In the table below are given Percentage change in cereal production under climate change scenarios in 2060.

Area	*Reference scenario (2060)without climate change(mmt)*[a]	*Scenario with climate change GISS (%)*	*GFDL (%)*	*UKMO (%)*
Developing	1836	-11.0	-9.2	-10.8
Developed	1449	11.3	5.2	-3.5
Central and South America	274	-23.7	-15.7	-5.8
Africa	296	-19.3	-20.9	-11.1
West Asia	133	-9.8	-14.3	-11.2
South and South East Asia	690	-9.1	-4.2	-15.2
Global	3286	-1.2	-2.8	-7.6

Consequences of WORLD FOOD TRADE

Effects on food production

1. Coming Days in the Absence of Climate Alterations—Thinking that there will be no effects of climate change on crop yields, but population growth and economic growth as given on p. 80, world cereal production is assumed at 3286 million metric tons (mmt) in 2060 (cf. 1795, in 1990). The estimate for cereals includes wheat, rice, maize, millet, sorghum and minor grains contained in the FAO AGROSTAT database.

Rice is included as rice milled equivalent (a factor of 0.67 is used to shift from rice paddy to milled rice). Cereal prices are estimated at an index of 121 (1970=100). The number of people at risk from hunger is assumed at about 640 million (cf. 530 million in 1990).

2. Without Adaptation, Impact of Climate Change, with Internal Adjustment in the Model—Keeping in mind the estimated effects of climate change and atmospheric CO_2 on crop yields, the effects on cereal production are given in Tables. These estimations are based upon changing simulation by the BLS that allow the world food system to respond to climate-induced supply reductions of cereals and consequently higher commodity prices through dynamic increases in production factors, cultivated land, labour, and capital, and inputs as like fertilizer. World cereal production is estimated to decrease between 1 and 7 per cent, depending on the GCM climate scenario.

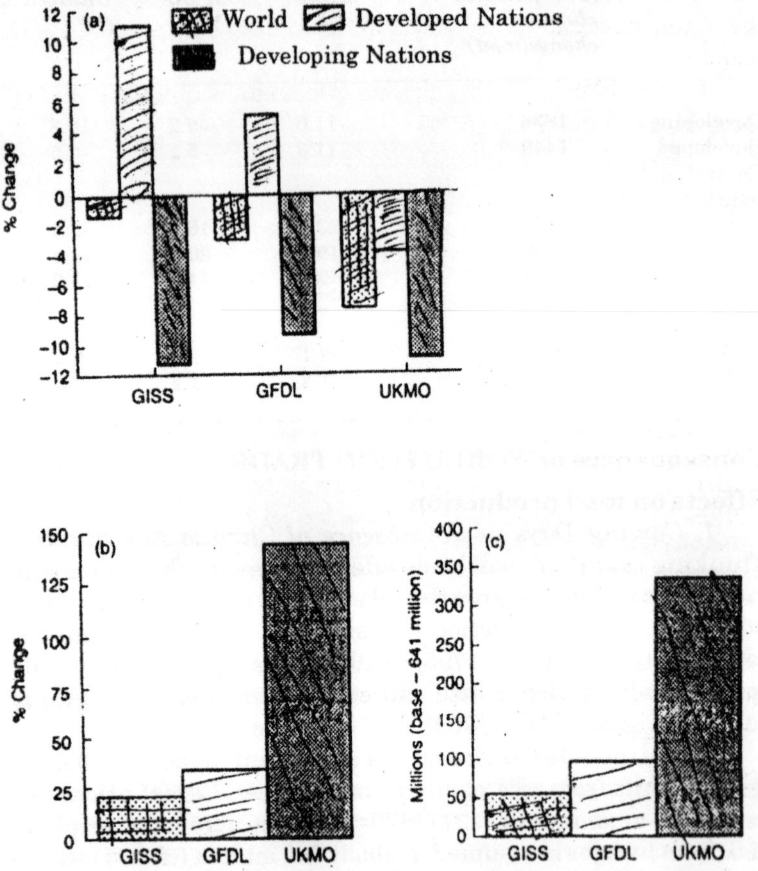

Effects of climate change on cereal production, prices, and number of people at risk from hunger under climate change scenarios in 2060. (a) Change in cereal production; (b) increases in cereal prices; (c) additional number of people at risk from hunger.

Under the UKMO scenario, global production is estimated to decrease by more than 7 per cent, but under the GISS scenario (which assumes lower temperature increases) cereal production is estimated go done by just over 1 per cent. The largest negative changes occur in developing countries, which average 9 per cent to –11 per cent. By contrast, in developed countries production is estimated to rise under all but the UKMO scenario (+11 per cent to –3 per cent). Thus, existing disparities in crop production between developed and developing countries are estimated to expand.

Consequences for production, under adaptation level 1 (AD1) and adaptation level 2 (AD2)

Region	*Changes in cereal production (per cent of 2060 reference)*		
	GISS	*GFDL*	*UKMO*
World			
Without adaptation	–1.2	–2.8	–7.6
AD1	0.0	–1.6	–5.2
AD2	1.1	–0.1	–2.4
Developed			
Without adaptation	11.3	5.2	–3.5
AD1	14.2	7.9	3.9
AD2	11.0	3.0	0.8
Developing			
Without adaptation	–11.0	–9.2	–10.8
AD1	–11.2	–9.2	–12.4
AD2	–6.6	–5.6	–5.7

Effects of Climate Change Under Different Levels of Adaptation

With AD1

As has been shown above, the effects of level 1 adaptation on estimated changes in cereal production. These largely offset the negative climate change yield effects in developed nations, improving their comparative advantage in world markets. In these regions cereal production increases by 4-14 per cent over the reference case. However, developing countries are estimated to gain little from adaptation (–9 to –12 per cent). Averaged global production is altered 0 to –5 per cent from the reference case.

As a consequence, world cereal prices are estimated to go up by c. 10-100 per cent, and the number of people at risk from hunger by c. 5-50 per cent. This indicates that level 1 adaptations would have comparatively little influence on reducing the global effects of climate changes.

Martin Parry

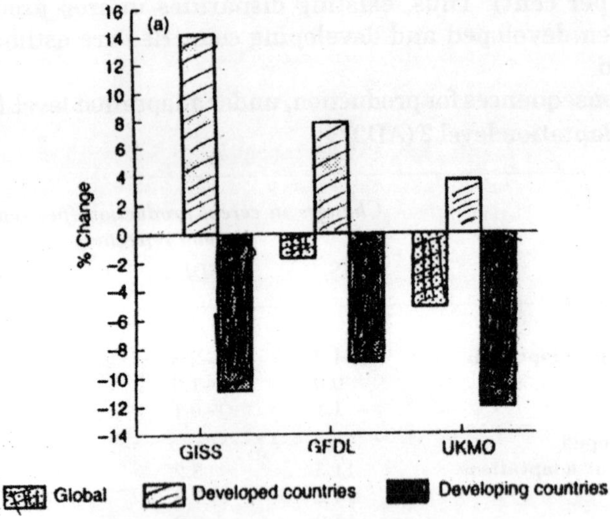

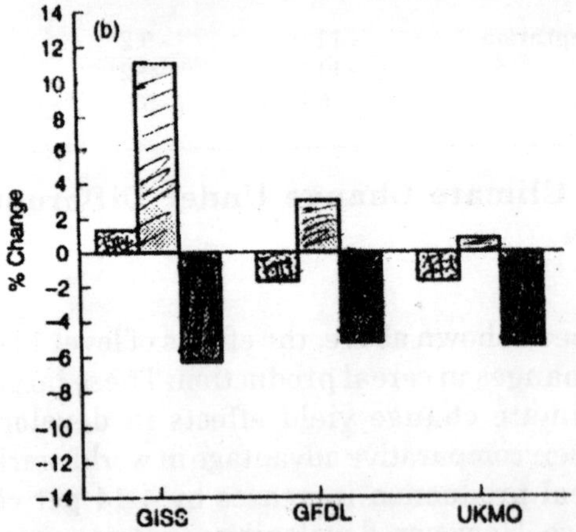

Alterations in cereal production under climate change scenarios in 2060, assuming various levels of adaptation. (a) AD1 (b) AD2.

With AD2

Wider spread amount of adaptation virtually eliminates negative cereal yield impacts at the global level under the GISS and GFDL climate scenarios and decreases impacts under the

UKMO scenario by one third. However, the decrease in comparative advantage of developing countries under these scenarios leads to less cereal acreages in these countries. Cereal production in developing countries still decreases by about 5 per cent. Globally, however, cereal prices hike only by c. 5-35 per cent, and the number of people at risk from hunger is altered by between –2 per cent and + 20 per cent from the reference case.

This suggests that level 2-type adaptations are needed to mitigate the negative effects of climate change, and still do not eliminate them in developing countries. Net imports of cereals into developing countries increase under all scenarios. The change in cereal imports is mostly determined by the size of assumed yield change, the change in relative productivity in developed and developing regions, the change in world market prices, and changes in incomes of underdeveloped countries.

Under the GISS climate scenario, productivity is depressed mainly in favour of developed countries, resulting in pronounced increases of net cereal imports into developing countries. Under the UKMO scenario, great cereal price hikes limit the increase of imports to developing countries. As a result, despite its beneficial impact for developed countries, the adaptation level 1 scenarios show only little improvement in developing countries compared to the corresponding impacts without such adaptation.

Consequences for production assuming full trade liberalization (REF-FTL)

		Changes in cereal production in 2060 (% REF-FTL)			
Region	*Ref.(2060) (mmt)*	*REF-FTL (mmt)*	*GISS (%)*	*GFDL (%)*	*UKMO (%)*
Global	3286	3356	–0.9	–2.6	–8.2
Developed	1449	1472	12.5	6.5	–3.7
Developing	1836	1884	–11.3	–9.7	–11.6

Consequences Assuming Complete Trade Liberalization, and Lower Economic and Population Growth Rates.

1. Total liberalisation of trade: Thinking that full trade liberalization in agriculture by 2020 provides for more efficient resource use, leading to a 3.2 per cent more value added in agriculture globally; and a 5.2 per cent higher agriculture GDP in developing countries (excluding China) by 2060 compared to the reference scenario. This policy change results in around 20 per cent fewer people at risk from hunger. Global cereal production is up 70 mmt, with most of the production increases occurring in developing countries.

World level impacts due to climate change are slightly reduced under most climatic scenarios, with enhanced gains in production accruing to developed countries, but losses in production higher in developing countries. Price increases are reduced slightly from what would occur without full trade liberalization, and the number of people at risk from hunger is decreased by about 100 million.

Consequences for production with assumption of a low rate of monetary growth (REF-E)

Area	*Changes in cereal production in 2060 (% REF-E)*				
	Ref.(2060) (mmt)	REF-E (mmt)	GISS (%)	GFDL (%)	UKMO (%)
Global	3286	3212	–1.0	–2.7	–7.9
Developed	1449	1428	12.5	6.0	–3.6
Developing	1836	1786	–11.6	–9.7	11.3

2. Decreased level of economic growth: To some extent, estimates were also made of impacts under a lower growth scenario (10 per cent lower than reference). Lower economic growth results in lower supply situation, higher prices, and more people below the hunger threshold. Prices are 10 per cent higher and the number of people at risk from hunger is 20 per cent greater.

The effect of climate change on these trends is generally to lessen production, increase prices, and increase the number of people at risk from hunger by about the same ratio as in the case with a larger economic growth rate. But the absolute amounts of change are greater.

3. Altered levels of population growth: The greatest effect of any of the considered policies would result from an accelerated reduction in population growth in developing countries. Simulations grounded on rates of population growth according to UN low estimates result in a world population about 17 per cent lower in year 2060 when compared to UN mid-estimates as used in the reference run.

The corresponding decrease in the developing countries (excluding China) would be about 19.5 per cent from 7.3 billion to 5.9 billion. The combination of more GDP per capita (about 10 per cent) and less world population produces an estimated 40 per cent less people at risk from hunger in the year 2060 compared to the reference scenario. Even under the most adverse of the three climate scenarios (UKMO) the estimated number of people at risk from hunger is some 10 per cent less than that estimated for the reference scenario without any climate alterations. Increases in world prices of agricultural products, in particular of cereals, under the climate change scenarios employing the low population projection are approx 75 per cent of those using the UN mid-estimate.

Consequences for production assuming UN low estimate of population growth (REF-P)

Area	*Changes in cereal production in 2060 (% REF-E)*				
	Ref. scenario (mmt)	REF-E (mmt)	GISS (%)	GFDL (%)	UKMO (%)
Global	3286	2929	–0.7	–2.6	–7.1
Developed	1449	1349	10.3	4.8	–3.9
Developing	1836	1582	–10.1	–8.9	–9.9

Thus, in nutshell, one can say that the Climate change induced by increasing greenhouse gases is likely to affect crop yields differently from region to region all over the globe. Under the climate change scenarios adopted in this study, the effects on crop yields in mid- and high-latitude regions appear to be less adverse than those in low-latitude areas. However, the more favourable effects on yield in temperate regions depend to a large extent on full realization of the potentially beneficial direct impact of CO_2 on crop growth. Decreases in potential crop yields are likely to be caused by shortening of the crop growing period, decrease in water availability due to increases rates of evapotranspiration, and poor vernalization of temperate cereal crops. When adaptations at the farm level were examined (e.g., change in planting date, switch of crop variety, changes in fertilizer application and irrigation), compensation for the detrimental effects of climate change was more successful in developed Nations. When the economic implications of these changes in crop yields are explored in a world food trade model, the relative ability of the world food system to accomodate impacts decreases with the magnitude of the impact. Regional variations in effects remain noticeable: developed countries are expected to be less affected by environmental change than developing economies. Dynamic economic adjustments can compensate for lower-impact scenarios such as the GDS and GFDL climate scenarios but not larger effect ones such as the UKMO scenario. Prices of agricultural products are related to the magnitude of the climate change impact and incidence of food poverty goes up in the least negative climate change scenario tested. When the consequences a lower future population and economic growth rates and trade liberalization were tested in the food trade model, less population growth rates would have the largest impact on minimizing the impact of climate change. Less monetary hike results in tighter food supplies, and consequently would result in higher rates of food poverty. Full trade liberalization in agriculture on the other hand, provides for more efficient resource use and would decrease the number of people at risk from hunger by about 100 million (from the reference case of a 640 million in 2060.) However, all of the scenarios of future climate adopted in this study increase the estimates of the number of people at risk from shortage of food items.

5

Sustainable Power and the Environment

The present chapter looks into corelation between the use of power and the environmental impacts. We flick a switch and energy flows. Energy is provided so easily for the developed world that thought is rarely given to where it is supplied from, whether it will ever run out or whether is harming the environment. Energy is also cheap enough that little serious attention is paid to conserving it. However, if the emissions of greenhouse gases into the atmosphere are to be decreased, a large proportion of the reduction will have to occur in the energy sector.

There is a need, therefore, to concentrate the minds of policy makers and indeed of everyone on our energy needs and usage. This chapter tries to find out how future energy might be provided in a sustainable manner.

Most of the energy we use can be traced back to the sun. For fossil fuels it has been stored away over millions of years in the past. If wood (or other biomass including animal and vegetable oils), hydro-power, wind or solar power itself is used, the energy has either been drawn from sunlight almost immediately or has been stored for short duration. These latter sources of energy are renewable; they will be considered in more detail later in the chapter. The sole common form of energy that does not originate with the sun is nuclear energy; this comes from radioactive elements which were there in the Earth when it was formed.

(a) Traditional Sources: Before the Industrial Revolution, energy for human society was provided from 'traditional' sources like wood and other biomass and animal power. Since 1860, as industry has developed, the rate of energy use has gone up by about a factor of 30 ; at first mostly through the use of coal followed, since about 1950, by rapidly increasing use of oil. In 1990 the world consumption of energy was almost 8,730 million tonnes of oil equivalent (toe). This can be converted into physical energy units to give an average rate of energy use of about 12 million watts (or 12 Terawatts=12×10^{12}W)[2].

(b) Variations in Amount of Energy Consumption: Large disparities exist in the amount of energy used per person in various parts of the world. In 1990 each person in the world consumed on average 1.65 tonnes of oil equivalent (toe), an average consumption of energy of about 2.2 kilowatts (kW). The highest amounts of energy consumption are in North America where the average citizen in 1990 used nearly 8 toe, similar to an average rate of consumption of about 11 kW. By contrast the average Indian used only one twentieth of that amount or 0.4 toe approximately, equivalent to an average rate of consumption of 0.5 kW, mainly in the form of traditional fuels.

Resources of Fossil Fuel: Estimate

Source	*Proven Reserves in 1990 (Gtoe)*	*Ratio: to current annual use (years)*	*Ultimately recoverable resources (Gtoe)*
1. Coal (excluding lignite)	496	197	3400 (coal and lignite)
Lignite	110	293	
2. Conventional oil	137	40	200
3. Unconventional oils (heavy crude, natural bitumen, oil shale)			600
4. Natural gas	108	56	220

In fact about half the world's population rely wholly on traditional fuels and do not presently have access to commercial energy in any of its forms. It is interesting to see how the energy we consume is used. Taking the world average, about 20 per cent of primary energy is used for transportation, about 40 per cent by industry and the 40 per cent in commercial activity and in homes. It is also perhaps interesting to know how much energy is consumed the form of electricity. About one-third of primary energy goes to make electricity at an average efficiency of conversion of about one-third. Of this electrical power about, 50 per cent on average, is utilised by industry and the other half in commercial activities and in homes.

Expenditure

Taking the world as a whole, the amount spent every year by the average person for the 1.65 toe of energy used, is about 5 per cent of annual income. Despite the very large disparity in incomes, the proportion spent on primary energy is almost the same in developed countries and developing ones.

(c) Future Assumptions: If we continue to generate most of our energy from traditional sources like coal, oil and gas, do we have enough to keep us going? Present knowledge of proven recoverable reserves indicates that known reserves of fossil fuel will meet demand for the period up to 2020 and substantially more. Around mid-century, if demand continues to expand, oil and gas supplies will come under increasing pressure. Further exploration will be stimulated which will cause exploitation of more sources, although induced difficulty of extraction can be expected to lead to a rise in price.

So far as coal is concerned, there are plentiful supplies for well over a hundred years. Estimates have also been made of the ultimately recoverable fossil fuel reserves, known as those potentially recoverable assuming high but not prohibitive prices and no significant bans on exploitation.

While these are bound to be somewhat speculative, they show that, at current rates of use, reserves of oil and gas are likely to be available for 100 years and of coal for duration longer than 1000 years.

It is important have to mention that likely reserves of uranium for nuclear power stations should also be included in this list. When converted to the same units they are sure to be at least 3,000 and possibly as high as 9,000 Gtoe, substantially greater than likely fossil fuel reserves.

There are some more future assumptions made by many energy experts, individuals and organizations who have attempted to look into the crystal ball of the future and estimate future energy demand next century and how it might be fulfilled. Any such attempts are bound to be fraught with a lot of uncertainty and to include assumptions of dubious accuracy; no one really knows how human beings will behave or which political or technical developments may occur.

Nevertheless a range of possibilities must be considered in order to predict what climate change might occur. The predictions of climate change on the basis of a business-as-usual scenario prepared under the auspices of the IPCC (scenario IS 92a) estimated future energy demand on the assumption that no controls or limits for environmental reasons were applied. It is interesting to compare the energy assumptions of that scenario with four energy scenarios prepared by the World Energy Council (WEC). These scenarios (box) take into account possible population growth and energy sources and a realistic view of the rate of technical change.

One of the scenarios, the 'high growth' case (A), assumes a higher rate of economic growth in developing nations. An 'ecologically driven' case (C) assumes that environmental pressures have a major influence on energy demand and growth. The other scenarios (B and B1), denoted reference cases, are based on moderate assumptions about economic growth.

Details, of the scenarios disclose that it is only in the developed world that there is potential for fulfilment of future energy demand. Population growth and the need for economic development in developing countries make it inevitable that they might for many decades, consume increased amounts of energy. For all the scenarios fossil fuels will control the energy mix over the next few decades.

World Energy Council

Case Name	*A High growth*	*B_1 Modified reference*	*B Reference*	*C Ecologically driven*
Monetary Growth per cent p.a.	High	Moderate	Moderate	Moderate
OECD	2.4	2.4	2.4	2.4
CEE/CIS	2.4	2.4	2.4	2.4
DCs	5.6	4.6	4.6	4.6
World	3.8	3.3	3.3	3.3
Intensity of Energy per cent p.a.	High	Moderate	High	Very high
OECD	-1.8	-1.9	-1.9	-2.8
CEE/CIS	-1.7	-1.2	-2.1	-2.1

DCs	-1.3	-0.8	-1.7	-2.4
World	-1.6	-1.3	-1.9	-2.4
Transfer of	High	Moderate	High	Very high
Institutional impr-ovements(Global)	High	Moderate	High	Very high
Possible total demand (Gtoe)	Very high 17.2	High 16.0	Moderate 13.4	Low 11.3

World Energy Council's Scenarios to the Year 2100

Case		*A*		*B*		*C*	
	1990	2050	2100	2050	2100	2050	2100
1. Global energy demand (Gtoe)	8.8	27	42	23	33	15	20
2. Fossil fuels (per cent of primary energy)	77	58	40	57	33	58	15
3. Nuclear (per cent of primary energy)	5	14	29	15	28	8	11
4. New renewables (per cent of primary energy)	2	15	24	14	26	20	50
5. Annual CO_2 emissions from fossil fuels	6.0	14.9	16.6	12.2	11.7	7.3	2.5
6. Annual CO_2 emission from fossil fuels (per cent change on 1990)		152	181	107	98	24	-59

It is also said that the contribution from nuclear power is assumed to grow in all the cases. New renewable energy sources perform an increasing role, although apart from Case C their contribution is modest. For the 'ecologically driven' WEC scenario C the energy demand in 2020 is about 30 per cent more than that in 1990 and 30 per cent less than that for scenario A. That scenario C, following the WEC Committee on Renewable Energy, assumes both that there will be large increases in efficiency leading to a reduced energy demand and also a substantial growth in the share of primary energy supply coming from new renewable energy sources ('modern' biomass, solar, wind and so on). An increase in energy supply from these new renewable sources from 2 per cent in 1990 to 12 per cent in 2020 (by when, 1.4 Gtoe per annum would be coming from these sources) is thought to be just about feasible if their development is provided sufficient support; by the year 2100 under scenario C, 50 per cent of energy supply is assumed to come from these sources.

The WEC report tells that 'cost effective research, development and installation involving financing which only governments can supply will be required if these sources of energy are to be implemented on the large scale shown in the Ecologically Driven Case C'.

(d) Comparison of WEC and IPCC: By the year 2020, the energy demand and the carbon dioxide emissions for IS 92a are similar to those of the WEC Reference scenario B1. Then about the middle of the century later, the WEC scenarios assume more than the IPCC ones that growth in energy demand and also in carbon dioxide emissions will start getting limited by the increasing scarcity and price of oil and gas. For all the scenarios, except WEC scenario C, atmospheric concentrations of carbon dioxide continue to rise throughout next century.

The WEC scenario C comes near to stabilizing emissions over the period to 2020 and to stabilizing atmospheric concentrations by the year 2100.

Sustainability and Energy Conservation

If we turn lights off in our homes when we do not need them on if we reduce the thermostat by a degree or two so that we are less warm, we are conserving or indeed saving energy. But are such actions significant in overall energy set up? Is it realistic to plan for really worthwhile savings in our use of energy?

To examplify what might be possible, let us consider the efficiency with which energy is currently used. The energy available in the coal, oil, gas, uranium, hydraulic or wind power is *primary energy*. It is hardly used directly, but is transformed into light, useful heat, motor power and so on. The process of energy conversion, transmission and transformation into its final usable form involves a proportion of the heat being wasted. To provide 1 unit of electrical power at the point of use typically needs almost 3 units of primary energy. An incandescent light bulb is about 3 per cent efficient in changing primary energy into light energy.

Efficiency of Appliances

In Table, figures are given for the average annual electricity consumption of typical domestic appliances used in a home in the United Kingdom. If, in replacing applicances, everyone bought the most efficient available, their total electricity consumption could easily drop by more than half.

Savings in electricity also deliver a net economic return to the user. Take for example fluorescent light bulbs which are as bright as ordinary light bulbs, but use a quarter of the electricity and last eight times as long before they have to be replaced. A 15 watt compact fluorescent bulb (equivalent to a 60 watt ordinary incandescent light bulb) costing £10 will use about £10 worth of electricity over its lifetime. To cover the same period eight ordinary bulbs would be needed costing about £4 but using £40 worth of electricity. The net saving is therefore about £24. Similar calculations could be carried out for the other appliances.

Absorption of Appliance Electricity per year in kWh per year

Appliances	*1990 stock(UK)*	*Average new model (UK)*	*Best available model (global)*
Cooker	840	780	370
Washing machine	210	180	70
Dishwasher	500	430	300
Refrigerator	350	300	60
Fridge/Freezer	730	500	275
TV	200	140	100
Lighting	370	370	105

Table :Two Different Models

Different Components	*Models 1 Improper insulation*	*Model 2 Proper insulation*
Walls 150m^2 total area	Brick + cavity+block U-value 0.7	Brick+cavity+block with insulation in cavity of 75mm thickness U-value 0.3

Different Components	*Models 1 Improper insulation*	*Model 2 Proper insulation*
Roof 64m^2 area	Uninsulated U-value 2.0	Covered with insulation of thickness 150mm U-value 0.2
Floor 64m^2 area	Uninsulated U-value 1.0	Includes insulation of thickness 50mm U-value 0.3
Windows 12m^2 total area	Single glazing U-value 5.7	Double glazing with low emissivity coating U-value 2.0
Heat losses (inkw) with 10^{0}C temperature difference from inside to outside		
Total heat loss (kilowatts)	4.2	1.05
Add heat (in kilowatts) needed for air changes (1.5 per hour)	1.60	1.60
Total heating required (kilowatts)	5.8	2.65

Uses of Controlling Lighting

Unnecessary use of lighting reduces the overall efficiency to perhaps no more than 1 per cent. Assessments have been made across all energy uses comparing actual energy use with that which would be used by ideal devices providing the same services. Although there is some difficulty in defining precisely the performance of such 'ideal' devices, assessments of this type come up with world average end-use energy efficiencies of the order of 3 per cent . That sort of figure suggests that there is a huge room for improvement in energy efficiency, perhaps by at least three-fold.

The following paragraphs consider three areas where there are genuine possibilities of savings: in buildings, in industry and in transport.

1. In Buildings: So that we are comfortable in them we heat them in cold weather and we cool them in summer. In the United States, for instance, about 36 per cent of the total use of energy is made in buildings, including about 20 per cent for their heating (including water heating) and about 3 per cent for cooling them. Two ways in which really substantial energy savings can be done in buildings are (a) by improving their insulation and (b) by improving the efficiency of appliances. Many countries, including the UK and the USA still have relatively poor standards of building insulation as compared to Scandanavian countries. There are also large possibilities for the improvement of the efficiency of appliances at relatively small cost.

Through the findings of a study in the United States, some of the large savings which could be made in the electricity used in buildings. The cost of such action would be less than the cost of the savings electricity overall therefore there would be a substantial net saving.

This kind of savings would also be possible in other developed countries. Major savings at least as large in percentage terms could also be made in these countries with economies in transition and in developing countries if existing plant and equipment were better used with more efficiently.

Ownership of Cars in 1991

Sr. No.	*Nation*	*Person per car*
1.	USA	1.7
2.	Italy	2.0
3.	UK	2.4
4.	Japan	3.3
5.	Czechoslovakia	4.8
6.	Malaysia	8.4
7.	India	121.4
8.	Republic of Korea	15.5
9.	Ex-USSR	17.0
10.	China	680.0

2. In Industry: A room for efficiency savings exists in industry also. The installation of relatively simple control technology often provides large potential for energy reduction at a substantial net saving in expenses. The cogeneration of heat and power, which already enables electricity generators to make better use of heat which would otherwise be useless, is particularly applicable to some industrial plants where large amounts of both heat and power are required. For example; British Sugar with an annual turnover of £700 million now spends about £21 million on energy. Since 1980 the energy consumed per tonne of sugar has been decreased by 41 per cent through low grade heat recovery, cogeneration schemes and better control of heating and lighting. Many research studies in industrialized countries indicate that savings of 30 per cent or more could be made in the industrial sector at a net saving in overall economic terms.

3. In Transport: 20-25 per cent of energy use is for transport is in developed world and it is a rapidly growing proportion. Road transport accounts for the largest proportion of this, over 80 per cent in industrialized countries; air transport comes next at 13 per cent. In the United Kingdom, for instance, if the present trend in motor-car use does not stop, in about thirty years there will be twice as many cars doing twice as many miles and the situation is very similar elsewhere. The proportional growth in developing countries could be ever more fast. The advantages conferred by the motor-car, the convenience, freedom and flexibility which it brings, mean that growth in its use is bound to continue. Grown prosperity also brings with it increased movement of freight.

One can suggest two types of action which can be taken to curb the energy use of transport.

(a) The first is increase the efficiency of fuel use. As we cannot expect the average car to compete with the vehicle which, in 1992, set a record by covering over 12,000 km on one gallon of petrol—a distance which serves to illustrate how inefficiently we use energy for transport! But technology is available now through which the average fuel absorption of the current fleet of motor cars could be halved while maintaining an adequate performance.

(b) Next action is to plan cities and other developments so as to lessen the need for transport and to make personalized transport less required— work, leisure and shopping should all be easily accessible by public transport, or by walking or cycling. Such planning is already being made seriously in some countries where the need to reverse some current trends (for instance the growth of large out-of-town shopping developments) is also recognized.

We cannot close down the question of energy efficiency, till two other areas are mentioned. First, there are the questions of how far the efficiency of large power stations or other installations burning fossil fuels can be made better and also of whether their carbon dioxide emissions could be stopped from entering the atmosphere. The efficiency of coal-fired power stations, for instance, has gone better from about 32 per cent, a typical value of 20 years ago, to about 36 per cent for a current fluidized bed plant of today. Such an improvement is significant in environmental terms and it is important that means be provided for the latest, most skilful technology to be available and attractive to rapidly industrializing countries such as China. Substantial further gains in overall efficiency can be achieved by making sure that the large quantities of low-grade heat generated by power stations is not wasted but utilised, for example in Combined Heat and Power (CHP) schemes.

In the case of gases like carbon dioxide removal from the flue gases, it must be realized that the amounts are very large; the gas to be removed weighs thousands of millions of tons. Numerous proposals for such removal have been proposed, for instance pumping the carbon dioxide into spent oil or gas wells or into the deep ocean.

However, even in the most favourable circumstances (like when power stations are close to oil or gas fields), the cost of removal would be significant and for deposition in the deep ocean would be large. Moreover, if deposition in the deep ocean is seriously contemplated, the potential hazards associated with it need to be very carefully assessed.

Table: Renewable Resources and Supply of Energy

Renewable sources of Energy	*Year 1990*		*Year 2020*	
	Mtoe	*per cent of World Energy*	*Mtoe*	*per cent of World Energy*
1. Present Bio Sources	121	1.4	561	5.0
2. Natural: Solar	12	0.1	355	3.1
3. Natural: Wind	1	0.0	215	1.9
4. Geothermal	12	0.1	91	0.8
5. 'Small' hydro	18	0.2	69	0.6

Renewable sources of Energy	*Year 1990*		*Year 2020*	
	Mtoe	*per cent of World Energy*	*Mtoe*	*per cent of World Energy*
6. Natural: Oceanic	0	0.0	54	0.5
7. Total(new renewable sources)	164	1.8	1345	11.9
8. 'Large' hydro	465	5.3	661	5.8
9. 'Traditional' biomass	930	10.6	1060	9.3
Total (all renewables)	1559	17.7	3093	27.0

Non-Commercial Energy from Traditional Sources

One more area needing brief consideration is that of the 10 per cent or so of world energy which is not commercial and which comes from traditional sources, mainly from wood or other biomass. This is the only source of energy for half the world's population. Although all of these sources are renewable, it is still necessary that they are employed efficiently, and a great deal of room for increased efficiency exists.

For example, much cooking is still carried out on open fires where only about 5 per cent of the heat reaches the inside of the cooking pot. The introduction of a simple stove can raise this to 20 per cent or with a little elaboration to 50 per cent. There is often considerable consumer resistance to the introduction of such stoves, but if they were widely used, the saving worldwide in fuelwood would be enormous. Other means of reducing fuelwood demand would be to enhance alternatives such as the use of fuel from crop wastes, of methane from sewage or other waste material or of solar cookers.

Recyclable Power

When we bring our energy use in context, it is interesting to realize that the energy incident on the Earth from the sun amounts to almost 180 thousand million million watts (or 18,000 Terawatts, ITW=10^{12} W). This is about 15,000 times the world's average energy use of about 12 million million watts (12TW). As much energy arrives at the Earth from the sun in 40 minutes as we use in a whole year. Therefore, providing we can harness it satisfactorily and economically, there is plenty of renewable energy coming in from the sun to provide for all the demands human society can conceivably make.

Methods of Making Solar Power Usable

We can find various ways in which solar energy is converted into forms that we can use; it is interesting to look at the efficiencies of these conversions. If the solar energy is concentrated, by mirrors for example, almost all of it can be made available like heat energy. Between 1 and 2 per cent of solar energy is converted through atmospheric circulation into wind energy, which although concentrated in windy places is yet distributed through the whole atmosphere.

Almost 20 per cent of solar energy is used in evaporating water from the Earth's surface which eventually falls as precipitation, giving the possibility of hydro-power. Living material converts sunlight into energy through photosynthesis with an efficiency of around 1 per cent for the best crops. Finally, photovoltaic (PV) cells turn sunlight into electricity with an efficiency which for the best modern cells can be over 20 per cent. Around the year 1900, very early on in the production of commercial electricity, water power was a common obvious source and from the beginning made an important contribution. Hydroelectric schemes now supply about 6 per cent of the world's commercial energy. Other renewable sources of commercial energy have, however, not been slow fast enough to take off. In 1990, only about 2 per cent of the world's commercial energy came from all renewable sources other than large hydro. Of this 2 per cent, almost three-quarters was from 'modern' biomass, the other 0.5 per cent being shared between solar, geothermal, wind energy and small hydro sources.

Coming back to commercial energy generation, in order to put renewable sources into context, it is important to inspect the detailed projection of the WEC for the contributions from different 'new renewable' sources which make up the 12 per cent of total energy supply in the year 2020 assumed for the WEC scenario C. The major growth expected is in energy from 'modern' biomass and from solar and wind energy sources.

Given below are some of the main renewable sources as are described in turn and their possibilities for growth considered.

Most of them are employed for the production of electricity; in the case of biomass, liquid or gaseous fuels too can be produced.

Hydro-electric

This, the oldest form of renewable energy, is well established and is competitive economically with electricity generated by other means. Some hydroelectric schemes are quite large. Two of the world's largest schemes, each of over 10,000 MW capacity, are in South America at Guri in Venezuela and at Itaipu on the borders of Brazil and Paraguay. It is estimated that there is potential for more exploitation of hydroelectric capacity to three or four times what has currently been developed, much of this undeveloped potential being in the former Soviet Union and in developing nations. Large schemes, however, can have significant social impact, environmental consequences like loss of land, of species and of sedimentation to the lower reaches of the river and problems of their own such as silting up, which have to be seriously addressed before they can be undertaken.

One very significant facility provided by some hydro schemes is that of pumped storage. Using surplus electricity available in off-peak hours, water can be pumped from a lower reservoir to a higher one. Some times, by reversing the process, electricity can be generated to meet periods of peak demand. The efficiency of conversion can be as high as 80 per cent and the response time a few seconds, decreasing the need to keep other generating capacity in reserve. In 1990 about 75GW of pumped storage capacity was available worldwide with a further 25GW under construction.

Dry and Wet Waste

Next in current importance as a renewable energy source is the use of biomass as a fuel. The word biomass in this context includes domestic, industrial and agricultural dry waste material, wet waste material and crops, all of which can be used as fuel to power electricity generators and some of which are good to use for the manufacture of liquid or gaseous fuels.

We also get to see everyday considerable public awareness of the vast amount of waste produced in modern society. The United Kingdom, for instance, generates each year somewhat over 30 million tonnes of domestic solid waste, or about half a ton for every citizen; this is a typical value for a nation in the developed world. Even with major programmes for recycling some of it, huge quantities would still remain. If it were all incinerated for power generation about 1.7 GW could be generated, about 5 per cent of the UK's electricity needs.

Generation of Greenhouse Gases

But a question that still remains unanswered is, what about the greenhouse gas generation from waste incineration? Carbon dioxide is of course produced from it, which contributes to the greenhouse effect. However, the alternative method of disposal is landfill (most of the waste in the UK presently is disposed of that way). Decay of the waste over time produces carbon dioxide and methane in roughly equal quantities. Some of the methane can be gathered and used as a fuel for power generation. However, only a fraction of it can be captured; the rest leaks away. Since methane is a much more effective greenhouse gas than carbon dioxide, the leaked methane makes a substantial contribution to the greenhouse effect.

Comprehensive calculations show that if all United Kingdom domestic waste were incinerated for power generation rather than landfilled, the net saving every year in greenhouse gas emissions would be equivalent to about 10 million tons of carbon as carbon dioxide. As this is about 5 per cent of the total United Kingdom greenhouse gas emissions, we can infer that power generation from waste could be a noteworthy contribution to the reduction in overall emissions. These figures for electricity generation and saving in greenhouse gases could be about enhanced if in addition to the domestic waste the potential for power generation from industrial and agricultural waste was also taken into account.

Other Agricultural Activities

These are, such as sewage sludge and farm slurries and manures. Bacterial fermentation in the absence of oxygen (anaerobic digestion) of these wastes produces biogas which is mostly methane and which can be used as a fuel to generate energy. Although not a large potential energy source, there is room for its contribution to go up.

Crops as Fuel

The third potential biomass contribution is from the use of crops as a fuel. Here the potential is large. It is a truely renewable resource in that the carbon dioxide which is emitted when the biomass is burnt and turned back again into carbon, through the process of photosynthesis, in the reproduced biomass when it is grown again. Many different crops can be employed as biomass for energy production.

In Brazil, for example, since the 1970's large plantations of sugar cane have produced alcohol for use as a fuel mainly in transport, generating, incidentally, much less local pollution than petrol or diesel fuel from fossil sources. Great potential has been recognized for the sugar cane industry to produce both sugar and energy together with other byproducts as well. Biomass from wood plantations on agricultural land no longer required for food crops features as an important future source in Sweden's energy plans; the most efficient use of the biomass is first to currect it into biogas and then burn it in a gas turbine to produce electricity. For the UK, trails indicate that the most promising wayout is willow and poplar grown in coppices.

Owing to the low efficiency of conversion of solar energy to biomass, the amount of land required for significant energy production by this means is high and it is important that land is not taken over which is required for food production. However, there is in principle no this shortage of land for purpose. Plenty of suitable crops are available which could be grown on land only marginally useful for agriculture. The main deficiency is the cost of energy production from biomass.

The basic cost of electricity generated by this way is currently about twice that generated from fossil fuel sources, and the cost of alcohol from biomass as a fuel for transport is almost twice the basic cost of petrol or diesel. However, in some countries the expenditure which would otherwise be incurred in keeping aside of land from agricultural use for food production could be set against that extra cost.

Air Power

Drawing energy from the wind is not new. Two hundred years ago windmills were a common feature of the European landscape; in the year 1800 there were over 10,000 working windmills in Britain. During the past few years they have again become familiar on the skyline, for example, in south-west England and Wales. Slim, tall, sleek objects silhouetted against the sky, they do not have the rustic elegance of the old windmills, but they are, quite efficient. A typical wind energy generator will have a two or three-bladed propeller 33m in diameter and a rate of power generation in a wind speed of 12m/sec (43km/hr, 27mph or Beaufort Force 6), of 300 kilowatts.

It has been found that on a site with an average wind speed of about 7.5m/sec (an average value for the west of Great Britain) it will generate an average power of about 100kW. The generators are generally sited close to each other in wind farms which may include several dozen such devices. From the point of view of the electricity generating companies the difficulty with the generation of electrical power from wind is that it is intermittent. There are substantial periods with no generation at all. The generating companies can handle this in the context of a national electricity grid which pools electrical power from different sources providing that the proportion from wind sources is not too high.

Energy produced from the wind depends on the cube of the wind speed: a wind speed of 12.5m/sec is twice as effective as one of 10m/sec. It makes sense thus to mount wind farms on the windiest sites available. The west coasts of the British Isles have some of the strongest winds in Europe and are therefore appropriately suitable. It has been estimated that wind energy could within reasonable cost contribute up to 10 per cent of the UK's electricity supply. This kind of a provision would require more than 40,000 330kW wind generators; these would need to be carefully sited if visual amenity were not to be lost.

It would also require that the electricity grid be reinforced so that power produced in the Hebrides islands off the coast of Scotland can be transmitted south to England. In the longer term this provision could perhaps be doubled, especially if an effective way for energy storage were developed. Many other countries with windy coast lines or mountain regions could also make substantial usage of wind energy. Wind energy is also particularly suitable for the generation of electricity at isolated sites to which the transmission expenses of electricity from the other sources would be unacceptable. Because of the wind's intermittency, some storage of electricity or some back-up means of generation has to be provided as well.

Small wind turbines also form an ideal means for charging batteries in isolated locations; for instance, about 83,000 are in use by Mongolian herdsmen. Wind energy is mostly also an ideal source for water pumps. With the large growth during the last few years in the installations of wind generators, economies of scale have reduced the cost of the electricity generated. Eventually it can be expected to approach the cost of electricity generated from fossil fuels.

Solar Power

Earliest way of making use of energy from the sun is to turn it into heat. A black surface directly facing full sunlight can absorb about 1 kilowatt for each square metre of surface.

I. In regions with a high incidence of sunshine it is an effective and cheap means providing domestic hot water, which is extensively employed in nations such as Australia, Israel, Japan and the southern states of the United States of America. In tropical countries, a solar cooking stove can make an efficient alternative to stoves burning wood and other traditional fuels.

II. Thermal energy from the sun can also be used effectively in buildings, in order to provide a modest boost towards heating the building in winter and, more importantly, to provide for a greater degree of comfort and better environment.

III. Heat from sun can also be employed to provide heating to produce steam for the generation of electricity. To produce significant quantities of steam, the solar power has to be concentrated by using mirrors. One arrangement employs trough-shaped mirrors aligned east-west which focus the sun on to an insulated black absorbing tube running the length of the mirror. Numerous such installations have been built, particularly in the United States, where solar thermal installations provide over 350 MW of commercial electricity. The high capital expenditure of such installations, however, assuming a reasonable pay-back period, translates into an electricity cost which, at the moment, is at least three times that from most conventional sources.

IV. This also can be converted directly into electricity by means of photo-voltaic (PV) solar cells. They seem in a variety of ways in everyday life; as power sources, for example for small calculators or watches. Spacecraft are covered with 'solar panels' or possess 'solar arrays' covered with PV cells providing electrical power for the spacecraft. Their efficiency for conversion of solar energy into electrical energy is today generally between just under 10 per cent and 20 per cent. A panel of cells of area one square metre facing full sunlight will therefore deliver between 100 and 200 watts of electrical power. The cost of energy from solar cells has gone down dramatically over the past twenty years; so much so that they can now be employed for a wide range of applications and can also begin to contribute to the high scale generation of electricity.

V. More to it, small PV installations are eminently suitable, especially for developing countries, to provide local sources of electricity in rural pasts. About a third of the world's population have no access to electricity from a central source. Their predominant need is for small amounts of power for lighting, for radio and TV, for refrigerators (for example, for vaccines at a health clinic) and for pumping water. The cost of PV installations for these purpose is now competitive enough with other means of generation (such as diesel units) and around 100,000 DLKs (Domestic Lighting and broadcast reception charging Kits) have now been installed worldwide. Bigger installations are required for public buildings such as hospitals. A small hospital, again in Sri Lanka, through assistance from the Australian government, has installed a 1.3kW solar array, supported by a 2,200 amp-hour battery, to provide for lighting, refrigeration for vaccines, autoclave sterilization, pumping for hot water (generated through a solar thermal system) and radio.

Region Specific More Renewable Energies

Till now have been covered the renewable energy sources for which there is potential for growth on a scale which can make a significant contribution to overall world energy requirements. We should also mention briefly other renewable energy technologies which contribute to global energy production and which are of particular importance in certain regions, like geothermal energy from deep in the ground and energies from the tides, waves or thermal gradients in the ocean.

As has been said earlier, the presence of geothermal energy from deep down in the Earth's crust makes itself apparent in volcanic eruptions and less dramatically in equipments like geysers and hot springs. The energy available in favourable locations may be employed directly for heating purposes or for generating electrical power. While very important in particular places, for instance in Iceland, it is currently only a small contributor (between

0.1 and 0.2 per cent) to total world energy; its contribution could increase to the order of 1 per cent during the next few decades.

Huge amounts of energy are in principle available in the movements and the temperature gradients of the ocean; but they are mostly not easy to exploit. Tidal energy is the only one currently contributing significantly to commercial energy production. The largest tidal energy installation is at La Rance in France; it has a capacity of 240MW. Many estuaries in the world have been extensively studied as potential sites for tidal energy installations. The Severn Estuary in the United Kingdom, for instance, has the potential to produce a peak power of over 8,000MW or about 6 per cent of the total UK electricity demand. Although the cost of the electricity generated from the largest schemes could be at par with others, the main deterrents to such schemes are the high capital up-front cost and the significant environmental impacts that are expected.

Estimates for Expenditure

This energy on the scale envisaged by WEC scenario C will only be realized if it is seen to be competitive in cost with energy from other sources and if the investment it needs is made available. Considering electricity and the cost of various sources of its supply, comparison is made between these costs and the carbon dioxide emissions from the various sources.

Under some circumstances renewable energy sources are already competitive in cost, like in providing local sources of energy where the cost of transporting electricity or other fuel would be significant. Anyway, if renewables are to begin to displace fossil fuels to the extent required by scenario C, there will be required financial arrangements to bring about the change.

Allocating the Environmental Cost

A method of engineering such arrangements would be to allocate an environmental cost to carbon dioxide emissions. Supposing,for instance, that an enviro- nmental expenses of between $50 and $100 per tonne of carbon were to be associated with carbon dioxide emissions, between one and two per cents per kWh would be added to the cost of electricity from fossil fuel sources which could begin to bring some renewables (for instance, biomass and wind energy) into competition with them. Electricity, however, only accounts for about 33 per cent of the world's primary energy use. What about the possibility of renewable energy replacing solid and liquid fuels used for heating, for industry and for transport?

It has already been said that currently, liquid fuels such as ethanol derived from biomass are about twice as expensive as those derived from oil. Although there is a hope that the processing of biomass will become more efficient —the rapid development of technologies in bioengineering will help—it is unlikely that in the short duration the substitution of biomass-derived fuels will happen on a large scale without the application of appropriate financial incentives. Arrangements of a similar kind to those we have already mentioned for electricity generation would need to be put into place. Looking at the investment required, annual investment in the world's energy industry is already large; it presently runs at between 3 and 4 per cent of GWP.

The WEC estimates that cumulative world investment in energy supply will continue at least at the same level and up to the year 2020 will approach 30 million million US dollars at 1992 rates. They also estimate that to achieve the WEC scenario C, investment of at least 2.4 million million US dollars in new renewable energy sources would be needed over the same period. Although this latter sum is less than 10 per cent of the world's total investment in energy, right encouragement and incentives will be required if it is to be realized.

Longer Lived Knowhow

Here, we have has concentrated mostly on what can be achieved with available and proven technology during the next few decades. It is also interesting to assume about the more distant future and what relatively new technologies may become dominant later next century. In doing so, of course, we are almost definitely going to paint a more conservative picture than will actually occur.

Imagine how well we would have done if asked in 1890 to speculate about technology change by the 1980s! Technology will certainly astonish us with possibilities not thought of at the moment. But that need not deter us from being speculative. Of the renewable energy sources mentioned earlier, the direct conversion of sunlight into electricity by photovoltaic (PV) cells is in many ways the most attractive. There are many parts of the world where sunshine is plentiful and where suitable land not useful for other purpose would be readily available. It is a very clear, non-polluting technology, easily adaptable to mass production. The cost of PV electricity has been reducing rapidly a trend which is likely to continue especially with an increased scale of production.

Drawbacks of this Method

Power from PV installations is only available during the day and such installations will usually be remote from areas where the electricity is to be used. Means of energy storage and transport are therefore required. The best suggestion here is for hydrogen gas to be brought in use as a storage medium. It can be generated directly from the PV electricity by the electrolysis of water. This can prove to be a very efficient process; over 90 per cent of the electrical energy can be stored in the hydrogen. The hydrogen can then be brought by pipeline or by bulk transport. Again, hydrogen is an extremely no-polluting energy source, which can easily be applied to most of the uses for which energy is required.

Without doubt, it is particularly attractive for vehicle transport as, by means of a fuel cell, the energy in the hydrogen can be transformed into electricity for driving the vehicle, again rather efficiently and cleanly. All the technology necessary for a solar-hydrogen energy economy is available now, although the cost of energy supplied this way would at the moment be much more times that from fossil fuel sources. As the technology for its further development progresses, the cost will undoubtedly come down substantially. If its attrac- tiveness from an environmental point of view were recognized as a dominant reason for its rapid development, the solar-hydrogen economy could take off more fast than most energy analysts are currently predicting.

Nuclear Energy

A rarely mentioned energy source is nuclear energy. It is not strictly a renewable source, but it has considerable attractiveness from the angle of sustainable development.

(a) It does not produce greenhouse gas emissions (apart from a small amount which is used in making the raw materials employed in the construction of nuclear power stations) and because the rate at which it uses up resources of radioactive material is small compared to the total resource available.

(b) It is only efficiently generated in large units, so is suitable for supplying power to national grids or to large urban connurbations, but not for small, more localized supplies. The cost effectiveness of nuclear energy compared with energy from fossil fuel sources is often a subject of debate; exactly where it falls in relation to the others depends on the return expected on the up-front capital cost, which represents a large element of the total.

(c) Another advantage of nuclear energy installations is that the technology is known; they can be built now and therefore contribute to the reduction of carbon dioxide emissions in the short term.

(d) Further significance of nuclear energy is recognized in the WEC energy scenarios, which all assume growth in this energy source next century. How much growth will be realized will depend to a large degree on how well the nuclear industry is able to make happy the general public of the safety of its operations; in particular that the risk of accidents from new installations is negligible, that nuclear waste can be safely disposed of, that the distribution of disastrous nuclear material can be effectively controlled and that it can be stopped from getting into the wrong hands.

This is important here to reproduce that a further potential nuclear energy source depends on fusion rather than fission. When, at extremely high temperatures, the nuclei of hydrogen (or one of its isotopes) are fused to form helium, a large amount of energy is discharged. This is the energy source which powers the sun; if a suitable method for harnessing and containing the process on the Earth could be evolved virtually limitless supplies of energy could be provided. A great deal of research is being put into fusion technology, but the economic generation of power by this method still appears to be many decades away.

Thus, to conclude the chapter, we can say that it has outlined the ways in which energy for human life and industry is currently provided. Growth in conventional energy sources at the rate necessary to meet future energy needs will generate much increased emissions of greenhouse gases. The WEC have taken a lead by proposing a future energy scenario (scenario C) supported strongly by environmental considerations which would lead to the stabilization of carbon dioxide concentration in the atmosphere by the end of the 20th century.

We can conclude the chapter with the following points:

1. Various studies have shown that in most developed countries energy savings of 20 or 30 per cent can be achieved at no net cost or even at some overall saving. But industry and individuals will need not just encouragement, but modest incentives if the savings are to be realized.

2. Such energy sources are renewable, (especially 'modern' biomass, wind and solar energy), which can begin to replace energy from fossil fuels, must be demised. One means of providing an incentive could be by including a component to the cost of fossil fuels which recognizes the environmental cost associated with their use.

3. An assurance is needed that technology is available for developing countries to develop their energy designs with high efficiency and to deploy renewable energy sources (for instance local solar energy generators) as widely as possible.

4. Now that the world investment in the energy industry running at around one million US dollars in a year, there is a great responsibility on both governments and industry to ensure that these investments take long-term environmental requirements fully into account.

Thus, these are some tips for a sustainable power use keeping in mind the limits of environment. These are important to be observed by all academicians and researchers, industrials and individuals. Unless and until this is done, we cannot expect our energy power use to be a sustainable safe development.

6

Environmental Safety and the Coal Policy

In the previous three chapters, are have seen what development are taking place at international level policy making in general and what the difference between the developed and the developing nations. But this chapter especially deals with the recent coal agreements vis-a-vis environmental protection. A positive development is that with the signing of the Climate Convention at the UNCED in Rio de Janeiro in 1992 a first important step was made in the direction of a coordinated-climatic and environmental protection policy. Germany is the host of the first Conference of Parties to be held in Berlin from 28 March to 7 April 1995. It is the ambition of the German government to initiate concrete action at this conference. These activities will be observed in light of the fact that the government has committed itself, as a first step, to a tough 25-30 per cent reduction in CO_2 emissions for West Germany and a reduction closer to 30 per cent by 2005 relative to 1987 for all of Germany.

The increasing impression is that the reduction target will be missed and that in many sectors of energy and transport policy decisions are being made that militate against climate and ecosystem safely even beyond 2005. Whether there is cause for this concern is investigated in this paper. On the basis of actual hard coal and brown coal policies as well as oil and gas developments, it will be proven what the likelihood is of meeting the CO_2 reduction target by 2005, Moreover, three policy scenarios of the Enquete-Commission of the German Parliament are used to show what the policy options are for meeting the German reduction goal. This chapter reaches a clear conclusion, namely that the government's energy and transport policies are not compatible with its CO_2 reduction target and thus its climate protection policy. It is therefore necessary to alter the current policy.

As we have said above, the ultimate objective of the Climate Convention is the protection of the climate and the ecosystems. To attain this, the greenhouse gas concentrations in the atmosphere must be stabilized at levels that will not endanger the climate system. For this it must be made that a mean global warming ceiling of ca. 2 °C is not exceeded by 2100 relative to 1860, and that from now on the rate of temperature change is confined to approximately 0.1 °C per decade (ECGP, 1991). Using climate modelling in reverse mode it can be calculated by to what extent the emissions of CO_2 and other green house gases, such as CH_4, N_2O and CFCs, must be reduced by certain reference years so that above temperature boundaries are not exceeded (Jain).

A number of scenario runs taking into account demographic, economic, technological and ecological considerations shows that the following combination of worldwide emission reductions from 1990 to 2100 would fulfil the above limits: 100 per cent for CFCs, H-CFCs and halons; 70 per cent for CO_2; 50 per cent for N_2O and 5 per cent for CH_4.

After start of the reduction process it is advisable to concentrate on the lead gas CO_2 and on the first reduction period from 1987 to 2005. Using accurate emission reductions for the other greenhouse gases, it can be shown with the help of climate modelling that it would suffice at the global level to cut back the CO_2 emission in 2005 to the 1987 level. In fact, the reductions would have to come, above all, from the economically strong countries, such as Germany, and would have to be of the order of 25-30 per cent. On the basis of the recommendation of the Climate Enquete-Commission of the Parliament, the German government accepted this target as a first step to be achieved by 2005. In spite of this commitment the impression grows that this tough reduction goal will not be reached.

Moreover, in many areas of energy and transport policy decisions are made that militate against climate and ecosystem protection for decades after 2005.

To questions that arise are:

(a) Can Germany meet its CO_2 reduction target of 25-30 per cent by 2005?

(b) What are the policy options for achieving such a tough reduction target?

Let us start with the structure of CO_2 emissions from 1975 to 1992 for each type of fossil fuel separately for West and East Germany, and Germany as a whole, see the German coal policy (there is no specific policy for the other energy carriers) and its effect on the reduction target, report on policy options that could conceivably help attain the reduction goal, and end by summarizing the major findings and recommendations for action.

Basics of the Policy

In the duration of past 17 years total German CO_2 emissions have varied from close to 1100 to about 900 Mt pa in more recent years. With an amount of *ca.* 1000 Mt pa Germany contributed about 4.5 per cent to the total global power energy related CO_2 emissions from fossil fuel use, placing it in fifth position as one of the major CO_2 emitters. About 80 per cent of the German CO_2 emissions was given by West Germany, reflection the population distribution of *ca.* 63 million West Germans and *ca.* 17 million East Germans. The relative contributions of the different fossil fuels to CO_2 emission varied markedly between West and East Germany. In West Germany between 40 and 50 per cent of the CO_2 emissions came from oil (See Table) About 25-30 per cent was derived from hard coal and about 15 per cent each were produced by brown coal and gas. Between 1982 and 1992 hard coal went on with its downward trend reaching a CO_2 reduction of 4.5 per cent, while gas showed an increasing trend with about 12 per cent. On the other hand, in East Germany, brown coal was the dominant source of CO_2 emission with a share of 70 to 80 per cent of the total emission. Oil was next with 15-20 per cent and both hard coal and gas were minor contributors with about 5 per cent each.

As a result of the breakdown of the East German energy economy in the aftermath of unification there were major CO_2 reductions amounting to about 59 per cent for hard coal, 56 per cent for brown coal and 23 per cent for gas between 1987 and 1992. The growth of 18 per cent in the oil sector may be considered as a harbinger of CO_2 growth with increasing motorization. For Germany as a whole, oil and brown coal were the two contributors to CO_2 emission, with oil rising to almost 40 per cent from increasing traffic, and brown coal decreasing to 26 per cent because

Table: Statistics Regarding the German CO_2 Emissions Related Fossil Fuels for the Duration, 1975-1992

Region	Amount (Mt pa)								Share (per cent)							
	1975	1980	1985	1987	1989	1990	1991[a]	1992[a]	1975	1980	1985	1987	1989	1990	1991[a]	1992[a]
(A) West Germany																
Hard coal	172	200	209	199	194	196	200	190	24	25	29	28	28	28	27	26
Brown coal	111	125	115	99	103	103	106	108	16	16	16	14	15	14	15	15
Mineral oil	353	355	304	316	285	300	316	318	50	46	42	44	42	43	43	44
Natural gas	76	99	90	98	101	104	111	110	10	13	13	14	15	15	15	15
Total	712	779	718	712	683	703	733	726	100	100	100	100	100	100	100	100
(B) East Germany																
Hard coal	19	20	15	17	13	11	8	7	6	6	4	5	4	4	4	4
Brown coal	224	237	282	281	276	243	164	125	76	76	83	82	83	81	75	69
Mineral oil	44	42	31	33	31	33	37	39	15	14	9	9	9	11	17	22
Natural gas	8	11	13	13	13	11	9	10	3	4	4	4	4	4	4	5
Total	296	310	341	344	333	298	218	181	100	100	100	100	100	100	100	100
(C) Germany																
Hard coal	191	220	224	216	207	207	208	197	19	20	21	20	20	21	22	22
Brown coal	336	362	397	380	379	346	270	233	33	33	37	36	37	35	28	26
Mineral oil	398	397	335	349	316	333	353	357	39	37	32	33	32	33	37	39
Natural gas	84	111	103	111	114	115	120	120	8	10	10	11	11	11	13	13
Total	1008	1089	1059	1056	1016	1001	951	907	100	100	100	100	100	100	100	100

Source: Deutscher Bundestag (1999) and own calculations.

of the dismantling of the very inefficient (< 30 per cent efficiency) energy plants in East Germany. The share of hard coal was steady at a little over 20 per cent, and that of gas was increasing to about 13 per cent Overall, between 1987 and 1992 CO_2 emissions went up by about 2 per cent in West Germany, and decreased by *ca.* 47 per cent in East Germany resulting in a total reduction of ca. 14 per cent.

There is no doubt that this reduction is greatly the result of the breakdown of the East German energy economy and not of any specific reduction measures. Especially worrisome is the fact that the large West German CO_2 emissions which dominate the total Germans CO_2 budget, show no sign of a decrease.

Possibilities and Doubts of Target Meet

(a) Policy regarding hard coal

The popular Century Treaty between the government and the coal industry, which guarantees the sale of a fixed quantity of coal for electricity and steel production, will be terminated by the end of 1995. For the duration of 1996 to 2005 the new Energy Policy Act of April 1994 will guarantee for German hard coal an appropriate amount for the production of electricity and long-distance warming.

The Act also regulates the subsidies. Since German hard coal is at *ca.* DM290/tce much more expensive than imported coal at *ca.* DM70/tce, it can be subsidized with DM7.5 billion in 1996 and DM7 billion per year from 1997-2000. This money will come from a levy on electricity use amounting to 8.5 per cent in West Germany and 4.25 per cent in East Germany, the latter slowly increasing to the level of West Germany.

Table : CO_2 Emission Shifts from Fossil Fuel use and Proposed Changes in a Trend Scenario for Germany in the Past and Future

Fossil fuels	*Changes in CO_2 emissions* 1987-1992[a] (Mt)	per cent	*1992-2005[b]* (Mt)	per cent	*1987-2005[b]* (Mt)	per cent
(A) West Germany						
Hard coal	–9	–4.5	4	2.1	-5	-2.5
Brown coal	9	9.1	–9	–8.9	0	0.2

Fossil fuels	*Changes in CO_2 emissions* 1987-1992[a] (Mt)	per cent	1992-2005[b] (Mt)	per cent	1987-2005[b] (Mt)	per cent
Mineral oil	9	0.6	−4	−1.3	−2	−0.7
Natural gas	12	12.2	27	27.2	39	39.5
Total	14	2.0	18	2.5	32	4.5
(B) East Germany						
Hard coal	−10	−58.8	24	142.7	−14	83.9
Brown coal	−156	−55.5	−33	−11.9	−189	−67.4
Mineral oil	6	18.2	15	45.0	21	63.2
Natural gas	−3	−23.1	19	146.7	16	123.6
Total	−163	−47.4	25	7.2	−138	−40.2
(C) Germany						
Hard coal	−19	−8.8	28	13.1	9	4.3
Brown coal	−147	−38.7	−42	−11.1	−189	−44.8
Mineral oil	8	2.3	11	3.0	19	5.3
Natural gas	9	8.1	46	41.2	55	49.3
Total	−149	−14.1	43	4.0	−106	−10.1

[a]Based on Dautscher Bundestag (1994). [b]Based on a trend scenario by Prognos (Eckerle *et al.* 1991).

At present, Germany imports about 13 Mtce pa or 18 per cent of its hard coal demand. At a rate of DM72/tce for imported coal and at a price of DM289/tce for indigenous coal in 1993 (RWE, 1994) this saves the utilities some DM 1.8 billion pa. No wonder that they are eager on increasing the import quota. However, reducing indigenous hard coal production is a very sensitive issue in the two hard coal mining *Lander* Nordrhein-Westfalen and Saarland, as so many jobs depend on it. In 1992 the 80,000 employees met an output of *ca.* 72 Mtce pa. so that a reduction of 1 Mtce pa translates into a loss of some 1350 jobs. This hard coal policy for the period up to 2005 implies the use of the following amounts of hard coal.

Coal from indigenous mining in West Germany is set at *ca.* 50 Mtce pa, of which some 35 Mtce pa and *ca.* 15 Mtce pa are to be used for electricity generation and steel production, respectively. With the liberalization of the energy market of the EU this is expected to be supplemented by 30-35 Mtce pa of imported coal. Almost two-thirds of the latter is to be used in West Germany in new hard coal power plants and in the iron and steel industry. The other one-third goes to East Germany for use in new power plants (e.g., Rostock and Stendal).

This coal policy has led and will probably lead to certain CO_2 emission changes. For West Germany there has been a decrease of *ca.* 4.5 per cent between the years 1987 and 1992. The trend scenario by Prognos (Eckerle *et al*, 1991), which takes account of this coal policy, expects hike of *ca.* 2 per cent from 1992 to 2005, and an overall decrease of 2.5 per cent for the total period 1987-2005. The reduction in indigenous coal is to some extent compensated for by imported coal.

In East Germany CO_2 emissions from hard coal have went down by more than 50 per cent from 1987-92, but they are expected to more than double from 1992-2005. These relative increase should not be overinterpreted since they refer to more modest amounts. The overall increase of about 4 per cent for all of Germany mainly arises from imported coal.

(b) Policy Regarding Brown Coal

There is major open pit brown coal mining both in West as well as East Germany. In West Germany the largest deposits are in the Rhine area being exploited by Rheinbraun. The 1987 mining became about 30 Mtce pa. The long-term mining plans involve the replacement of the exhausted pits by new ones in Hambach (13 to 16 Mtce pa), Garzweiler II (10 to 13 Mtce pa), and Inden (ca. 6 Mtce pa), which cames to virtually the same amount as in 1987. There is much opposition from local people for environmental and displacement reasons. In spite of this, North Rhine Westphalian government is expected to issue a permit in 1994 for the exploitation of Garzweiler II. The pits in Lower Saxony, Hesse and Bavaria are so tiny as to be insignificant.

In East Germany there are two large pit areas, the Central German Area (CGA) south of Leipzig, run by MIBRAG, and the Lausitz Area (LA) north-east of Dresden, run by LAUBAG. CGA goes on to mine in four open pits (*ca.* 8 Mtce pa) mainly for electricity production. In 1993 MIBRAG was bought by an Anglo-American syndicate. In 1993 LAUBAG used some 10 open pits with a capacity of ca.25 Mtce pa almost exclusively for electricity production.

In 1994 the *Lander* governments of Brandenburg and Saxony granted long-term permits until 2030/40 for the amounts of 5-7

Mtce pa for CGA and 16-20 Mtce pa for LA, giving a total of 21-27 Mtce pa. Together with West Germany this comes to almost 60 Mtce pa for Germany as a whole. In West Germany brown coal use increased by *ca.*3 Mtce pa resulting in a 9 per cent CO_2 increase from 1987-1992 (Table). However, as per the plans brown coal is to be stabilized at about the 1987 level of 30 Mtce pa so that from 1992-2005 CO_2 emissions are expected to drop by the same 9 per cent, leading, overall, to no after between 1987 and 2005. In East Germany the breakdown of the brown coal economy resulted in a 56 per cent CO_2 reduction between 1987 and 1992.

This was the result of the shutdown of some of the most inefficient power plants, the decreased sale to industry and decreasing briquette production. The anticipated long-term use of close to 28 Mtce pa would lead to a CO_2 reduction of above 67 per cent from 1987-2005.

(c) Use of Gas and Oil

Oil Consumption in West Germany showed only small changes so that also the CO_2 emission stayed almost the same from 1987-1992. This is expected to carry on, leading to virtually no change between 1987 and 2005. Two opposing trends are responsible: continuously rising motorized traffic causing more petrol use, and both efficiency measures and substitution of oil through gas in the residential sector requiring less oil use. In East Germany oil consumption has gone up by *ca.* 18 per cent from 1987-1992, and it is expected to continue its rise leading over the entire period of 1987-2005 to a CO_2 increase of more than 60 per cent. This is due to the enormous pent up demand in the transport sector and a small increase in the area of power plants and residential heating. In West Germany the use of gas is expected to carry on its strong growth leading to an increase in CO_2 emission of almost 40 per cent over the period of 1987-2005.

Strong growth is expected, above all, in the residential heating sector and in the industrial sector. The breakdown of industry in East Germany led to a remarkable decrease in gas relate CO_2 emission of about 23 per cent from 1987-92. However, by 2005, a substantial growth of around 124 per cent in CO_2 emission is expected. Some reasons are the shift from city gas to natural gas, a switch from brown coal to gas fired power plants for district heating, the extension of the gas network, and the recovery of industrial production (Schmitz and Bazkorn, 1994).

Initial Results

Depending upon the above analysis an attempt is made to give an answer to the first question of whether Germany can meet its reduction target of 25-30 per cent by 2005. The modest hike in CO_2 emission of 2 per cent in West Germany, and the drastic reduction of 47 per cent in East Germany leading to an observed total reduction of 14 per cent between 1987 and 1992 is not about to continue in the future. Rather it is expected that over the entire period 1987-2005, CO_2 emission will increase by 4.5 per cent in West Germany reduction by *ca* 40 per cent in East Germany so that for Germany as a whole only a modest decrease of 10 per cent is reached.

This analysis, which is based on actual policy (BMU, 1993; Uhlmannsiek, 1994; Schwarz, 1993a; 1993b); and a plausible trend analysis (Eckerle *et al*, 1991) reveals that the government's CO_2 reduction target of 25-30 per cent to be met by 2005 will be missed by a wide margin. This is because the amounts of hard and brown coal as well as those of oil and gas intended to be used over the coming 10 years or so are not compatible with the German CO_2 reduction target. It is therefore necessary for the government to alter fundamentally its current energy policy. The options at disposal for meeting the government's reduction target are addressed in the next section.

Alternatives for Achieving the German CO_2 Reduction Target

Central question is how coal policy as well as the oil and gas consumption can be made compatible with the government's CO_2 reduction target. This was investigated by about 50 agencies in 150 studies commissioned by an Enquete-Commission of the German Parliament (ECGP, 1991).

The following three reduction scenarios were considered: (a) scenario 'energy policy', in which the share of electricity from nuclear power of 31.2 per cent in 1987 is maintained until 2005; (b) scenario 'nuclear energy phase out' by and 2005; (c) scenario 'nuclear energy expansion', in which the part of nuclear electricity is almost doubled to 60 per cent, and the share in primary energy use is more than doubled from 11.4 per cent in 1987 to 24.6 per cent in 2005 (ECGP, 1991; Jochem, 1991; Bach, 1991).

The three scenarios were designed to come close to the desired CO_2 reduction of 25 per cent to 30 per cent by 2005.

Table: Expected Decrease in fossil fuels and CO_2 emissions in various policy scenarios for West Germany in 2005 relative to 1987

S.No.		*Base year 1987*	*Enquete-scenarios in 2005*[b] *Energy Policy*	*Nuclear energy Phase out*	*Expansion*
A.	**Fossil Fuels (Mtce pa)**[a]				
	Hard coal	73.2	45.0	54.7	42.6
	Brown coal	30.7	18.6	16.5	13.7
	Mineral oil	144.3	90.8	66.1	97.0
	Natural gas	59.8	71.9	88.5	69.5
	Total	307.9	226.3	225.8	222.7
B.	**CO_2- emissions (Mt pa)**				
	Hard coal	199	122	149	116
	Brown coal	99	60	53	94
	Mineral oil	316	199	145	212
	Natural gas	98	118	145	114
	Total	712	499	492	486
C.	**Emissions Change (per cent)**				
	Hard coal	0	–39	–25	–42
	Brown coal	0	–39	–48	–55
	Mineral oil	0	–37	–54	–33
	Natural gas	0	20	48	16
	Total	0	–30	–31	–32

In the following analysis, we concentrate on West Germany since the Enquete scenarios were carried out only for that part of the country. German hard coal policy envisages the use about 50 Mtce pa in 2005. Table above shows that only scenario 'nuclear phase out' comes close of this goal with about 55 Mtce pa. In this scenario hard coal fulfils the bridging function from the coal era to the solar age (Uhlmannsiek, 1994).

In contrast, with *ca.* 43 Mtce, scenario 'nuclear expansion' allows for the smallest amount of hard coal; for cost reasons both coal as well as nuclear must be used predominantly in base load leading to fierce competition between the two energy carriers. German brown coal policy is based on opening up new open pits in Garzweiler II, Hambach and Inden, with a capacity of about 30

Mtce pa replacing almost the same amount mined in the present pits. Table reveals that this is not compatible with any one of the three CO_2 reduction scenarios whose analyses result only in a permissible brown coal consumption of about 14 to 19 Mtce pa. The smallest coal demand is with close to 14 Mtce pa in scenario 'nuclear expansion'. This is because of the strong competition of the brown coal and nuclear for the same electricity market. All three energy policy scenarios make it clear that brown coal use must be cut in about half by 2005. Rest permissible oil and gas use is given to a large extent by the coal policy on the supply side and by the efficiency policy on the demand side. Scenario 'nuclear phase out', which permits for job reasons the smallest decrease (25 per cent) in hard coal, and for environmental factors the largest increase (48 per cent) in gas, results in the strongest oil reduction (54 per cent) of the three scenarios (See Table). This requires a drastic reduction in the transport sector, which would be significant not only for climatic and environmental protection reasons, but also for health, planning and a variety of other reasons. On the other hand, in case of 'nuclear expansion' gas, which of all fossil fuels is most environmentally benign, shows the least increase (16 per cent), while oil shows the least decrease (33 per cent). A number of the members of the Enquete-Commission favoured the middle of the road scenario 'energy policy'. A very significant and somewhat surprising result as shown in Table was that even a considerable increase in the use of nuclear energy did not result in a significant reduction of CO_2 emissions over a phase out of nuclear power.

In all three scenarios the overall CO_2 reduction potential came out to be about the same, at 30-32 per cent, by 2005 relative to 1987. While the reduction potential for the individual fossil fuels was quite diverse (See Table). This means that there is big room for action on a desired reduction policy, and that a nuclear phase out is compatible with an effective climate protection policy. This leads to the important observation that both environmental threats, namely the climatic change and nuclear energy risks, can be reduced simultaneously by a consequent policy which emphasizes the better efficient use of energy, but deemphasizes the use of fossil fuels and nuclear energy. CO_2 reduction of 40 per cent for total fossil fuels in East Germany in the continuing scenario of Prognos as evident from the Table can hardly be reduced further by any specific measures within the next ten years. In this case it is justified to combine the trend scenario of East Germany with the policy state of West Germany. This results in mixed policy scenarios for all of Germany with a CO_2 reduction potential of the order of about 33 per cent for total fossil fuels.

As per the Enquete-Commission another 5 per cent CO_2 reduction could come from behavioural changes (ECGP, 1991). If the proposed climate protection steps underlying the policy scenarios were from now on expeditiously implemented, it would perhaps still be possible to come close to the 25 to 30 per cent CO_2 reduction target by 2005, in spite of the government's four years of inaction since the publication of the scenarios.

Summing up

To conclude, there is no doubt that in the absence of an effective climate protection policy the official German CO_2 reduction target of 25 to 30 per cent by 2005 almost to 1987 will not be met. With the continuation of the current policy a CO_2 reduction of only 10 per cent is expected, thus missing the target by a wide margin. The main factors behind this are mistaken policy decisions with regard to coal on the supply side, and a lack of policies to save energy and reduce transport on the demand part. Only if and when the bundle of measures underlying the Enquete-Commission's scenarios is implemented, can a reduction potential of more than 30 per cent be activated. These steeps should be expeditiously taken. The German hard coal policy sets an upper ceiling of 50 Mtce pa until 2005. This can be best achieved by scenario 'nuclear phase out' of the Enquete-Commission (See Table). In the case of CO_2 it is only the quantity of fuel used that determines the amounts of emissions.

However, for reasons of saving exhaustible resources and costs, it is paramount to use the hard coal greatly in cogeneration as well as gas and steam power plants.

In the presence of the Federal Transport Act the government gives the wrong signals. This will ensure that the dramatic increase in petrol use in the transport sector will continue. It is important that this adverse trend be reversed through an active policy of reducing consumption using more efficient cars and avoiding too much traffic. Moreover, oil use must be drastically decreased in existing and new buildings through better insulation, more efficient heating systems and substitution.

Last but not the least, hard coal, brown coal and oil should be substituted for in the heating area by gas, because it has a much lower specific CO_2 emission. The largest CO_2 reduction can be effected by using gas in combined heat and power plants and neighbourhood cogeneration systems.

7

Role and Rules of International Agreements

The GATT

Global environmental change are bound to cause tensions in international relations. Therefore, the relationship between open trade and environmental protection (and their often conflicting objectives) has been the centre of increased attention in recent years. At the centre has been the General Agreement on Tariffs and Trade (GATT) which governs international trade related disputes; including trade and environment disputes. However, since 'environment' is not expressly referred to in the GATT, the perception has been that dispute resolution has been skewed in favour of trade. Whether or not this is precise perception is not particularly relevant for the purposes of this article.

What is important to note is that under the GATT the adoption of decisions of dispute panels requires common agreement, itself an act of diplomacy, and there is always the possibility that the adoption could be affected by a small number of States. Thus, whichever side disagrees with a result could block its adoption, be it the environmental or trade interest. Through this, the development and evolution of international law is slowed.

Formation of WTO

However, in 1994 the Uruguay Round of Multilateral Trade Negotiations was formally concluded and the World Trade Organization (WTO) was established. The WTO, which includes and expands the GATT, also expressly recognizes the aim of sustainable development.

In addition, the WTO contains a detailed chapter on general dispute settlement and is indicative of a movement far from the diplomatic resolution of disputes to a more legalistic and adjudicatory approach.

The following article will briefly narrate and compare the rules under the WTO and the *Understanding of Dispute Settlement of 1979* (1979 Understanding) governing the establishment and composition of panels as well as the acceptance of panel reports.

According to 1979 Understanding, a GATT party could request the Contracting Parties to establish a panel to enquire a dispute between itself and another party regarding the implementation of GATT obligations. Any such panel could only be established after one more party to the dispute had had an opportunity to study the complaint and respond to it before the Contracting Parties.

Under the WTO, however, a party is entitled, as a matter of right, to the establishment of a panel unless the Dispute Removal Body (DRB) decides by consensus not to establish one. The creation of a 'right' to a panel serves to remove the political uncertainty of whether or not a panel will be established. Moreover, it will also effectively prevent a party from blocking or delaying the appointment of a panel and thus will contribute to the period bound resolution of disputes. With respect to panel composition; under the 1979 Understanding, the panel could be comprised of either three or five members.

Although non-governmental panellists were approved, the stated preference was for governmental members even though they would be serving in their individual limits and not as government representatives. Under the WTO, any panel shall be composed of three members unless the Parties to the dispute expressly agree to a five member panel. The parties of the panel can be either governmental or non-governmental so long as they have demonstrated experience in international trade matters.

As with the 1979 Understanding, panellists cannot be citizens of the country which is a party to the dispute. The deduction of panel members from five to three is a reflection of existing practice (the last five member panel was in 1981). This preference for three member as opposed to five member panels flows not only from the fact that a three member panel is easier to convene and manage but also from the fact that smaller panels known to be more likely to achieve unanimous conclusion based on consensus, compromise and mutual understanding between the panellists.

It is a matter of chance that there is less opportunity for majority and minority findings and the attendant confusion associated with adoption and precedent setting, that after decisions, in the international context would invite. The elimination of the preference for government affiliated panellists, represents an opportunity for the Contracting Parties to enlarge the skills and expertise base from which they draw. However, while the exclusion against government persons sitting on a panel hearing a dispute between their government and another is not generally objected to criticism of the extension of this exclusion to all nationals of a party to a dispute has arisen.

It has been argued that the inclusion of a panel member with expertise in the trade law and policy of the party alleged to be in violation would assist the other panellists in defining and deciding on the issues. Above all, because many of the recognised GATT specialists are national of either the United States, the EC or Japan, and because the majority of disputes involve at least one of these three major economic powers, the exclusions of these nationals precludes the GATT/WTO from utilizing their expertise. The most important single change to the dispute settlement process concerns the adoption of panel reports. As mentioned, prior to the WTO, consensus was needed in order for a panel report to be accepted and, as a result, a single party, usually the losing side of a dispute, could block or delay a report's adoption. Under the WTO, anyway, the adoption of a panel report is presumed unless the DRB decides not to adopt the report, by consensus and within 60 days of the report's release by the panel, or provided the report is appealed by one of the parties to the dispute.

The inverted consensus requirement will effectively prevent a disgruntled party from blocking the adoption of a report and thus, the effectiveness of a decision. The creation of an appellate body is a completely new innovation under the WTO as no similar parallel organization existed before this. The appellate body, which will only review disputes on points of law, will be composed of seven persons who are unaffiliated with any government, any three of which will be involved on appeal on a given case.

Establishment to the appellate body will be for a period of four years as opposed to the *ad hoc* basis for panellists. As with panel reports, appellate body reports shall be accepted, unless the DRB decides against their adoption by consensus and within 30 days of their release. The purpose of the appellate body is dual. First, it provides a review mechanism which will help ensure that the decisions of the panel are sound. Secondly, the appellate body, through the consistency of its members, will help to make sure that there is a corresponding consistency amongst rulings. This in turn should help to promote legal certainty in world trade matters. While the preceding discussion has focused on panels, it should be recalled that recourse to a panel is a last resort in a dispute and that consultation and conciliation attempts need first to be exhausted. Furthermore, it should be noted that panel reports are, *de jure*, only bound on the parties to the dispute although it has become GATT practice to generally follow precedent.

Consequently, the role the politics and diplomacy is by not at all eliminated under the WTO. These points notwithstanding, the fact remains that the changes to the panels discussed above, together with the application of stricter time limits will foster a more formal, rule orientated approach to dispute resolution. To the extent that these rules and procedures reflect a more legalistic approach to dispute resolution, the whole process is likely to become more adjudicatory and less diplomatic and panel reports could have an even greater precedential effect. The willingness of States to be bound by the rules, regulations and decisions of a supra-national authority is evidence of the willingness of States to cede some of their sovereignty and marks a significant departure from past practice.

In this context, the changes made by the WTO in the field of dispute settlement are truly 'developments, in international law. Still given the link between trade and environment, as has been expressly recognised in the WTO, careful attention will have to be given to the reports rendered by the panels to ensure that they do, in fact, promote sustainable development,that environmental considerations are not governed by purely trade considerations nor that environmental considerations are used as a form of illogical safety guidelines.

Meeting the Expenditure

With the end of century, there is a recognition that many environmental problems have the properties of a global public good, or, perhaps better expressed, a global public 'bad'. If goods produce human well-being, bads detract from it. Public goods are shared by all because their consumption by one person (or one country), entails their consumption by another person (or another country). For a good to be genuinely public it must also be effectively impossible to exclude these 'joint consumers' through pricing or other means. A global public bad, then, is a loss of global well-being brought about by the actions of individual any countries and which it is impossible or very difficult, for any one individual and country to neglect. The solutions to such problems tend to involve a deliberate change in property rights, usually through the creation of an international agreement to protect the global environment.

Effectively, such agreements change what were global *open access* resources into global *common property* resources. With open access there are no owners. With common property there are communal owners and their success in controlling the problem will rely on the design of incentives to maintain the agreement. Two such agreements relating to global resources were negotiated at the Earth Summit in Rio de Janeiro in June, 1992: (a) the Framework Convention on Climate Change, and (b) the Convention on Biological Diversity (for the texts of these Conventions, see Johnson). Prior to that, the Montreal Protocol on the protection of the earth's ozone layer had already been negotiated in 1987. These agreements can be interpreted as signs that the world has come to its senses regarding global pollution.

Despite all this still exists there a major underlying problem and, not surprisingly, it lies with the issue of making the relevant resource transfers from North to South.

One, it has to be questioned whether global agreements carry with them the financial power to make other than cosmetic differences to the situation of the global environment. The targets agreed under the Conventions are modest enough, and their very modesty, when contrasted with the scale of the problems they seek to address, is testimony to the concern of the nation that 'saving the world' should not be too expensive a business.

Decision in the Agreements

During the pilot study the Global Environment Facility will have disbursed funds of around US$1 billion in a three-year period, i.e., US$300-400 million pa. In its operational phase, commencing in 1994, it will have some US$2 billion over a similar duration. By comparison with the scale of the problems, the sums are trivial. In comparison with official aid comes they are perhaps 1.5 per cent of the total. Then, if transfers are made to secure a global good, are these transfers to be seen as part of conventional development aid, or are they intrinsically something different? Conventional aid is meant for development within nations. A reasonable, first orders, test of the potential success of such aid is that the economic benefits to the developing nation should exceed any costs it bears from the development.

This is orthodox benefit-cost analysis as embodied in numerous guidelines, manuals and texts, but intervening to obtain the global good may not be consistent with conventional aid criteria: for example, benefits to the developing nation may be less than the costs, but the global benefit may exceed the net costs. From the global angle the intervention is worthwhile. From the developing country standpoint, it is not, unless its share of global benefits exceeds the net domestic costs.

Self-evidently, the transfer must overcompensate the developing country for the excess domestic cost. But developing nations may see greater gains by diverting resources to lobby developed nations and international agencies to make the global transfers more development oriented. In fact, that is exactly what is happening in the debate over prospective international transfers under the Rio conventions, and under the not-binding and absolutely wide-ranging document Agenda 21 agreed at Rio.

Lastly, persuading developing countries to undertake actions for the global benefit may be difficult given the mostly starkly contrasting priorities of the developing and developed world. For most developing countries the priorities are food, shelter, energy, health and education—the basic needs—and the prospect of economic betterment. The conservation of biological diversity will often appear a low priority against such a backdrop, while even global warming control strikes few chords outside the island and deltaic states.

There are some problems for which the following interim conclusions have been suggested:

1. That official transfers to secure global benefit will be small in any event, and that if global problems are of concern, other sources of transfer have to be tapped;

2. That transfers for global benefit must exploit, wherever possible, gains from trade, but with the trades having spin offs in the kind of development opportunities, i.e., all parties must be better off.

Management of Resources

Besides the fact that much has been done to make the flow of funds going from rich to poor countries more sensitive to environmental impacts, and more targeted at resource conservation and the enhancement of environmental quality, the true flow that can be identified as truly green still remains unknown. The OECD countries spend approximately 1-1.5 per cent of their GNP on their own environmental safety—a combination of public and private expenditures. If they spent that same fraction on conserving the global environment and the environments of the poor nations that cannot afford better environments, total green resource flows might total some US$100-150 billion per annum. This is very similar to the actual total official development finance (ODF) of all types of US$70 billion in 1991, plus around US$55 billion of private flows (foreign direct investment, bank lending, etc) or some US$130 billion in total. Put another way, if the OECD countries invest as much on global and developing country environmental protection as they spend on their own environments, they would double the total resource flows to the developing countries.

World Bank Estimates

The World Bank estimates that extra costs of some US$70 billion pa will be needed by the year 2000 to met selected total environmental programmes in the developing world—water and sanitation, air emissions control, diffusion of effluent and solid waste management, soil conservation and family planning. To conserve and expand by 50 per cent the protected areas of the developing world would, they estimate, cost another US$2.5 billion per year. Addressing global and local LDC problems, then, is unlikely to cost more than, say, US$100 billion per year. If that was all to be paid for by the OECD countries, it would add a cost of about 0.8 per cent of GNP to public and individual resource transfers in the year 2000.

Though much of the cost could be met from sustained economic growth in the developing world, a significant sum would remain as transfers from rich to poor countries. It has then to be borne in mind that the aggregate of official development assistance from OECD countries has remained at a fairly constant 0.35 per cent of OECD GNP since 1970. In other words, if much of the cost of improving the global and local LDC environments has to flow from official aid, the prospects look grim. If foreign aid has not changed as a proportion of the rich world's income in response to poverty, it hardly seems likely that it will respond differently to environmental concerns.

Major Reason behind the World level Changes

We have evolved in this section an elementary framework for assessing the potential for mutually beneficial trades in global environmental benefits. The fundamental forces giving rise to biodiversity loss arise mainly from two factors: *One*, competition between humans and non-humans for the remaining ecological niches on land and in coastal regions; and secondly, failures in the workings of international and national economic systems.

Undoubtedly, other causes are at work as well. In a comprehensive view we would need to add misdirected past policies by bilateral and multilateral aid agencies, corruption, the non-involvement of much big business to environmental concerns, the results of international indebtedness and perhaps poverty itself. Besides all this, contrary perhaps to widespread opinion, these factors are not well understood and a popular mythology has emerged about them, usually more in keeping with preconceived political agendas than with any respect for right research and judgement.

Table 1. Soil Conservation 1977/9-1987/9

	Continent	*Cropland*	*Pasture*	*Forest*	*Other*
1.	Africa	+8	–4	–25	+22
2.	North and Central America	+3	+11	+7	–20
3.	South America	+14	+20	-41	+11
4.	Asia	+4	–2	–29	+29
5.	Europe	22	23	+2	+4

Table 2. Estimates for Global Population

	1990	*2100*	*2150*
Global population %in	5.4	12.0	12.2
Asia/Oceania	59.4	57.0	56.8
North and South America	13.7	11.0	10.8
Africa	11.9	23.9	24.5
Europe	15.0	8.1	7.9

Race between Humanity and Nature for Space: Big amount of the competition for space between man and Nature shows up in the conversion of land to agriculture, aquaculture, infrastructure, urban development, industry and unsustainable forestry. Table 1 discloses land use conversions by world region between 1977 and 1987. The loss of the world's forests, rich sources of biodiversity, is apparent, especially in Asia and South America. Unless the causes behind these conversions are understood, the outlook for the conservation of biodiversity is bleak. Above figures suggest that sheer pressure of human beings on space will displace other living species. Some authors have argued that the benefits of this possibly outweight the costs, but one suspects that such views arise from a lack of appreciation of the economic values embodied in biodiversity.

The displacement hypothesis should, however, be tested empirically. Brown and Pearce bring together the observations of a number of studies on the factors that are statistically linked to one major environmental change—tropical deforestation. There it is suggested that population change is indeed a factor that is connected with forest loss. The economic theory of species extinction was evolved mainly in the water context and very largely in terms of fisheries (see Clark). There it is comparatively straightforward to see that a combination of open access property rights (no one owning the sea) and profitability (the difference between revenues and the cost of fishing effort) does much to describe overfishing and the loss of mammalian species. Once the theory is moved to land, the additional factor is the sheer competition for niche occupancy, and the theory need to alter, as Swanson has so elegantly demonstrated. Rather than saying open access explains excess harvesting effort, the question is why nation states allow open access conditions to prevail. In other words, why do governments not invest more in conservation land practice? There are three immediate reasons and they comprise the second major strand in the description of biodiversity loss: an economic theory of biodiversity loss.

Financial Loss

(a) Loss in Regional Market: First, underinvestment arises for the classic economic reason of 'market failure'. What this means is that the interplay of market forces will not achieve the economically correct balance of land conversion and land conservation. This is because those who convert the land do not have to compensate those who suffer the local consequences of that conversion—over pollution and sedimentation of waters from deforestation, for example. The corrective solutions to this problem are well known—a tax on land conversion, zoning to restrict detrimental land uses, environmental standard and so on. From this it concludes that we cannot rely on market forces to save the world's biodiversity as long as biodiversity loss is one of the incidental effects of those market forces. Notice, however, that the measures required to correct this market failure do not result in zero biodiversity loss. In the economist's language there is an 'optimal' rate of loss. Though, it is less than what happens now, but it is not zero.

(b) Government Failure: Next and a more recent explanation, is 'intervention failure' or 'government failure' - the deliberate intervention by governments in the working of market forces. This can coexist with market failure: both forces are at work at the same time. The instances are, by now, well known and include the subsidies to forest conversion for livestock in Brazil up to the end of the 1980s; the subsidies to beef in Botswana, raised by the preferential tariffs in European Community; hedgerow removal and overintensive farming arising from above equilibrium guaranteed prices under the European Common Agricultural Policy; the undercosting of irrigation water whether in California or Pakistan and so on. What government intervention does is to distort the competitive playing field. We are used to hearing businessmen using this language but, while they generally see environmental regulations as the means of hampering their competitive efficiency, the truth is that the same argument shows powerfully why the conservation of biological diversity is an uphill struggle. Governments effectively subsidize the pace of return to land conversion, tilting the economic balance against conservation.

(c) World Missing Markets: What this means in the biodiversity context is that systems of habitat and species are serving valuable activities which are not marketed. Effectively, then, no one values these functions because there is no obvious mechanism for capturing the values. Local market failure described this phenomenon within the context of the country or local area. But there are missing global level markets as well. We can consider two such global markets which are highly relevant to biodiversity: what economists call the 'non-use' or 'existence' value possessed by individuals in one country for wild life and habitat in other nations, and the carbon storage values of tropical forests.

(d) Human Contribution: Researcher use methods of measuring individual preferences, as revealed through individuals' willingness to pay to conserve biodiversity. The methodologies include contingent valuation (CVM), which functions through sophisticated schedules which ask people their willingness to pay, and other techniques such as the travel cost method, the hedonic property price approach and the production function approach. The money values that are captured in this way are likely to be a mix of potential use value and non-use values, Use values relate to the valuation placed on the resource because the respondent makes use of it or might desire to make use of it in the future. Non-use values, or passive use values, as they are also called, relate to positive willingness to pay even if the respondent makes no use of the resource and has no intention of making the best out of it.

It is very tragic that Global valuations of this kind are still few and far between. Table assembles the results of some CVMs in several countries. These report desire to pay for species and habitat conservation in the respondents own country. These studies remain controversial, especially in light of the findings of the recent 'blue ribbon' panel on contingent valuation in the states, although that same panel basically gave CVM a good bill of health provided rigorous rules of investigation are pursued. While we cannot say that similar kinds of expressed values will arise for safety of biodiversity in other countries, even a benchmark figure of, say, US$ 10 pa for the rich countries of Europe and North America would produce a fund of US$ 4 billion per annum, around four times the mooted size of the fund that will be available to the Global Environment Facility (GEF) in its operational phase as the financial mechanism under the two Rio Conventions and its continuing role in capturing global values from the international waters point of view, and perhaps 10 times what the GEF will have available for helping with biodiversity conservation under the Rio Convention.

Table: Species and Habitats at Risk (US$pa per person in1990)

Species		
Norway	Brown bear, wolf and wolverine	15.0
USA	Bald eagle	12.4
	Emerald shiner	4.5
	Grizzly bear	18.5
	Bighorn sheep	8.6
	Whooping crane	1.2
	Blue whale	9.3
	Bottlenose dolphin	7.0
	California sea otter	8.1
	Northern elephant seal	8.1
	Humpback whales[a]	40-48(without information) 49-64(with information)
Habitat		
USA	Grand Canyon (visibility)	27.0
	Colorado wilderness	9.3-21.2
Australia	Nadgee Nature Reserve NSW	28.1
	Kakadu Conservation Zone, NT	40.0 (minor damage) 93.0 (major damage)
UK	Nature reserves	40.0 (experts only)
Norway	Conservation of rivers	59.0-107.0

Scientists can well understand that all forests store carbon so that, if cleared for agriculture there will be a release of carbon dioxide which will contribute to the accelerated greenhouse effect and hence global warming. With the objective to derive a value for the 'carbon credit' that should be ascribed to tropical forest, we need to know (1) the net carbon released when forests are converted to other uses; and (2) the economic value of one tonne of carbon thrown to the atmosphere. Carbon will be released at different rates according to the method of clearance and subsequent land use. With burning there will be an immediate release of CO_2 into the atmosphere, and some of the rest will be locked in ash and charcoal which is resistant to decay.

The slash not converted by fire into CO_2 or charcoal and ash gets destroyed over time, releasing most of its carbon to the atmosphere within 10-20 years. Studies of tropical forests indicate that significant amounts of cleared vegetation become lumber, slash, charcoal and ash. The proportion varies for closed and open forests; the smaller stature and drier climate of open forests result in the combustion of higher proportion of the vegetation. If tropical forested land is changed to pasture or permanent agriculture, then the amount of carbon stored in secondary vegetation is equivalent to the carbon content of the biomass of crops planted, or the grass grown on the pasture. If a secondary forest is allowed to develop, then carbon will accumulate, and maximum biomass density is attained after a relatively short time.

Table illustrates the net carbon storage effects of land use conversion from tropical forests; closed primary, closed secondary, or open forests; to shifting cultivation, permanent agriculture or pasture. The negative figures convey emissions of carbon; for example, conversion from closed primary forest to shifting agriculture results in a net loss of 194 tC/ha. The greatest loss of carbon involves change of land use from primary closed forest to permanent agriculture.

These figures also represent the once and for all change that will occur in carbon storage as a result of the various land use conversions. The data suggest that, allowing for the carbon fixed by subsequent land uses, carbon thrown from deforestation of secondary and primary tropical forest is of the order of 100-200 t of carbon per hectare. This carbon contributes to global warming, and we now have several estimates of the minimum economic damage done by global warming, leaving aside catastrophic events. Latest work by Fankhauser suggests a 'central' value of US$ 20 of damage for every tonne of carbon released.

One always wonders how do these estimates relate to the development benefits of land use conversion? We can illustrate with respect to the Amazon region of Brazil. Schneider mentions upper bound values of US$ 300 per hectare for land in Rondonia.

The figures suggest carbon credit values 2-15 times the price of land Rondonia. These carbon credits also compare favourably with the value of forest land for timber in, for example, Indonesia, where estimates are of the order to US$ 2000-2500 per hectare. All this suggests the scope for a global bargain. The land is worth US$ 300 per hectare to the forest colonist but several times this to the world at large. If the North can transfer some amount of money greater than US$ 300 but less than the damage cost from global warming, there are mutual gains to be obtained. Note that if the changes did take place at, say, US$ 500 per hectare, then the cost per tonne carbon reduced is of the order of US$5 tCF(US$ 500/100 tC/ha). These unit costs compare favourably with those to be achieved by carbon emission reduction policies through fossil fuel conversion.

Avoiding deforestation becomes a legitimate and potentially significant means of reducing global warming rates.

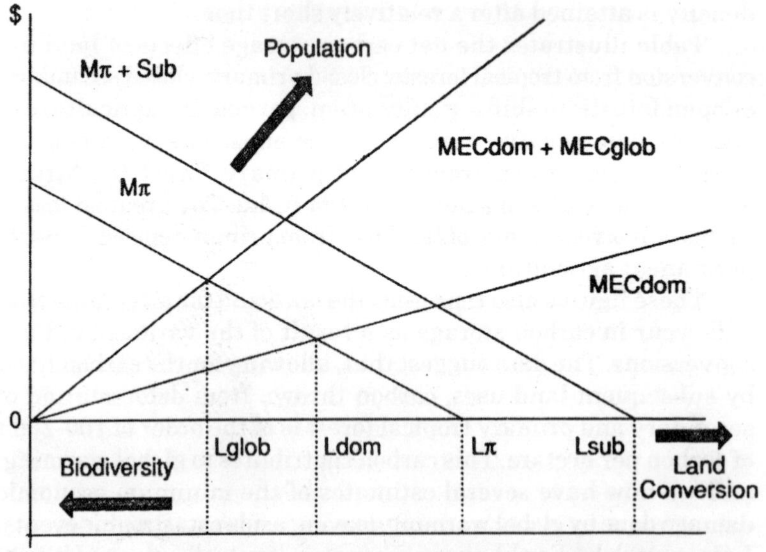

Fig. 7.1. Economic and Biodiversity Loss.

In the figure given above, we see together the economic analysis of conservation 'failure'. The vertical axis shows money (US$). The horizontal axes show the extent of land conversion, the main factor contributing to biodiversity loss, and the 'amount' of biodiversity (BD) conserved. Land conversion and BD are therefore inversely related. The curves shown are marginal benefit and cost activities. Thus, MII is the marginal profit accruing to the country from land conversion. MII + SUB shows the effect of subsidizing land conversion. More land is converted, with the result that there is less biodiversity. MEC_{dom} is the low external damage from land conversion and which is borne by the country itself, say in the form of loss of watershed protection, reduced medicinal plants etc. $MEC_{dom} + MEC_{glob}$ shows the externality from land conversion, but now including the loss in global usefulness.

Through inspection of the diagram we also see that point A is the overall optimum where the optimal amount of local and global externality occurs. Point B is the domestic optimum allowing for domestic externalities only. Point C is the free market alternatives when there are no subsidies, and point D is the solution when there are subsidies. The distance CD is intervention failure; distance BC is domestic market failure; and distance AB is global market failure. The gap between A and D describes the total level failure due to market, intervention and global failure. Clearly, this distance could be very large. Note that the more land is conserved, the greater the opportunity cost of that conservation.

Let us take the example of Kenya, it has been estimated that land conservation for biodiversity purposes (including wildlife tourism) costs Kenya around 2.5 per cent of its GNP.[23]

There are clear opportunities for no regrets or win–win situations that can be produced by the removal of market and government failure, as discussed above. Terminology like win-win may be something of an exaggeration-subsidy measures offen have their own social purposes-but it is often true. A great deal of biodiversity can be conserved by setting domestic policies right. This must not be used to argue that resource transfers are not appropriate; there should still be resource transfers from North to South regardless of the existence of no regret measure. Similarly, it cannot be argued that all biodiversity conservation requires financial transfers. North and South perspectives often differ on this issue, as is revealed in the text of Rio Biodiversity Convention. Article 11 clearly makes effort to locate some responsibility in the developing world for biodiversity loss through domestic distortions:

"Each contracting party shall, as far as possible and as appropriate, adopt economically and socially sound measures that act as incentives for the conservation and sustainable use of components of biological diversity."

At the same time, Article 20.4 asserts:

"The extent to which developing country Parties will effectively implement their commitments under this Convention will depend on the effective implementation by developed country Parties of their commitments under this Convention related to financial resources and transfer of technology and will fully take into account the fact that economic and social development and the eradication of poverty are the first and overriding priorities of the developing country Parties."

Formation of World Level Markets

There are several ways in which global appropriation failure can be set right through creating global environmental markets. We distinguish between private and public (official) ventures, and between those that are regulation induced and those that are spontaneous market initiatives. Public regulation-induced activity takes place because of international agreements, such as the Biodiversity and Climate Change Conventions. Table that follows sets out the resulting schema. The examples listed are dealt with more fully below.

Table: Planning for Global Environment Markets

	Regulation Induced	*Spontaneous Market*
Public/official ventures	Instances: Government measures under joint implementation provisions of the Rio treaties: Norway, Mexico, Poland,GEF	Instances: Governme ment involvement in market ventures:Swiss Green Export aid; debt-for-nature swaps
Private sector ventures	Instances: carbon offsets against carbon taxes and externality adders.	Instances:purchase of exotic capital-Merck and Costa Rica.

Anticipated Regulations: The first way in which markets are emerging is through the existence of regulations or anticipated regulatins. In turn, these regulations are international and national but since implementation is always at the national level we can treat them together.

National to Nation Trade: One instance of an international regulation is the Framework Climate Convention negotiated at Rio in 1992. As per the Convention each ratifying country will have an obligation to cut back on CO_2 emissions, but the Convention quite explicitly recognizes that it is often cheaper for one country to cut back on emissions in another country and also making its own domestic effort to cut back. Similarly, it may be cheaper to create 'sinks' for CO_2 in another country rather than cutting back domestically.

This scope for carbon offsets or common implementation is potentially large, and the first joint implementation agreement has already been agreed between Norway, Poland and Mexico, through the medium of the GEF. Norway gives consent to create additional financing (through the revenues from its own carbon tax) for GEF carbon reducing projects in Mexico (energy efficient lighting) and Poland (converting from coal burning to natural gas). The US Environmental Defence Fund is known to be in the process (1993) of developing a reforestation project in Russia. The US government announced the Forest for the Future Initiative (FFI) in January 1993 under which carbon offset agreements will be decided between the USA and several countries, including Mexico, Russia, Guatemala, Indonesia and Papua New Guinea. The aim is for the US Environmental Protection Agency to broker deals involving the private sector.

Since the procedures for joint implementation under the Convention are not agreed and it is likely that more deals will develop once the ground rules have been established.

(c) Non-governmental Trades: The European Community Draft Directive on a carbon tax and other European legislation also provides an incentive to trade in this way, as does state regulation on pollution by electric utilities in America. While not strictly a private enterprise trade, in the Netherlands, the state electricity generating board (SEP) has established a non-profit making enterprise (FACE—Forest Absorbing Carbon Dioxide Emissions) and is pondering to invest in forest rehabilitation to absorb CO_2 in Czechoslovakia, Indonesia, Ecuador, Costa Rica and the Netherlands itself.

The FACE Foundation already has a contract with Innoprise in Sabah, Malaysia for the fertilisation of degraded forest lands. In the US case the offset deals are currently not directly linked to legislation, but several have occurred which are clearly a mix of assumption of regulation and global good citizenship. These include the New England Electric System's investment in carbon sequestration in Sabah, Malaysia through the reduction of carbon waste from unskilled logging activities. The forest product enterprise is run by Innoprise.

New England Electric estimate that some 300,000 to 600,000 tonnes of carbon (C) will be offset at a cost of below US$ 2tC. Rain Forest Alliance will provide help in monitoring the project. New England Electric regard the Innoprise project as the first of a series aimed at assisting with the Corporation's plan to reduce CO_2 emissions by 45 per cent by the year 2000. PacifiCorp, an electric utility in Oregon, is thinking reforestation projects and urban tree planting programmes in the USA, and an international sequestration project. Two pilot projects have been announced: (1) a rural sequestration project in Southern Oregon which gives funds for planting subject to constraint of no harvesting for 45-65 years, at an estimated cost of around US$ 55 tC; and (2) an urban tree programme in Salt Lake City, Utah at a provisionally estimated expenditure of US$15-30 tC sequestered. Tenaska Corporation is considering sequestration projects in the Russian boreal forests. Ultimately, some 20,000 ha of forests may be created in the Saratov and Volgograd areas at a cost of US$1-2 tC. Russian partners in the venture include the Russian Forest Service, the Ministry of Ecology and others. The US Energy Policy Act of 1992 needs the Energy Information Administration to develop guidelines for the establishment of a database on greenhouse gas offsets, together with an offset bank. The Keystone Center in the USA is also setting up an interchange of information with a number of electric utilities to explore the issues involved in the establishing offset deals.

(d) Committed Common World Level Human Concerns: Several offset deals appear to have been undertaken quite independently of law or anticipation of regulation. Applied Energy Services (AES) of Virginia has also undertaken sequestration investments in Guatemala (agroforestry) and Paraguay and is in the process of setting up another project in the Amazon basin.

The Guatemala project is introduced to offset emissions from a 100 MW coal fired power plant being built in Uncasville, Connecticut. The intermediary for the project is the World Resources Institute and in Guatemala the implementing organisation is CARE. The project involves tree planting by some 40,000 farm families. Carbon sequestration is estimated to be 15.5 Mt of carbon. The US$ 14 million expenditure includes US$ 2 million contribution from AES; US$1.2 million from the government of Guatemala; US$1.8 million from the CARE, with the balance coming in kind from USAID and the Peace Corps. Note that the motivation forces for involvement vary. AES,s involvement relates to its concern to offset CO_2 emissions, whereas other partners are concerned with the local development and environmental benefits the deal brings about. Dixon et *al*. report the sequestration cost as US$ 9 tC overall, but inspection of the data suggests it may be less than this, US$ 9 tC would be expensive for carbon sequestration alone, but there are other benefits from the scheme, including local monetary benefits. In the Paraguay deal, AES is planning to advance money to the (US) Nature Conservancy for investment in some 57,000 ha of endangered tropical forest. AES hopes to sequester some 13 million tC at around US$1.5 per tonne of carbon. Local benefits include eco-tourism, scientific research, recreation, agroforestry and watershed protection.

(e) Exotic Capital: Monetary transfers may take place without any regulatory push. The consumer demand for green products has already resulted in companies planning to invest in conservation either for direct profit or because of a mix of profit and conservation motives. The Body Shop is an example of the mixed motive, as is Merck's royalty deal with Costa Rica for pharmaceutical plants and Pro-Natura's expanding venture in marketing indigenous tropical forest creations. There is, in other words, an incentive to purchase or lease exotic capital in the same way as a company would buy or lease any other form of capital. The contract between Merck and Co, the world's largest pharmaceutical company, and INBio (the National Biodiversity Institute of Costa Rica) is already well documented and studied (Gamez *et al.,* Sittenfield and Gamez, and Blum). According to the agreement, INBio collects and processes plants, insect and soil samples in Costa Rica and supplies them to Merck for assessments. In return, Merck pays Costa Rica US$ 1 million plus a share of any royalties should any successful drug be made from the supplied material. The royalty agreement is reputed to be of the order of 1 per cent to 3 per cent and to be shared between INBio and the Costa Rican government. Patent rights to any successful drug would lie with Merck. Biodiversity is protected in two ways by conferring commercial value of the biodiversity, and through the earmarking of some of the payments for the Ministry of Natural Resources.

To what extent is the Merck-INBio deal likely to be repeated? Numerous caveats are in order to offset some of the enthusiasm over this single deal. First, Costa Rica is in the vanguard of biodiversity conservation, as its strong record in debt for nature swaps shows. Second, Costa Rica has a good and bold scientific base and a considerable degree of political stability. Both to these characteristics need to be present and their combination is not typical of very many developing countries.

Third, the economic value of this type of deals is least unless the royalties are actually paid and that will mean success in developing drugs from the relevant genetic material. The chances of such developments are dim-perhaps one in one to 10,000 of plant species screened. INBio has undertaken to supply 10,000 samples under the initial agreement. There is therefore a chance of one such drug being developed. But successful drugs could result in several hundreds of million of dollars in revenues.

Finally, there are two views on the extent to which deals of this kind could be given added impetus by the Biodiversity Convention. The Convention stresses the role of intellectual property rights (IPRs) in securing conservation and is sufficiently vaguely worded for there to be wide interpretation of its provisions. But it also appears to threaten stringent conditions concerning those right and technology transfer and it remains to be tested how the relevant protocols are worded. If so, parties to the Convention may find private deals being turned into overtly more political affairs with major constraints on what can be negotiated.

(f) Risk Constraints in Private Sector: Authors like Newcombe and de Lucia have drawn attention to another potentially very large private trade which has global environmental benefits. Investment by the private sector in the developing world is invariably hampered by risk factors such as exchange rate risks, repayment risks, political risks and so on. Insofar as this investment benefits the global environment, as with, say, the development of natural gas to displace coal, the emergence of the risks reduces of flow of investment and hence the global environmental benefits. But these risk might be shared (bought down) by having an international agency, such as the GEF, provide some funds or services which are useful to reduce the risk. Given the scale of private investment flows, the potential here is enormous. Nor is there any reason why it should not benefit biodiversity, either indirectly as a joint benefit of other investment in for instance, raising agricultural productivity and hence in reducing the pressure for land degradation, or directly through afforestation schemes.

Thus, to conclude, we can say after undergoing the above that with population set to double in the next 80 years or so, it is unrealistic to expect to save the world's current biodiversity in total. Much of it will be lost. But much of it can be saved. There is a major role to be played by regulations and agreements, but the prospects for real action must lie in (1) leveraging the flow of funds that will take place under international agreements; and (2) exploiting every possibility for mutual economic gain that also generates biodiversity conservation benefits. The idea of exploiting mutual economic gain will strike many as morally unacceptable, but that viewpoint while heartfelt-partly describes why we have the problem in the first place. Taking the moral high ground may be satisfying for the moralist, but it has not yet produced the wave of resources needed to contain the problem, nor is likely to. The answer is to pioneer on all platforms. The economic approach looks especially more useful. This paper has argued that there is substantial potential for mutual gain through global trades. This should not divert attention from the present need to correct domestic policies in the developing and developed world alike. All forms of economic failure need to be addressed.

8

Obstacles for Third World Countries

In this chapter, we are going to discuss severe risks facing developing nations from rapid climatic changes with steps that both the industrialized and developing world can take to prevent or mitigate the worst effects. The world is already committed to some climatic changes because of gases emitted over the past century. Slowing the rate of future change can increase the time available to understand and prevent the worst impacts and reduce the risks of international disputes and conflicts. For nearly two decades since the landmark 1972 United Nations Conference on the Human Environment in Stockholm, Sweden, the major environmental worries facing most nations have concerned air and water quality, soil conservation, and proper food supplies. Although some environmental progress has been made in recent years, notably improving air and water quality in industrialized nations, number of problems remain to be solved. In particular, environmental deterioration in developing countries continues at an alarming rate.

Not only this, equally alarming, new large-scale environmental problems have came forward that threaten to aggravate international relations, behaviour, and security. These problems include acid precipitation, Arctic haze, the depletion of stratospheric ozone, species extinction, and global warming. Unlike past concerns about air and water pollution, these threats have implications that are truly global in scope—they know no political distinctions and they follow no international boundaries. As a result, finding satisfactory solutions will be especially difficult.

What else the issue of global climatic change, the so-called "greenhouse effect;" epitomizes these concerns. With the exception of the results of nuclear war, no other environmental problem has the scope or the potential for such widespread societal impacts. Now analysts and policy-makers have begun to express concern about the international implications of climatic changes. In 1987, the World Commission on Environment and Development (WCED) said:

"Environmental threats to security are now beginning to emerge on a global scale. The most worrisome of these stem from the possible consequences of global warming caused by the atmospheric build-up of carbon dioxide and other gases. Slowing, or adapting to, global warming is becoming an essential task to reduce the risks of conflict."

And then, Toronto Conference on the Changing Atmosphere also concluded in June 1988:

"The Earth's atmosphere is being changed at an unprecedented rate by pollutants resulting from human activities, in efficient and wasteful fossil-fuel use and the effects of rapid population growth in many regions. These changes represent a major threat to international security. The best predictions available indicate potentially severe economic and social dislocation for present and future generations, which will worsen international tensions and increase risk of conflict between and within nations."

Other symptoms that the issue of greenhouse warming has reached the international political agenda can be seen through statements by General Secretary Gorbachev, Prime Minister Brundtland, Prime Minister Mulroney, President Reagan, and President Bush and members of his cabinet.

This environmental change will affect more than just traditional East-West concerns. Indeed, while the principal responsibility for the production of greenhouse gases remains with the industrialized countries, some of the worst societal impacts will fall on developing countries. This discrepancy has the potential to deteriorate existing tensions and to raise new disputes between industrialized and developing nations and between poorer nations themselves. This chapter discloses severe risks facing both developed and developing nations from rapid climatic change and proposes actions to prevent or mitigate the worst international differences that may arise. If nations act today to slow the rate of climatic change, it may be possible to increase the time available to understand and prevent the worst impacts, and to reduce the chances of international disputes and conflicts.

Some Future Assumptions for Developing Nations

As we have already seen, atmospheric concentrations of carbon dioxide and other trace gases are increasing as a result of the combustion of fossil fuels, other industrial activities, and cutting of forests. These gases retain heat in the atmosphere that would otherwise be reradiated into space, thus raising the temperature of the Earth and changing major climatic patterns. State-of-the-art climate studies estimate that global average temperatures will increase between 2 and 5°C with an equivalent doubling of the atmospheric CO_2 concentration, a concentration that will be reached in the first half of the next century within present rates of fossil-fuel use and deforestation.

In the fall of 1987, climate scientists and policy-makers met in Villach, Austria under the auspices of the Beijer Institute, the World Climate Programme of the World the Meteorological Organization (WMO), the UN Environment Programme, and several other organizations to discuss plausible future climatic impacts and possible policy responses.

There is no doubt that the expected rise in temperature will be accompanied by many other climatic and geophysical effects, including changes in precipitation patterns, changes in the frequency and intensity of storms, and a hike in sea level due to both thermal expansion of the oceans and melting of land ice.

Concerns have also been raised about the possibility of surprises—sudden abrupt shifts-in the way the oceans and atmosphere may react to climate perturbations. State-of-the-art climate models can neither predict such surprises, nor rule out the possibility that they will occur. Considerable uncertainties remain about the nature, timing, magnitude, and regional details of climatic changes. Although we could wait for more research and more comprehensive information on the environmental and economic impacts of climatic changes before taking actions, this approach has two serious flaws.

1. The complexity of climate modelling means that the necessary research will be slow and difficult. Yet any delay in reducing the emissions of greenhouse gases commits the earth to greater and greater climatic changes.

2. Any international agreement to avoid major climatic change may be complicated by a desire of certain actors (countries, subnational groups, corporations, alliances) to capitalize on perceived regional advantages in the midst of larger-scale negative impacts. Those actors who perceive themselves to be beneficiaries

of a warmer earth—even if that perception turns out later to be wrong—may decide not to cooperate in international negotiations to address the issue of climatic change. More recently, attention has begun to focus on the rate of climatic change.

In 1987, the Villach and Bellagio climate conferences stated that slowing the rate at which temperature and sea level will rise is as important for preventing severe societal and ecological disruptions as is an extreme limit on climatic changes. This focus arises because of constraints on the ability of natural and societal systems to adapt. Of particular concern are limits to how fast natural ecosystems can respond to climatic changes. Inland migration of wetlands is limited by sedimentation rates; upward growth of coral reef islands cannot exceed levels defined by temperature, tidal action, and nutrient availability; forest and plant communities move at rates constrained by soil conditions, water availability, and vegetation succession dynamics.

Because of these concerns, attention is now shifting to identifying critical rates of change in order to set long-term environmental targets that may have some use as regulatory guides. This kind of targets could be supplemented with absolute limits to climatic change, since unlimited warming must eventually be prevented.

Changing Relation Patterns

Future tensions over climate changes are assumed to result from changes in superpower relations (East-West concerns) and from disparities between developed and developing countries (North-South concerns). Many fundamental factors suggest strongly that North-South tensions will be the most problematic.

First, the industrialized countries are primarily responsible for the production of greenhouse gases.

Second, the consequences of climatic changes will be far more widely distributed among both rich and poor nations.

Table: World Production of Carbon Dioxide and Chlorofluorocarbons (CFCs)(32-34) in Percentage

		CO_2	*CFC-11*	*CFC-12*
1.	United States	24	23	30
2.	Western Europe and Canada	16	49	33

	CO_2	*CFC-11*	*CFC-12*
3. Japan, Australia, New Zealand	6	20	15
4. Soviet Union and other CPEs	26	6	19
5. All others	28	2	3

- Figures given above also included carbon dioxide from fossil fuel combustion and industrial fuel use, but do not include the contribution from biomass burning.

CPEs: Centrally-planned economies.

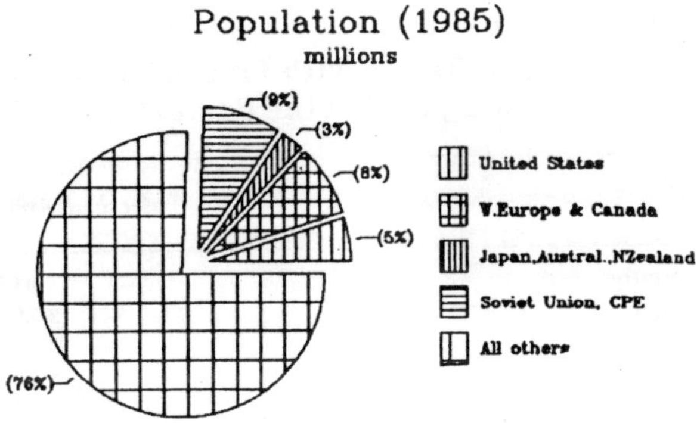

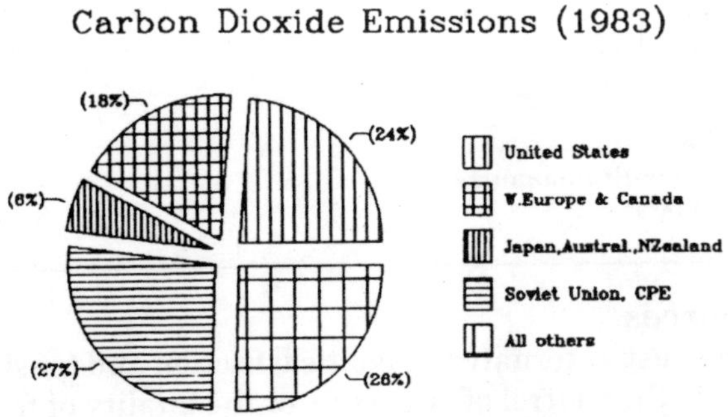

Fig. 8.1. Distribution of 1985 population by country and region. Note the low population of the industrialized countries, which make up only 25 per cent of global population.

Figure 3b. Distribution of 1983 carbon dioxide emissions by country and regin. The industrialized countries are responsible for nearly 75% of global carbon production. Although this may decrease as developing countries increase their energy use, the principal responsibility for greenhuse gas emissions will rest with the industrialized nations for a long time.

Lastly, developing countries have far fewer technical and economic resources at their disposal for adapting to or mitigating the effect of climatic changes than do the industrialized nations. The industrialized world is primarily responsible for the production of greenhouse gases. The industrialized countries of the Northern Hemisphere are presently responsible for about 70 per cent of the global production of CO_2 and nearly all chlorofluorocarbon production, while having only 1¼th of the world's population. Although rapid population growth in developing countries will lead to large increases in energy use, this disparity in per capita production of greenhouse gases is likely to continue for a long time.

Table: Flowing of Rivers with Five or More Nations Forming Part of the Basin(19)

		#	*Watershed Area (km²)*
1.	Danube	12	817 000
2.	Niger	10	2 200 000
3.	Nile	9	3 030 700
4.	Zaire	9	3 720 000
5.	Amazon	7	5 870 000
6.	Zambezi	8	1 419 960
7.	Rhine	8	168 757
8.	Lake Chad	6	1 910 000
9.	Mekong	6	786 000
10.	Volta	6	379 000
11.	Elbe	5	144 500
12.	Ganges-Brahmaputra	5	1 600 400
13.	La Plata	5	3 200 000

New Sources

In the past, international political friction and tensions have arisen over the control of, access to, or the quality of freshwater resources. In the absence of climatic changes also, pressures on existing water resources are growing due to increases in population, industrial water demand, and development. With these pressures grow, the probability of conflict over remaining water resources will also increase. Greenhouse climate changes will have extensive effects on both water availability and quality of water.

Rising temperatures will increase the demand for water for urban and agricultural uses, and elevated temperatures will alter snowfall and snowmelt patterns. Changes in precipitation patterns will stress the timing and availability of freshwater runoff, increasing flood risks in some regions and drought frequencies and intensities in other regions. Warmer waters and altered flows could further deteriorate existing water-quality problems. And the hydrological changes anticipated will greatly complicate operating and managing our present system of aqueducts, reservoirs, and dams, which aimed at past climatic conditions, not future ones. In regions where water resources are widely shared, these physical effects will have important political implications. Freshwater resources are often shared by two or more countries. Nearly 50 countries on four continents have more than three-quarters of their total land area falling within international river basins, while globally 47 per cent of all land past falls within international river basins. Over 200 river basins are multinational, including 57 in Africa and 48 in Europe. Table below lists thirteen major rivers with five or more nations forming part of the watershed, although conflicts may occur when rivers are shared by only two nations. Areas with a history of international tension or competition over water resources include the Jordan and Euphrates rivers in the Middle East, the Nile, Zambezi, and Niger rivers in Africa, the Ganges in Asia, and the Colorado and Rio Grande rivers parts of in North America.

An important measure of the greater risks facing developing countries is the extent to which they share freshwater resources. Of the thirteen river basins, ten are shared mostly by developing states. Indeed, many of the wealthier nations, like the US, Canada, the Soviet Union, Australia, New Zealand, and Japan have few or no shared river basins due to their size, location, or geography. Climate-induced water-resources difficulties may be particularly severe in arid and semiarid regions where water is already in short supply. Developing countries predominate in these areas. One measure for evaluating this vulnerability is per capita water supply—the amount of reliable streamflow available per person. There have been several efforts to define these terms more precisely. Falkenmark, for example, discusses relative levels of "water competition" as the number of people that must be supplied per million cubic metres of water per year.

Using her definition, problems of absolute water scarcity tend to arise when this value rises above 1000 (i.e., 1000 people per million cubic metres per year). Another measure of water availability is "per-capita water availability".

One more factor that highlights the vulnerability of developing countries to changes in water resources is their relative lack of facilities such as flood-control dams or water-supply reservoirs. Natural disasters like floods and droughts are mitigated by controlling excessive flows or storing water for extended dry periods. Most facilities for these purposes, however, are found in developed nations able to afford the large costs necessary to construct and operate them. While climatic change may well change the frequency and severity of floods and droughts, and hence the design and operating requirements of main reservoirs, countries with no or little physical water-resource infrastructure will be more vulnerable to adverse hydrologic events than industrialized countries.

Growth of Food Items and Plantation

Threats to food supplies and agricultural systems have been reason for past frictions and tensions between nations and may be cause for future problems as population growth puts increasing pressures on food growth. Mechanisms for such threats include trade embargoes, political manipulation of access to food, environmental degradation such as loss of soil fertility, or competition among controversial land uses.

The disparity in food needs and food resources between the developing and the developed world has long hinted at the possibility of future conflict over access to food resources. A number of countries are already acutely vulnerable to natural climatic variability that may cripple food production, reduce supplies, or raise the price of foodstuffs on the world market. Agriculture, based on rains, the principal form of agriculture, in many developing countries, is particularly sensitive to the vagaries of weather, especially the timing and length of the rainy season, the total amount of rain received, and the pattern and excesses of storms. Rainfed arid and semiarid lands support nearly one billion people. (1) These lands remain largely underdeveloped and agricultural investment is low. Rainfall in these parts is highly variable and unpredictable on both a seasonal and annual basis—indeed, some blame the recent decline in food production in Africa on recent, persistent adverse drought conditions exacerbated by development pressures with the global temperatures begin to increase and rainfall patterns begin to change, the food situation in these areas is likely to grow more precarious. At all latitudes, the most severe agricultural impacts may be found in marginal areas, although we know little about how climate will change in these areas. What else, analysis of the net effect (both regionally and globally) of climatic changes on food production is greatly complicated by two factors; One, the difficulty of estimating how climatic changes and higher CO_2 concentrations will destroy yields; and two, the difficulty of estimating the effect of changes in yields on world agricultural markets.

Food availability depends on a complex array of physical and institutional factors, including patterns and productivity of planting and harvesting, buying ability of nations, and the operation of food-distribution systems. Short-term reductions in yields alone are not necessarily bad for overall long-term productivity and food availability. Confounding elements include the size of stocks, subsequent investment in other regions, planting patterns, international prices, and the character and mechanisms of trading agreements. This may, changes in the comparative advantage of different international actors can play a greater role than absolute changes in agricultural productivity. The advantage, however typically benefits rich industrialized nations.

Table: Water Availability in Nation Dominated by International River Basins Per Person

Nation	*10^3 m^3 per year per person**	*Land area in international river basins (per cent)***
High Water Availability		
Bangladesh	12.1	86
Brazil	35.2	61
Burma	27.0	73
Cameroon	18.8	65
Colombia	34.3	64
Ecuador	29.9	51
Guatemala	13.0	54
Kampuchea	10.9	87

Nation	*10^3 m^3 per year per person**	*Land area in international river basins (per cent)***
Lao People's Dem	59.5	94
Nepal	9.4	100
Venezuela	44.5	80
Low Water Availability		
Afghanistan	2.5	91
Belgium	<1	96
Botswana	0.8	68
Bulgaria	2.0	79
Czechoslovakia	1.8	100
Egypt**	<1	30
Ethiopia	2.3	80
Germany (Dem Rep.)	1.0	93
Germany (FRG)	1.3	88
Ghana	3.4	75
Hungary	0.6	100
India**	2.3	<30
Iraq	1.9	83
Israel**	0.4	6
Jordan**	0.2	6
Kenya	0.6	64
Luxembourg	2.8	100
Pakistan	2.7	>75
Peru	1.8	78
Poland	1.3	95
Portugal	3.3	56
Romania	1.6	98
Spain	2.8	57
Sudan	1.2	81
South Africa	1.4	66
Syria	0.6	72
Togo	3.4	77

- **Statistics are useful for internally available renewable water resources. Some of the largest developed countries, such as the Soviet Union, Japan, Australia, New Zealand, Canada and the United States have few or no internationally shared rivers.**

Table: Prominent Storm Disasters in South Asian Coastal/Delta Parts (38)

Sl.No.	*Year*	*Region*	*Estimated Human loss*
1.	1963	Bangladesh	22 000
2.	1965	Bangladesh	17 000
3.	1965	Bangladesh	30 000
4.	1965	Bangladesh	10 000
5.	1970	Bangladesh	250 000-500 000
6.	1971	India	10 000-25 000
7.	1977	India	10 000
8.	1985	Bangladesh	10 000

Hike in Sea Water Level

Rising sea-level due to both thermal expansion of the oceans and melting of glaciers and land ice will have deadly effects on coastal nations. While the rise in sea-level will most likely be incremental, the damages caused by this rise will occur during extreme events like storm surges, hurricanes, and typhoons. Some observations can be made about the differences in vulnerability to sea-level rise of underdeveloped and developed countries. Most major cities in both developed and developing nations will be protected from sea-level rise, but a great cost. In developing countries, however, sea-level rise will be most severely felt by exposed coastal habitats and by agricultural developments in deltaic areas. Three highly-populated developing countries, India, Bangladesh, and Egypt, are known to be especially vulnerable because their low-lying coastal plains are already extremely vulnerable to storms. Since 1960, the first two have been struck by at least eight tropical cyclones that each killed more than 10,000 people.

Not only this, river deltas are also vulnerable to the activities of upstream states. Activities by India, Nepal, China, and Bhutan, for example, all affect the flow characteristics of the Ganges, which is felt downstream by Bangladesh. Difference already exist between India and Bangladesh over the construction of dams on the Ganges, over the use of major upstream tributaries, and over river diversions. One solution—population migration away from the most threatened areas—suggests a way of reducing human vulnerability, but at the high societal and political cost of relocation and absorption of those displaced.

An Analysis

1. Amongst all the pressing large-scale environmental problems facing society, global climatic changes appear to have the greatest potential for provoking disputes, worsening tensions, and changing international relations between developed and developing countries. Two routes to conflict can be identified.

One, the climatic changes associated with global warming will affect freshwater availability and quality, food productivity, and access to other resources, goods, and services. The societal effects of these climatic changes will be widely distributed, but they are likely to be felt far more severely by poorer countries, posing important and still unresolved questions about equity, fairness, and international environmental ethics.

Two, the inequitable responsibility for the production of greenhouse gases has started to provoke calls from developing countries for prompt actions to reduce these emissions. With few exceptions, developing nations are least able to mobilize the resources for adapting to severe and rapid impacts, while developed countries are more likely to prefer to adapt to climatic changes than to drastically change their energy and industrial infrastructures. This fundamental dichotomy is likely to lead to international disputes between the two, unless mechanisms can be worked out to more equitably share the cost of limiting climatic impacts.

2. This is true that technical and political solutions are available, although none appear capable of preventing at least some climatic changes due to greenhouse gases already emitted. Among the technical options are:- (a) reducing the rate of climatic change through increased energy efficiency, greater use of non-fossil-fuel energy sources, reforestation, controls on other greenhouse gases, and the sequestering of carbon dioxide away from the atmosphere, like deep in the ocean; (b) mitigation of the most severe impacts through larger grain shortage, better international distribution of agricultural production, more flexible water-resources systems, more water conservation, and protection from the sea-level rise; and (c) adaption to climatic impacts such as through population migration, land abandonment, and shifts

in agricultural practices. In fact, the actual responses to climatic changes are likely to include all of the above.

3. A number of political actions are also available depending on the perception of the severity of climatic impacts and on the economic and technological sources available for responding. Unilateral actions can be taken by those countries that have a major responsibility for greenhouse gas production or that face particularly extreme climatic impacts. While unilateral actions are likely to be only marginally effective at slowing climatic changes, they set good ethical examples and some of them can be justified for other good reasons. Like increased energy efficiency reduces the economic, political, and environmental costs of energy use while slowing the rate of emission of greenhouse gases. Same way, increasing the robustness of existing agricultural and water-resource systems would ease many existing food and water problems, while helping to prepare for identical problems caused by future changes in climate. Restrictions on ozone-destroying chlorofluorocarbons protect human health and also slow the rate of climate change.

To conclude, better effective are multilateral actions on the part of the industrialized world. Coordinated actions to control trace-gas emissions should be the responsibility of there countries and would help address the problem about equity. Joint international research into alternative energy resources is another possibility, as would be an agreement by major coal consumers, such as the United States, the Soviet Union, and China to decrease their dependence on coal through an agreement to share natural gas resources and energy efficiency technologies. Lastly, comprehensive international agreements, such as the Law of the Sea, or the Montreal Protocol developed for protecting the ozone layer, would be most helpful and supportive at slowing the rate of climatic change. Such agreements are however, the most difficult to negotiate and implement. Nevertheless, ever reducing the rate of change by slowing the rate of production of the major trace gases can provide considerable "breathing room" to allow us to not only improve our understanding of climatic impacts but also to negotiate and implement equitable international responses.

9

Global Agencies on Environment

Though some international panels, conventions and conferences have been discussed here and there in the previous chapters, the present chapter brings out in sequential organised manner efforts at the same and more international platforms to cope with the global environmental problems that affect no single nation but all or at least—a group of nation—may be developed on developing.

The Panel on Climate Change

Growing threat to environment has generated awareness at least among the intelligentsia. The basic science of the greenhouse effect has been known for nearly a century: certain trace gases present in the atmosphere,, chiefly water vapor but also anthropogenic gases which include carbon dioxide (CO_2), methane (CH_4), and nitrous oxide (N_2O), reflect heat radiated off the Earth's surface back toward the surface, thus raising global average temperatures.

In the mid-1980s, as scientific understanding of the subject and the potential impacts of on-going human-induced modification of the global atmosphere increased, the scientific community and the public at large began to stress for a governmental response. Following a series of scientific and nongovernmental conferences and declarations, culminating in the June 1988 Toronto Conference on the Changing Atmosphere, the World Meteorological Organization (WMO) and the UN Environment Programme (UNEP) established the Intergovernmental Panel on Climate Change (IPCC) in November 1988. During its first session, held in Geneva in November 1988, the IPCC divided its work into three working groups to deal respectively with scientific analysis, socioeconomic impacts and policy responses.

To improve coordination among the working groups, a bureau was set up comprising the chairman, vice-chairman, and Rapporteur of IPCC; chairmen of the three working groups; and vice-chairmen of these three working groups (two each from Working Groups I and II, and five from Working Group III). It was soon felt that not enough attention was being given to ensuring the participation of developing countries. Therefore, a Special Committee on the Participation of Developing Countries was formed chaired by France. The IPCC has several features that distinguish it from similar initiatives launched by international organizations in the past.

Though its Terms of Reference stress the peer review process, and though participation in the various working groups and subgroups is expected to be at a technical level, its participants have been essentially either chosen by their governments or associated with various governmental departments in the member countries. The *First Assessment Report,* adopted at the Fourth Plenary of the IPCC, outlined the conclusions of the three IPCC working groups as well as the suggestions of the Special Committee on Developing Countries. The IPCC has subsequently produced a 1992 Supplemental Report, as well as reports on impacts and response strategies.

Framework Convention

Before the approval of the first IPCC report, resolutions had been passed by WMO and UNEP to convene the first open-ended negotiating session on the Framework Convention on Climate Change. The first series of these meetings was held in Geneva in September 1990, attended by over seventy countries. UNEP's executive director emphasized at this meeting that both he and the secretary general of the WMO had been appealed by their governing bodies "to prepare for negotiations now."

The said proposal set out a number of points to be taken into consideration in the negotiating process, including; which gases the atmospheric concentrations, of which should be subject to policy regulation; stabilization and emission reduction targets; proposed deadlines and base years for comparison of emissions; and criteria for calculating emissions levels for individual countries (e.g., per capita, per unit of GNP or GDP, as per the geographic size, its climatic conditions, the size of natural carbon sinks, energy consumption per unit of production, or a mixture of these and other criteria).

Despite the fact that there was disagreement on the details of what the future convention should accomplish, there appeared to be consensus from the outset that "a meaningful act for adoption in 1992 should be a target." The fundamental question, however, was whether this should be accomplished if the price meant agreeing to a weak and potentially ineffective treaty. The resolve expressed by the executive heads of UNEP and WMO was formally adopted by the Second World Climate Conference, which was held in Geneva in November 1990. The United States offered to host the first formal negotiating meeting. The UN General Assembly accepted the United States offer but appointed an Intergovernmental Negotiating Committee (INC) under its own auspices to conduct negotiations for a framework convention on climate change. On the substantive side, progress at the first session, especially on the organization of the work, was less than satisfactory. Many countries stressed the importance of addressing the issue of global climate change in an integrated and comprehensive style, taking full account of the special circumstances and needs of developing countries.

Yet, there was great opposition to considering emissions reductions, preservation and expansion of sinks, and monetary and technical assistance in separate working groups. Developing countries feared that, if these topics were addressed separately, less attention would be paid to emissions reductions and financial and technical assistance.

These countries were also concerned that forests in developing countries would be targeted as a panacea for the global warming issue, since they are a sink for carbon dioxide, a principal greenhouse gas. It was clear, however, that all of these tapics could not be addressed in the plenary. After intensive discussions, agreement was reached on the establishment of two working groups; one to take care of commitments and the other with mechanisms. The progress made by the working groups was integrated by the plenary, and the final text treated as one package. During the first session and part of the second one, many delegations submitted texts ranging from specific elements to be contained in the convention to an entire draft convention. A significant number of these came from developing countries, whose active participation signaled the fact that these countries would not be idle bystanders but would advance clear specific stands in the negotiations. Group of 77 (G-77) countries submitting detailed proposals included the following: Malaysia/Malta, Republic of Korea, India, Vanuatu, China, Singapore, Kenya, Kuwait/Saudi Arabia, Micronesia, and Malaysia.

The initial job for the Bureau and the Secretariat was to compile these submissions. At the end of the second session, the compilations were discussed with a view to streamlining the text as per the general structure of international agreements.

Negotiations began in earnest in the third and fourth sessions, which concentrated on the consideration of text that should appear in the framework convention. One element that retarded progress in the third session was the first by delegations to ensure that texts submitted by them were incorporated verbatim in the documents produced by the Bureau. It required considerable diplomacy on the part of the Bureaus of the INC and the working groups to overshadow delegates insistence on maintaining their own special wording of proposals. Several new proposals contained ideas such as "pledge and review," "targets and timetables," "joint implementation," "emissions trading," and the requirement of specific protocols. Discussions on these proposals have been inconclusive.

However, it was decided that if delegates agreed on what protocols should contain, then the substance of the potential protocols should reflect from the framework convention itself, rather than in supplementary documents. When the negotiations began, many delegations were scared that the developing countries would form a coalition to impede progress. But open differences among the G-77 resulted in three distinct groupings: the Alliance of Small Island States (AOSIS), the oil-producing countries, and the other developing countries. Thus, despite dark forebodings that emerged from time to time, the group as a whole could not unite to form a blocking coalition. When it was time to agree on the Convention, almost as if by a miracle, these disparate groupings of nations and the various coalitions among industrialized countries came together and signed it. In this way, barely fifteen months after the INC began its work, negotiations for a framework convention were completed.

The Convention, signed at the United Nations Conference on Environment and Development— the Rio Earth Summit—in June 1992, received the required several ratifications on December 22, 1993 and entered into force on March 21, 1994. The total number of ratifications exceeded 120, by the time the first Conference of the Parties met in Berlin in March/April 1995, and the number went on to grow.

These environmental talks are both complex and extremely significant for the future of international relations. In his statement at the first session of the INC, the UN Secretary General characterized the significance of the climate negotiations by saying that a parallel exists there between the San Francisco Conference that created the United Nations and the process being set in motion at the INC meeting. In the same manner, many commentators have seen a parallel in terms of complexity of subject matter between the climate negotiations and the 1982 UN Convention on the Law of the Sea (UNCLOS), which took nine years to negotiate, accept and adopt.

Many have gone further, saying that the climate negotiations are more complex than UNCLOS. Even a casual observer of the negotiations to draft and implement the Convention will attest to both the importance and the inherent complexity of the task that faced the INC and that now faces the COP.

The Conference of the Parties to FCCC

As we have already said that the adoption of the FCCC was aided by three essential factors: a sense of urgent scientific need that was new to the wider international community; a strong coalition that had been forged between the scientific and environmental advocacy communities; and the negotiating target dates provided by the fact of the Summit itself, which was to be attended by heads of state and government. By 1995, when the first Conference of the Parties convened, these factors had changed. The most important issue addressed by the COP was the review of the adequacy of commitments under the FCCC. The so-called "Berlin mandate" that resulted from the Conference concludes that the current political commitments under the Convention are inadequate to fulfil the Convention's ultimate objective. It establishes a two-year negotiating process to strengthen the specific commitments of industrialized countries and further implement the present general commitments of developing countries.

The mandate establishes an ad hoc body to elaborate a protocol or other legally binding instrument for adoption at the third Conference of the Parties to be held in 1997. This body is authorized to expand policies and measures that could limit or reduce greenhouse gas emissions, as well as to "set quantified limitation and reduction objectives within specified time-frames," which means set targets and timetables for emissions reductions beyond the year 2000. Agreement was also reached on the establishment of a pilot phase for joint implementation of measures to mitigate environment change, though the Conference was unable to adopt rules of procedure.

There were further adopted a host of recommen-dations negotiated at previous meetings of the INC, addressing, *inter alia:* preparation and submission of national communications from Annex 1 parties; first communications from non-Annex 1 parties; methodo-logical aspects, maintenance of the interim arrangements with the Global Environment Facility (GEF); and initial guidance on policies, programme priorities, and eligibility criteria to the operating entity or entities of the financial system. It defined the general functions of the Subsidiary Bodies on Scientific and Technological Advice and the Subsidiary Body for Implementation, as well as the specific tasks and schedule of meetings to be held before COP_2.

It requested the secretariat to report on activities undertaken by industrialized country parties to comply with their technology transfer commitments and to compile an inventory of technologies which could either mitigate or adapt to climate change. Finally, the COP established an ad hoc working group of technical and legal experts to look into establishing a multilateral consultative process that could resolve questions of implementation.

After three years had passed from Rio, with COP_1 concluded and the negotiators embarking on their next round of negotiations, the science of environmental change has grown more certain, which tells us only that the assumptions and projections on which the FCCC was based remain valid; the nongovernmental community is now mainly focus on implementation of the Convention at the national level; and the pressure provided by Rio is gone, which means that COP_3 could be postponed with little political cost. Unluckily, despite the weight of the scientific evidence, the history of climate negotiations shows that specific, significant emissions reductions will not necessarily be forthcoming.

Analytical Review

After we have looked at the international developments in the previous pages of this chapter, we can say that the approach followed in the global climate change issue is vastly different from that pursued in the attempts to safeguard the ozone layer—and also from the other experiences incorporated in this volume. Yet, shades of the process adopted in the ozone negotiations are obviously sufficient. The success of the current climate change approach depends on how and when governments consent for binding international legal agreements specifying clear commitments; defined responsibilities, targets, and schedules; and workable, equitable institutional mechanisms.

Negotiable Factors: Some of the determinants of effectiveness encompass factors that can not be directly overpowered by those charged with negotiating the terms of international treaties or conventions.

Applying lessons phrased in general terms to specific situations, moreover, is seldom a straightforward, let alone a mechanical, process. Much similar to the more familiar process of deploying general principles or rules of law to deal with specific cases, the design of institutional arrangements applicable to particular issue areas requires both an in-depth understanding of the issue and an ability to think imaginatively about ways to realize the ideas embedded in general principles under the conditions prevailing in actual situations. Nonetheless, the discussion at the 1991 Dartmouth conference shifted repeatedly to the practical concerns of those responsible for applying our understanding of the determinants of regime effectiveness to specific cases.

Given the decision of the conference's organizers to concentrate on atmospheric issues as the target for applications, as well as the intense interest in the problem of climate change at the present time, it will come as no surprise that the ongoing effort to generate an effective regime to protect the Earth's climate system loomed particularly large in this discussion. In this section, therefore have been made some concluding observations about climate change. In addition, endeavour has also been made to distill from the deliberations of the Dartmouth conference and the preceding discussion a set of recommendations about the international environmental governance that should be of interest to those now charged with the task of building a regime to save the Earth's climate system.

Research Findings Meant for Governments: The study of environmental change is characterized both by profound uncertainties and by rapid advances resulting from ongoing research. It follows that any governance system in this region must seek not only to stimulate the growth of knowledge but also to provide mechanisms for integrating new insights into the system without triggering a time-consuming and highly politicized ratification process. But more than this, the success of governance systems is linked to the development of broader cognitive constructs capable of providing the intellectual underpinnings for institutional arrangements. In the case of climatic change, such a construct is likely to involve the articulation of a new worldview (that is, an integrated set of principles, propositions, and norms) that redefines human aspirations and gives birth to a restructured ethical system to guide human beings in their relationships with their environment. Almost certainly, this worldview will take as its point of departure the perspective of ecology, which emphasises linkages among the elements of complex systems, in contrast to the perspective of technology, which emphasizes the separation of complex systems into discrete parts that can be coped with as self-contained entities. Success in developing an effective governance system for the Earth's climate will require a concerted effort to nurture these new intellectual underpinnings as well as an attempt to design the specific elements of the regime being established under the terms of the Climate Convention.

Need for Conventions: The question arises is why do we need a formal instrument, such as the convention, instead of letting the regime evolve more informally through the development of what is commonly referred to as "soft law"? Advocates of formalization stress the role treaties and conventions can play in establishing legal obligations and in minimizing opportunities for members to ignore the dictates of regimes with impunity. "Soft law" advocates, by comparison, emphasize the virtues of more informal arrangements in avoiding the complications of the ratification process and in allowing regimes to adapt the changing circumstances in a dynamic manner.

The discussions at Dartmouth resulted in the conclusion that there is no need to think of these alternatives as posing an either/or choice. To be effective, a climate regime will need the loyalty of both public and private actors throughout the world. Partly, this is a matter of providing opportunities for all members of the international community to participate in a meaningful way in making provisions to be implemented through the framework of the Climate Convention. Even more profoundly, however, support for the evolving governance system must come from the roots as well as from the top down. Meaningful consultation requires in turn the empowerment of those directly affected so that there is some recognized method for bringing their voice into the process.

Addressing the Concerns of Developing Countries: The environmental efforts cannot succeed without concerted effort to address the concerns and priorities of the world's developing countries. While the affluent residents of the industrialized countries are growingly attentive to matters of environmental quality, many developing country leaders are understandably concerned that a focus on environmental issues will deflect worldwide attention from their financial problems or even lead to the promulgation of restrictive rules that hinder their efforts to achieve sustained economic growth and a reasonable standard of living for their citizens. Given the facts that the growth of greenhouse gases resident in the Earth's atmosphere in modern times are attributable in large measure to the industrialization of First World countries and that no climate regime can be useful in the absence of acceptance and active participation on the part of the principal countries of the developing world, there is no avoiding the need to accommodate the development concerns of developing countries as part of a planetary bargain concerned with to climate change.

While it is certainly desirable to focus attention on the follow-up negotiations on the Climate Convention, much of the work of bringing the terms of the resultant regime to bear on concrete problems must happen in more circumscribed settings by private actors. Partly, this is a matter of encouraging individuals, industrial enterprises, and the governments of specific countries to alter present patterns of behaviour. Partly, it is a matter of facilitating the efforts of pairs or small groups of states to transcend rigid insistence on simplistic principles, such as the doctrine of polluter pays, and to enter into mutually beneficial agreements ensuring net reductions in greenhouse gas emissions.

Underlying all these approaches is the need to set aside any expectation that the provisions of the climate regime will be adhered to in practice just because they are included in a convention, and to begin thinking about the development of an array of techniques to implement and strengthen its provisions. It is futile to ask governments of member states to take steps are not feasible in economic, technical, or administrative terms. While we often assume that governments desiring to achieve well-defined goals have the capacity to improve the behaviour of their citizens in the prescribed manner, the reality in many instances is far different. This is particularly true of many developing countries and former socialist countries, whose governments are relatively weak in their ability to stick to commitments made in good faith in connection with the creation of international regimes. It follows that an effective governance system for climate change must provide substantial support to governments prepared to make a concerted effort to implement the rules of the regime within their own jurisdictions. The appropriate tools for such an effort include technology transfers, training facilities, and additional development support earmarked for those endeavouring to implement the terms of the climate regime. As the history of development assistance clearly indicates, success in such ventures cannot be achieved in the absence of a concrete effort on the part of recipients to help themselves and to make the most of the assistance they receive. But this in no way diminishes the importance of making assistance available on attractive terms to those formed to make good use of it.

Compliance with treaty provisions seldom flows primarily from the threat of formal sanctions. In this connection, there is much to be said for developing a globally accepted greenhouse index (that is, a quantitative measure of net contributions to worldwide emissions for all major greenhouse gases on a country-by-country basis) and requiring members of a climate regime to report on their performance in this context—subject to periodic checks carried out by international inspectors—on a regular basis using a standard measurement protocol. Over time this would make it exceedingly difficult for individual countries to disobey the terms of the climate regime in secrecy, and it would facilitate the mustering of public pressure as an effective compliance mechanism (the NGOs might play a particularly beneficial role as watchdogs in this regard). It would also allow states that succeed in improving their performance regarding emissions of greenhouse gases to publicize their accomplishment effectively.

Need for Sophisticated Organisational Arrangements: While the burden of proof should always lie with those who propose the creation of new organizations to administer international regimes, there is little doubt that the governance system under consideration here will need sophisticated organizational arrangements. The functions to be performed include: (1) managing a compensation fund, (2) administering programmes featuring technology transfers, training, and additional development support, (3) compiling and updating the greenhouse index, and (4) assessing emerging arguments for and against international actions to achieve additional reductions in aggregate greenhouse gas emissions. Thinking that it makes sense to deal with these functions in an integrated rather than a piecemeal fashion, the case for a strong institutional mechanism is forcing.

Thus, to conclude, we can say that in focusing on the establishment and administration of the international climate regime, it is important not to lose sight of the significant social forces that drive increase in anthropogenic emissions of greenhouse gases. These forces include speedy growth of human populations, the introduction of technologies whose use accelerates anthropogenic emissions of greenhouse gas emissions, and the strength of consumer preferences and consumption patterns revolving around the exploitation of material goods whose production is energy intensive. Ultimately, no governance system designed of decrease or even to regulate emissions of greenhouse gases can succeed in the absence of vigorous efforts to affect and alter these forces. Without doing this minimum possible, one cannot dream about fighting with the problems arising from environmental and climatic changes.

10

Global Development of the Last Decade: Concept of Justice

The centerpiece of the 1992 Rio Earth Summit was the signing of the United Nations Framework Convention on Climate Change (FCCC). The signatories to the Convention, numbering more than 160 countries, committed themselves to the goal of achieving "stabilization of greenhouse gas concentrations in the atmosphere at a level that would prevent dangerous anthropogenic interference with the climate system." To begin to reach this objective, the Annex I countries agreed to voluntarily stabilize greenhouse gas emissions (GHGs) at 1990 levels by the year 2000. It soon became clear that while the European Union was likely to keep its commitment, the United States, Australia, New Zealand, Japan, Canada, and Norway would not. In the year 1995 the parties to the FCCC adopted the Berlin Mandate: they pledged that by the end of 1997 they would reach an agreement establishing binding "quantified, limitation, and reduction objectives" for Annex I nations, and that no new obligations would be imposed on other countries during the compliance period. From December 1 to 10, 1997, the parties met in Kyoto, Japan to try to negotiate the agreement. In the run-up to Kyoto there was grave conflict between the developed and developing countries, as well as within both groups. The United States wanted an agreement that required stabilization at 1990 levels between 2008 and 2012.

The European Union forced for 15 per cent reductions by 2010. On July 7, 1997, Foreign Minister Alexander Downer said that "the only target that Australia could agree to at Kyoto would be none that allowed reasonable growth in our greenhouse emissions" (Australian Conservation Foundation 1998). The Alliance of Small

Island States (AOSIS), whose very existence is at risk by sea-level rise, proposed stronger measures than anyone would accept. India and China were mainly interested to avoid undertaking new commitments but some Latin American countries, such as Chile and Argentina, signaled a willingness to do more.

In the duration even less than five months before the Kyoto meeting, the US Senate unanimously passed the "Byrd Resolution," directing the president not to sign any agreement that requires the United States to limit or reduce GHGs, unless the same agreement also "mandates fresh specific scheduled commitments to limit or reduce greenhouse gas emissions for Developing Country Parties within the same compliance period." The Clinton Administration, which had agreed to the Berlin Mandate, also stood by the Byrd Resolution, declaring that it would strengthen the American hand at Kyoto. When President Clinton announced the American negotiating position on October 22, 1997, he declared that "the United States will not assume binding obligations unless key developing nations meaningfully participate in this effort." The Kyoto meeting was "make-or-break" moment in the strengthening of the international climate regime. Had the parties to the convention not been able to reach an agreement in Kyoto it is likely that the global effort to limit GHG emissions would have fallen apart. But after pulling some "all-nighters," the delegates to the conference anyhow managed to hammer out an agreement.

Provisions of Kyoto Protocol

Four provisions are central to the Kyoto Protocol: (1) The Annex I countries agreed to differentiated, binding targets that would decrease GHG emissions to about 5 per cent below 1990 levels sometime between 2008 and 2012. (2) Performance in meeting these targets will be assessed on the grounds of "sinks" (e.g., tree planting) as well as "sources," and virtually all GHGs, not only carbon dioxide, will be taken into account. (3) Emissions trading among Annex I countries and between Annex I countries and developing countries will be allowed. (4) The Protocol reaffirmed that developing countries will not be subject to binding emissions limitations during the compliance duration of this Protocol.

There are mandering in the background enormous uncertainties about how emissions can be monitored and how changes in sinks can be measured. But many important issues were left unresolved even in principle by the last-minute compromise obtained in Kyoto.

Let us see an example, the Protocol does not specify sanctions for nations that do not keep their commitments. Nor does it address the extent of emissions trading and exactly how it will be implemented. As it is now clear that the United States as well as some other Annex 1 countries plan to reach their targets primarily by purchasing credits rather than by reducing emissions, this issue is rapidly moving to the centre of the debate. Though some progress has been made on these issues in subsequent meetings in Buenos Aires in November 1998, and Bonn in November 1999, most major decisions have been deferred. Debates about environmental change are as much about the distribution of wealth, power, and authority as they are about whether or not scientists have accurately depicted the natural and human systems that contribute to climate change. How we as individuals should act in the presence of the rapid anthropogenic environmental changes that are now sweeping the globe with disastrous consequences for many of our contemporaries, future generations, and nonhuman nature is one of the most attendable and important ethical issues that climate change confronts us with. But just as important are the ethical questions that underlie our collective responses to climate change. For what is big deal in these debates are the moral principles that will govern future global environmental governance.

As Miller and Edwards point out, rising atmospheric concentrations of carbon dioxide and other greenhouse gases generate important questions not only about the nature and extent of anthropogenic degradation of the world environment but also about "how people of vastly unequal technological capacity and means are going to live together on the planet."

Here, we are going to address some competing conceptions of global environmental justice that lie at the heart of the North-South debate about climate change. It can be argued that the post-Kyoto process must find ways of addressing contentious normative issues, including those bound up with scientific representations of nature, if we are going to be able to mobilize support among different and far-flung publics for the kinds of foundational social and economic changes that will be needed to seriously address climate change. As Sheila Jasanoff has observed, scientific knowledge can only win public credibility and "political authority when the boundaries of the relevant moral-political space [are] redrawn so as to accommodate the interests of all parties."

(A) Technical Information Vs. Justice: As we shall see, the issue of relationships between scientific knowledge and conceptions of justice is a large one. The simplest thing to say (echoing Hume) is that an "ought" cannot be derived from an "is," and so insofar as science is a purely descriptive enterprise it can no way tell us how the world ought to be. While this is true, it does not take us as far as it may seem. Logical derivation is one relation that may hold between beliefs, but it is not the only one.

It is also hard to defend the idea that science is a purely descriptive enterprise. Scientific knowledge informs normative commitments, undermines them, and shapes them in all sorts of other ways both gross and subtle. While it is difficult to provide a full account of the relations between science and conceptions of justice here, let us discuss some examples of these relations in the context of climate change.

1. Mutually Affected Interests: One principle at work is this: In order for the language of justice to come into play, there must at least be the serious possibility of people significantly affecting each other's interests. What it means in the context of climate change is that if human activity does not pose a threat to climate stability, then questions of global environmental justice do not arise with respect to GHG emissions. This principle describes in part why the discussion of climate change has focused so centrally on science. A strong case for skepticism about the reality of climate change undercuts the debate about what are ethically acceptable (or required) policy responses.

2. The Commitment: Next general principle at work is that *"ought implies can."* People or nations cannot be morally obliged to do what they cannot do. Thus, there can be no ethical injunction that requires humans to fly or cats to be vegetarian. Similarly, some argue that the United States cannot reasonably be required to conform to the Kyoto reductions since it would not be possible for the United States to do so. This argument definitely trades on treating a lack of political will as if it were equivalent to some strong form impossibility such as physical impossibility. Science indulges into the debate about justice in various other, more subtle, ways as well. Scientific debates about "the facts" are often proxies for debates about moral responsibility. For example, a recent study suggests that North America is such a large carbon sink that USA may be neutral with respect to its contributions to concentrations of atmospheric carbon dioxide. Many scientists are disposed not to trust these results. Some worry that "groups opposed to the Kyoto treaty will seize on the estimate to argue that the United States doesn't need to reduce its emissions to comply with the accord" (Kaiser 1998, 386).

Sure enough, Steven Crookshank from American Petroleum Institute says that this finding "calls into question the scientific basis on which we are making these decisions, when we still don't know if the United States is even emitting any carbon in the net". (Kaiser 1998, 387). Scientific and moral authority are sometimes explicitly connected. The science most influential in shaping the discussion relating to the FCCC has been that collected and organized by the Intergovernmental Panel on Climate Change (IPCC). In 1998 the IPCC was organised by the World Meteorological Organization (WMO) and the United Nations Environmental Program (UNEP). The IPCC published major reports in 1990 and 1996, and has also created a stream of occasional studies, assessments and discussion papers.

Hundreds of scientists from all over the world have been involved with the IPCC in various ways. The IPCC process is one of the most ambitious efforts ever mounted to mobilize science for the purposes of making international law and policy. Despite its scientific credentials, different constituencies see the IPCC in different ways. Since most of the scientific expertise relating to climate change is in the industrialized world, and truely in only a few highly specialized research centers (Hadley in the United Kingdom; CCCMA in Canada; Max Planck Institute in Germany; GISS, GFDL, Livermore, Lamont-Doherty, and NCAR in America Macquarie University in Australia, among others), the IPCC's attempts at inclusiveness are seen by some as a noble dream and by others as a cruel deception.

Researchers who write in the tradition of science studies have seen the IPCC as a paradigmatic institution for creating apparently natural facts through the artful benefit of social processes (Jasanoff and Wynne 1998). Environmentalists typically view the IPCC as the voice of reason and dispassionate objectivity in the cacophony of greed and self-interest characteristic of environmental politics.

But leftists who criticise "globalism" and rightists who are against "internationalism" have seen the IPCC as a malevolent conspiracy. Even some who champion the IPCC see it as a conspiracy, but one that is benign (Lahsen 1999). The value and authority of the IPCC rests, in part, on perceptions of its moral and political authority.

If we are not biased, the above observations may help to explain cross-national differences in the acceptance of scientific claims about climate change, especially those emanating from the IPCC. From the start, the IPCC's conclusions were more warmly embraced in Europe than in United States. This is part of the reason why during the 1990s most European countries were reducing GHGs while the United States of America was still increasing them. By the early 1990s the European debate had already moved away from the science of climate change to discussion of policy responses.

Developing-country views of climate science show how the credibility of science is conditioned by the moral and political structures of global society. One of the peculiarities of the climate change debate in the United States is that much of the science that advocates the case for climate change has been produced in that country, yet skepticism about climate change is more influential in the United States than in any other industrial country. This has certainly hurt the credibility of the case for climate change in the developing world.

Americans who have promoted the idea of climate change have not been able to convince many of their fellow citizen (e.g., the Republican Congress) of its truth, much less have they succeeded in motivating them to take significant actions in response. When this apparently self-refuting nature of American climate-change science is united with the standing skepticism that many Third World people have about knowledge produced in the developed world, it is not shocking that many developing countries have refused to take the climate change issue seriously even though they may have the most to lose if climate change is in fact underway.

Last instance give here of how perceptions of moral authority can condition particular scientific claims emerges from recent activities in the United States that have fragmented the unity of industrial opposition and pushed move the American debate over climate change away from the question of whether climate is changing toward the question of what we should try to do about it. During a speech at Stanford University in 1997, Sir John Browne,

CEO of British Petroleum, acknowledged the threat of climate change and went on to sketch some steps to address it. This was the first major crack in the united front that leading corporations had erected to defend their interests against possible climate stabilization policies. In his October 22 speech later that year, President Clinton began to reframe the domestic political discussion of environmental change when he declared that "the problem is real" (Clinton 1997).

While most of the American business community opposed the Kyoto Agreement, their coalition continued to fragment throughout 1998, the hottest year since at least 1856. In May 1998, the Pew Center on Global Climate Change was launched with the support of such corporations as American Electric Power, BP America, and Weyerhauser. The Pew Center explicitly supports "the views of most scientists" and views Kyoto as the first step in addressing climate change. Throughout the unusually warm summer of 1998 the President and Vice- President repeatedly connected various weather anomalies to climate change. On October 20, 1998, executives from General Motors, Monsanto, and British Petroleum held a joint press conference with the World Resources Institute in which they announced that "climate change is a reason for concern, and precautionary action is justified now" (*Greenwire* 1998). In 1999 such companies as Ford Motor Company followed Shell Oil, United Technologies, and BP Amoco in withdrawing from the Global Climate Coalition, the industry lobbying group that campaigns not in favour of climate change measures. Shell, United Technologies, and BP Amoco went on to join the Pew Center's "Business Environmental Leadership Council."

Although a stubborn band of contrarians carries on to have the ear of the Republican Congress, warmer temperatures and the breakup of the industrial coalition have fractured the moral authority supporting critiques of climate science, and the discussion has dramatically shifted away from climate models toward economic models.

(B) Role of America

1. Reduction in GHG Emissions based on National Interest: In this country, the debate about reducing GHG emissions centers on self-interest and national interest rather than on appeals to morality. Studies have been thrown around about how compliance with the Kyoto Protocol would affect the economy or put Americans at a competitive disadvantage. The debate has been dominated by hypersensitivity to the domestic politics of which sectors would win and which would lose as a consequence of controlling GHGs.

There is also a backlash, at least in Congress, against government regulation, and the Kyoto Protocol is seen as underwriting government intrusion in the economy. In addition to these factors, the United States is in a state of confusion and ambivalence about its role in the world. This is well symbolized by a series of votes in April 1999, in which the US House of Representatives both failed to support the NATO air campaign against Serbia, and advocated twice as much money for carrying out the campaign as the president had requested. In his October 22, 1997, speech President Clinton did make a moral appeal when he declared that "if there are dislocations caused by the changing patterns of energy use in America, we have a moral obligation to respond to those to help the workers and the enterprises affected." Also, the president noted that "the United States has less than 5 per cent of the world's people, enjoys 22 per cent of the world's wealth, but emits more than 25 per cent of the world's greenhouse gases," he did not make this observation in the language of morality. Instead he went on to say that " we must begin now to take out our insurance policy on the future" (Clinton 1997). Since American opposition to Kyoto might therefore be viewed as resting on national interests, these conceptions of interests are constructed against a backdrop of moral claims about such issues as efficiency, feasibility and fairness.

2. Effective Permanent Wayout: The other argument appeals to feasibility. Just as the United States could not remain half slave and half free, so restricting the emissions of only a small number of countries and leaving the emissions of maximum countries uncontrolled cannot possibly be an effective permanent solution. Two arguments are given for why this is so. First, in the post-Kyoto world, energy-intensive industries in the developed nations will simply move offshore to escape emissions limitations. The same GHGs emissions will happen but the developed countries will no longer benefit from them. Another view is that by 2020 the developing countries will be the largest emitters of GHGs, and over the next century their emissions will swamp.

3. Outcasting a Handful of Countries Unjustified: One more argument against the Kyoto Protocol that is commonly given has a more distinctively moral tone: "It just ain't fair to single out a handful of countries for emmissions control when the rest of the world goes unregulated." If climate change truely is a global problem, then everyone in the world should do their part in solving it. The Kyoto Protocol violates a principle of equality that requires all countries to be treated the same, or (perhaps more subtly) a principle about the fair sharing of burdens.

Among these arguments are not seen as particularly persuasive. Probably most Europeans see the developed world as getting off easy in the Kyoto Protocol. Even countries like Australia, Norway, and New Zealand, which argued for growth in their emissions, did not for the most part argue on the basis of general principles like efficiency or equality. Instead they claimed that they were special cases and should be exempted from requirements forcibly imposed on larger, richer industrial countries with more diversified economies.

If we go analytically, the most serious of these arguments given for the view from above is the second one. Anyone who appreciates the seriousness of climate change should value the importance of eventually bringing at least some of the developing countries into an emissions control regime. The question is how to do this in a way that is both fair and effective. Indeed, proposals not seen as justful by developing nations are not likely to be effective in bringing them into an emissions control regime.

(C) Developing Countries and Their Role: Just like the Annex I countries, the developing countries are a large and diverse group of nations. We shall focus mainly on the picture of global environmental justice that is commonly expressed in the climate negotiations by countries such as India and China. Roughly, their view is that if there is a problem about climate change, it has been generated by the developed countries; therefore, they are the ones who should be addressing it. This is really a version of the "polluter pays" principle. In this case the developed countries are the polluters, therefore they should pay to mitigate the damages.

The state of affairs can be bolstered by appeal to various principles of equality. One version of such a principle would ask which countries can afford to address GHG emissions without hurting the serious interests of their citizens. The answer would be the same one that the delegates to Kyoto arrived at: the developed countries. Another version of the appeal to equality would assert that decreasing inequality between nations is in itself a good thing. So the provision of any global public good that requires developed but not developing countries to pay is a good thing.

In their own justification, the developing countries point out that throughout the nineteenth and twentieth centuries the nations of Europe and North America became affluent by developing powerful industrial economies driven by fossil fuels. Four out of five pounds of carbon dioxide currently in the atmosphere were emitted by these countries. (Carbon dioxide has a residency time of 120 years in the atmosphere.) While in recent years emissions have been growing in the less developed countries, the United States is still by far the world's largest emitter, with annual emissions one-third greater than China's and two-thirds greater than India's. Every year since 1990 the actual increase in American carbon emissions has been greater than that of any country except China and greater than the total carbon emissions of Brazil.

On a per capita basis, Americans can be held responsible for more than seven times the emissions of the Chinese and eighteen times the emissions of the Indians. Moreover, it is unfair to equate the "necessary" emissions of the developing world, in their thirst for minimally decent lives for their citizens, with the "luxury" emissions of the industrialized world produced by gas-guzzling second cars and overheated and overcooled homes and offices. It is hardly difficult to see why most developing countries are unwilling even to think about controlling their emissions until they see some real progress on the part of the developed countries in reducing theirs. The rich countries are the ones that have created the problem, continue to emit more than their fair share per capita, and have the resources to develop and adopt alternative technologies. Moreover, they promised to stabilize their emissions at Rio in 1992 but failed to fulfil their promise. Even worse, it now appears that at least some Annex I countries are planning to fulfil their Kyoto agreements through clever bookkeeping rather than through emissions decrease. The Kyoto loopholes that make this possible involve counting sinks as well as sources in assessing performance, emissions trading, and reductions keyed to 1990 emissions rates. The Australian government plans to make advantage of the first loophole. By planting trees (many of them plantation pines that will be harvested for timber) in areas in which native forest was cleared before 1990, Australia may earn sufficient credits for increasing its sinks to significantly increase its emissions.

The United States plans to achieve 75 to 85 per cent of its emissions reductions by purchasing credits from other countries, many of them from the earlier communist countries (President's Council of Economic Advisers 1998). The latter's GHG emissions have declined precipitously since 1990 as a result of their falling economies, leaving them with many salable permits. However, these permits really reflect what is sometimes called "hot air" (rather than emissions that would actually occur if they were not sold).

Thus, emissions trading not only allows some nations to avoid reducing their own emissions at home, but also results in GHG emissions that would otherwise not occur. Paradoxically the Kyoto Protocol has the potential for increasing GHG emissions rather than decreasing them. This enrages environmentalists and many in the European Union. It also does little to convince the developing world that the rich countries are serious about the issue and problem of climate change.

(D) A Meeting Point—Synthesis: Developments within the climate regime seems likely to continue to elude negotiators so long as North and South continue to remain deadlocked over such basic moral issues. Is it possible to envision a way forward? In this section, we offer a modest proposal. The proposal is modest in that it conjoins two ideas that are very much alive in the policy world, each of which has strong supporters. However, the conjunction that constitutes this proposal has not been forcefully advocated because those who support one conjunct typically oppose the other. The proposal has been discussed by a number of writers, however, in varying degrees of detail (see Rayner *et al.* 1999 and the literature cited therein).

This modest proposal is important both for its intrinsic fairness, and because it provides an example of how an explicit focus on normative principles might help shift grounds of debate, thus opening new opportunities for settlements that can bridge rather than exacerbate existing differences.

In my view both developed and developing countries have a right point. The emphasis on efficiency being promoted by the

United States is potentially good for the world as a whole. But the emphasis on equality on the part of the developing countries seems to me to be ethically unassailable. The main problem with emissions trading as it is developing is that no serious thought is being given to what might be called the end game and start game: the total global emissions that we should permit and how permissions to emit should be granted we propose that we give the Americans what they want—an unrestricted market in permits to emit GHGs—but that we distribute these permits according to some plausible principle of justice. What can be such a principle? I can think of the following general possibilities:

(a) Grant permissions on a per capita basis
(b) Grant permissions on the basis of productivity
(c) Grant permissions on the basis of existing emissions
(d) Grant permissions on the basis of some other principle
(e) Grant permissions on the basis of some combination of these principles

While number 4 and 5 are principles of last resort, and principle 3 is implausible. The present pattern of emissions primarily reflects temporal priority in the development process, rather than any moral entitlement. In general, it is hard to see why temporal priority in exploiting a commons should create any presumptive claim to continue the exploitation. There is a point in principle 2 . Surely we would not want to allocate emissions permissions toward unproductive uses. If the world can only stand so many GHG emissions, we have an interest in seeing that they are granted toward efficient uses. But what this point bears on is how emissions should be allocated, not on how they should initially be distributed. Markets will allocate permissions toward beneficial uses. But it is difficult to see why those who are in a position to make the most productive use of GHGs should therefore have the right to emit them for free.

This is certainly not a principle that we would accept in any domestic economy. The most plausible distributive principle is one that simply asserts that each one of us has a right to the same level of GHG emissions as every other person. It is hard to see why being American or Australian would thereby give someone a right to more emissions, or why being Brazilian or Chinese should give someone not equal a right. The problem with this proposal is that it provides an incentive for pronatalist policies. A nation can generate more permissions to emit only by generating more people. But this problem is easily addressed.

For other purposes the FCCC has seen the importance of establishing baseline years. There is no miracle in 1990 as the reference year for emission stabilization. But if 1990 is a good year for that purpose, let us just say that every nation should be granted equal per capita emissions permissions, indexed to its 1990 population. If there is dislike for 1990, then index to another year. It is important to the present proposal that per capita emissions be indexed to some year, but exactly which year is open to negotiation.

Four Prominent Problems

(a) In indexing emissions to 1990 populations there should be in effect for the developed countries their historical emissions for free. But don't the same considerations that suggest that everyone who was alive in 1990 should have equal permissions apply to everyone who has ever lived? There is some logic to this objection. But knowledge of the consequences of GHG emissions does seem to some extent to be morally relevant. Suppose that when one's mother grazed her cows on our common property, the world was very different. Neither of them thought of what they were doing as eroding common property. Indeed, neither of us thought of the area on which the cows were grazing as property at all. They benefited from the activities of my mother, but neither of mothers were aware of any harms being produced.

(b) The second objection is that some would insist that it matters where GHG emissions take place, not because of their impact on climate, but because of their effects on quality of life. High quality of life it is argued is associated with high levels of GHG emissions. But what this objection brings out is that a bad market in emissions permissions would be even worse than no market at all. In a properly functioning market, nations, would only sell their emissions permissions if the value of the offer was worth more to them than the permission to emit. But though no international market in emissions permissions could be expected to run perfectly, there is no reason to think that they cannot run well enough to make better the welfare of both buyers and sellers.

(c) Last and third objection would come from some developing countries. This proposal brings them into the regime before developed countries have taken the first steps to reduce emissions. True enough, but the developing countries have the most to lose from environmental change. If the regime is to be effective they will have to enter at some point anyway, and the terms that have been proposed are the most favourable ones they will get by a long shot. This leads to the problems of monitoring, enforcement, and compliance. These are tough problems for any climate regime, but it is clear that any meaningful emissions control will require vast improvement in these areas.

The scheme that has been suggested has many advantages. It would stabilize emissions in a way that would be both efficient and fair. It would also entail a net transfer of resources from the developed to the developing countries, thus reducing global inequality. Too unfortunate that it does not have much chance of being adopted.

(E) Acceptance of Environmental Agreements

Before October, 2000, the Kyoto Protocol had been signed by eighty-four countries and ratified by twenty-nine. What happens in the America is especially important since, in order to take effect, the Protocol must be ratified by fifty-five countries that together emitted 55 per cent of GHGs in 1990. Since the United States was responsible for around 38 per cent of the world's emissions in 1990, the Protocol is unlikely to become law without American ratification. USA signed the Protocol in November 1998, but the Clinton administration has stated that it will not submit the Protocol to the Senate for ratification until it gets "key developing countries to meaningfully participate." During the Fourth Conference of the Parties in Buenos Aires, Nauru, Niue, Argentina, and Kazakhstan volunteered to reduce the rate of their increases in GHGs on the same timetable as the Annex I countries. A good case can also be prepared for supposing that many developing countries, including China, are taking steps to reduce the rate of their increases of GHG emissions.

But clearly the American government is unimpressed. The administration's level of "meaningful participation" is weaker than the Senate's requirement that there be an agreement than mandates specific limitations or reductions for developing countries, but the administration needs more from the developing countries than it got in Buenos Aires before it is willing to argue the case for ratification. Senator Hagel, the leading Republican sponsor of the Byrd resolution, was clearly dismissive of Argentina's commitment to reduce its rate of increase in GHG emissions. Ultimately, however, what is important about the Byrd Resolution is not its language but rather its unanimous approval, which indicated just how much opposition there was to the Kyoto Protocol in the US Senate. The 1998-2000 Republican Senate was unlikely to ratify the Protocol under any situation and even if the Democrats had taken control of the Senate in the elections of 2000 it would still have faced serious opposition. However, even if the United States succeeds in extracting more concessions from developing nations and the Kyoto Protocol is submitted and ratified in the future, it is far from clear that the United States would be able to keep its commitments. The heavy reliance on emissions trading in the administration's plan is in part a response to the major political, economic, and social obstacles to trying to get Americans to change their energy-profligate ways.

The *New York Times* has reported that "since the early 1970s, as the average household has shrunk by a sixth, the average new home has grown by a third" (October 22, 1998, A-1). And since American GHG emissions have been on an upward trajectory since the country's 1992 promise to reduce emissions, meeting the Kyoto target will require a reduction of more than 30 per cent from "business-as-usual" scenarios. Even if every country kept its Kyoto promises, the effect on the atmosphere would be relatively slight. In 2010 the difference between a world of perfect conformity to the Kyoto Protocol and a world without any such agreement at all is 1.5 parts per million (ppm) of carbon dioxide, the difference between an atmospheric concentration of 382 ppm and 383.5 ppm (Bolin 1998).

To place the point in perspective, in the 1990s we have had a 0.25°C warming from the 1961-1990 baseline; perfect conformity to the Kyoto agreements would reduce the assumed warming in 2050 from 1.4°C to 1.395°C (Parry 1998). But much more may be at stake than 1.5 ppm of carbon dioxide or .005°C of warming. In the positive scenario the FCCC process is like the ozone regime. The initial greatly publicized agreements at Vienna and Montreal were not sufficient for repairing the ozone layer, or even to prevent further depletion. The really strong agreements to phase out CFCs happened afterwards, in London and Copenhagen, with much less publicity.

From this perspective what is important is to bring the countries of the world into an emissions-control regime by getting them to agree to take the first steps, and then to restart this agreement as the science develops and the consequences of a warming are felt. Moreover, mandatory limits, even if they are relatively weak at present, send signals to the markets that the era of fossil fuels is finished. New investment with move away from fossil fuels toward renewables, bringing about technical innovation and lower prices. However, the more likely outcome is that the attempt to control GHG emissions will fall apart. Diplomats may carry on to fly around the world having meetings and coining acronyms, but none of this will matter much on the ground. Or perhaps in a fit of international honesty we may just give it all up.

Either way, the world will shift toward adaptation. Indeed, influential voices in the research community are calling for just this shift in focus (Rayner and Malone 1997; Pielke 1998; Parry 1998).

In the older perspective, it is said that there are three options in responding to climate change: prevention, mitigation, and adaptation. But if the science is at all credible, then for some time prevention has not been an alternative. The debate is over mitigation. Will the world succeed in significantly mitigating climate change, or will we have a global policy of adaptation? There is much to be said for adaptation. Most countries are not currently well adapted to the variability that is part of a stable climate regime. But a policy of adaptation without mitigation runs serious practical and moral risks.

The practical risk is that a GHG forcing may drive the climate system into some unanticipated, radically different state, to which it is difficult to adjust. The moral risk is that a policy of adaptation will be one that hits the developing countries hardest. For a global policy of adaptation is an expression of the "polluted pay" principle rather than the "polluter pays" principle. This is so because adaptation policies are typically national or subnational and require resources and knowledge. Since the developed countries have resources and knowledge, they will succeed in adapting to climate change.

Because the developing countries do not have (the right sort of) resources and knowledge, they will suffer the worst effects of climate change. We could try to internationalize adaptation by generating a global fund that countries contribute to on the basis of their GHG emissions and make withdrawals from on the basis of the climate change impacts that they suffer. In fact, something like this is supported by those in the research community who win adaptation.

The vocabularies of "at risk populations" and "humanitarian assistance" are already at play in the West, and in America, for example, funds the International Research Institute for Climate Prediction in an effort to help developing countries respond to El Nino-like events (Glantz and Jamieson, forthcoming). Still, the affluent countries, especially the United States, have the political equivalent of attention deficit disorder. Grand promises are made and big money is promised when a hurricane devastates Honduras, still all this is forgotten when the next humanitarian crisis erupts.

A "Global Marshall Plan" would need a level of non-crisis-sustained commitment that most Western societies seem incapable of maintaining. Had we have to conclude, we can say that the moral and political resources to internationalize adaptation, the Kyoto Protocol would succeed and we could effectively mitigate the effects of environmental change. The positive scenario envisioned by the optimists would prevail, and we would not need to focus our attention exclusively on adaptation. In nutshell, we examined one of the ethical problems posed by global environmental change. The approach to mitigating climate change that would be both just and efficient. But a more likely option is an approach to mitigation that is not very responsive to concerns about justice, or what is even more likely, a step toward adaptation, an outcome that is likely to be the most unjust of all.

11

Awareness Generation about the Changing World Environment

The present chapter is a study of reception of the images of planet earth in America and through her mediation, in the international environmental politics. In the last year of the last Millennium, as the mood of the West turned retrospective and millennial, it became clear that the images by which Western societies were defining the meaning of this stretch of history had changed their form and emphasis—from pictures of division and conflict for the first three-quarters of the century to those of interconnectedness at its end. War and destruction dominate the frames through which we look at most of the gone hundred years : the disjointed march of troops from nowhere to nowhere on the battlefields of the Great War, the emaciated bodies and charred cities of the second and wider World War, the eruptions of American firepower in the fields and rural parts of Vietnam, and the mass evacuations that presaged the killing fields of Cambodia.

These images have not faded from our collective consciousness. Rather, they have gained secondary and tertiary currency through the commemorative contribution of contemporary historians, novelists, filmmakers, and museologists, all intent, it seems, on finding at this emotionally charged calendrical moment the appropriate visual languages to memorialize the century's vast conflicts. One need think only of the controversies surrounding the U.S. Vietnam memorial and their resolution through Maya Lin's inspired and reflective roll call of names, the attack against perceived revisionism in the *Enola Gay* display at the US National Air and Space Museum (Harwit 1996), Stephen Spielberg's embrace of black-and-white cinematography in his 1993 opus *Schindler's*

List, and the lengthy, emotional discussions about how best to commemorate the Holocaust in Berlin, the once and future capital of reunified Germany. Sometime during the last three decades of the century, however, images of the like, of dissolving boundaries, began to supplement, and at times crowd out, division in our visual and imaginative space.

President Richard Nixon's controversial trip to China in 1972 was perhaps a starting point, providing compelling television footage of one of the world's most committed cold warriors visiting the shrines and monuments of the very nation he had fought so doggedly to throw them out from communion with the West. The watershed year of 1989 brought additional stirring images, with the fall of the Berlin wall on November 9 signaling the official end of bipolar disturbance and, to some, even "the end of history" (Fukuyama 1992).

And on January 1, 1999, months before war-torn Kosovo gripped the television screens, the pictures of a new common currency, the Euro—as yet available just in virtual form—made concrete the extraordinary, voluntary ceding of sovereignty-through which eleven European nations sought to erase the scars and trenches of the two world wars that had divided their continent.

A particular image perhaps more than any other has come to symbolize the Western world's heightened perceptions of connectedness at the end of the millennium: that of the earth suspended in a void, caught by the cameras of the US space program beginning with the Lunar Orbiter in 1966 and culminating with *Apollo 17,* the last mission to land men on the moon.

The image confronts Americans today at every step from the revolving globe used as a background for so many televised, and now networked, news programs to the logo that wordlessly asserts the world level reach of credit cards, airlines, automobile manufacturers, telephone companies, bookstores, academic programs, and virtually every other product or service that travels. It is also an image that catches the spirit of contemporary environmentalism, one among late modernity's signature social movements.

The picture of the earth hanging in space not only renders visible and immediate the object of environmentalists concern, but it resonates with the motto of finiteness and fragility, and of human dependence on the biosphere, that have provided growing impetus for environmental mobilization since the 1960s. It is as well a strong political image, subordinating as it does the notional boundaries of sovereign power in favour of swirling clouds that do not respect the lines configured by human conquest or legislation. It is in this respect a fitting emblem of Western Environmentalism's changing ambitions.

Despite the fact that many have pointed to the image of earth from space as an artifact that fundamentally altered human consciousness, there have hardly been systematic attempts to explore how, when, or to what extent such a transformation occurred, let alone how this potent visual resource interacted with the other, better and more commonly recognized political forces (for example, scientific knowledge, economic interests, or hegemonic power) in the formation of shared environmental awareness (for an exception, see Sachs 1994).

There are several reasons why it is important to do away with this gap. To begin with, the televised distribution of standardized visual symbols, and visual language more generally, is creating a global communicative resource whose political implications need closer exploration. Images may transcend cultural lines in ways that words cannot, thereby helping to create communities of meaning and shared responses or demands that cut across ordinary linguistic and governmental splits.

More generally, there is growing interest in the social sciences in the power of visual representation to sway both belief and action (Scott 1998). Sight moreover, like any sense, is now viewed as something that has to be manipulated and disciplined in order for people in the aggregate to see things in the same ways. "The politics involved in constructing common vision has accordingly started to draw attention.

Objectives and Aims

As we have said in the beginning that it is a study of the reception of the image of planet Earth in American and, through US mediation, international environmental politics. At a theoretical level, this project can be seen as contributing to the interpretive shift in international relations theory by attempting to understand better the role of ideas in promoting trans-national cooperation and conflict (Keohane 1988; Haggard and Simmons 1987; Haas 1990b; Litfin 1994).

More particularly, it extends earlier work on epistemic communities by probing, within visual culture, one possible source of shared beliefs about the environment. At the same time, the project also fits comfortably within the deep research agenda of science and technology studies: it explores the creation of new knowledge about nature and its diffusion to varied audience through technologically mediated visual representations. The chapter's organization reflects these paired objectives. It is being began by reviewing major strands in international relations theory and science and technology studies that deal with image making and its power to foster shared social and political awareness. We shall, then successively discuss the emergence of Earth consciousness in post-war politics, the early history of responses to the image of planet Earth, and its later thematization and uptake in the discourses of risk, politics, economics, and morals. The chapter ends with reflections on the merits of the planetary image as a resource for global action to protect the environment.

I. Major Theories: The question here arises is what makes people from different societies believe that they should act to further common aims, even if these goals require them to sacrifice or postpone perceived economic and social interests? In a world in which political will has classically been exercised through national institutions, how can we account for the increase of transnational coalitions, such as the contemporary environmental movement, that seem to articulate their objectives in defiance of the positions of nation states?

How, more generally, do people form commitments to collective action on a worldly scale, and from where do they derive notions of an international common good that are strong enough to override the intense but parochial pull of national self-interest?

(a) Anderson's Sense of Nationalism

A promising place from which to begin addressing these questions is Benedict Anderson's influential study *Imagined Communities* (1991), which sought to explain how nationality became modernity's most compelling social identifier. Why, Anderson asked, has nationality proved to be such a strange robust form of ideology, resisting for instance Marxism's brave attempts to reclassify world politics in terms of shared class allegiances?

Why are people willing to go to war, courting death in pretence of nationhood, and why do they agree to do this even when, as in the case of Indonesia, the entity that commands their loyalty is a loosely connected string of islands with no plausible claims to dialectic or cultural unity? Rejecting geographic determinism as improper, Anderson defined the nation as "an imagined political community—and imagined às both inherently limited and sovereign" (Anderson 1991, 6). The move from physical to imagined demarcation proved deeply liberating to theoreticians of the state. Anderson and his many followers were able to probe the mechanisms by which people come to think that they are associated with something so invisibly put together as a nation, and which, in short, endow the concept of nationhood, with meaning. The turn to "imagined communities" made it possible to encompass within a single theoretical frame such disparate expressions of nationhood as Austria-Hungary, Indonesia, and the ultimately failed construct of postpartition Pakistan, its brackets not firmly enough welded through a shared Islamic faith to withstand the element of intervening Hindu India. Print capitalism plays a central role in Anderson's story of nationalism. Newspapers, he argued, exerted a profound pull on social imagination, making it possible for people in far-flung areas to read about and react to the same events at the same time. The printed page became the instrument through which people who previously had no connection with each other could now *imagine* that they were part of a same community, experiencing and participating in a single national drama.

Readers were bound together by the newspaper's inbuilt clock, which inexorably marked off the days (and, through morning and evening papers, even times of days), juxtaposed incidents from around the world in a collage of adventitiously related events, and rendered them obsolete the very next day with another collection of stories, equally random though united by the same apparently inevitable logic. Anderson originally ascribed to the controllers of the printed page an almost unlimited capacity to mobilize nationalism, but in the book's second edition he included a chapter, more Foucauldian in inspiration, on three other institutions of power—the census, the map, and the museum—through which modern states have tried to discipline their citizen's nationalistic imaginations.

With the help of these institutions, enterprising states could manufacture or erase boundaries and histories, connections and divisions. A telling exercise in image making occurred at the fifteenth anniversary celebration of Cambodia's freedom in November 1968, in honor of which Nationalism as "logoization," imagination highly expressed by image making—all possible, so Anderson argued, through a means of production that permitted images to be removed from context, made infinitely reproducible, and so inscribed in people's minds as seedlings of national fellow-feeling. This account of political community building strikingly resonates with work in science and technology studies that attempts to explain how scientific representations of the natural world obtained a hold on people's beliefs.

No one perhaps has done more to illuminate this process than Bruno Latour, the French ethnographer and philosopher of science, for whom the investigation of scientific knowledge in the formation has long been coextensive with trying to understand what gives scientific images and inscriptions their special persuasive power (Latour and Woolgar 1979). In one of his best-known expositions of the issue, Latour argues that the difference between "savage," or prescientific, and "civilized," or scientific, knowledge lies not so much in how people perceive reality but in the ability of modern science to circulate its perceptions by keeping them "mobile, flat, reproducible, still, and of varying scales" (Latour 1990, 45). Latour called the resulting inscriptions "immutable mobiles" since unlike the *objects* that science observes (countries, planets, microbes)—representations of them (maps, photographic plates, Petridishes) can move around in fixed forms created by the exertions of scientists.

(b) Latour's Still Inscriptions

Here, we find a startling family resemblance between Anderson's logoized nations and Latour's immobilized inscriptions: both move, both can be mobilized, both are torn away from the specific circumstances of their production, gaining more power through this erasure of history and context. Yet the two writers are profoundly at odds in their understanding of the forces that create mobility. For Anderson, capital is the prime mover. Without its support, nations could not control the printing presses that produce the maps and images that impress themselves, in turn, on the awaiting minds of protonationalist citizens. Latour turns this argument on its head, stressing that it is the mundane craftsmanship of visualization that moves things and people, and so gives rise to power. In passages that read almost as if they were written to counter Anderson, or like Foucault, Latour says that we continually misunderstand the relationship between science and power "because we take for granted that there exist, somewhere in society, macroactors that naturally dominate the scene: Corporation, State, Productive Forces, Cultures, Imperialism, "Mentalites," etc... Far from being the key to the understanding of science and technology, these entities are the very things a new to which sociologists of science are keen to attach "interests" are immaterial in practice so long as precise mechanisms to explain their origin or extraction and their changes of scale have not been proposed."

Thus, in this manner, Latour's commitment is to elaborating the details of scientific practice (not, characteristically, of science funding), the workaday routines of sampling and observation, recording and classification through which complete Amazonian forest, for example, can be transformed into tractable, movable catalog of soil types and plant varieties, and ultimately even a theory of causation to explain whether the forest is advancing or going back (latour 1995).

The question now here, does the aggregated power of money control the technologies of representation, which then function as levers of ideology? Or does mastery of the craftwork of representation cumulatively give push to power, lodged, as Latour (1990, 59) memorable puts it, in "centers of calculation" that in effect *make* the world by circulating particular interpretations of it? Or is the relationship of image and imagination altogether more complex, requiring visual stimuli to resonate with cultures of interpretation that help define their ultimate meanings in time and place? Let us turn to an actual state. In this chapter we will investigate more exactly how a single image, that of planet Earth, became an inhabitor of Western consciousness and an icon, more particularly, of US environmentalism. Through this act, we will not (following a typically Latourian program) seek chiefly to retrace the networks of rocket and satellite production, nor the labyrinths of the military-industrial establishment, that importantly enabled the making of the true image. Rather, we will focus on less a easily encapsulated dimension of the story, that of the image's transmission, uptake, and interpretation within disparate groups of discourse and action. Unlike Anderson and Latour, both of whom link their studies of power primarily to the technologies of image of making and circulation, I aim to look more closely at the imagination audience—and the self-conscious consumers-of this potent symbol human and natural interconnectedness. Without the participation of these ordinarily unsung actors, images would not be invested with the meaning that push political action.

II. New Look

US commentators have frequently written of the transforming impact of picture of Earth suspended in space, as captured on film by successive Apollo mission astronauts. The late astronomer Carl Sagan, whose televised program Cosmos won him something close to cult status in the 1980s, was one of those who helped to popularize this theme:

"While almost everyone is taught that the Earth is a sphere with all of us somehow glued to it by gravity, the reality of our circumstance did not really begin to sink in until the famous frame-filling *Apollo* photograph of the whole Earth—the one taken by the Apollo 17 astronauts on the last journey of humans to the Moon." (Sagan 1994, 5).

More it is necessary to reproduce that Sagan selected a particular image as his icon, the one that shows Earth in the round, with no clouds concealing (to a culture familiar with conventions of mapping) the readily imaginable outlines of countries in Arabia and the horn of Africa. Environmentalists as a rule are inclined to agree with Sagan's judgement about the importance of that image. Writing in 1990, the ecologist Daniel Botkin stated.

It is more than 20 years since the phrase "spaceship Earth" was coined and made popular and 20 years since the Apollo astronauts took this famous photograph of the Earth from space—a blue globe, enveloped by swirling white clouds, against a black background—creating an image of a small island of life floating in an ocean of empty space. (Botkin 1990, 5)

Another similarly significant point was made some years earlier by the World Commission on Environment and

Development (WCED) in its influential report, *Our Common Future:*

"In the middle of the 20th century, we saw our planet from space for the first time. Historians may eventually find that this vision had greater impact on thought than did the Copernican revolution of the 16th century, which upset humans' self-image by revealing that the Earth is not the centre of the universe. From space, we see a small and fragile ball dominated not by human activity and edifice but by a pattern of clouds, oceans, greenery, and soils. Humanity's inability to fit its activities into that pattern is changing planetary systems fundamentally." (World Commission on Environment and Development 1987, 308)

Introduction of the idea of a "scientific revolution" held particular appeal for others who commented on the *Apollo* picture. Laurence Tribe, at one time a critic of technology's instrumental rationality and then a constitutional scholar at Harvard Law School, remarked that this image-"the earth as a dramatically finite and surpringly delicate blue-green globe" (Tribe 1973, 620)-had ushered as toward "the fourth discontinuity". "It was a moment that displaced the human ego by making it conscious of the physical limitations of the place it inhabits. This decentering effect, Tribe and other have said, was at par with three great intellectual discontinuities of the past: the Copernican revolution, which displaced the earth from the center of the universe; the Darwinian revolution, which displaced human beings from the pinnacle of the tree of creation, and also, the Freudian revolution, which exposed the working of the unconscious mind and made humankind aware that we are not, after all, masters in our own house.

Carrying on with the theme of scientific revolutions, some suggested that the picture of our lonely planet brought about nothing less than a paradigm shift in ways of thinking about how the world works. Lynton Caldwell, a leading figure in the new environmentalism of the 1970s, clearly took this position:

"The change from the belief that the sun, moon, and stars revolved around the earth to the Copernican view of the earth's place in the solar system was a paradigm shift. The change marked by [the aftermath of Apollo] is from the view of an earth unlimited in abundance and created for man's exclusive use to a concept of the earth as a domain of life or biosphere for which mankind is a temporary resident custodian. The newer view sees it as an ultimately unified system that may supply man's needs as long as he observes the system's rules." (Caldwell 1990, 21)

One more author, Joseph Campbell, suggested that the making and broad costing of the Apollo 17 tip had "transformed, deepened, and extended human consciousness to a degree and in a manner that amount to the opening of a new spiritual era".

Above written all the observations credit the planetary image with inducing a sudden, radical, and far-ranging shift in political consciousness, as human beings redefined their understanding of what it means to live together on the earth. But the widespread acceptance of this number by environmentalists runs counter to much of what we know about cultural responses to imagery. Whether in the history of science or in the history of art, it seems that images become persuasive only when options of looking at them have been carefully prepared in advance, through the creation of a stylized visual idiom or an interpretive tradition that knows how to respond to special types of images. The meaning of pictures is inseparable from the context that supplies the idioms of interpretation. What, then, were the historical, political, economic and cultural circumstances in which vision of planet Earth acquired its now-canonical readings? Did the image the give rise to demonstrably new forms of understanding about the environment and associated concepts of governance, or did it merely reinforce older habits and patterns of political association?

III. Descriptive Rituals

A number of the themes invoked in connection with the *Apollo* image predated the photographs that gave them unforgettable embodiment. In particular, reflections on the earth's finiteness, its fragility, its confined resources, the interconnectedness of its physical and biological systems, and the flimsiness of its geopolitical boundaries were all current in Western thought and writing quite before the astronauts of *Apollo* 17 brought back the most famous icon of the floating planet.

(a) Imaginary Concepts: Thus, the maverick American engineer and inventor R. Buckminster Fuller (1969), who prided himself on having seen the earth imaginatively before there were astronauts, coined the term *Spaceship Earth* to describe humanity's flight on a superbly designed, self-contained vehicle lacking only an intelligible operating manual.

Fuller's metaphor speedily became popular in enlightened political circles. The influential British economist and environmentalist Barbara Ward borrowed the term, finding it a congenial hook on which to stick her own ideas about transnational harmony, sustainable development, and the need for global redistribution of wealth. Ward's friend and philosophical ally, the noted liberal Democrat Adlai Stevenson, then American Ambassador to the United Nations, observed in a speech before the UN Economic and Social Council in dated July 1965, "We travel together, passengers on a little spaceship, dependent on its vulnerable resources of air and soil; all committed for our safety to its security and peace; preserved from annihilation only by the care the work and, I will say, the love we give our fragile craft".

While Fuller and others spoke of the earth as a spaceship, it was the University of Michigan economist Kenneth Boulding who explicitly connected the planet's roundness with a global imagination of the environmental impression. Air travel, Boulding observed, had begun to accustom people since World War II with "the notion of the spherical earth and a closed sphere of human activity" (Boulding 1966, 3). The idea of the planet as an enclosed system had gradually replaced the image of the frontier, with its wide open spaces and promise of endless resources. The new era, Boulding argued, would require a new type of economic discipline: a "spaceman economy," in which "man must find his place in a cyclical ecological system," replacing the earlier "cowboy economy," which countenanced "reckless, exploitative, romantic, and violent behavior," particularly with respect to resource consumption.

(b) Effect of Population: Many more authors had begun to note that the triad of population, consumption, and pollution might place irreversible stresses on the planet's health. Among the earliest and most influential voices in America was that of Rachel Carson, whose 1962 book *Silent Spring* offered a part-scientific, part-elegiac exposition of how the indiscriminate use of chemical pesticides was killing bird populations throughout North America and gravely threatening all earthly life (Carson 1962). The Club of Rome, a prestigious association of scientists and intellectuals, went further. Using newly devised techniques of computer modeling, its controversial report, *The Limits to Growth,* predicated a sudden and drastic collapse of the Earth's economic, social and environmental systems (Meadows *et al.* 1972).

In spite of many methodological criticisms, the report's catastrophist vision persisted as one of the enduring themes of modern environmentalism.

(c) Perceptions about Earth as a Closed System: This inspired less calamitous scientific stories as well. Most widely discussed perhaps in the so-called Gaia hypothesis, originated in the early 1970s by James Lovelock, a physicist working for the National Aeronautics and Space Administration (NASA), and further prepared with Lynn Margulis, microbiologist known for the theory of the origins of eukaryotic cells. Versions of the hypothesis range from a weak (and uncontroversial) form that merely posits complex connections between biological and nonbiological activity at the earth's surface to stronger claims that the earth's atmosphere maintains a steady state for the express purpose of sustaining life, and that biological organisms actively manipulate their environment to this extent.

It is not the validity or theoretical coherence of Lovelock's and Margulis's scientific ideas that is important for our purposes, but rather their integrative, planetary vision. An outgrowth of NASA's interest in the possible existence of life on Mars, the Gaia hypothesis illustrates how the technology of space discoveries fostered a global science of biogeochemical interactions. Even before the space age allowed humanity actually to look the earth in the face, scientific imagination were constructing narratives on a global scale about what was taking place at the earth atmosphere interface.

Is not it tragic to know that if the conquest to flight ushered in an age of environmental claustrophobia, it also made geopolitical division seem more vulnerable. By the late 1940s, the world's major powers were already arrayed into the strong dualities of the Cold War. The earth as globe dominated the visual renditions of this new political dispensation. The standard view adopted by the superpowers looked down on the global scene from the North Pole. From this standpoint, image makers were free to decide only how much of the Southern Hemisphere they would include in their field of vision.

A 1947 report sponsored by the Council on Foreign Relations, for instance, displayed the polar perspective as adapted from a official chart used by the US Air Force. The map was cut off at the

30th parallel, showing the top of the north Africa and fringes of Iran and India, still nothing at all of Latin America. "Strategists," the report observed, "term the area between the 30th and 65th parallels the key zone since all modern wars have started there" (Baldwin 1947). The same projection seems as a logo to this day on publications of Harvard University's Belfer Center for Science and International Affair, an institution whose identity was molded during the Cold War. Image and imagination, even now powerfully fused, deny the emergence of a more complex, less bipolar political order.

Besides their various assumptions, the implications of the global perspective have always been thoroughly ambiguous. The view from the pole could be read, on one hand, as an invitation to strengthen state sovereignty. A 1948 report by the President's Air Policy Commission followed just this tack, using the polar projection to underscore the threat of aerial war.

Observing the world from a position near Point Barrow, Alaska, and looking 7,000 miles along the earth's surface in all directions, the Commission graphically illustrated the existence of "a new element through which this country may be attacked—the air". The report called for a stronger air force as "the best conceivable defense" against air attack (President's Air Policy Commission 1948, 11). But the polar gaze equally supported sounds of peaceful coexistence in the post-war world, as evidenced by the United Nations logo adopted in the same period. Although the North Pole again occupied the image's center, no nation however away from the central viewing point, was excluded from the UN's encompassing vision.

Even Australia appears outlined in full at the outer margins of the UN world. Last but not the least, no account of interpretive conventions that have grown up around the earth image would be complete without the voices of the astronauts who saw as eyewitnesses what the remaining of humanity experienced only through pictures and television. Unwitting seers, confronting a vision for which little in life prepared them, these observers tell what it was similar to see the earth before anyone else had appropriated the images. Some were stirred to uncharacteristic eloquence. William Anders, a member of the December 1968 *Apollo* 8 mission that for the first time saw the earth whole, set the tone for many coming interpreters. Imagining the earth as "little

Christmas-tree ornament against an infinite black backdrop of space," Anders commented on its "fragility and finiteness":

"I find it somewhat ironic that we went up there for the moon, but probably it was Earth and the perspective of it that most impressed hard-bitten test pilots like us—and I guess of the rest of the world—the most. Because the pictures of the first Earthrise and the first full earth floating in space, I think, have been a major contribution of helping people get a better feeling for the Earth's place in our lives and in the universe. You realize that Earth is about as physically significant as one grain of sand on a beach. But it's our only home."

It can be seen in Anders's groping phrases some familiar strains of contemporary environmentalist discourse: fragility finiteness, insignificance, the unavoidable dependence of human life on this planet ("our only home"). Yet mere three and a half years later, when NASA was winding up the first phase of lunar exploration, the "hard-bitten" edge was back, and some members of the *Apollo* 17 crew seemed able to take the spectacular earthscape for granted. Eugene Cernan reproduces the following conversation with his fellow-traveller Harrison "Jack" Schmitt:

"C: "Oh, man—Hey, Jack, just stop. You owe himself 30 seconds to look up over the South Massif and look at the Earth."

S: "what? The Earth?!"

C: "Just look up there."

S: "Aaah! You've seen one Earth, you have seen them all."

While astronauts on the moon could so quickly accustom themselves to one of the twentieth century's grandest displays, then it hardly seems probable that the rest of humanity, preoccupied with innumerable local cares and conflicts, was formed by the image to an all-new, enduring global ecoconsciousness. Did its mere dissemination—as capitalist logo or scientific "immutable mobile"—compel people to reimagine their political affiliations on a worldwide scale? It is not so. As we will see, connections between the global image and an imagined global community evolved along intricate pathways, as human actors and institutions strove in disparate method to assimilate, or exploit, the photographic evidence of their common destiny. Associated shifts from local or national to global environmental thinking—although they can be documented—have been neither seamless nor smooth, but instead subtle, sporadic, partial, and unevenly distributed among the world's political communities.

Numerous World Experiments

Global environmental consciousness, we are suggesting, did not coalesce all at once in response to a striking visual stimulus, but took shape gradually at once in response to a striking visual stimulus, but took shape gradually in diverse domains of social and political practice during the final decades of the twentieth century. Strands of growing global awareness can be traced in the discourses of risk, politics, commerce, and ethics. In each context, we observe a selective uptake of themes prevalent in older narratives of earthwatching, but reinforced and given fresh persuasive power through association with the *Apollo* photographs.

Preparing World Level Risk Factors

A number of observers of American environmental politics agree that something happened to alter its character in the decade roughly marked by the publication of *Silent Spring* in 1962 and the celebration of the first Earth Day, a nationwide event involving some 300,000 citizens, on the day of April 22, 1970. Often termed the *new environmentalism,* the movement born in this period of ferment diverged from earliest forms of environmental activism in its focus on people and their shelters rather than on the preservation of nature for its own sake. It was founded, according to one expert, on "a broader conception of the place of man in the biosphere, a more sophisticated understanding of that relationship, and a note of crisis that was greater and broader than it had been in the earlier conservation movement".

Aims and objectives of this, however, were initially local. They concerned first and foremost the effects of pollution on common people's homes and lives. Rachel Carson's ground-breaking vision, as noted back, took as its central theme the harms caused by pervasive use of chemical pesticides.

Although she imagined a whole world deprived of birdsong (her book started with a fable of poisoned landscapes and dying animals and vegetation), some of her most telling vignettes involved ordinary citizens reporting on changes in their immediate surroundings: the disappearance of robins in one town, the decimation of swallows in another. These regional insults added up to a problem of concededly national proportions. In 1970, President Nixon ordered the creation of the Environmental Protection Agency largely on the basis that a new organization was needed to coordinate a nationwide fight against pollution. But local issues continued to predominate in environmental politics. In 1978, for example, toxic chemicals found in the underground of homes in the Love Canal area of Niagara Falls, New York, precipitated an intense flurry of pollution centered legislative and regulatory activity (see for example Levine 1982).

This and similar episodes fueled the century's is most powerful form of environmental mobilization, the NIMBY, a social movement whose tightly bounded, *local* imagination was synonymous with the slogan "not in my backyard." Chemical pollution of communities continued to be a guiding theme of US environmentalism well into the 1980s. It was not until the later 1980s that a global conception of environmental protection rooted itself in Western consciousness. Almost imperceptibly, the causes and extent of environmental downfall (for example, deforestation, desertification, ozone depletion) began to be defined across political domains far larger than individual communities and even more encompassing than nation states. Attention started to shift from end-of-pipe controls on specific polluting facilities to questions of prevention and lifestyle change. A new term—*sustainability*—came into common use in policy discourse, bridging what had in the past seemed and irreconcilable contradiction between environmental protection and human development. Appropriately enough, the book that heralded this new era was not the work of a single author with a distinctively individual vision, but of an international committee of experts, the World Commission on Environment and Development, chaired by Norway's prime minister Gro Harlem Brundtland. Both in its title and by explicit reference (as quoted above), *Our Common Future* conveyed, and helped crystallize, a sense of the full human condition, framed by the planetary image and global in its prescriptive scope. No longer would if be sufficient for environmental activism to concentrate its energies mainly on the invasion of individual backyards by chemical pollution.

World Level Polities

Right from NIMBY to a global politics of the environment, however, was no easy, step. The transition arguably began with the age to space exploration, but its progress is not yet complete. That the image of planet impels many observers to "think globally" has been apparent ever since the early satellite launches. Barbara Ward, for example, imagined the solidarity that US astronauts should feel with their Soviet counterparts and speculated that their feat would erase the cold war's central political conflict:

"When the astronauts spin through more than a dozen sunrise and sunsets in a single day and night; when the whole globe lies below them with California one minute and Japan the next; when as they return from space, they feel spontaneously, wit the first Soviet spaceman: "How beautiful it is, *our* earth"; it is inconceivable that no modification of consciousness or imagination occurs, no sense that quarrels are meaningless before the majestic yet vulnerable reality of a single planet carrying a single human species through infinite space."

These comments interestingly foreshadowed Ander's testimony that the earth is "as physically significant as one grain of sand" and yet "it's our only home." Perhaps self-consciously echoing Anders, Ward and her renowed environmentalist colleague Rene Dubos published a book in 1972 with the title *Only One Earth*. This became the official theme of that year's Stockholm conference on the environment. Carl Sagan in turn presented the image an explicitly political spin, while reiterating the theme of humanity's insignificance:

"We are too small and *our statecraft too feeble* to be seen by a spacecraft between the Earth and the Moon. From this vantage point, our obsession with nationalism is nowhere in evidence. The Apollo pictures of the whole Earth conveyed to multitudes something well known to astronomers: On the scale of worlds-to say nothing of stars or galaxies—humans are inconsequential, a thin film of life on an obscure and solitary lump of rock and metal."

In the same manner, the World Commission on Environment and Development juxtaposed the transitory geopolical constructions of the globe against an enduring ecological opinion: "From space, we see a small and fragile ball dominated not by human activity and edifice but by a pattern of clouds, oceans, greenery, and soils".

Though it is true that astronauts, astronomers, and international experts identified the earth image with coexistence and political interdependence, the use and enjoyment of environmental resources remained for many other actors tightly bound to national interests.

One important case in point was President Ronald Reagan's astonishing and emphatic rejection of the draft Law of the Sea (LOS) convention following his election in 1980. Here was an accord applicable on the oceans that had enjoyed bipartisan support in the Nixon, Ford, and Carter administrations and had seemed virtually ready for adoption by the late 1970s. It presented US navigational freedom, simplifying and counteracting a patchwork of jurisdictional claims by coastal states, in return for decrease in the right of mine seabed resources, including manganese nodules, which third world countries saw as the common heritage of mankind. For those committed to the negotiation, the two issues were inextricably liked. Concession on seabed mining was the inevitable price for avoiding the expanding territorial ambitions of coastal states. Yet as the negotiations went on for decades, fissures appeared in the US position corresponding to changing perceptions of costs and benefits between some of the parties to the negotiation.

American mining interests, in particular, came to believe that the draft treaty was penalizing them more than was warranted by corresponding gains on the side of navigation. As support crumbled for a wide solution, combining navigation and mining, a few Republican administration began to think the unthinkable and pulled the United States out of the almost-completed negotiations.

We can well see in front of an eyes fate of the LOS conference in the 1980s can be seen in retrospect as triumph of persistent nationalist claims to global environmental resources over nascent internationalist global. This point was well understood by Richard Darman, vice chair of the US delegation to the 1977 session of the third LOS conference and perceptive participant observer of the treaty process. In his write up *Foreign Affairs,* Darman argued that the conference was being driven, to the detriment of US interests, both pragmatic and ideological, by a community of

"internationalist lawyer-condifiers. The inter-nationalists' tendency to favor collective over individual action is combined with the codifiers' tendency to wish to see the world in neat static terms. Above and beyond practical considerations, there is an aesthetic antipathy toward the "disaster" of nonuniformity, and a general distrust of the possible benignness of self-regulating, dynamic processes."

What else, further Darman conceded that foiling the internationalist vision of a single regime of navigational and seabed governance carried a risk. The oceans occupying two-thirds of the earth's surface might be "carved up" within geopolitical lines in ways that would benefit developed countries over developing ones. Political boundaries would in effect be drawn where none had previously existed.

This, in turn, would cause a problem of equity that might affect US strategic interests. But this issue, Darman urged, should be addressed on its own terms through mechanisms such as loan guarantees and technology shifting. International equity did not require the United States to recognize the oceans as the common property of humankind or to countenance the development of new international institutions whose mandates would certainly erode national sovereignty. Equity problems, in other words, could be redressed without having to accept the case for global ownership or control of the oceans. When the Clinton adminis-tration signed a revisited LOS convention in July 1994, the official explanation declared a victory for free-marked centralized planning and for sovereignty over failure of national control. A government fact sheet on LOS posted on the World Wide Web notes that the United States has won a guaranteed seat on key committees, increased power to block adverse decisions and credit for exploration already undertaken by US companies. Clearly, framing the seas as an economic resource ran opposite to the planetary imagination. A view founded on the necessity—even the rightness—of competition among nations blocked the emergence of transnational management institutions and a truely global politics of resource allocation.

Another this type of resurgence of national sovereignty can be observed under the Convention on Biological Diversity (CBD), even though this treaty, too, was initially conceived as an instrument for effectuating allegedly global environmental interests. By the late 1980s, alarm about fast world-wide extinctions of species and associated activism by leading biologists had created a demand for international action to protect the earth's scarce biological resources (Takacs 1996).

In reply, the United Nations Environment Program (UNEP) initiated in 1988 a series of expert and intergovernmental deliberations with the aim of preparing a legal factor for the conservation and sustainable use of biodiversity. Consistent with these goals, the convention sought to address economic and social concerns along with scientific ones. The experts convened by UNEP were asked to take into notice "the need to share costs and benefits between developed and developing countries" as well as "ways and means to support innovation by local people." The text of the CBD was adopted in Nairobi in May 1992 and opened for signature in June of that year at the United Nations Conference on Environment and Development (the Rio "Earth Summit"). It came in force in December 1993, ninety days after the thirtieth ratification. From the beginning, however, international efforts to balance conservation against development, equity against economics, and global management against national sovereignty proved to be greatly contentious. A test of the convention's attempted global framing of biodiversity arose in 1999 at a meeting in Cartagena, Colombia, to approve an international biosafety protocol applicable genetically modified organisms. Acrimony between developing countries and major grain exporters caused the meeting to break down without any agreement being reached. A new round of negotiations in Montreal in early 2000 proved more meaningful, although the agreement reached there represented more a working compromise among contrary interests than a global accord on basic presumptions. As in the case of LOS, environmentalism's world ambitions bowed to pressure from economic interests defined at the national level.

Amongst the few environmental regimes in which the political ideal of "One Earth" arguably has come closer to fruition is that governing climate change (popularly better known as "global warming"). Here, there has been a convergence between the *scientific* formation of a problem that transcends national boundaries (see Miler, chapter 8, this volume) and *normative* construction that recognizes the rights of developing as well as developed countries to be safeguarded against the worst consequences of greenhouse-gas accumulation in the atmosphere. Even on the scientific side, considerable work was needed to define climate change as something other than the total of local weather patterns—in other words, as a problem of "whole-earth" dimensions. Prerequisites included the formation of the Intergovernmental Panel on Climate Change and its hard-fought acquaintance of credibility as body capable of representing the best scientific judgement with respect to climate change. This evolutionary story stands markedly at odds with the traditional account of the earth image as herald and harbinger of a sudden paradigm shift in environmental consciousness. The emergence of climate change as a global phenomenon, moreover, concided as we will see, with the appearance of moral discourse that had no precursor in the politics of either LOS or biodiversity.

Environmental Advertising

American environmentalists were not alone in sizing up the symbolic potential of the earth image. The picture of the planet became almost an instant classic in the visual repertoire of advertising, at first retaining its connections to themes of environmental stewardship, but slowly shedding these in favour of something more like "universalism" or simply "global reach." Commerce, environment, and the earth in space were first connected together in 1968 in the *Whole Earth Catalog*, an entrepreneurial venture that both articulated and capitalized on the values of the new environmental movement. The cover picture showed the North American land mass almost totally obstructed by a large white cloud; below appeared the caption "THE UNIVERSE: from plan Earth on a sunny day." Inside, the *Catalog's* offerings emphasized environmental restoration, community building, simplicity, authenticity, and medical self-help. Supplements published over the next five years all carried the same cover picture associated by the same message. A new version planned for the millennium continued several themes of the late 1960s. Consumers were still made available "tools for producing knowledge, reporting and broadcasting the news as you see it, and creating communities according to your own value and ideals".

Modern advertisers of services and products no longer link globality so explicitly to environment-friendly lifestyles. Instead, the planetary symbol tends to stress the deployer's capacity to move pcople and products without much attempt around the globe. Not surprisingly, the picture has become an important property for CNN, the cable news service that built its empire by bringing viewers face to face with event from the furthest approach of the earth—with an immediacy prized equally in the White House and in the headquarters of some of the United State's most intransigent enemies. Not only for CNN, but for many other advertiser, it is the assumed shrinking of time and distance between the consumer and the object of consumption that has become the image's most alluring message.

Through advertisements also we illustrate the infinite interpretive flexibility of an image that has achieved iconic status throughout Western culture. Just as the Mona Lisa, the world's most popular painting, has been adapted interpreted, and sometimes subverted, to suit every taste, so too has the planet's portrait been manipulated in varied ways to create a universally approachable visual counterpoint to messages of persuasion and seduction. One commonplace strategy is to focus on the part of the globe on which the advertiser's commercial activities are specifically targeted. Another is to superimpose the image on something else—like, a burning, spherical candle or a pair of clasped hands—thereby hybridizing the instantly comprehensible sign of global interconnection with other, less normalized messages, which then are empowered to travel, as it were, on the neck of the earth.

"There's Antarctica at what Americans and Europeans so readily regard as the bottom, and then all of Africa stretching up above it: You can see Ethiopia, Tanzania, and Kenya, where the earliest humans lived. At top right are Saudi Arabia and what Europeans call the Near East. Just barely peeking out at the top is the Mediterranean Sea, around which so much of our global civilization emerged. You can make out the blue of the ocean, the yellow-red of the Sahara and the Arabian desert, the brown-green of forest and grassland."

Through trade discourse, by contrast, Earth has no fixed, humanmade coordinates. It is, as often as not, a dream image, as in an advertisement for Thai Airways, which shows an incredibly remote planet held at the eye of the huge silvery needle in turn of black velvet sky and a ribbon of deep purple, the advertiser's signature color. Through their very ubiquity, however, these modified pictures reinforce the status of the underlying "original" image as common cultural resource; they look and disappear as figments of our common imagination, even as they cater to our culturally calibrated desires.

Human Morals

Present environmentalism includes at its core a widely acknowledged, if only imperfectly realized, ethical imperative to renegotiate human beings' relationship with nature in the light of new scientific understandings. More than a generation back, Boulding observed in his article on Spaceship Earth that we were as yet "very far from having made the moral, political, and psychological adjustments which are implied in [the] transition from the illimitable plane to the closed sphere". Now, more than two decades later the first landing on the moon and the first photographic portrayals of the earth from space, it is possible to identify at least three strains of ethical discourse that appear specifically to derive their force from a global, as against a national or local, framing of humanity's environmental predicament.

(1) Slow Extension of Policy: Leading on is a gradual extension of the pre-cautionary principle into transnational environmental policy. This legal precept originated in German law as one of five basic principles governing environmental decisions. Briefly stated, the precautionary principle asks for restraint on human activities that could hurt the environment when there is not enough evidence to determine for sure whether such harm will occur. American environmental law has opted on the whole for a seemingly more pragmatic, risk-based approach that permits development to proceed when the benefits are calculated to exceed the probable harm.

Regarding the environmental hazards of global scope, however, the utilitarian calculus of risks and benefits is harder to sustain than in the context of localized pollution troubles from a waste dump or chemical factory. Uncertainties loom larger, and, within the contested frameworks of global politics, practices of analysis and reassurance cannot be as readily stabilized through well-worn channels of expert pondering.

The result has been to introduce what some international theorists have termed a *bias shift* away from problem solving toward a set of actions geared more toward prevention (Ruggie 1986). For instance, as Karen Litfin has argued, the Montreal accord on the control of ozone-depleting substances would not have adopted nearly so stringent a set of targets had it not been for the invention of the Antarctic ozone hole, which atmospheric science had not predicated and for which there was no obvious nonanthropogenic explanation.

(2) Sustainable Environment for Future Generation: Next strand of an emergent global ethical discourse centers on the idea of sustainability and more specifically on concepts of stewardship for future generations. The World Commission on Environment and Development built the norm of stewardship into its very meaning sustainability in *Our Common Future,* endorsing only those patterns of development that would leave future generations no worse off than their forebears today. Lynton Caldwell, for one, explicitly ties this shift to the *Apollo* image, which in his telling induced a move "from the view of an earth unlimited in abundance and created for man's exclusive use to concept of the earth as a walk of life or biosphere for which mankind is a temporary resident custodian" (Caldwell 1990, 21). The elaboration of intergenerational ethics as a legal principle likewise rests on a recognition of "the planet" as the proper spatial framing for sustainable environmental action. Edith Brown Weiss's important treatise on the legal foundations of intergenerational ethics begins on a note known to all earthwatchers: "The human species inhabits a small, relatively new, and so far as we know, unique planet-Earth. It is also a fragile planet" (Weiss 1989,1).

(3) Responsible Northern Countries: This ethical stand has to do with the obligations of the developed North to the developing South in matters of environmental policy. The recognition of such an obligation is not in itself new, as is evident from our previous discussion of the Law of the Sea negotiations. Thus, even while espousing a position of unilateralism and national self-interest, Darman rejected the prospect of a highly inequitable regime for exploiting world seabed resources. Ethics, however, was embedded within the discourse of rational choice, where it became simply one more item to tote up along with other national interests. Acting ethically was no more important in principle than respecting the requirements of the mining industry or of commercial shipping. Efforts to treat equity as higher-order variable within LOS proved unsuccessful.

Truely, in his analysis of the US withdrawal from LOS, the negotiation theorist James Sebenius has argued that developing nations' attempt to promote a supervening, *transnational* moral discourse—that of the New International Economic Order

(NIEO)—was a prime reason for the formation of a "blocking coalition" and the eventual breakdown of the conference. Claims about equity have received a more sympathetic hearing under regimes that have (unlike LOS and CBD) successfully constructed environmental problems on a transnational level, maximum known ozone and climate change. Thus, an Indian environmental group, the Centre for Science and Environment, successfully deconstructed the tacit normative assumptions incorporated within early attempts to create objective measures of the "global warming potential" of greenhouse gases (Agarwal and Narain 1991). Perhaps more important, the very kinds of equity arguments that were rejected by Northern countries when put forward by the South under the label NIEO now seem to carry greater moral as well as political weight. Terms like *vulnerability* and *equity* have entered the language of global environmental agreements. Both the ozone and climate change regimes explicitly recognize the special economic and ethical claims of developing nations through legal provisions ensuring delayed implementation, funding, and technology shifting.

A Synthesis

Strength of words to force action has been a subject for philosophical and political analysis from Plato down to modern times. The power of images may be no less profound, especially in this era of mass visual communication, but it has yet to get the same sustained scrutiny from social theorists. My object in this chapter has been to trace the complex pathways by which one images—that of planet Earth—has come to inhabit our political consciousness as an icon of world environmentalism. A closer look at the image's reception suggest that its connections with environmental thought and action have been nothing but straightforward. The picture, to begin with, picked up and reinforced themes of the earth's fragility and finiteness that had begun to percolate through policy discourses decades before the space age started. In this way, it may have subtly helped to shift the perception of environmental risk from issues of purely local scope to longer-term concerns for human survival.

Yet although it was appropriated early on to advocate arguments for global environmental governance (witness the "Only One Earth" theme of the 1972 Stockholm conference), such thinking failed to move entrenched national interests in resource management regimes starting from seabed mining to the protection of biodiversity. The image's widespread exploitation by commerical enterprise has underscored its iconic components but arguably blunted its moral and political connotations. Possibly the most important consequence to flow from the planetary image is the visual anchor it has provided for emerging, globally articulated ethical concepts, like precautionary principle, sustainability and intergenerational equity.

Still global stewardship remains a deeply contested concept. Battles over the Law of the Sea and biodiversity throw into sharp relief some of the risks that people around the world. The planetary image, also conveys a serene disregard for the human condition. Not only does it seem to erase the territorial claims of nation states, but it also renders invisible the day-to-day environmental insults suffered by billions of the world's poorest citizens: dirty air, polluted water, inadequate sanitation, infectious diseases, damaged crops, loss of green lanes, and the decay of built environments. Indeed, people themselves are eliminated from this image of environmentalism, as in some of the darker fantasies of ecofascism. As a dazzling offshoot of the last century's most destructive technological impulses, the photograph that preeminently symbolizes planetary togetherness ironically undermines its own authority in the eyes of skeptics. It promises an imagined community as significant as the earth itself, but is this a community in which those without the power to patrol the heavens, to map and perhaps to devastate the earth, can ever meaningfully participate?

Conclusion

Here, we would like to end this chapter on a note of mild optimism. Seldom in the course of preparing an academic publication have we encountered so much spontaneous interest among my US conversation partners as in discussing the topic of this piece. It seemed everyone's favourite associations with the Earth image; many admitted to possessing a variant of it on some prized but mundane object, such as a T-shirt, a tote bag, or a poster. If general circulation models and integrated calculations belong to the "high" scientific language of global environmentalism, then for most Americans the picture of planet Earth surely belongs to its vernacular. It is not, if it ever was, an arcane "immutable mobile" that simply goes beyond the dominance of instrumentally rational ways of perceiving the environment. Nor is it a decontextualized, impersonal logo through which an unscrupulous, hegemonic power is asserting its hands across the globe. Thoroughly domesticated and sustaining multiple meanings, the image may, after all, rekindle an associationism through which America's too self-centered political culture can hug in imagination those billions of others who also regard Earth as their sole home.

12

Background of Environmental Records

Before setting any guidelines for the future environmental precautions, it is important to look into the pages of history, records of environmental hazards and on the basis of that, draw lessons, for future course of Action. The chapter is divided in three sections:

1. Past century
2. Past Millennium
3. Past Million years.

The Last Century

The years of 1980s and early 1990s have brought some unusually warm years for the globe as a whole; seven of the eight warmest years during the past 100 years, have occurred during this period. 'Warmest' means only a few tenths of a degree Celsius at most, but in terms of the world average such differences are quite significant. An increase over this period has occurred between 0.3°C and 0.6°C. Although there is a distinct trend, the increase is by no means a uniform one; in fact, some times of cooling as well as warming have occurred.

Whatever the case may be, temperature varies from place to place, from season to season and from day to day by many tens of degrees. How, then, can a global average changing by a few tenths of a degree have any meaning?

In the beginning, just how is a change in global average temperature estimated from a combination of records of changes in the near surface temperature of land and changes in the temperature of the sea surface. To estimate the changes over land, weather stations are chosen where regular observations have been taken from the same location over a substantial proportion of the whole 130 year period. Changes in sea surface temperature have been assumed by pròcessing over sixty million observations from ships—mostly merchant ships—over the same period. All the observations, from land stations and from ships, are therefore located within a grid of squares, say 1^0 of latitude by 1^0 of longitude, covering the Earth's surface.

Observations within each square are averaged; the world average is obtained by averaging (after measuring them by area) over the averages for each of the squares.

A huge group of research groups in the world in different countries have made careful and independent analyses of these observations. In somewhat different ways they have made allowances for reasons which could have introduced artificial changes in the records. For instance, the record at some land stations could have been influenced by changes in their surroundings as these have become more urban.

In the case of ships, the standard method of observation used to be to insert a thermometer into a bucket of water taken from the sea. Small level changes of temperature have been shown to occur during this process; the size of the changes varies between day and night and is also rely on several other factors including the material from which the bucket is made.

Over the years wooden, canvas and metal buckets have been variously employed; now-a-days, a large part of the observations are made by measuring the temperature of the water entering the engine cooling system. Careful analysis of the effects of these details on observations on land as well as from ships has enabled appropriate corrections to be made to the record, and good agreement has been achieved between analyses made at different centres. Confidence that the observed variations are true is increased by noticing that the trend and the shape of the changes are similar when different selections of the total observations are made. For example, the separate records from the land and sea surface, and from the northern and southern hemispheres are tightly in accord. In the period of last twenty years or so observations have been available from satellites orbiting around the Earth. Their great advantage is that they automatically offer data with global coverage, which is generally lacking in other data sets. The length of the record from satellites, however, is generally less than two decades, a comparatively short period in climate terms.

It has been suggested that satellite measurements of lower atmospheric temperature since 1979 are not in tune with the trend of rising temperatures in surface observations; a careful analysis, however, does not confirm this as a significant inconsistency.

Here, it is important that the most obvious feature of the climate record is that of considerable variability, not just from year to year, but from decade to decade. Some of this variability will have came up through causes external to the atmosphere and the oceans, for instance, as a result of volcanic explosions such as those of Krakatoa in 1883 or of Pinatubo in Philippines in 1991 (the low global average temperature in 1992, compared with 1990 and 1991, is probably due to the Pinatubo volcano). But there is no need to invoke volcanoes or other external causes to describe most of the variations in the record. Their most likely cause is internal variations within the total climate system, for instance between various parts of the ocean.

Owing to the degree of natural variability shown by the climate record, it is clearly difficult to be certain that the growing trends in global average temperature over the past century and over the past decade are due to global warming arising from the rise of greenhouse gases. For instance, the particular increase from 1910 to 1940 is too rapid to have been due to the rather small hikes of greenhouse gases during that period. Eventually, as the greenhouse gases increase further, the amount of warming is expected to become sufficiently huge that it will swamp the natural variations in climate; then it will be evident that global warming has almost certainly been observed. In the meantime, the global average temperature may continue to increase or it could show days of decrease. However, over the next few years and the next decade or two scientists will be inspecting climate changes and climate events most carefully as they happen, to try to detect signs of global warming and to see to what extent actual events can be related to scientific forecasts.

Past Millennium

Complete systematic record of weather elements such as temperature, rainfall, cloudiness and the like presented above for the last century and which covers a good proportion of the globe is not available for earlier periods. Further back, the record becomes much more sparse and doubt goes up over the consistency of the instruments used for observation. Most thermometers in use two centuries ago were not well calibrated or carefully exposed.

However, many diarists and writers kept records at different times; from a wide variety of sources weather and climate information can be pieced together. Indirect means such as are provided by ice cores, tree rings and records of lake levels, of glacier advance and retreat or of pollen distribution in the gone days, can also yield information to assist in building up the whole climatic story. From, a variety of sources, for example, it has been possible to put together a systematic atlas of weather patterns covering the last five hundred years for China.

In the same manner, from direct and indirect sources, Professor Hubert Lamb of the Climate Research Unit of the University of East Anglia has prepared a record of the average temperatures for Central England for the past thousand years. Its main features are of a medieval hot period between about AD 1100 and 1300 when vines were grown as far north as Yorkshire, and the 'Little Ice Age' between the period about AD 1400 and 1850, during which freezing of the Thames in winter was not uncommon.

There is plenty of evidence that the 'Little Ice Age' extended throughout whole of Europe and North America; indications from glaciers in other part of the world including the southern hemisphere suggest that it could have been experienced globally. There is as yet no certain explanation for these warm and cold periods during the last Millennium. Volcanic activity has sometimes been suggested as a possible cause.

One of the largest eruptions during the period was that of Tambora in Indonesia in April 1851, which was followed in many places by two excessively cold years; 1816 was described in New England and Canada as the 'year without a summer'. But the impact on the climate even of an eruption of the magnitude of Tambora only lasts a few years at most. Others have postulated that changes in the output of energy from the sun might be a reason.

However, there is no direct evidence for such variations so their possibility must remain speculative. Nor can it be said that greenhouse gases such as carbon dioxide and methane have been the cause of change; for the millennium before 1800 their concentration in the climate was rather stable, the carbon dioxide concentration, for instance, varying by less than 3 per cent.

The most likely reason is, in fact, not due to any factors external to the atmosphere. As with the shorter-term changes mentioned earlier, such variations of climate can go up naturally from internal variations within the atmosphere and the ocean and in the two-way relationship—coupling—between them.

Last Million Years

Before going back to recorded human history, scientists have to rely on indirect methods to unravel much of the story of the past climate. A specifically valuable information source in the record stored in the ice which caps Greenland and the Antarctic continent. These icecaps are several thousands of metres thick. Snow collected on their surface gradually becomes compacted as further snow falls, becoming solid ice. The ice moves steadily downwards eventually flowing outwards at the bottom of the ice-sheet. Ice near the top of the layer will have been deposited fairly recently; close to the bottom will have fallen on the surface many tens of thousands of years ago.

Analysis of the ice at different levels can, therefore, provide information about the conditions prevailing at different times in the gone days. Deep cores have been drilled out of the ice at several locations in both Greenland and Antarctica. At Russia's Vostok station in east Antarctica, for example, drilling has been carried out for about twenty years. The longest and most recent core reached a depth of over 2.5 km; the ice at the bottom of the hole fell down as snow on the surface of the Antarctic continent over 200,000 years ago. More recently cores of similar length from the Greenland icecap have been drilled by teams of Europe and America. Small bubbles of air are trapped within the ice.

Analysis of the composition of that air tells what was present in the atmosphere for the time at which the ice was formed—gases like carbon dioxide or methane, or dust particles that had probably come from volcanoes or from the sea surface.

Further information is provided by analysis of the ice itself. Small quantities of different oxygen isotopes and of the big isotope of hydrogen (deuterium) are contained in the ice. The ratios of these isotopes that are present depend clearly on the temperatures at which evaporation and condensation took place for the water in the clouds from which the ice originated. These they in turn are dependent on the average temperature near the surface of the Earth. A temperature record for the polar regions can thus, constructed from analyses of the ice cores.

This type of reconstruction from a Vostok core for the temperature and the content of carbon dioxide and methane for the past 160,000 years, also includes the period of the last climatic cycle. It shows the last major ice age which started about 120,000 years ago and began to come to an end about 20,000 years ago. It also demonstrates the close connections which is present between temperature and carbon dioxide and methane concentrations. Data from ice cores can carry us back 200,000 years or so. To go further back, over the past million years, the composition of ocean sediments can be enquired to yield information. Fossils of plankton and other small sea creatures deposited in these sediments also carry different isotopes of oxygen. In particular the amount of the heavier isotope of oxygen (^{18}O) compared with the more bulky isotope (^{16}O) is sensitive both to the temperature at which the fossils were formed and to the total volume of ice in the world's ice-caps at the period of the fossils' formation. From the variety of paleoclimate data which is present, variations in the volume of ice in the ice-caps can be reconstructed over the greater part of the last million years.

In this record six or seven major ice ages can be identified with warmer periods in between, the period between these main ice ages being approximately 100,000 years. Other cycles are also evident in the record. The most obvious place to look for the reason of regular cycles in climate is outside the Earth, in the sun's radiation.

Has this varied in the past in a cyclic way? So far as is known the output of the sun itself has not changed to any significant limit over the last million years or so. But because of variations in the Earth's orbit, the distribution of solar radiation has different in a more or less regular way during the last millennium. Three regular variations take in the orbit of the Earth around the sun. The Earth's orbit, although nearly circular, is in fact an ellipse. The eccentricity of the ellipse (which is related to the ratio between the greatest and the least diameters) varies with a duration of about 100,000 years; that is the slowest of the three variations.

The Earth also spins on its own axis, the axis of spin being tilted with regard to the axis of the Earth's orbit, the angle of tilt varying between 21.6° and 24.5° (currently it is 23.5°) with a period of about 41,000 years.

The next variation is of the time of year when the Earth is closest to the sun (the Earth's perihelion). In the present configuration, the Earth is closest to the sun in January; the time of perihelion moves through of months of the year with a time of about 23,000 years. As the Earth's orbit changes its relationship to the sun, while the total quantity of solar radiation reaching the Earth varies very little, the distribution of that radiation with latitude and season within the Earth's surface changes considerably. There changes are especially large in polar regions where the variations in summer sunshine, for example reach about 10 per cent.

James Croll, a British scientist, first pointed out in 1867 that the major ice ages of the past might be connected with these regular variations in the seasonal distribution of solar radiation reaching the Earth. His ideas were evolved in 1920 by Milankovitch, a climatologist from Yugoslavia, whose name is usually linked with the theory.

Inspection by eye of the relationship in the variations of polar summer sunshine and global ice volume shown in indicates a strong connection. Careful study of the correlation between the two curves confirms this and shaves that 60 per cent of the variance in the climatic record of global ice volume falls close to the three frequencies of regular variations in the Earth's orbit, thus giving support for the Milankovitch theory. More careful study of the relationship between the ice ages and the Earth's orbital variations tells that the size of the climate changes is larger than might be expected from forcing by the radiation changes alone.

Other processes which could enhance the effect of the radiation changes (in other words, positive feedback processes) have to be initiated to explain the climate variations. The strong correlation observed the climatic record between average atmospheric temperature and carbon dioxide concentration tells that one such feedback arises from the changes in carbon dioxide influencing atmospheric temperature through the greenhouse impacts. Such a correlation does not prove the existence of the greenhouse feedback; in fact part of the correlation arises since the atmospheric carbon dioxide concentration is itself influenced, through biological feedbacks, by reasons related to the average global temperature. However, as we shall see in later chapters, climates of the past cannot be modelled successfully without considering the influence on climate of variation in carbon dioxide concentration.

Some Observation About the Past

Here, it is important to tell that the major climate changes considered so far in this chapter have taken place relatively slowly. The growth and recession of large polar ice-sheets between the ice ages and the intervening warmer interglacial durations have taken on average many thousands of years. Over the last 8000 years or so, which can be investigated more thoroughly than previous epochs, the climate has shown some slow changes but no dramatic fluctuations.

Without any doubt, there is substantial evidence from data from the Greenhouse ice cores that the last 8000 years have been unusually stable and that much more big variations have been typical of earlier epochs. At the summit of the Greenland icecap, the rate of accumulation of snow has been more than that at the drilling locations in Antarctica. Because of this, a period of, say, ten years in the past is represented by a bigger length of ice core from Greenland and more detail of variations over relatively short periods of a few years is therefore available.

Moreover, it appears that the fluctuations of temperature over Greenland have been larger than those found over Antarctica. Variations of a few degrees Celsius taking place with in a few hundred years during the ice age period about 30,000 years back were reported from Greenland ice core data in 1989. But in 1993, Professor Dansgaard from Denmark and his colleagues found proof that rapid variations of the Arctic temperature frequently occurred during the glacial period up to 100,000 years ago.

These variations have been of up to five or six degrees Celsius and have sometimes happened over periods of less than a hundred years (Fig.). Comparison between the results from ice cores drilled at different locations within the Greenland icecap confirm the details till 100,000 years ago. But the records from previous times that time may have been distorted by ice movements and it is not yet clear from the ice core record whether the periods of fast temperature variation extend into the interglacial warm period around 120,000 years back. Another particularly interesting period of climatic history, more recently, is the Younger Dryas event (so called because it was marked by the spread of an arctic flower, the *Dryas octopetala*) which happened over a period of about 1500 years between about 12,000 and 10,700 years ago. For 6,000 years before the start of this event the Earth had been warming up after the completion of the last ice age. But then during the Younger Dryas period, as demonstrated from many different means of paleoclimatic data, the climate swung back again into much colder conditions similar to those at the end of the last ice age.

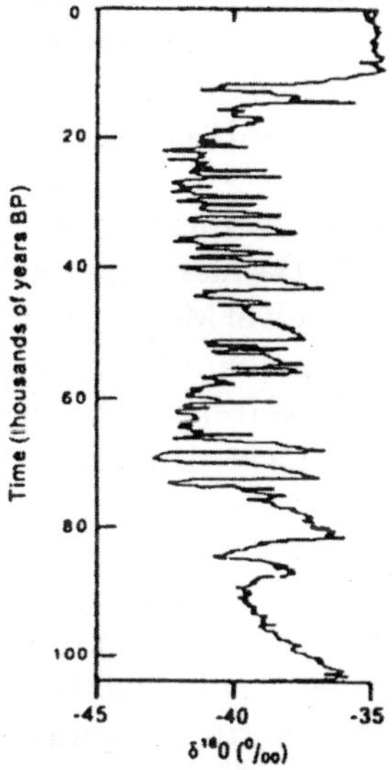

Fig. 12.1. Variations in Arctic temperature over the past 100,000 years as deduced from oxygen isotope measurements (in terms of ^{18}O)[9] from the 'Summit' ice core from Greeenland. A change of 5 parts per thousand in 18° in the ice core corresponds to about a 7°C change in temperature.

The ice core record shows that by the end of the event, 10,700 years ago, the warming in the Arctic of about 7°C occurred within only about 50 years and was associated with decreased storminess (shown by a dramatic fall in the amount of dust in the ice core) and an increase of precipitation of almost 50 per cent. Two main possible reasons for these rapid variations in the past have been given.

One suggestion particularly applicable to ice age conditions is that, as the ice-sheets over Greenland and eastern Canada have prepared; major break-ups have occurred from time to time, releasing massive numbers of icebergs into the north Atlantic.

The second possibility is that the ocean circulation in the north Atlantic region has been greatly affected by injections of fresh water from the melting of ice.

At present the ocean circulation here is strongly influenced by cold salty water sinking to deep ocean levels as its saltiness makes it dense; this sinking process is part of the 'conveyor belt' which is the major feature of the circulation of deep ocean water around the world. Huge quantities of fresh water from the melting of ice would make the water less salty stopping it from sinking and there by altering the whole Atlantic circulation. This connection between the melting of ice and the ocean circulation is a key feature of the explanation put forward by Professor Wallace Broecker for the Younger Dryas event.

As the great ice-sheet over north America started to melt at the end of the last ice age, the melt water at first drained through the Mississippi into the Gulf of Mexico. Eventually, however, the arrival of the ice opened up channel for the water in the region of the St Lawrence river. This influx of fresh water into the north Atlantic reduced its saltiness, therefore, Broecker postulates, cutting off the formation of deep water and that part of the ocean 'conveyor belt. Warm water was thus prevented from flowing northward, resulting in a reversal to much colder conditions. The suggestion is also that a reversal of this process with the beginning the Atlantic 'conveyor belt' could lead to sudden appearance of warmer conditions. While debate continues regarding the details of the Younger Dryas event, there is considerable evidence from paleodata, particularly those from ocean sediments, for the main element of the Broecker explanation which involves the deep ocean circulation.

It is also evident from paleodata that large changes have occurred at different times in the past in the formation of deep water and in the deep ocean circulation. Our perspective regarding the possibilities of the future climate change has to take into account the rapid climate changes which have occurred in the past.

13

Learning from Past, Lessons for Future

In the previous chapter, we have been past environmental records. Here, we shall see how and what lessons should be learnt for future. It may appear strange to begin a study of climatic change which focuses on the future with an excursion into the past, not just to recent centuries but to the last ice age and beyond. However, an axiom of the well-known climatic historian Professor Hubert Lamb (1982) is that for the purpose to understand present-day climate, and how it might vary in the future, it is first necessary to appreciate how and why climate has fluctuated in the past. Information about past climates provides a ground for testing hypotheses about the causes of climatic change. By reconstructing past climates on a range of time-scales we can gauge the degree of natural variability in the climate system.

The 'forcing factors' (changes forced on the climate system which alter its radiative balance) which have operated in the past to produce climatic changes will continue to affect climate in the future. Any changes resulting from the man-made greenhouse effect will be superimposed upon, and will interact with, these natural fluctuations. Reconstructing past climates helps to place contemporary climates in perspective, making it easier to identify styles and periodicities. Unless we can understand the natural variability of climate, it will be hard to isolate those influences deriving from human activity. Climates from the recent and more distant past provide yardsticks against which we can evaluate the scale of possible future climatic changes, especially those resulting from greenhouse gas increases.

After laying stress on this, it is sobering to reflect that the upper end of the range of temperature increases which have been predicted to occur by Ad2100 - 5.5°C above present averages - would make global temperatures higher than they have been at any time during the past three million years, bringing them close to what they are thought to have been in the Cretaceous period over 65 million years ago. A more modest increase of 3°C would still produce warmer conditions than at any time in the past 125,000 years, while a rise of only 2°C would take us beyond anything that has been experienced since the end of the last glaciation.

The question arises is, how do we know what climate was like in the past? Instrumental weather records are available for the last 200 or so years providing a precise, quantitative (though far from complete), picture or climate variation during the period in which human involvement with the composition of the atmosphere has become increasingly evident. Going further back we have less and less information about past climatic conditions. However, qualitative weather analysis and many indirect or proxy indicators allow more general reconstructions of climate in some parts of the world back to medieval times (Flohn 1985).

Beyond this, and more recently for those parts of the world where written records start late, a wide range of scientific techniques can be applied to different kinds of environmental evidence to provide a picture of climatic variation. The study of palaeoclimates is a complex, inter-disciplinary sector and it is impossible here to do more than briefly review some of the most important methods of climate reconstruction which are currently available, starting with those relating to more recent times before moving on to handle which concern the more distant past. Having examined these techniques, we can then consider the evidence they provide about past climatic variations, initiating on a time-scale of hundreds of thousands of years and moving towards the twentieth century with an increasingly sharp focus.

Historical and Archaeological Data

Though in the previous chapter, we have seen past records, but they only cover short part of climatic history, one where there has been a steady trend towards warming, and a much longer where perspective is needed to identify and understand the full range of climatic variation which has happened. For many parts of the world, qualitative records of weather conditions and weather-related phenomena—such as droughts, floods, the freezing of rivers and lakes, the flowering of trees and ripening of grapes—reveal information about past climates which is less precise than instrumental records but is more abundant and sometimes extends several centuries further back in time (Ingram *et al.*, 1981). Ships' logs, for example, carry a good deal of information on weather conditions (Oliver and Kingston 1970). Medieval manorial records are a useful source of information on weather events such as droughts, severe snowfalls and storms, along with providing information on the impact of such events on society (Titow 1960 and Dury 1984). Historical data, however, have to be interpreted with care. It is necessary to understand the background of diarists, researchers, and observers. Early descriptions of weather conditions in North America should be treated with some caution if the writers had not been in an area for long enough to gain an impression of what caused 'normal' conditions (Bradley and Jones 1992). A winter described as 'hard' by a seventeenth-century diarist like Pepys was not necessarily comparable with one described in similar terms by medieval monastic chronicler.

The frost fairs on the River Thames in Pepys, day certainly reflected winter conditions colder than those experienced in recent times by they may also concern in part to the 'ponding back' of fresh water by old London Bridge, making the river freeze more easily than it does today.

Information about the pressure and circulation patterns has allowed climatic historians to take individual stray weather observations and combine them to produce seasonal pictures of conditions all over the Europe as far back as the fifteenth century (Lamb, 1982).

The French historian Le Roy Ladurie (1971) established trends in post-medieval climate in the Alps by reforming glacier fluctuations from maps and documentary sources. A similar approach by Jean Grove (1985, 1988), using Norwegian tax records, has established a rather different chromology of advances and retreats of glaciers and climatic changes in southern Scandinavia during the period between the sixteenth and nineteenth centuries. Le Roy Ladurie (1980) also pioneered the use of local records dating the start of the grape harvest in France and adjacent countries.

Variations in the date at which the harvest commenced provided a useful indication of conditions during the previous spring and summer going back to late medieval days.

In the regard, Archaeological data can be used to examine the relationship between climatic changes and fluctuations in settlement and cultivation limits, though care must be taken not to follow a simple 'cause and effect' approach (McGhee 1981 and Neuman 1993). Parry (1977), studying the Lammermuir Hills in south-east Scotland, was able to show that, during the twelfth and thirteenth centuries, with more warm and more dry conditions than today, settlement and cultivation expanded over all but the highest part of this rolling plateau area, with cultivation occurring at altitudes where crops of oats would not ripen in about any year at the present time. He also linked the progressive abandonment of settlements and their field systems in this area from the fourteenth to the eighteenth century to the steady downward shift in viable cultivations limits as conditions got progressively colder and wetter (Figs. 12.1, 12.2). In highlighting the changes in cultivation limits, Parry was careful to stress that climatic change was probably only a background influence which may have supported to tip the balance in favour of abandonment when other short-term economic, social and political factors were unfavourable.

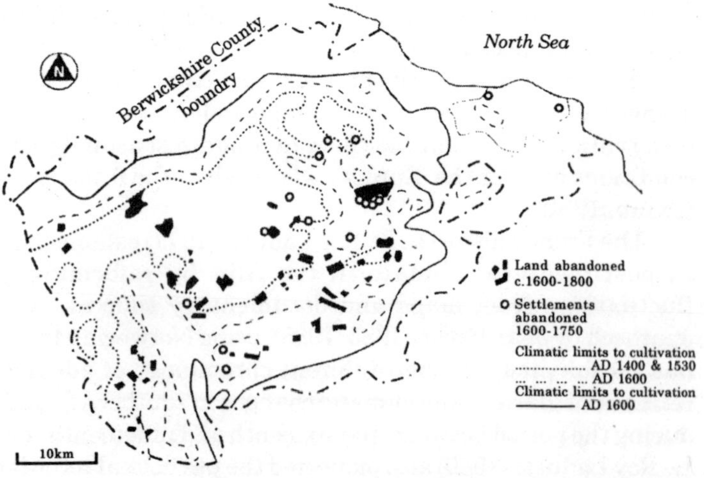

Fig. 13.1. Scraped farmland and lowered climatic limits to cultivation in the Lammermuir Hills, south-east Scotland, 1600-1750. (After Parry, 1977).

Above given examples relate to the more densely populated areas of western and central Europe, one of the best documented parts of the world in the last few centuries. For some more remote parts where climatic conditions are particularly sensitive we are fortunate in having detailed written observations predating instrumental records. For example, information on the extent of summer sea ice around Iceland goes back to the Norse settlement in the 9th century (Ogilvie 1984). For Arctic Canada, records of the Hudson's Bay Company provide a wealth of data on past weather and sea ice conditions from the mid-eighteenth century (Ball 1992 and Catchpole 1992).

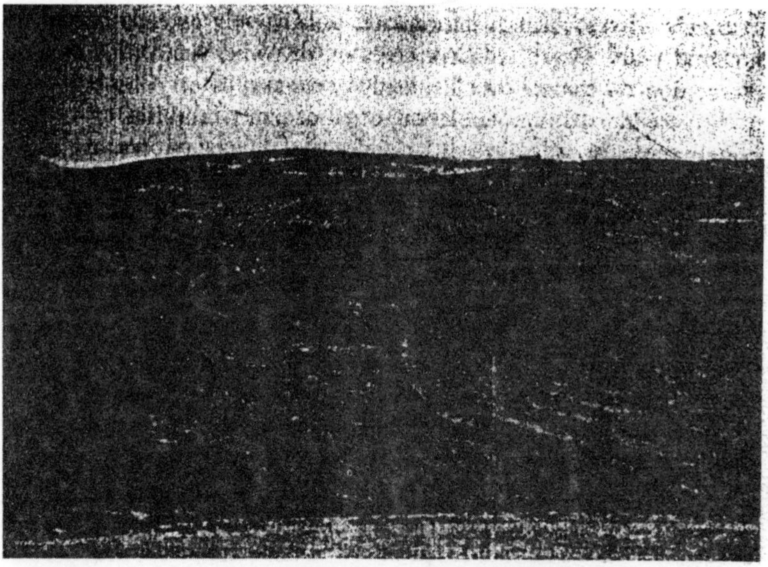

Fig.13.2. Condemned cultivation ridges at high altitude in southern Scotland: a casualty of the Little Ice Age? (Photo: 1, Whyte).

The Company's ships went by regular sailing routes from England to the Hudson Strait at the same time each year in order to fit it with the short ice-free season. The logbooks of the vessels, which were kept in a standardised format from 1751, present details of sea ice conditions. By comparing modern year-to-year sea ice variations with climatic data it is possible to use the logbook entries to make deductions about gone circulation patterns and temperature conditions. Records from the Company's trading posts also contain a wealth of weather-related information— like the annual dates of freezing and thawing of rivers like the Red River at Winnipeg, and the date of the arrival of migratory geese in spring—together with direct weather observations like the onset of spring thaws and the first autumn snowfalls (Ball 1983; Bradley and Jones 1992; Catchpole and Faurer 1983 and Rannie 1983). Graphical representation of such data presents short-term warm and cold spells to be identified and linked to the position of the Arctic Front. On a longer time-scale, the start of the modern warm phase in the late nineteenth century is also clearly detectable.

Indicators Used for Environment

There is a lacunae of the subject that historical records do not take us back very far though. Fortunately a wide range of natural phenomena are climate-dependent and become sealed into stratified deposits containing built-in proxy measures of past climates (Bradley 1985). A wide range of proxy data is now accessible relating to environments in different parts of the world. Each technique of climatic reconstruction has its own strengths and limitations. The further one goes into the past, the more broad-brush is the scenario of climate they provide.

One significant aspect of such indicators is the quality of their time resolution. Sources which provide data on a seasonal or annual basis, such as tree rings and ice cores, allow climatic fluctuations to be dated accurately. However, such information usually only goes back a few thousand years. Ocean sediment cores on the other hand provide proxy information on climate over hundreds of thousands of years but with a much more blurred time resolution, generally of many centuries.

It is now clear that some proxy records, such as ice and ocean sediment cores, are continuous. Others, like moraines marking the extent of glacier advances or shorelines indicating former high lake levels, provide discontinuous information. Proxy data respond to environmental changes at different speeds. Records of fossil beetles show that these insects responded rapidly to temperature changes while variations in fossil pollen demonstrate that plants took far longer to adapt to the same changing conditions.

Remains of Plants and Animals

(A) Plants: Another fact is that fossil pollen grains, which can be identified to the level of the family and, for many trees, the genus, preserve well in peat bogs, buried soils and lake sediments. If cores are taken from these deposits and the pollen assemblages studied for examples at different depths, variations in the vegetation cover over time can be identified.

Inferences can then be made regarding the environmental changes, including climatic fluctuations, that generated the vegetation to alter.

Pollen analysis was developed in Sweden and Britain in the early twentieth century and has been widely used in reconstructing postglacial environments, at first within Europe and more recently somewhere else in the world (Lowe and Walker 1984; Birks and Birks 1980; and Birks 1981). The time resolution of the environmental changes preserved in the pollen record is fairly coarse as the response of vegetation to climatic changes often involved a substantial time lag. Nevertheless, the analysis of pollen variations from sites in Britain and elsewhere in western Europe provided the first clear chronology of climatic changes in the early part of the Holocene (postglacial) period. Anyway, it was soon recognised that much of the variation in pollen assemblages could be attributed to purely local environmental changes, such as drainage conditions, instead of the direct effects of climate (Barber 1985).

As human population increased, especially with the spread of agriculture, changes in the pollen record came increasingly to reflect local human interference in the vegetation cover in place of background changes in climate. In addition, pollen macro-remains of plants, such as trees buried at the base of growing peat, provide information on altitudinal and latitudinal vegetation limits and have been used in measuring summer temperatures at the period of maximum postglacial warmth.

(B) Animals: Animal remains can also provide clues to past climates. The hard parts of Coleoptera (beetles) are often abundant and well preserved in peat and sedimentary deposits. Fossil beetle remains can often be identified at species level. From studying their modern counterparts it is known that different species have marked preferences for particular environments and can generally thrive only within set temperature ranges. Their ability to respond quickly to temperature changes and to colonise suitable new areas makes them a much faster-moving indicator of climate than vegetation (Coope 1977).

During the last interglacial period the assemblage of beetles inhabiting lowland England was comparable to that found in southern Europe today, suggesting that summer temperatures were almost 3°C higher than they are now. Because of their quick reactions, studies of changes in beetle assemblages during the last 50,000 years have allowed the identification of warm periods which were too short-lived to be noticed by changes in vegetation. For example, about 43,000 years ago temperatures for perhaps 1,000 years or so were 1-2°C above those of today. Central England nevertheless remained devoid of trees which never had sufficient time to migrate in before the return of colder conditions and this warm phase does not register in the pollen record.

A similar series of events occurred during the Windermere ***Interstadial*** (a brief warm phase) around 13,000-12,500 years ago. By the time the birch woods had moved into southern Britain and were beginning to spread, the height of warmth had already passed and assemblages of beetles were changing with an increase in the proportion of less warmth-loving species.

Increase and Decrease of Glacier

Fluctuations in glacier are the result of changes in the balance between the accumulation of snow which nourishes them and loss by melting or the calving of icebergs. A glacier advance reflects a positive mass balance due to climatic conditions which motivate accumulation over melting. Glacier fluctuations provide a good barometer of past climatic variations because they can amplify small fluctuations in temperature and/or precipitation into perhaps several hundred metres of ice advance or retreat (Porter 1981).

The rise in mean global temperatures of about 0.5°C which has occurred in the last century has been associated with by the worldwide retreat of glaciers and small ice caps (Lamb 1982) (Fig). The spectacular scale of this retreat can often be calculated by comparing present glacier limits with those recorded on old maps or early pictures. Earlier periods of glacier, growth in Europe can be established from documents and moraine limits. Moraines can be dated by a variety of techniques such as radiocarbon dating or lichenometry—measuring the growth rates of lichens on boulders incorporated in moraines to estimate roughly when they first emerged from under the ice (Matthews 1975 and Matthews and Shakesby 1984).

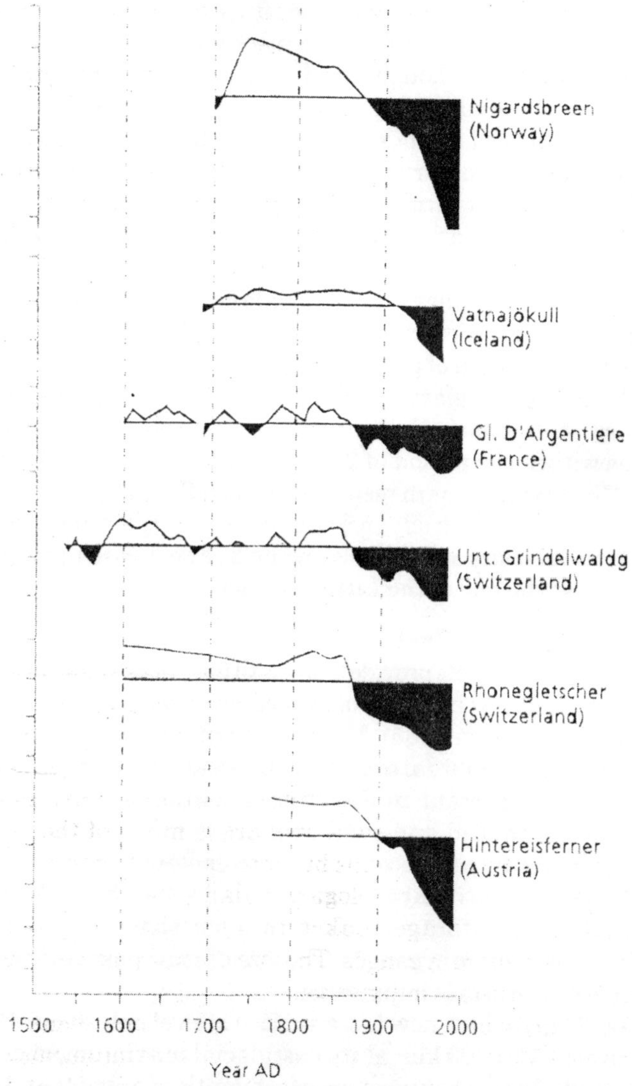

Fig. 13.3. Progress and Retreat of Selected European Glaciers.

The morphological record of glacier variations is, undoubtedly, only a partial one because any ice advance tends to obliterate traces of previous movements of lesser magnitude. However, if all the glaciers within an upland region are considered, fragments of moraine from a whole series of earlier fluctuations can most of the time be identified (Karlen 1973). The response of glaciers to climatic changes is not simple though (Bradley, 1985). Many combinations of climate can produce changes in their mass balance. Variations in precipitation and temperature have to be considered. Colder winters may not necessary bring more snow while milder winters with a more vigorous atmospheric circulation may lead to more snowfall and accumulation. Equally, glacier advances can be linked to cool, cloudy summers when melting is reduced. There is also a time lag between changes in mass balance and the position of a glacier front, while downwasting of ice can happen without any change in the position of glacier margins. Time lags are a function of the length of the glacier, its slope, thickness and the overall geometry of its basin. Some glaciers may respond to climatic changes within the period of 25 years or less, others take much longer. Due to variations in response times, different glaciers within the same region may be advancing and retreating simultaneously. Some Arctic glaciers are still advancing as a response to more cool conditions at the end of the Little Ice Age.

Lake Levels of the Past

Previous lake levels provide a low-latitude counterpart to glacier moraines as indirect evidence of past climatic fluctuations (Street-Perrott and Harrison,1985). Much environmental reconstruction focuses on past temperatures and the study of changes in lake hydrology is important in directing attention to variations in precipitation. In arid and semi-arid areas much of the surface drainage go not into the oceans but into enclosed basins. In such basins changes in the hydrological balance can have dramatic effects on water storage. Lakes in such situations can act, effectively, as giant rain gauges. The size of some past lakes during pluvial (wet) periods is impressive.

Lake Chad, which now has a surface area of only about 10,000 km^2, covered 300,000 km^2 at its postglacial maximum, though it was very shallow reaching a greatest depth of only 50 m. In the south west USA the Great Salt Lake is only a shrunken remnant of the much larger pluvial Lake Bonneville which covered 50,000 km^2 and was over 330 m deep. In closed lake basins, high lake levels may show wetter phases or periods when evaporation was reduced. Low lake levels reflect arid spells or periods of increased evaporation. Whether variations in the levels of pluvial lakes reflect changes in precipitation, evaporation or may be, both is a controversial topic but the question can be explored using hydrological balance models, while there is often enough evidence of past temperature conditions to provide an indication of which was the most significant variable at work. Former high lake shorelines can be recognised by features such as abandoned cliffs, beaches, bars and deltas.

Periods of low lake levels can be determined by evaluating cores taken from lake floor sediments, with layers of evaporite marking periods when lakes dried up completely (Fig. Street-Perrott, 1994). Much early work on postglacial climate history concentrated on higher latitudes rather than on tropical areas. The evidence of lake level fluctuations has provided valuable indications of the climatic history of Africa. Radiocarbon dating of material in lake deposits has made former periods of high and low water to be dated, allowing correlation across the Sahel and East Africa (Street and Grove 1979).

Fig. 13.4. Salt Crust on Dried Land of Lake Magadi, Kenya. (Photo: Dr. P. Barker).

It was originally believed that pluvial phases in semi-arid areas corresponded to periods of glacial advance in upper latitudes. The extensive pluvial lakes in the south-west USA did indeed reach their maximum extent at this time. Evidence from sub-Saharan Africa has shown, however, that the important pluvial phase was not contemporary with the last glacial maximum but with the postglacial climatic optimum. Studies of present water regimes and knowledge of past temperatures, allowing evaporation rates to be measured, have enabled scientists to establish that, at the height of the postglacial pluvial phase, rainfall over East Africa was around 65 per cent higher than today and in the Sudan and Mauritania between twice and four times today's precipitation levels (Roberts 1989). Even in more recent times lake levels and precipitation have fluctuated significantly. For Lake Malawi, one of the world's largest lakes, sediment cores reveal that the lake dropped by 100 m between AD1450 and 1850 and that rainfall at this time may have been only 50-70 per cent of that of the twentieth century. The recent chronology established for East Africa varies from that of West Africa, where the level of.

Lake Chad was high in the sixteenth and seventeenth century and lower in the eighteenth and early nineteenth (Maley, 1977 and Nicholson 1978) demonstrating the regional contrasts which were present. Apart from showing that climate in sub-Saharan Africa has been as variable in recent centuries as in parts of Europe during the Little Ice Age, lake level data also show that the latest drought which has affected the area since the late 1960s is not unique and is more likely to be a natural fluctuation than a symptom of man-induced climatic change.

Annual Cycling

Dendroclimatology is based on the long-appreciated fact that trees in many parts of the world grow in an annual cycle, influenced by climatic variations, which sheds annual rings when the trunk is sectioned. The rings represent the alternation of large, thin-walled cambium cells in spring and summer and more densely packed thick-walled cells later in the growing season. Trees happen over much of the world though in tropical climates the lack of seasonality may mean that clear rings do not form. Tree rings also have the advantage that they can be accurately dated, so that their time resolution is good. Wide rings show favourable environmental conditions, narrow rings adverse ones.

In semi-arid areas the main influence on tree growth and ring width is the availability of moisture. On the cooler margins of temperate climate like Scotland or Scandinavia the principal influence on tree growth is temperature (Fig.) Dendroclimatology was pioneered early this century as a source of identifying precipitation variations in the arid south-west USA (Fritts 1976 and Fritts *et al.*, 1981). In this region living examples of Bristlecone Pine can be up to 5,000 years old, providing a chronology of precipitation variation with an annual time resolution approaching back halfway through the postglacial period.

The use of wood from dead trees allowed the chronology to be pushed back even further to over 8,000 years. The technique has also been in practice in Europe and Russia, the Mediterranean, the Himalayas, China and Australasia (Bradley and Jones 1992). It is particularly useful for areas where instrumental records

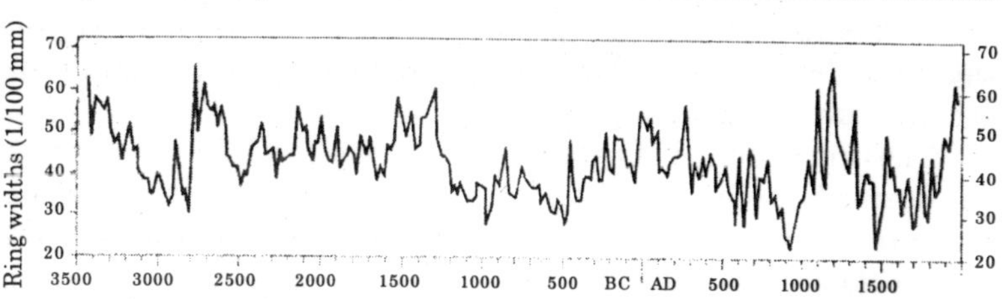

Fig. 13.4. Differences in ring widths (twenty-year moving averages) of Bristlecone Pine near the treeline in the White Mountains of California. In this part, changes in ring width indicate variations in summer warmth. (After Lamb, 1982).

started comparatively recently. Work on trees from Irish peat bogs has generated a chronology nearly as long as that for the Bristlecone Pine. Comparison of tree ring width variations in recent times against modern climatic data show which climate variable have most influence on tree development in particular areas. This allows inferences about earlier climatic patterns to be made from tree ring information alone. Trees growing near the limits of survival of their species make a better record than those in more favourable locations in the middle of their range.

Tree ring width calibrations can be used to identify individual bad years but the data are more beneficial if they are averaged out over longer periods such as decades. The ring widths of individual trees contain variations due to the process of ageing, and changes in local site conditions. Chronologies for particular locations are made from sets of ring width data from many individual trees. These are carefully chosen to reduce the extent of purely local non-climatic influences. The technique has been refined and expanded throughout North America allowing the geographical distribution of past phases of drought and temperature variation to be mapped and related to variations in atmospheric circulation (Fritts and Lough, 1985).

Oxygen Isotope in Water Molecules

Amongst the main sources of information on palaeoclimates on longer time-scales is the oxygen isotope content of the water molecules of snow crystals. An isotope is a variant of a normal component whose atoms have a different atomic weight. For oxygen, atoms with the normal atomic weight of 16 make up nearly 99.8 per cent of the total but 0.2 per cent are heavier with an atomic weight of 18. These lighter and heavier atoms are found in the atmosphere and in water.

The proportion of ^{18}O atoms to ^{16}O is around 1:500 on average but varies between 1:495 and 1:515 according to temperature. The minute oxygen is incorporated in a stratified deposit such as a layer of snow on a glacier surface or in the calcium carbonate of a shell in ocean sediments, the ratio between 18° and 16° atoms is frozen, providing a record of the temperature conditions of air or water taking place at the time that the deposit was laid down.

Oxygen isotope data can be extracted from various stratified deposits but the most useful for reconstructing past climates have been centres from ice caps and ocean sediments. The snow which accumulates each year on the world's ice caps and glaciers is eventually compacted to form ice. Within the ice, however, annual layers of accumulation can still be recognised, sometimes to a considerable depth. Variations in the oxygen isotope content, and other features discussed below, provide a valuable environmental record. The isotope ratio in a particular ice layer is a function of the temperature at the time that the original water vapour condensed. Ice cores were first crushed into the Greenland ice cap in the 1960s and then in different parts of the Arctic and the Antarctic, choosing sites where the deformation of annual layers due to ice movement was minimal. New cores and more sophisticated ways of analysing them are providing more detailed information about climatic changes on time-scales reaching back to the last interglacial period (Bolton, 1993). The Vostok core in the Antarctic has inserted to ice which is over 200,000 years old but another 1 km or 500,000 years of ice has still to be drilled and analysed (Jousel *et al.,* 1993).

Fascinating as the details of climate suggested by these cores are, they nevertheless relate to areas remote from centres of population whose climates did not necessarily totally mirror global conditions. More recently it has been appreciated that, by careful choice of site to minimise dislocation caused by ice movement, useful data can be obtained from other areas; cores from start ice caps in Tibet and the Andes have provided the first details of climatic fluctuations in the tropics. It is generally assumed that oxygen isotope measurements from ice cores are a good proxy means of information about past temperatures. In fact other influences such as changes in patterns of storm tracks, affecting the origins of the moisture which produced the snow, can also influence ^{18}O levels.

Moreover, the deeper layers may have originated up-glacier from the sampling point and have accumulated under slightly different climatic conditions. So it is not easy to translate ^{18}O variations directly into a record of temperature fluctuations though, for present times, ^{18}O variations in snow and ice layers can be calibrated against instrumental records of temperature. Annual layers of accumulation in the ice can be detected from melt features and seasonal differences in the ^{18}O levels—higher in summer, lower in winter—but this is difficult to do beyond a certain depth. For the Camp Century core in Greenland it was possible to identify individual years going back almost 10,000 years.

The seasonal signal of the ^{18}O isotope is gradually smoothed out as the snow is compacted into firn and it may not be preserved at all where the annual level of accumulation of new snow is low. This makes the identification and precise dating of annual layers of snow more difficult in areas such as the centre of the Antarctic where precipitation is less compared with Greenland. As well as variations in oxygen isotope content, ice layers also carry other evidence relating to past climates. Differences in the thickness of the annual layer reflect changes in snowfall amounts. Layers of dust from volcanic eruptions are kept safe and form useful chronological markers.

The electrical conductivity of different layers of ice also varies. Ice formed during cold periods has a higher alkaline content and lower conductivity than ice from warmer periods. Electrical conductivity assessment provides a quicker and less expensive way of getting a broad-brush impression of changes throughout an ice core, allowing the identification of key periods of climatic change which can then be examined in more detail by more labour-intensive methods, such as oxygen isotope analysis. The upper levels of snow in Greenlands provide a sensitive barometer of other environmental changes due to man. Atmospheric lead reates, for instance, have risen around 200 times in recent years due to the use of leaded petrol in motor vehicle engines in the developed countries of the northern hemisphere. In the past 20 years, however, lead levels in Greenland snow have fallen dramatically, apparently due to the increasing use of unleaded petrol in North America from the 1970s (Rosman *et al.* 1993). More generally, variations in the dust component of ice layers provide indications of past patterns of storminess and changes in wind direction associated with different atmospheric circulation patterns.

Past concentrations of greenhouse gases i.e., carbon dioxide and methane can be calculated from bubbles of air trapped within the ice. The latest cores from Greenland, an area of high snow accumulation, allow climatic changes to be established on a time-scale of decades or less for the last 240,000 years, going back beyond the last interglacial period.

Observations of oxygen isotope variations from ocean floor sediment cores provided the first long-term chronology of climatic changes stretching back through the Quaternary era into the Tertiary (Bradley 1985). Variations in the oxygen isotope composition of sea water are kept in the shells and skeletons of marine creatures incorporated in sea-floor sediments as a result of the oxygen absorbed from sea water during the making of the shells. Lighter molecules of water carry ^{16}O atoms evaporate more easily than the ^{18}O ones. During glacial periods large quantities of ^{16}O were locked up in ice leaving the oceans relatively richer in ^{18}O atoms.

The melting of ice sheets returned huge volumes of ^{16}O enriched water to the oceans. The proportion of ^{18}O in marine shells depends partly on temperature conditions and partly on the isotopic content of sea water. It is believed, however, that the oxygen isotope variations mainly reflect changes in the volume of land ice rather than ocean temperatures. They, thus, provide a chronology of glacial advances and retreats which indirectly points to changes in climate.

Now that in recent years developments in the analysis of cores from ice caps and ocean sediments have provided clearer evidence of past climatic changes on time-scales of tens and hundreds of thousands of years. A great discovery has been that the Earth's climate, rather than changing slowly over long time periods, has often been very unstable, changing sharply and quickly.

For example, analysis of cores from the Greenland ice cap has shown that the transition to warmer conditions at the end of the last glaciation occurred swiftly; certainly within a century, possibly within 30 years. The end of the severe cold snap popularly known as the Younger Dryas event about 11,500 years ago (see below) seems to have occurred within 20 years. A core from the Quelcaya ice cap in the Peruvian Andes shows that the post-medieval cool phase, widely mentioned as the Little Ice Age, came within two or three years around AD1800 (Thompson 1992).

To conclude, this chapter has looked at some of the ways in which past climates can be reconstructed on time-scale ranging from annual to glacial/interglacial cycles. Taken together, the different sources of evidence examined provide an increasingly detailed picture of climatic variations. However, due to the complexity of the climate system and the forcing factors that have affected it, each new piece of evidence tends to throw up more queries than it answers. The next chapter looks at the scale and nature of the climatic changes that have occurred and some of the possible underlying influences which have generated them.

14

Precautionary Principle (Regarding Environmental Change)

This chapter is an extract of the arguments presented to all delegations both governmental and non governmental at the UN Climate Change Negotiations (INC-7) New York, 15-20 March, 1993.

Equity and Survival

Human induced global climate change is now in an unnecessary condition of gathering fossil GDP driven risk. This contravenes the 'precautionary principle' which says that "risks which do not have to be taken, should not be taken." The dangers of fossil-dependence are great and there are alternatives to fossil fuels. In order to understand the political and the ecological nature of this risk, the global relationship between fossil-GDP-economics and global ecopolitics must be assessed. This assessment should recognise that the climate change threatened global economy is a single system within which equity is now inextricably linked to survival. 'Equity' is the trans-temporal equal sharing of rights, risks, responsibilities, rewards and restraints. Our global survival interests depend on understanding this and preventing powerful minority fossil fuel interests from continuing to raise the levels of risk and obliging the majority to face risks which violate universal survival prospects. The UN Climate Convention may yet be the legal instrument which embraces these fundamentals. Preventing dangerous anthropogenic interference with the climate system is its stated objective.

Vested Interest

To this end, the case for initiating immediately the displacement of fossil fuels in favour of renewables, is now more compelling than is the case for refining their use through 'efficiency gains' so as to justify their retention. Efficiency arguments are relevant, but alone are incapable of solving the climate problem. They should not be used to postpone fossil fuel displacement. The only arguments which can be (and are) put up for efficiency alone are those inequitably based on unnecessary and dangerous risk-enhancement in violation of the precautionary principle. The fundamental judgment against the continuation of fossil energy investment and dependence is really only opposed by vested fossil fuel interests. These interest groups have resorted to the so-called "no-regrets" arguments. These energy-efficiency and cost-effectiveness arguments are divorced from the precautionary principle. The no-regrets idea is, "if it makes economic sense to do it anyway, do it anyway". The arguments try and minimize the public's perception of the risks of climate change whilst trying to maximize the image of their proponents as caring and competent in the management of risk. The proponents' track record however, has been in the management of financial risk. And this has been in a context of unsustainable resource deployment and unaccountability over the creation of social and environmental disbeneficiaries. In reality these vested interests are a monopoly of self-interested primary fuel and energy producers in a global fossil economy which is still 90 per cent dependent on the combustion of fossil fuels for energy.

The IPCC and CO_2 Emissions Cuts

If further deterioration in the global climate is to be avoided, the Intergovernmental Panel on Climate Change (IPCC) atmosphere stabilising CO_2 emissions cuts must be initiated promptly. The IPCC stated in 1990 that in order to stabilise the rising atmospheric concentrations of CO_2 at 1990 levels, immediate minimum 60 per cent cuts in the emissions of CO_2 were required. (See chart). It was not clear whether that represented an optimistic or a pessimistic view of where the levels of atmospheric CO_2 should be stabilised to avoid interference with the climate system. The IPCC did however, exclude from that estimate the effect of what they described as the probably positive feedbacks which would further accelerating the warming trend.

It is in the lead economies of OECD from where these emission cuts must be led. The Convention text already acknowledges this requirement. Historically, the industrialised countries are responsible for at least 83 per cent of the CO_2 output (the principal greenhouse gas) from industry (see chart one). Currently, OECD alone is still responsible for nearly 50 per cent with only 16 per cent of global population and the US is responsible for 50 per cent of this amount with only 3 per cent of global population.

Polluters

In order to solve the problems of human-induced climate change, a per capita fossil GDP indicator needs to be established. Three years after the IPCC warned of the need to reduce CO_2 emissions, emissions are still rising, dangerously provoking global climate change. The difficulty is the global economy and its Gross Domestic Product (GDP) are currently 90 per cent linked to the combustion of fossil fuels for energy. Inevitably fossil CO_2 emissions and GDP trajectories are very closely inter-related. We can therefore measure what GCI calls this *'fossil GDP'*. (See chart two and the US/Japan charts at the end of the booklet—and for detailed discussion of this, see GCI "GDP:CO_2=B-A-U:I-O-U").

However, despite this context, rising per capita GDP is still taken as a valid monetary measure of economic benefit. It is the World Bank's principal so-called 'development indicator'. But attention is not given to its fossil fuel component, and rising per capita GDP is assumed to be a universally achievable phenomenon giving rise to a universally accurate indicator of benefit. The truth is in a fossil GDP economy, universally rising per capita GDP is only possible (if at all) in the context of rising CO_2 emissions, rising environmental impact and rising risk of climate change adversity.

Consequently we believe that, "per capita fossil GDP is— and should be made— the principal indicator of environmental impact globally." It is for this reason and in the understanding of equity as defined above, we assert that 'responsibilities for' rather than 'rights to' environmentally finite and vulnerable resources—like stable climate—should be allocated by income. We will return later to the detailed consequences of using this indicator to calculate the "sustainable per capita fossil GDP threshold" and what this reveals about consumption globally.

The World Bank and others advocate the reverse saying that environmental rights should be allocated by income. The 1992 Development Report contains a description of why they feel CO_2 emissions entitlements should be allocated by income. Allocating rewards to income is normal in the bank's normal line of business. It is the business-as-usual incentive of positive feedback for capital. However, in the management of climate change this approach is clearly problematic. Rising global temperature indicates net positive feedback (or self-reinforcing reactions) coming into play in the global climate system. For example, heat trapping gases accumulating in the atmosphere raise global temperature and this in turn causes other temperature raising phenomena to manifest—examples of this are polar ice melting as a consequence of temperature rise which causes the incoming heat from the sun to be less efficiently reflected back into space with more heat retained—as more heat begets more heat, the oceans warm up releasing more CO_2 and so on— this is a sampling of positive feedback.

On the other hand, the global economic system seeks growth operating on a series of deliberately applied positive feedback mechanisms such as interest and profit. Here the practice of seeking financial gain is facilitated by rewarding capital and capital transactions with the incentives of interest, growth and/or commissions. In fact, 'growth is an expression of net positive feedback within any frame chosen for observation. In the economic process, investors and traders naturally try to take out more than they put in for personal and corporate reasons. But the global climate crisis is really about this very point—if you take out more than you put in, the system will eventually compensate for the imbalance. The neo-classic economic law of diminishing returns should really be viewed in this context; the current net fossil GDP growth phenomenon (i.e., in spite of the diminishing returns), and the growth of risk (i.e., the diminishing prospect of climate stability).

By proposing as the Bank does, that rights to emit CO_2 should be allocated on the extent of fossil GDP income which a country derives from the global fossil economy, the Bank and others are effectively formalizing the marriage of the deliberate positive feedback of the financial system on the one hand, to the already

Industrial CO_2 emissions by region 1860-1990 incrementally by decade and as regionally disaggregated per cents of total global output

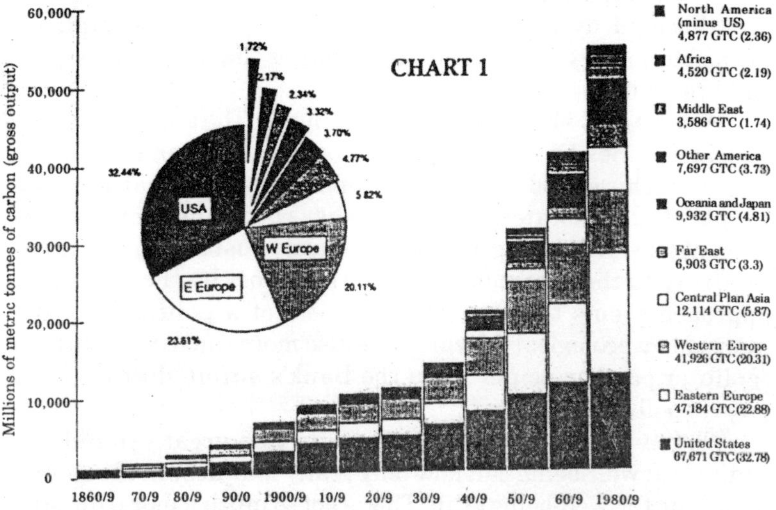

Industrial CO_2 emissions past and projected, 1955-2025, with IPCC suggested stabilisation cut (60%) reflected from 1990 forward.

CHART 2

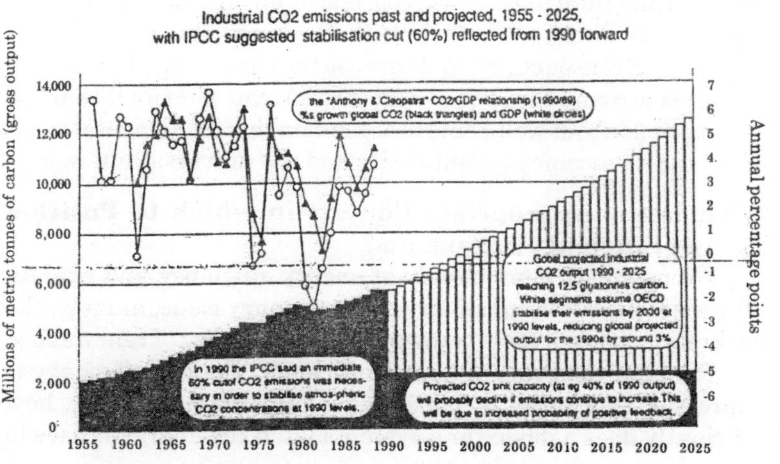

positively fossil fuel sensitized climate feedbacks on the other. De facto, this approach exists already. Formalised, it would simply consummate folly. But the Bank describes it as *"more feasible"* than their Aunt Sally alternative. The Aunt Sally is where rights are allocated by population and then regarded as implicitly infeasible because the high income countries "have exhausted their right to emit."

What they should be recognising is that by allocating responsibilities by income, causers of climate change would be targeted. This would enable responsibility for remedial actions to be specifically allocated to those who have been and continue to be responsible for creating and unnecessarily sustaining this crisis. Contrary to the assertion made in the report by the Bank, this approach seems to have more prospect of a political—not-to-mention an ecological—future. It is also more consistent with the "polluter pays principle" than the Bank's adroit shift to the "it pays to pollute principle."

At the heart of this crisis there is this great conundrum. Individual well-being can now only really manifest in the context of seeking the well-being of all. This is not so much a moral question as an economic question. Self-interest needs to be redefined to embrace the universal interest. The indicators of progress, development, impact and change which we choose, need therefore to be universally valid as well. The narrow self-interest of profit and the business of seeking this in the short-term at the expense of second and third parties, will continue to ensure the irresponsible investment decisions which still dominate the global fossil economy. In consequence, and because the threat of global climate change is so comprehensive, we must re-educate personally narrow assumptions about well-being to assimilate this fundamental sense of per capita income accountability and the universal interest.

What is the Appropriate Context in which to Position Energy Efficiency Arguments?

We now look more closely at energy efficiency and explain why we believe it is subsidiary to the primary issue, namely, the early start to fossil fuels being displaced in favour of renewables.

First the meaning of energy efficiency. Energy efficiency is expressed as a ratio. It has a technology component, i.e., how efficiently does a device or a system match the energy it uses to produce the usable energy it puts out. In economics, energy efficiency is taken as the ratio between the money or GDP generated by the energy/economic system on the one hand, and the energy units required by this system to generate the GDP on the other. In the context of the global fossil economy, it is the ratio of dollars of GDP generated per unit of carbon (from CO_2 emissions from the fossil fuels) used to generate the dollars of GDP.

For example

Global GDP in 1990 totalled around twenty and a half trillion dollars ($20,500,000,000,000);

Global CO_2 emissions from industry in 1990 (according to US energy department statistics) containded around six billion tonnes (that is metric tonnes) of carbon (6 gigatonnes, or 6 GTC, or 6,000,000,000 metric tonnes of carbon);

Fossil fuels supplied 90 per cent of the energy required to generate the global GDP, so the twenty and a half trillion dollars should be reduced by 10 per cent to make the calculation of the dollar/carbon rations more precise, this gives a figure of $18.45 trillion;

The 1990 global average energy efficiency ratio was therefore $18.45 trillion/6 GTC or $3,075 per tonne of carbon from fossil fuel burning. For comparison the:-

Japanese	energy efficiency ratio for 1990 was $10,839 per tonne of carbon,
US	energy efficiency ratio for 1990 was $3,852 per tonne of carbon,
Chinese	energy efficiency ratio for 1990 was $596 per tonne of carbon.

Of the group, Japan was clearly the most energy efficient economy, China very inefficient by comparison (there are grounds, for regarding the available Chinese GDP figure as an under-estimate) and the US is about average. However, if every one of the 5.2 billion people on the planet in 1990 had emitted industrial CO_2 even at the 1990 efficiency rate of the average Japanese person (i.e., 2.35 tonnes of carbon per person), the actual global CO_2 output of 6 billion tonnes would have been more than doubled to over 12 billion tonnes of carbon. If every one of the 5.2 billion people on the planet in 1990 had emitted industrial CO_2 at the 1990 rate of the average US person (i.e., 5.23 tonnes of carbon per person), the actual global CO_2 output of 6 billion tonnes would have been more than quadrupled to over 27 billion tonnes of carbon.

The point of this observation is to show that in the context of rising energy demand and the need for universally valid indicators as already argued, even by the standard of the conventionally most energy efficient economy on the planet (Japan), five-fold universal average gains in energy efficiency (or an 80 per cent reduction in the amounts of carbon per $) would be required to meet a 2.4 GTC maximum output level—or the IPCC atmospheric CO_2 concentrations stabilisation requirement of a 60 per cent cut in the 1990 levels of CO_2 emissions. Even assuming such a technological miracle could happen; it would take years to achieve by which time the cut requirement would have increased because of further atmospheric CO_2 build-up.

So the real point of this is to back up the main assertion at the outset—namely, that the case for the immediate displacement of fossil fuels in favour of renewables, is more compelling than is the case for retaining them whilst refining their use in the name of efficiency gains. The efficiency gains will never outpace the positive growth in emissions unless this displacement is initiated immediately. The lead time for such a technology transition is considerable and even with an urgent action plan under way, it is not a foregone conclusion that we will beat the clock of fossil GDP-induced climate adversity, especially if the second hand of corporate efficiency arguments continues its sweep unchallenged.

A sustainable Per Capita Fossil GDP Threshold

We already know that the global average energy efficiency ratio for 1990 was $3,075 per tonne of carbon. We can also calculate the 1990 global average per capita carbon emission from industrial CO_2. It was 6 GTC divided amongst 5.2 billion people or 1.15 metric tonnes of carbon per person. This figure reduced by 60 per cent—consistent with the IPCC stabilisation cut—gives an "allowable" 0.46 tonnes per person per annum.

The sustainable per capita fossil GDP threshold for 1990 is calculated by seeing what globally averaged level of dollars could be generated, given the $3,075 per tonne efficiency average and the allowable 0.46 of a tonne per capita. The answer is $1,415 per person (or 0.46 tonnes of fossil carbon) and this is the sustainable per capita fossil GDP threshold for 1990. The results of applying this figure to the global economy are striking.

GDP 'debitors' and 'creditors' were assessed using the following method. The 'sustainable per capita fossil GDP threshold, figure $1,415 is allocated to each country by population. These 'sustainable fossil GDP quotas' are then compared with the actual 1990 GDP values for each country. When a country exceeds its quota, we call it a 'fossil GDP debitor'. The amount by which a country exceeds its quota, we call production dumping'. When a country shortfalls its quota, we call it a 'fossil GDP creditor, The amount by which a country shortfalls its quota, we call 'subsidy', Also 'Transfers' are calculated in the following way. The total amount of the transfer required, equals the total amount of the subsidy. The debitors settle this collectively with amounts calculated in proportion to the size of their debt. For example, the US debt represents 33 per cent of the total value of the debt, therefore they put up 33 per cent of the value of the transfer. After deductions in this way to liquidate the subsidy, all countries commit the balance of their economies unconditionally to the pursuit of sustainable development and displacement of fossil fuels. The diagram opposite summarises the actual fossil GDP quotas and related population imbalances on 1990 values.

The diagram segments are approximately proportional to the actual imbalances described. The actual 1990 $ amounts of fossil GDP are summarised in the table below. The proportions, expressed as percentages, are summarised in the table alongside. The actual full country breakdown appears on the full page chart overleaf entitled. "All countries as 1990 fossil dollar debitors and creditors with proportional transfers and sustainable development commitments."

The accumulated (1860/1990-segmented by decade) credits and debits, assessed on the basis of allocating sustainable per capita emissions quotas nationally and then calculating excess and shortfall emissions (see detailed explanation in, GCI "GDP:CO_2= B-A-U:I-O-U"), are summarised on the page beyond in the chart beyond entitled."1860-1990, accumulated debits, credits, proportional transfers and sustainable development commitments in 1990 fossil dollar values". The accumulated debt runs into hundreds of trillions of dollars. It is included here to contextualise

A	= unused allowable credito f-GDP quotas (or 'subsidy')
B	= Actual creditor f-GDP
A+B	= total allowable creditor f-GDP quotas
f	= creditor population
C	= transfers from debitors to creditors
D	= balance for sustainable development by debitors
D+C	= debitor quotas exceeded (or production dumping)
E	= fully used allowable debitor quotas
C+D+E	= total actual debitor f-GDP
B+C+D+E	= total actual creditor & debitor f-GDP
A+B+E	= total allowable f-GDP
G	= debitor population
I-I	= zero f-GDP quota and population line
H-H	= allowable f-GDP quota threshold

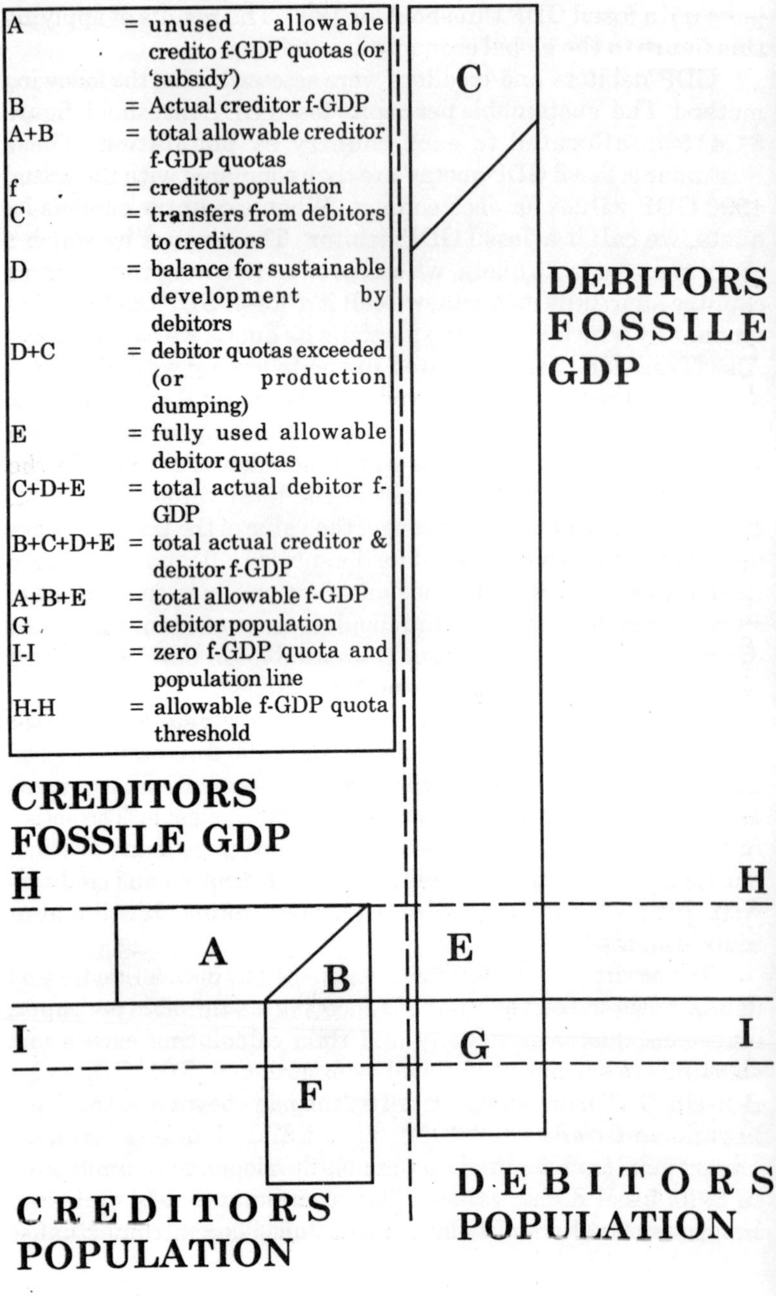

Table: Regarding the German CO_2 Emission Related Fossil for the Duration, 1975-1992

1990	*(diagram segments)*	*Debitors*	*(diagram segments)*	*Creditors*	*(diagram segments)*	*Total*	*(diagram (segments)*	*Balance for SD commit*	*(diagram segments)*	*Transfers*
actual f-GDP	C+D+E	\$17.3 trillion	B	\$1.2 trillion	B+C +D+E	\$18.5 trillion				
allowable f-GDP	E	\$2.4 trillion	A+B	\$4.2 trillion	A+B+E	\$6.7 trillion				
excess f-GDP	C+D	\$14.6 trillion					D	\$11.8 trillion		
shortfall f-GDP			A	\$3.1 trillion					C	\$3.1 trillion

historically the order of $ magnitude referred to in the discussion below about only current subsidy and redress.

1990 %f-GDP	*Debitors*	*Creditor*	*Total (Strillions)*
actual	94%	6%	$18.5=100%
allowable	36%	64%	$6.6=100%
excess	100%	na/	$14.6=100%
shortfall	n/a	100%	$3.1=100%
population	36%	64%	5.2=100%

Conclusions

In total, the energy subsidy received at the present by the debitor countries from the creditor countries, is worth $3.1 trillion annually on 1990 values. It is a serious distortion of the global political economy and shows clearly where the unsustainability of the present economic order is to be found and in what proportion. The energy subsidy actually assists the unsustainable production-dumping of $ 14.6 trillion worth of fossil-fuel products on the global market by the debitor countries. At least the current subsidy should be dealt with immediately. The fact this runs annually in the order of magnitude of trillions of dollars, makes risible the OECD countries' response to the issues outlined in this paper. They have yet to grasp the policy implications of their own enormous and unrestructured fossil debt overhang. What is required is structural adjustment of the fossil debitor economies and an end to the energy subsidy and the fossil production dumping. The diversionary response monies theoretically proposed so far by debitor countries are incapable of dealing with the structural issues. $6 billion are being offered conditionally through the World Bank's new Global Environmental Facility" (GEF) for global warming and biodiversity projects. Monies are even projected net of the value of the local benefit of any project. The World Bank's professed global outlook will founder if it continues to identify the universal interest based on the rationale of 'it pays to pollute'.

Equity and survival are linked, because it is clearly dangerous, anti-democratic and in violation of the precautionary principle to allow a subsidised 36 per cent of the world's population, controlling 93 per cent of the fossil derived income, to continue to raise the level of climate change risk which the global population is obliged to take in consequence. Income differentials of this kind are clearly the appropriation of the survival rights of the many by the inequitably and unsustainably subsidised few.

Adopting procedures like those outlined here, will allow us to phase out fossil fuel led GDP growth consistent with the precautionary principle. We can then concentrate on the strong and sustainable economic growth and development of democratic, decentralised, renewable, energy systems, This is the prerequisite of global ecological recovery.

For interest we include these final graphics. US and Japanese CO_2:GDP curves 1960-1990, floating, fixed and as shares of global. It is clearly precipitous to allow 5 per cent of world population to control 50 per cent of the unsustainably generated wealth. We also include (back cover) a chart comparing the 1991 UNDP assessment of skewed distribution, with GCI's. UNDP's income split is 6:1; GCI's income split at the sustainable fossil GDP threshold, is 16:1.

15

Inter-Governmental Panel on Climate Change—A Report of Working Group-II

Scientific- Technical Analysis of Impacts

Scope of the Assessment: The charge of Working Group II of the Intergovern-mental Panel on Climate Change (IPCC) was to review the state of knowledge concerning the impacts of climate change on physical and ecological systems, human health, and socioeconomic sectors. Working Group II also was charged with reviewing available information on the technical and economic feasibility of a range of potential adaptation and mitigation strategies. This assessment provides scientific, technical, and economic information that can be used, *inter alia,* in evaluating whether the projected range of plausible impacts constitutes "dangerous anthropogenic interference with the climate system," as referred to in Article 2 of the United Nations Framework Convention on Climate Change (UNFCCC), and in evaluating adaptation and mitigation options that could be used in progressing towards the ultimate objective of the UNFCCC (see Box 1).

Box 1. Ultimate Objective of the UNFCCC (Article 2)

"...stabilization of greenhouse gas concentrations in the atmosphere at a level that would prevent dangerous anthropogenic interference with the climate system. Such a level should be achieved within a time frame sufficient to allow ecosystems to adapt naturally to climate change, to ensure that food production is not threatened, and to enable economic development to proceed in a sustainable manner."

Table 1: Summary of Assumptions in the Six IPCC 1992 Alternative Scenarios

Scenario	*Population*	*Economic Growth*	*Energy Supplies*
IS92a,b	World Bank 1991 11.3 billion by 2100	1990-2025: 2.9% 1990-2100: 2.3%	12.000 EJ conventional oil 13.000EJ natural gas Solar costs fall to $0.075/kWh 191 EJ of biofuels available at $70/ barrel
IS92c	UN Medium -Low Case 6.4 billion by 2100	1990-2025: 2.0% 1990-2100: 1.2%	8.000 EJ conventional oil 7.300 EJ natural gas Nuclear costs decline by 0.4 per cent annually
IS92d	UN Medium-Low Case 6.4 billion by 2100	1990-2025: 2.7% 1990-2100: 2.0%	Oil and gas same as IS92c Solar costs fall to $0:065/kWh 272 EJ of biofuels available at $50 barrel
IS92e	World Bank 1991 11.3 billion by 2100	1990-2025: 3.5% 1990-2100: 3.0%	18.400 EJ conventional oil Gas same as IS92a,b Phase out nuclear by 2075
IS92f	UN Medium-High Case 17.6 billion by 2100	1990-2025: 2.9% 1990-2100: 2.3%	Oil and gas same as IS92e Solar costs fall to $0.083/kWh Nuclear costs increase to $0.09/kWh

[a]Approximate conversion factor: 1 barrel = 6 GJ.

Source : IPCC, 1992: Emissions scenarios for IPCC: an update. In: *Climate Change* 1992: *The Supplimentary Report to the IPCC Scientific Assessment* [J.T. Houghton. B.A. Callander, and S.K. Varney (eds.)]. Section A3, prepared by J. Leggett, W.J. Pepper, and R.J. Swart, and WMO/UNEP, Cambridge University Press, Cambridge, UK, 200 pp.

Nature of the Issue

Human activities are increasing the atmospheric concentrations of greenhouse gases which tend to warm the atmosphere and, in some regions, aerosols which tend to cool the atmosphere. These changes in greenhouse gases and aerosols, taken together, are projected to lead to regional and global changes in climate and climate-related parameters such as temperature, precipitation, soil moisture, and sea level. Based on the range of sensitivities of climate to increases in greenhouse gas concentrations reported by IPCC Working Group I and plausible ranges of emissions (IPCC IS92:see Table1), climate models taking into account greenhouse gases and aerosols project an increase in global mean surface temperature of about 1-3.5°C by 2100 and an associated increase in sea level of about 15-95 cm. The reliability of regional-scale predictions is still low and the degree to which climate variability may change is uncertain. However, potentially serious changes have been identified, including an increase in some regions in the incidence of extreme high-temperature events, floods and droughts, with resultant consequences for fires, pest outbreaks, and ecosystem composition, structure, and functioning, including primary productivity.

Human health, terrestrial and aquatic ecological systems and socioeconomic system (e.g., agriculture, forestry, fisheries, and water resources) are all vital to human development and well-being and are all sensitive to changes in climate. Whereas any regions are likely to experience the adverse effects of climate change— some of which are potentially irreversible— some effects of climate change are likely to be beneficial. Hence, different segments of society can expect to confront a variety of changes and the need to adapt to them.

Policymakers are faced with responding to the risks posed by anthropogenic emissions of greenhouse gases in the face of significant scientific uncertainties. It is appropriate to consider these uncertainties in the context of information indicating that climate-induced environmental changes cannot be reversed quickly, if at all, due to the long time scales associated with the climate system (see Box 2). Decisions taken during the next few years may limit the range of possible policy options in the future because high near-term emissions would require deeper reductions in the future to meet any given target concentration. Delaying action might reduce the overall costs of mitigation because of potential technological advances but could increase both the rate and the eventual magnitude of climate change, hence the adaptation and damage costs.

Box 2. Time Scales of Processes Influencing the Climate System

1. Turnover of the capital stock responsible for emissions of greenhouse gases: **Years to decades** (without premature retirement).
2. Stabilization of atmospheric concentrations of long-lived greenhouse gases given a stable level of greenhouse gas emissions: **Decades to millennia.**
3. Equilibration of the climate system given a stable level of greenhouse gas concentrations: **Decades to centuries.**
4. Equilibration of sea level given a stable climate: **Centuries.**
5. Restoration/rehabilitation of damaged or disturbed ecological systems: **Decades to centuries.** (some changes, such as species extinction, are irreversible, and it may be impossible to reconstruct and re-establish some disturbed ecosystems).

Policymakers will have to decide to what degree they want to take precautionary measures by mitigating greenhouse gas emissions and enhancing the resilience of vulnerable systems by means of adaptation. Uncertainty does not mean that a nation or the world community cannot position itself better to cope with the broad range of possible climate changes or protect against potentially costly future outcomes. Delaying such measures may leave a nation or the world poorly prepared to deal with adverse changes and may increase the possibility of irreversible or very costly consequences. Options for adapting to change or mitigating change that can be justified for other reasons today (e.g., abatement of air and water pollution) and make society more flexible or resilient to anticipated adverse effects of climate change appear particularly desirable.

The Climate Change

Article 2 of the UNFCCC explicitly acknowledges the importance of natural ecosystems, food production, and sustainable economic development. This report addreses the potential *sensitivity, adaptability,* and *vulnerability* of ecological and socioeconomic systems— sincluding hydrology and water resources management, human infrastructure, and human health—to changes in climate (see Box 3).

(a) Human-induced climate change adds an important new stress: Human-induced climate change represents an important additional stress, particularly to the many ecological and socioeconomic systems already affected by pollution, increasing resource demands, and nonsustainable management practices. The most vulnerable systems are those with the greatest sensitivity to climate changes and the least adaptability.

(b) Most systems are sensitive to climate change: Natural ecological systems, socioeconomic systems, and human health are all sensitive to both the magnitude and the rate of climate change.

(c) Impacts are difficult to quantify, and existing studies are limited in scope: Although our knowledge has increased significantly during the last decade, and qualitative estimates can be developed, quantitative projections of the impacts of climate change on any particular system at any particular location are difficult because regional-scale climate change predictions are uncertain: our current understanding of many critical processes is limited; and systems are subject to multiple climatic and non-climatic stresses, the interactions of which are not always linear or additive. Most impact studies have assessed how systems would respond to climate change resulting from an arbitrary doubling of equivalent atmospheric carbon dioxide (CO_2) concentrations. Furthermore, very few studies have considered dynamic responses to steadily increasing concentrations of greenhouse gases: fewer still have examined the consequences of increase beyond a doubling of equivalent atmospheric CO_2 concentrations or assessed the implications of multiple stress factors.

Box 3. Sensitivity, Adaptability, and Vulnerability

Sensitivity is the degree to which a system will respond to a change in climatic conditions(e.g., the extent of change in ecosystem composition, structure, and functioning, including primary productivity, resulting from a given change in temperature or precipitation).

Adaptability refers to the degree to which adjustments are possible in practices, processes, or structures of systems to projected or actual changes of climate. Adaptation can be spontaneous or planned, and can be carried out in response to or in anticipation of changes in conditions.

Vulnerability defines the extent to which climate change may damage or harm a system. It depends not only on a system's sensitivity but also on its ability to adapt to new climatic conditions.

Both the magnitude and the rate of climate change are important in determining the sensitivity, adaptability, and vulnerability of a system.

(d) Successful adaptation depends upon technological advances, institutional arrangements, availability of financing, and information exchange: Technological advances generally have increased adaptation options for managed systems such as agriculture and water supply. However, many regions of the world currently have limited access to these technologies and appropriate information. The efficacy and cost-effective use of adaptation strategies will depend upon the availability of financial resources, technology transfer, and cultural, educational, managerial, institutional, legal and regulatory practices, both domestic and international in scope. Incorporating climate change concerns into resource-use and development decisions and plans for regularly scheduled investments in infrastructure will facilitate adaptation.

(e) Vulnerability increases as adaptive capacity decreases: The vulnerability of human health and socioeconomic systems—and, to a lesser extent, ecological systems—depends upon economic circumstances and institutional infrastructure. This implies that systems typically are more vulnerable in developing countries where economic and institutional circumstances are less favourable. People who live on arid or semi-arid lands, in low-lying coastal areas, in water-limited or flood-prone areas or on small islands are particularly vulnerable to climate change. Some regions have become more vulnerable to hazards such as storms, floods, and droughts as a result of increasing population density in sensitive areas such as river basins and coastal plains. Human activities, which fragment many landscapes, have increased the vulnerability of lightly managed and unmanaged ecosystems. Fragmentation limits natural adaptation potential and the potential effectiveness of measures to assist adaptation in these systems, such as the provision of migration corridors. A changing climate's near-term effects on ecological and socioeconomic systems most likely will result from changes in the intensity and seasonal and geographic distribution of common weather hazards such as storms, floods, and droughts. In most of these examples, vulnerability can be reduced by strengthening adaptive capacity.

(f) Detection will be difficult, and unexpected changes cannot be ruled ou:. Unambiguous detection of climate-induced changes in most ecological and social systems will prove extremely difficult in the coming decades. This is because of the complexity of these systems, their many non-linear feedbacks, and their sensitivity to a large number of climatic and non-climatic factors, all of which are expected to continue to change simultaneously. The development of a baseline projecting future conditions without climate change is crucial, for it is this baseline against which all projected impacts are measured. As future climate extends beyond the boundaries of empirical knowledge (i.e., the documented impacts of climate variation in the past), it becomes more likely that actual outcomes will include surprises and unanticipated rapid changes.

(g) Further research and monitoring are essential: Enhanced support for research and monitoring, including cooperative efforts from national, international, and multi-lateral institutions, is essential in order to improve significantly regional scale climate projections; understand the responses of human health, ecological and socioeconomic systems to changes in climate and other stress factors; and improve our understanding of the efficacy and cost-effectiveness of adaptation strategies.

I. Aquatic Ecosystems

Ecosystems contain the Earth's entire reservoir of genetic and species diversity and provide many goods and services critical to individuals and societies. These goods and services include (i) providing food, fiber, medicines, and energy; (ii) processing and storing carbon and other nutrients; (iii) assimilating wastes, purifying water, regulating water runoff and controlling floods, soil degradation, and beach erosion: and (iv) providing opportunities for recreation and tourism. These systems and the functions they provide are sensitive to the rate and extent of changes in climate. Fig. 15.1 illustrates that mean annual temperature and mean annual precipitation can be correlated with the distribution of the world's major biomes.

The composition and geographic distribution of many ecosystems will shift as individual species respond to changes in climate; there will likely be reductions in biological diversity and in the goods and services that ecosystems provide society. Some ecological systems may not reach a new equilibrum for several centuries after the climate achieves a new balance.

(a) Forests: Models project that a sustained increase of 1° C in global mean temperature is sufficient to cause changes in regional climates that will affect the growth and regeneration capacity of forests in many regions. In several instances this will alter the function and composition of forests significantly. As a consequence of possible changes in temperature and water availability under doubled equivalent-CO_2 equilibrium conditions, a substantial fraction (a global average of one- third varying by region from one-seventh to two-thirds) of the existing forested area of the world will undergo major changes in broad vegetation types—with the greatest changes occurring in high latitudes and the least in the tropics. Climate change is expected to occur at a rapid rate relative to the speed at which forest species grow, reproduce and re-establish themselves. For mid-latitude regions, a global average warming of 1-3.5°C over the next 100 years would be equivalent to a poleward shift of the present isotherms by approximately 150-550 km. or an altitude shift of about 150-550 m; in low latitudes, temperatures would generally be increased to higher levels than now exist. This compares to past tree species migration rates that are believed to be on the order of 4-200 km. per century. Therefore, the species composition of forests is likely to change: entire forest types may disappear, while new assemblages of species, hence new ecosystems, may be established. Fig. 15.2 depicts potential distribution of biomes under current and a doubled equivalent CO_2 climate. Although net primary productivity could increase, the standing biomass of forests may not because of more frequent outbreaks and extended ranges of pests and pathogens, and increasing frequency and intensity of fires. Large amounts of carbon could be released into the atmosphere during transitions from one forest type to another because the rate at which carbon can be lost during times of high forest mortality is greater than the rate at which it can be gained through growth to maturity.

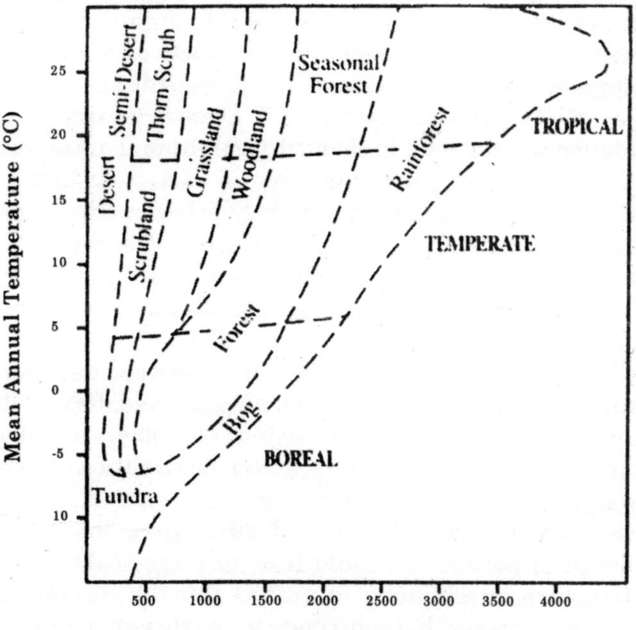

Fig. 15.1. The figure illustrates that mean annual temperature and mean annual precipitation can be correlated with the distribution of the world's major biomes. While the role of these annual means in affecting this distribution is important, it should be noted that the distribution of biomes may also strongly depend on seasonal factors such as the length of the dry season or the lowest absolute minimum temperature, on soil properties such as waterholding capacity, on land-use history such as agriculture or grazing, and on disturbance regimes such as the frequency of fire.

(b) Rangelands: In tropical rangelands, mean temperature increases should not lead to major alterations in productivity and species composition, but altered rainfall amount and seasonality and increased evapotranspiration will. Increases in atmospheric CO_2 concentration may raise the carbon-to-nitrogen ratio of forage for herbivores, thus reducing its food value. Shifts in temperature and precipitation in temperate rangelands may result in altered growing seasons and boundary shifts between grasslands, forests and shrublands.

(c) Deserts and Desertification: Deserts are likely to become more extreme— in that, with few exceptions, they are projected to become hotter but not significantly wetter. Temperature increases could be a threat to organisms that exist near their heat-tolerance limits. The impacts on water balance, hydrology, and vegetation are uncertain. Desertification, as defined by the UN Convention to Combat Desertification, is land degradation in arid, semi-arid and dry sub-humid areas resulting from various factors, including climatic variations and human activities. Desertification is more likely to become irreversible if the environment becomes drier and the soil becomes further degraded through erosion and compaction. Adaptation to drought and desertification may rely on the development of diversified production systems.

(d) Cryosphere: Models project that between one-third and one-half of existing mountain glacier mass could disappear over the next 100 years. The reduced extent of glaciers and depth of snow cover also would affect the seasonal distribution of river flow and water supply for hydroelectric generation and agriculture. Anticipated hydrological changes and reductions in the areal extent and depth of permafrost could lead to large-scale damage to infrastructure, an additional flux of CO_2 into the atmosphere and changes in processes that contribute to the flux of methane (CH_4) into the atmosphere. Reduced sea-ice extent and thickness would increase the seasonal duration of navigation on rivers and in coastal areas that are presently affected by seasonal ice cover, and may increase navigability in the Arctic Ocean. Little change in the extent of the Greenland and Antarctic ice sheets is expected over the next 50-100 years.

(e) Mountain: The projected decrease in the extent of mountain glaciers, permafrost and snow cover caused by a warmer climate will affect hydrologic systems, soil stability, and related socioeconomic systems. The altitudinal distribution of vegetation is projected to shift to higher elevation; some species with climatic ranges limited to mountain tops could become extinct because of disappearance of habitat or reduced migration potential. Mountain resources such as food and fuel for indigenous populations may be disrupted in many developing countries. Recreational industries—of increasing economic importance to many regions—also are likely to be disrupted.

*(f) **Lakes and Streams:*** Inland aquatic ecosystems will be influenced by climate change through altered water temperatures, flow regimes, and water levels. In lakes and streams warming would have the greatest biological effects at high latitudes, where biological productivity would increase and at the low-latitude boundaries of cold- and cool-water species ranges, where extinctions would be greatest. Warming of larger and deeper temperate zone lakes would increase their productivity: although in some shallow lakes and in streams, warming could increase the likelihood of anoxic conditions. Increases in flow variability, particularly the frequency and duration of large floods and droughts, would tend to reduce water quality and biological productivity and habitat in streams. Water level declines will be most severe in lakes and streams in dry evaporative drainages and in basins with small catchments. The geographical distribution of wetlands is likely to shift with changes in temperature and precipitation. There will be an impact of climate change on greenhouse gas release from non-tidal wetlands, but there is uncertainty regarding the exact effects from site to site.

(g) Coastal systems: Coastal systems are economically and ecologically important and are expected to vary widely in their response to changes in climate and sea level. Climate change and a rise in sea level or changes in storms or storm surges could result in the erosion of shores and associated habitat, increased salinity of estuaries and freshwater aquifers, altered tidal ranges in rivers and bays, changes in sediment and nutrient transport, a change in the pattern of chemical and microbiological contamination in coastal areas, and increased coastal flooding. Some coastal ecosystems are particularly at risk, including saltwater marshes, mangrove ecosystems, coastal wetlands, coral reefs, coral atolls, and river deltas. Changes in these ecosystems

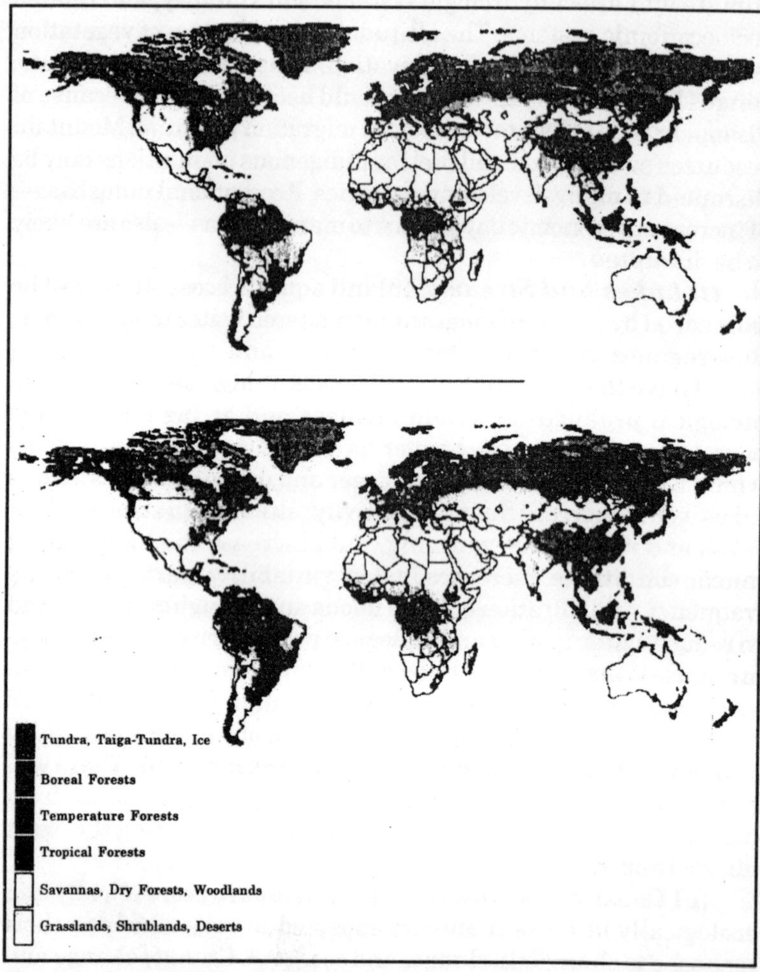

Fig. 15.2. Potential distribution of the major world biomes under current climate conditions, simulated by Mapped Atmosphere-Plan: Soil System (MAPSS) model (top). "Potential distribution" indicates the natural vegetation that can be supported at each site, given monthly inputs of precipitation, temperature, humidity, and windspeed. The lower product illustrates the projected distribution of the major world biomes by simulating the effects of 2xCO2-equivalent concentrations (GFDL, general circulation model), including the direct physiological effects of CO2 on vegetation. Both products are adapted from: Neilson, R.P. and D. Marks, 1994: A global perspective of regional vegetation and hydrology sensitivities from climatic change, *Journal of Vegetation Science,* 5, 715-730.

would have major negative effects on tourism, freshwater supplies, fisheries, and biodiversity. Such impacts would add to modifications in the functioning of coastal oceans and inland waters that already have resulted from pollution, physical modification and material inputs due to human activities.

(h) Oceans: Climate change will lead to changes in sea level, increasing it on average, and also could lead to altered ocean circulation, vertical mixing, wave climate, and reductions in sea-ice cover. As a result, nutrient availability, biological productivity, the structure and functions of marine ecosystems, and heat and carbon storage capacity may be affected, with important feedbacks to the climates system. These changes would have implications for coastal regions, fisheries, tourism and recreation, transport, off-shore structures, and communication. Paleoclimatic data and model experiments suggest that abrupt climatic changes can occur if freshwater influx from the movement and melting of sea ice or ice sheets significantly weakens global thermohaline circulation.

Hydrology: Climate change will lead to an intensification of the global hydrological cycle and can have major impacts on regional water resources. A change in the volume and distribution of water will affect both ground and surface water supply for domestic and industrial uses, irrigation, hydropower generation, navigation, instream eco-systems, and water-based recreation.

Changes in the total amount of precipitation and in its frequency and intensity directly affect the magnitude and timing of runoff and the intensity of floods and droughts; however, at present, specific regional effects are uncertain. Relatively small changes in temperature and precipitation, together with the non-linear effects on evapotranspiration and soil moisture, can result in relatively large changes in runoff, especially in arid and semi-arid regions. High-latitude regions may experience increased runoff due to increased precipitation, whereas runoff may decrease at lower latitudes due to the combined effects of increased evapotranspiration and decreased precipitation. More intense rainfall would tend to increase runoff and the risk of flooding, although this would depend not only on the change in rainfall but also on catchment physical and biologicalcharacte-ristics. A warmer climate could decrease the proportion of precipitation falling as snow, leading to reductions in springs runoff and increases in winter runoff.

The quantity and quality of water supplies already are serious problems today in many regions, including some low-lying coastal areas, deltas, and small islands, making countries in these regions particularly vulnerable to any additional reduction in indigenous water supplies. Water availability currently falls below 1,000 m^3 per person per year—a common benchmark for water scarcity—in a number of countries (e.g.,Kuwait, Jordan, Israel, Rwanda, Somalia, Algeria, Kenya) or is expected to fall below this benchmark in the next 2 to 3 decades (e.g., Libya, Egypt, South Africa, Iran, Ethiopia). In addition, a number of countries in conflict-prone areas are highly dependent on water originating outside their borders (e.g., Cambodia, Syria, Sudan, Egypt and Iraq).

The impacts of climate change will depend on the baseline condition of the water supply systems and the ability of water resource managers to respond not only to climate change but also to population growth and changes in demands, technology, and economic, social, and legislative conditions. In some cases—particularly in wealthier countries with integrated water-management systems—improved management may protect water users from climate change at minimal cost; in many others, however, there could be substantial economic, social and environmental costs, particularly in regions that already are water-limited and where there is a considerable competition among users. Experts disagree over whether water supply systems will evolve substantially enough in the future to compensate for the anticipated negative impacts of climate change on water resources and for potential increases in demand.

Options for dealing with the possible impacts of a changed climate and increased uncertainty about future supply and demand for freshwater include more efficient management of existing supplies and infrastructure; institutional arrangements of limit future demands/promote conservation; improved monitoring and forecasting systems for floods/droughts; rehabilitation of watersheds, especially in the tropics; and construction of new reservoir capacity to capture and store excess flows produced by altered patterns of snowmelt and storms.

Food and Fibre

(a) Agriculture: Crop yields and changes in productivity due to climate change will vary considerably across regions and among localities, thus changing the patterns of production. Productivity is projected to increase in some areas and decrease in others, especially the tropics and subtropics (Table 2). However, existing studies show that on the whole global agricultural production could be maintained relative to baseline production in the face of climate change modeled by General Circulation Models (GCMs) at doubled equivalent-CO_2 equilibrium conditions, but that regional effects would vary widely. This conclusion takes into account the beneficial effects of CO_2 fertilization, but does not allow for changes in agricultural pests and the possible effects of changing climatic variability.

Focusing on global agricultural production does not address the potentially serious consequences of large differences at local and regional scales, even at mid-latitudes. There may be increased risk of hunger and famine in some locations; many of the world's poorest people—particularly those living in subtropical and tropical areas, and dependent on isolated agricultural systems in semi-arid and arid regions—are most at risk of increased hunger. Many of these at-risk populations are found in sub-Saharan Africa; south, east, and south-east Asia, and tropical areas of Latin America, as well as some Pacific island nations.

Adaptation—such as changes in crops and crop varieties, improved water management and irrigation systems and changes in planting schedules and tillage practices— will be important in limiting negative effects and taking advantage of beneficial changes in climate. The extent of adaptation depends on the affordability of such measures, particularly in developing countries; access to know-how and technology; the rate of climate change; and biophysical constraints such as water availability, soil characteristics, and crop genetics. The incremental costs of adaptation strategies could create a serious burden for developing countries; some adaptation strategies may result in cost savings for some countries. There are significant uncertainties about the capacity of different regions to adapt successfully to projected climate change.

Livestock production may be affected by changes in grain prices and rangeland and pasture productivity. In general, analyses indicate that intensively managed livestock systems have more potential for adaptation than crop systems. This may not be the case in pastoral systems, where the rate of technology adoption is slow and changes in technology are viewed as risky.

(b) Forest products: Global wood supplies during the next century may become increasingly inadequate to meet projected consumption due to both climatic and non-climatic factors. Boreal forests are likely to undergo irregular and large-scale losses of living trees because of the impacts of projected climate change. Such losses could initially generate additional wood supply from salvage harvests, but could severely reduce standing stocks and wood-products availability over the long term. The exact timing and extent of this pattern is uncertain. Climate and land-use impacts on the production of temperate forest products are expected to be relatively small. In tropical regions, the availability of forest products is projected to decline by about half for non-climatic reasons related to human activities.

(c) Fisheries: Climate change effects interact with those of pervasive overfishing, diminishing nursery areas and extensive inshore and coastal pollution. Globally, marine fisheries production is expected to remain about the same; high-latitude freshwater and aquaculture production are likely to increase, assuming that natural climate variability and the structure and strength of ocean currents remain about the same. The principal impacts will be felt at the national and local levels as species mix and centers of production shift. The positive effects of climate change—such as longer growing seasons: lower natural winter mortality, and faster growth rates in higher latitudes—may be offset by negative factors such as changes in established reproductive patterns, migration routes, and ecosystem relationships.

Human Infrastructure

Climate change and resulting sea-level rise can have a number of negative impacts on energy, industry, and transportation infrastructure; human settlements; the property insurance industry; tourism and cultural systems and values.

In general, the sensitivity of the energy, industry, and transportation sectors is relatively low compared to that of agricultural or natural ecosystems, and the capacity for adaptation through management and normal replacement of capital is

Table 2: Selected Crop Study Results for 2 × CO_2 Equivalent Equilibrium GCM Scenarios

Region	*Crop*	*Yield Impact (%)*	*Comments*
Latin America	Maize	-61 to increase	Data are from Argentina, Brazil, Chile, and Mexico; range is across GCM scenarios, with and without CO_2 effect.
	Wheat	-50 to -5	Data are from Argentina, Uruguay, and Brazil; range is across GCM scenarios, with and without CO_2 effect.
	Soybean	-10 to +40	Data are from Brazil; range is across GCM scenarios, with CO_2 effect.
Former Soviet Union	Wheat Grain	-19 to +41 -14 to +13	Range is across GCM scenarios and region, with CO_2 effect.
Europe	Maize	-30 to increase	Data are from France, Spain, and northern Europe, with adaptation and CO_2 effect; assumes longer season, irrigation efficiency loss, and northward shift.
	Wheat	increase or decrease	Data are from France, UK, and northern Europe; with adaptation and CO_2 effect: assumes longer season, northward shift, increased pest damage, and lower risk of crop failure.
	Vegetables	increase	Data are from UK and northern Europe; assumes pest damage increased and lower risk of crop failure.
North America	Maize Wheat Soybean	-55 to+62 -100 to+234 -96 to +58	Data are from USA and Canada; range is across GCM scenarios and sites, with/without adaptation and with/without CO_2 effect. Data from USA; less severe or increase with CO_2 and adaptation.
Africa	Maize	-65 to+6	Data are from Egypt, Kenya, South Africa and Zimbabwe; range is over studies and climate scenarios, with CO_2 effect.
	Millet	-79 to -63	Data are from Senegal; carrying capacity fell 11-38 percent
	Biomass	decrease	Data are from South Africa; agrozone shifts.

Region	*Crop*	*Yield Impact (%)*	*Comments*
South Asia	Rice	-22 to +28	Data are from Bangladesh, India, Philippines, Thailand, Indonesia,
	Maize	-65 to -10	Malaysia, and Myanmar; range is over GCM scenarios, with CO_2
	Wheat	-61 to +67	effect; some studies also consider adaptation.
China	Rice	-78 to +28	Includes rainfed and irrigated rice; range is across sites and GCM scenarios; genetic variation.provides scope for adaptation.
Other Asia and Pacific Rim	Rice	-45 to +30	Data are from Japan and South Korea; range is across GCM scenarios; generally positive in north Japan, and negative in south.
	Pasture	-1 to +35	Data are from Australia and New Zealand; regional variation.
	Wheat	-41 to + 65	Data are from Australia and Japan; wide variation, depending on cultivar.

Note: For most regions, studies have focused on one or two principal grains. These studies strongly demonstrate the variability in estimated yield impacts among countries, scenarios, methods of analysis, and crops, making it difficult to generalize results across areas or for different climate scenarios.

expected to be high. However, infrastructure and activities in these sectors would be susceptible to sudden changes, surprises, and increased frequency or intensity of extreme events. The subsectors and activities most sensitive of climate change include agroindustry energy demand, production of renewable energy such as hydroelectricity and biomass, construction, some transportation activities, existing flood mitigation structures, and transportation infra-structure located in many areas, including vulnerable coastal zones and permafrost regions.

Climate change clearly will increase the vulnerability of some coastal populations to flooding and erosional land loss. Estimates put about 46 million people per year currently at risk of flooding due to storm surges. This estimate results from multiplying the total number of people currently living in areas potentially affected by ocean flooding by the probability of flooding at these locations in any year, given the present protection levels and population density. In the absence of adaptation measures, a 50 cm sea level rise would increase this number to about 92 million; a 1m sea-level rise would raise it to 118 million. If one incorporates anticipated population growth, the estimates increase substantially. Some small island nations and other countries will confront greater vulnerability because their existing sea and coastal defense systems are less well-established. Countries with higher population densities would be more vulnerable. For these countries, sea-level rise could force internal or international migration of populations.

A number of studies have evaluated sensitivity to a 1 m sea-level rise. This increase is at the top of the range of IPCC Working Group I estimates for 2100; it should be noted, however, that sea level is actually projected to continue to rise beyond 2100. Studies using this 1-m projection show a particular risk for small islands and deltas. Estimated land losses range from 0.05 percent for Uruguay, 1 percent for Egypt, 6 percent for the Netherlands, and 17.5 percent for Bangladesh to about 80 percent for the Majuro Atoll in the Marshall Islands, given the present state of protection systems. Large numbers of people also are affected for example, about 70 million each in China and Bangladesh. Many nations face lost capital value in excess of 10 percent of their Gross Domestic Product (GDP). Although annual protection coasts for many nations are relatively modest (about 0.1 percent of GDP), the average annual costs to many small island states total several per cent of GDP. For some island nations, the high cost of providing storm-surge protection would make it essentially infeasible, especially given the limited availability of capital for investment.

The most vulnerable human settlements are located in damage-prone areas of the developing world that do not have the resources to cope with impacts. Effective coastal-zone management and land use regulation can help direct population shifts away from vulnerable locations such as flood plains, steep hillsides, and low-lying coastlines. One of the potentially unique and destructive effects on human settlements is forced internal or international migration of populations. Programs of disaster assistance can offset some of the more serious negative consequences of climate change and reduce the number of ecological refugees.

Property insurance is vulnerable to extreme climate events. A higher risk of extreme events due to climate change could lead to higher insurance premiums or the withdrawal of coverage for property in some vulnerable areas. Changes in climate variability and the risk for extreme events may be difficult to detect or predict, thus making it difficult for insurance companies to adjust premiums appropriately. If such difficulty leads to insolvency, companies may not be able to honor insurance contracts, which could economically weaken other sectors, such as banking. The insurance industry currently is under stress from a series of "billion dollar" storms since 1987, resulting in dramatic increases in losses, reduced availability of insurance, and higher costs. Some in the insurance industry peiceive a current trend toward increased frequency and severity of extreme climate events. Examination of the meteorological data fails to support this perception in the context of a long-term change, although a shift within the limits of natural variability may have occurred. Higher losses strongly reflect increases in infrastructure and economic worth in vulnerable areas as well as a possible shift in the intensity and frequency of extreme weather events.

Human Health

Climate change is likely to have wide-ranging and mostly adverse impacts on human health, with significant loss of life. These impacts would arise by both direct and indirect pathways (See Fig. 19.4), and it is likely that the indirect impacts would, in the longer term, predominate.

CLIMATE CHANGES: TEMPERATURE, PRECIPITATION, AND WEATHER

Mediating Process	Health Outcomes
DIRECT	
Exposure to thermal extremes (expecially heatwaves) →	Altered rates of heat and cold related illness and death (especially cardiovascular and respiratory diseases)
Altered frequency and/ or intensity of other extreme weather events (floods, storms etc.) →	Deaths, injuries, and psychological disorders; damage to public health infrastructure
INDIRECT	
DISTURBANCES OF ECOLOGICAL SYSTEMS	
Effects on range and activity of vectors and infective parasites →	Changes in geographic ranges and incidence of vector-borne diseases
Altered local ecology of water-borne and food-borne infective agents →	Changed incidence of diarrheal and certain other infectious diseases
Altered food (especially crop) productivity due to changes in climate, weather events, and associated pests and diseases →	Regional malnutrition and hunger, and consequent impairment of child growth and development
Sea-level rise, with population displacement and damage to infrastructure (e.g., sanitation) →	Injuries increased risks of various infectious disease (due to migration, crowding, contamination of drinking water), psychological disorders
Levels and biological impacts of air pollution, including pollens and spores →	Asthama and allergic disorders other acute and chronic respiratory disorders and deaths
Social, economic, and demographic dislocations due to adverse climate change impacts on economy, infrastructure, and resource supply →	Wide range of public health consequences (e.g., mental health, nutritional impairment, infectious diseases, civil strife)

Note : Populations with different levels of natural, technical and social resources would differ in their vulnerability to climate induced health impacts.

Fig. 19.4. Ways in which climate change can affect human health

Direct health effects include increases in (predominantly cardiorespiratory) mortality and illness due to an anticipated increase in the intensity and duration of heat waves. Temperature increases in colder regions should result in fewer cold-related deaths. An increase in extreme weather would cause a higher incidence of death, injury, psychological disorders, and exposure to contaminated water supplies.

Indirect effects of climates change include increases in the potential transmission of vector-borne infectious diseases (e.g., malaria, dengue, yellow fever and some viral encephalitis) resulting from extensions of the geographical range and season for vector organisms. Projections by models (that entail necessary simplifying assumptions) indicate that the geographical zone of potential malaria transmission in response to world temperature increases at the upper part of the IPCC-projected range (3-5°C by 2100) would increase from approximately 45 per cent of the world population to approximately 60 per cent by the latter half of the next century. This could lead to potential increases in malaria incidence (on the order of 50-80 million additional annual cases, relative to an assumed global background total of 500 million cases). primarily in tropical, subtropical, and less well- protected temperate zone populations. Some increases in non-vector borne infectious diseases —such as salmonellosis, cholera, and giardiasis—also could occur as a result of elevated temperatures and increased flooding.

Additional indirect effects include respiratory and allergic disorders due to climate-enhanced increases in some air pollutants, pollens, and mold spores. Exposure to air pollution and stressful weather events combine to increase the likelihood of morbidity and mortality. Some regions could experience a decline in nutritional status as a result of adverse impacts on food and fisheries productivity. Limitations on freshwater supplies also will have human health consequences.

Quantifying the projected impacts is difficult because the extent of climate-induced health disorders depends on numerous coexistent and interacting factors that characterize the vulnerability of the particular population, including environmental and socioeconomic circumstances, nutritional and immune status, population density, and access to quality health care services. Adaptive options to reduce health impacts include protective technology (e.g., housing, air conditioning, water purification, and vaccination), disaster preparedness, and appropriate health care.

Option to Gases

Human activities are directly increasing the atmospheric concentrations of several greenhouse gases, especially CO_2, CH_4, halocarbons, sulfur hexafluoride (SF_6), and nitrous oxide (N_2O). CO_2 is the most important of these gases, followed by CH_4. Human activities also indirectly affect concentrations of water vapor and ozone. Significant reductions in net greenhouse gas emissions are technically possible and can be economically feasible. These reductions can be achieved by utilizing an extensive array of technologies, and policy measures that accelerate technology development, diffusion, and transfer in all sectors including the energy, industry, transportation, residential/ commercial, and agricultural/forestry sectors. By the year 2100, the world's commercial energy system in effect will be replaced at least twice, offering opportunities to change the energy system without premature retirement of capital stock; significant amounts of capital stock in the industrial, commercial, residential, and agricultural/ forestry sectors will also be replaced. These cycles of capital replacement provide opportunities to use new, better performing technologies. It should be noted that the analyses of Working Group II do not attempt to quantify potential macroeconomic consequences that may be associated with mitigation measures. Discussion of macroeconomic analyses is found in the IPCC Working Group III contribution to the Second Assessment Report. The degree to which technical potential and cost-effectiveness are realized is dependent on initiatives to counter lack of information and overcome cultural, institutional, legal, financial and economic barriers that can hinder diffusion of technology or behavioral changes. The pursuit of mitigation options can be carried out within the limits of sustainable development criteria. Social and environmental criteria not related to greenhouse gas emissions abatement could, however, restrict the ultimate potential of each of the options.

Energy

Global energy demand has grown at an average annual rate of approximately 2 per cent for almost 2 centuries, although energy demand growth varies considerably over time and between different

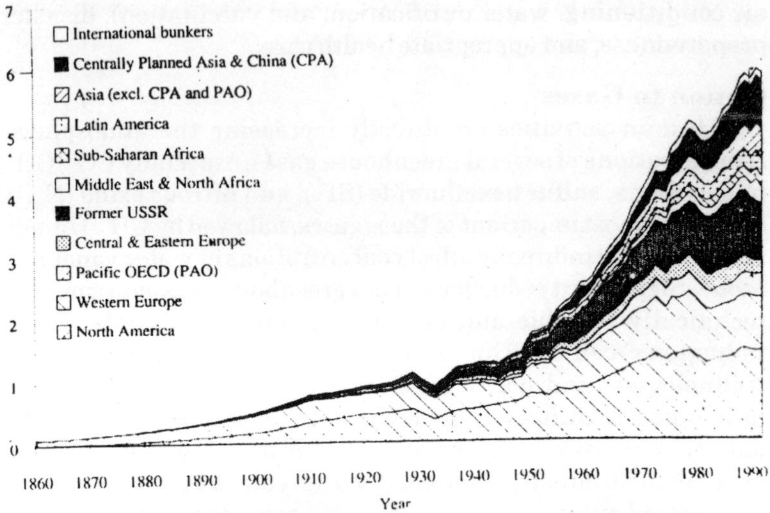

Fig. 19.5. Global energy-related CO² emissions by major world region in Gt C/ yr. Sources: Keeling, 1994; Marland et al., 1994; Grubler and Nakicenovic, 1992; Etemad and Luciani, 1991; Fujii, 1990; UN, 1952 (see the Energy Primer for reference information).

regions. In the published literature, different methods and conventions are used to characterize energy consumption. These conventions differ, for example, according to their definition of sectors and their treatment of energy forms. Based on aggregated national energy balances, 385 EJ of primary energy was consumed in the world in 1990, resulting in the release of 6 Gt C as CO_2. Of this, 279 EJ was delivered to end users, accounting for 3.7 Gt C emissions as CO_2 at the point of consumption. The remaining 106 EJ was used in energy conversion and distribution, accounting for 2.3 Gt C emissions as CO_2. In 1990, the three largest sectors of energy consumption were industry (45 per cent of total CO_2 releases), residential/commercial sector (29 per cent), and transport (21 per cent). Of these, transport sector energy use and related CO_2 emissions have been the most rapidly growing over the past 2 decades. For the detailed sectoral mitigation option assessment in this report, 1990 energy consumption estimates are based on a range of literature sources; a variety of conventions are used to define these sectors and their energy used, which is estimated to amount to a total of 259-282 EJ.

Figure depicts total energy-related emissions by major world region. Organisation for Economic Cooperation and Development (OECD) nations have been and remain major energy users and fossil fuel CO_2 emitters, although their share of global fossil fuel carbon emissions has been declining. Developing nations, taken as a group, still account for a smaller portion of total global CO_2 emissions than industrialized nations—OECD and former Soviet Union/Eastern Europe (FSU/EE)—but most projections indicate that with forecast rates of economic and population growth, the future share of developing countries will increase. Future energy demand is anticipated to continue to grow, at least through the first half of the next century. The IPCC (1992, 1994) projects that without policy intervention, there could be significant growth in emissions from the industrial, transportation, and commercial/ residential buildings sectors.

Energy Demand

Numerous studies have indicated that 10-30 per cent energy - efficiency gains above present levels are feasible at little or no net cost in many parts of the world through technical conservation measures and improved management practices over the next 2 to 3 decades. Using technologies that presently yield the highest output of energy services for a given input of energy, efficiency gains of 50-60 per cent would be technically feasible in many countries over the same time period. Achieving these potentials will depend on future cost reductions, financing and technology transfer, as well as measures to overcome a variety of non-technical barriers. The potential for greenhouse gas emission reductions exceeds the potential for energy use efficiency because of the possibility of switching fuels and energy sources. Because energy use is growing world-wide, even replacing current technology with more efficient technology could still lead to an absolute increase in CO_2 emissions in the future.

In 1992, the IPCC produced six scenarios (IS92a-f) of future energy use and associated greenhouse gas emissions (IPCC, 1992,1995). These scenarios provide a wide range of possible future greenhouse gas emission levels, without mitigation measures.

In the Second Assessment Report, future energy use has been re-examined on a more detailed sectoral basis, both with and without new mitigation measures, based on existing studies.

Despite different assessment approaches, the resulting ranges of energy consumption increases to 2025 without new measures are broadly consistent with those of IS92. If past trends continue, greenhouse gas emissions will grow more slowly than energy use, except in the transport sector.

The following paragraphs summarize energy-efficiency improvement potentials estimated in the IPCC Second Assessment Report. Strong policy measures would be required to achieve these potentials. Energy-related greenhouse gas emission reductions depend on the source of the energy, but reductions in energy use will in general lead to reduced greenhouse gas emissions.

(a) Industry: Energy use in 1990 was estimated to be 98-117 EJ and is projected to grow to 140-242 EJ in 2025 without new measures. Countries differ widely in their current industrial energy use and energy -related greenhouse gas emission trends. Industrial sector energy-related greenhouse gas emissions in most industrialized countries are expected to be stable or decreasing as a result of industrial restructuring and technological innovation, whereas industrial emissions in developing countries are projected to increase mainly as a result of industrial growth. The short term potential for energy efficiency improvements in the manufacturing sector of major industrial countries is estimated to be 25 per cent. The potential for greenhouse gas emission reductions is larger. Technologies and measures for reducing energy-related emissions from this sector include improving efficiency (e.g., energy and materials savings, cogeneration, energy, cascading steam recovery, and use of more efficient motors and other electrical devices); recycling materials and switching to those with lower greenhouse gas emissions; and developing processes that use less energy and materials.

(b) Transportation: Energy use in 1990 was estimated to be 61-65 EJ, and is projected to grow to 90-140 EJ in 2025 without new measures. Projected energy use in 2025 could be reduced by about a third to 60-100 EJ through vehicles using very efficient drive-trains, lightweight construction, and low air-resistance design, without compromising comfort and performance. Further energy-use reductions are possible through the use of smaller vehicles; altered land use patterns, transport systems, mobility patterns, and lifestyles, and shifting to less energy intensive transport modes. Greenhouse gas emissions per unit of energy used could be reduced through the use of alternative fuels and electricity from renewable sources. These measures, taken together, provide the opportunity for reducing global transport energy-related greenhouse gas emissions by as much as 40 per cent of projected emissions by 2025. Actions to reduce energy-related greenhouse gas emissions from transport can simultaneously address other problems such as local air pollution.

(c) Commercial/Residential Sector: Energy used in 1990 was estimated to be about 100 EJ, and is projected to grow to 165-205 EJ in 2025 without new measures. Projected energy use could be reduced by about a quarter to 126-170 EJ by 2025 without diminishing services through the use of energy efficient technology. The potential for greenhouse gas emission reductions is larger. Technical changes might include reduced heat transfers through building structures and more efficient space-conditioning and water supply systems, lighting and appliances. Ambient temperatures in urban areas can be reduced through increased vegetation and greater reflectivity of building surfaces, reducing the energy required for space conditioning. Energy-related greenhouse gas emission reductions beyond those obtained through reduced energy use could be achieved through changes in energy sources.

Mitigating Industrial Process and Human Settlement Emissions

Process-related greenhouse gases including CO_2, CH_4, N_2O, halocarbons, and SF_6 are released during manufacturing and industrial processes, such as the production of iron, steel, aluminium, ammonia, cement, and other materials. Large reductions are possible in some cases. Measures include modifying production processes, eliminating solvents, replacing feedstocks, materials substitution, increased recycling, and reduced consumption of greenhouse gas-intensive materials. Capturing and utilizing CH_4 from landfills and sewage treatment facilities and lowering the leakage rate of halocarbon refrigerants from mobile and stationary sources also can lead to significant greenhouse gas emission reductions.

Energy Supply

This assessment focuses on new technologies for capital investment and not on potential retrofitting of existing capital stock to use less carbon intensive forms of primary energy. It is technically possible to realize deep emissions reductions in the energy supply sector in step with the normal timing of investments to replace infrastructure and equipment as it wears out or becomes obsolete. Many options for achieving these deep reductions will also decrease the emissions of sulfur dioxide, nitrogen oxides, and volatile organic compounds. Promising approaches, not ordered according to priority are described below.

Greenhouse Gas Reductions in the use of Fossil fuels

(a) More efficient conversion of fossil fuels: New technology offers considerably increased conversion efficiencies. For example, the efficiency of power production can be increased from the present world average of about 30 per cent to more than 60 per cent in the longer term. Also, the use of combined heat and power production replacing separate production of power and heat—whether for process heat or space heating—offers a significant rise in fuel conversion efficiency.

(b) Switching to low-carbon fossil fuels and suppressing emissions: Switching from coal to oil or natural gas, and from oil to natural gas, can reduce emissions. National gas has the lowest CO_2 emissions per unit of energy of all fossil fuels at about 14 kg C/GJ, compared to oil with about 20 kg C/GJ and coal with about 25 kg G/GJ. The lower carbon-containing fuels can, in general, be converted with higher efficiency than coal. Large resources of natural gas exist in many areas. New, low capital cost, highly efficient combined-cycle technology has reduced electricity costs considerably in some areas. Natural gas could potentially replace oil in the transportation sector. Approaches exist to reduce emissions of CH_4 from natural gas pipelines and emissions of CH_4 and/or CO_2 from oil and gas wells and coal mines.

(c) Decarbonization of flue gases and fuels, and CO_2 storage: The removal and storage of CO_2 from fossil fuel power-station stack gases is feasible, but reduces the conversion efficiency and significantly increases the production cost of electricity. Another approach to decarbonization uses fossil fuel feed-stocks to make hydrogen-rich fuels. Both approaches generate a by-product stream of CO_2 that could be stored, for example, in depleted natural gas fields. The future availability of conversion technologies such as fuel cells that can efficiently use hydrogen would increase the relative attractiveness of the latter approach. For some longer term CO_2 storage options, the costs, environmental effects, and efficacy of such options remain largely unknown.

Switching to non-fossil fuel sources of energy

(a) Switching to nuclear energy: Nuclear energy could replace baseload fossil fuel electricity generation in many parts of the world if generally acceptable responses can be found to concerns such as reactor safety, radioactive-waste transport and disposal, and nuclear proliferation.

(b) Switching to renewable sources of energy: Solar, biomass, wind, hydro, and geothermal technologies already are widely used. In 1990, renewable sources of energy contributed about 20 per cent of the world's primary energy consumption, most of it fuelwood and hydropower. Technological advances offer new opportunities and declining costs for energy from these sources. In the longer term, renewable sources of energy could meet a major part of the world's demand for energy. Power systems can easily accommodate limited fractions of intermittent generation, and with the addition of fast-responding backup and storage units, also higher fractions. Where biomass is sustainably regrown and used to displace fossil fuels in energy production, net carbon emissions are avoided as the CO_2 released in converting the biomass to energy is again fixed in biomass through photosynthesis. If the development of biomass energy can be carried out in ways that effectively address concerns about other environmental issues and competition with other land uses, biomass could make major contributions in both the electricity and fuels markets, as well as offering prospects of increasing rural employment and income.

Integration of Energy System Mitigation Options

To assess the potential impact of combinations of individual measures at the energy system level, in contrast to the level of individual technologies, variants of a Low CO_2 Emitting Energy Supply System (LESS) are described. The LESS constructions are "thought experiments" exploring possible global energy systems.

The following assumptions were made: World population grows from 5.3 billion in 1990 to 9.5 billion by 2025 and 10.5 billion by 2100. GDP grows 7-fold by 2025 (5-fold and 14 fold in industrialized and developing countries, respectively) and 25-fold by 2100 (13-

fold and 70-fold in industrialized and developing countries, respectively), relative to 1990. Because of emphasis on energy efficiency, primary energy consumption rises much more slowly than GDP. The energy supply constructions were made to meet energy demand in (i)projections developed for the IPCC's First Assessments Report (1990) in a low energy demand variant, where global primary commercial energy use approximately doubles, with no net change for industrialized countries but a 4.4-fold increase for developing countries from 1990 to 2100 and (ii) a higher energy demand variant, developed in the IPCC IS92a scenario where energy demand quadruples from 1990 to 2100. The energy demand levels of the LESS constructions are consistent with the energy demand mitigation chapters of this Second Assessment Report.

Figure shows combinations of different energy sources to meet changing levels of demand over the next century. The analysis of these variants leads to the following conclusions.

- Deep reductions of CO_2 emissions from energy supply systems are technically possible within 50 to 100 years, using alternative strategies.
- Many combinations of the options identified in this assessment could reduce global CO_2 emissions from fossil fuels from about 6 Gt C in 1990 to about 4 Gt C/yr by 2050, and to about 2 Gt C/yr by 2100 (see Figure). Cumulative CO_2 emissions from 1990 to 2100 would range from about 450 to about 470 Gt C in the alternative LESS constructions.
- Higher energy efficiency is underscored for achieving deep reductions in CO_2 emissions, for increasing the flexibility of supply side combinations and for reducing overall energy system costs.
- Interregional trade in energy grows in the LESS constructions compared to today's levels, expanding sustainable development options for Africa. Latin America and the Middle East during the next century.

Costs for energy services in each LESS variant relative to costs for conventional energy depend on relative future energy prices, which are uncertain within a wide range and on the performance and cost characteristics assumed for alternative technologies. However, within the wide range of future energy

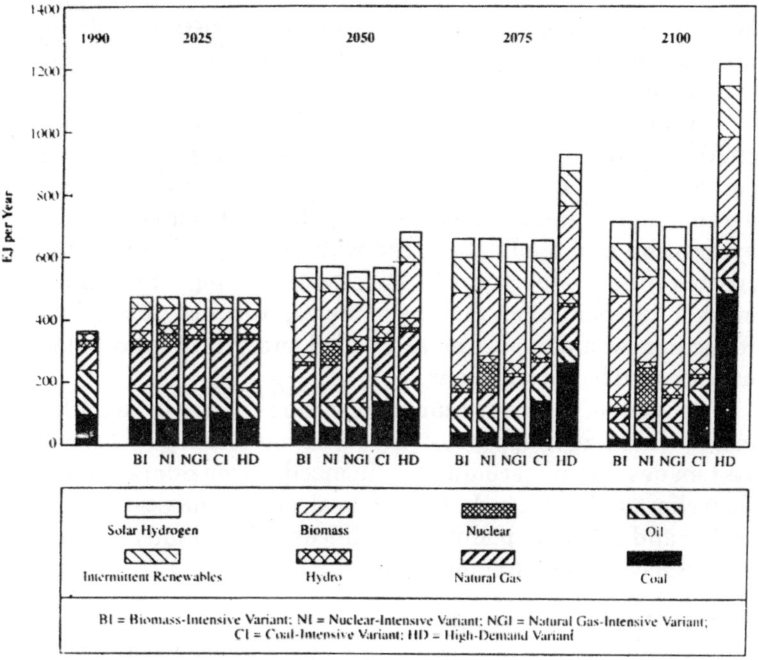

Fig. 19.5.1. Global primary energy use for alternative Low CO_2. Emitting Energy Supply System (LESS) construction: Alternatives for meeting different energy demand levels over time, using various fuel mixes.

prices, one or more of the variants would plausibly be capable of providing the demanded energy services at estimated costs that are approximately the same as estimated future costs for current conventional energy. It is not possible to identify a least cost future energy system for the longer term, as the relative costs of options depend on resource constraints and technological opportunities that are imperfectly known and on actions by governments and the private sector.

The literature provides strong support for the feasibility of achieving the performance and cost characteristics assumed for energy technologies in the LESS constructions within the next 2 decades though it is impossible to be certain until the research and development is complete and the technologies have been tested in the market. Moreover, these performance and cost characteristics cannot be achieved without a strong and sustained investment in research, development, and demonstration (RD&D).

Many of the technologies being developed would need initial support to enter the market and to reach sufficient volume to lower costs to become competitive.

Market penetration and continued acceptability of different energy technologies ultimately depends on their relative cost, performance (including envir- onmental performance), institutional arrangements and regulations and policies. Because costs vary by location and application, the wide variety of circumstances creates initial opportunities for new technologies to enter the market. Deeper understanding of the opportunities for emissions reductions would require more detailed analysis of options, taking into account local conditions.

Because of the large number of options, there is flexibility as to how the energy supply system could evolve, and paths of energy system development could be influenced by considerations other than climate change, including political, environmental (especially indoor and urban air pollution, acidification and land restoration), and socioeconomic circumstances.

Agriculture and Forestry

Beyond the use of biomass fuels to displace fossil fuels, the management of forests, agricultural lands, and rangelands can play an important role in reducing current emissions of CO_2, CH_4 and N_2O and in enhancing carbon sinks. A number of measures could conserve and sequester substantial amounts of carbon (approximately 60-90 Gt C in the forestry sector alone) over the next 50 years. In the forestry sector, costs for conserving and sequestering carbon in biomass and soil are estimated to range widely but can be competitive with other mitigation options. Factors affecting costs include opportunity costs of land; initial costs of planting and establishment; costs of nurseries; the cost of annual maintenance and monitoring; and transaction costs. Direct and indirect benefits will vary with national circumstances and could offset the costs. Other practices in the agriculture sector could reduce emissions of other greenhouse gases such as CH_4 and N_2O. Landuse and management measures include:

- → Sustaining existing forest cover
- → Slowing deforestation
- → Regenerating natural forests
- → Establishing tree plantations

→ Promoting agroforestry
→ Altering management of agricultural soils and rangelands
→ Improving efficiency of fertilizer use
→ Restoring degraded agricultural lands and range lands
→ Recovering CH_4 from stored manure
→ Improving the diet quality of ruminants.

The net amount of carbon per unit area conserved or sequestered in living biomass under a particular forest management practice and present climate is relatively well understood. The most important uncertainties associated with estimating a global value are (i) the amount of land suitable and available for forestation, regeneration, and/or restoration programs, (ii) the rate at which tropical deforestation can actually be reduced, (iii) the long-term use (security) of these lands and (iv) the continued suitability of some practices for particular locations given the possibility of changes in temperature, water availability and so forth under climate change.

Other Issues

Cross-sectoral assessment of different combinations of mitigation options focuses on the interactions of the full range of technologies and practices that are potentially capable of reducing emissions of greenhouse gases or sequestering carbon. Current analysis suggests the following:

- **Competing Uses of Land, Water and Other Natural Resource:** A growing population and expanding economy will increase the demand for land and other natural resources needed to provide, *inter alia*, food, fiber, forest products, and recreation services. Climate change will interact with the resulting intensified patterns of resource use. Land and other resources could also be required for mitigation of greenhouse gas emissions. Agricultural productivity improvements throughout the world and especially in developing countries would increase availability of land for production of biomass energy.
- **Geoengineering Options:** Some geoengineering approaches to counterbalance greenhouse gas-induced climate change have been suggested (e.g., putting solar radiation reflectors in space or injecting sulfate aerosols into the atmosphere to mimic the cooling influence of volcanic eruptions). Such approaches

generally are likely to be ineffective, expensive to sustain, and/or to have serious environmental and other effects that are in many cases poorly understood.

The Policy

Mitigation depends on reducing barriers to the diffusion and transfer of technology, mobilizing financial resources, supporting capacity building in developing countries, and other approaches to assist in the implementation of behavioural changes and technological opportunities in all regions of the globe. The optimum mix of policies will vary from country to country, depending upon political structure and societal receptiveness. The leadership of national governments in applying these policies will contribute to responding to adverse consequences of climate change. Governments can choose policies that facilitate the penetration of less greenhouse gas-intensive technologies and modified consumption patterns. Indeed many countries have extensive experience with a variety of policies that can accelerate the adoption of such technologies. This experience comes from efforts over the past 20 to 30 years to achieve improved energy efficiency, reduce the environmental impacts of agricultural policies, and meet conservation and environmental goals unrelated to climate change. Policies to reduce net greenhouse gas emissions appear more easily implemented when they are designed to address other concerns that impede sustainable development (e.g., air pollution and soil erosion). A number of policies, some of which may need regional or international agreement, can facilitate the penetration of less greenhouse gas-intensive technologies and modified consumption patterns, including:

- → Putting in place appropriate institutional and structural frameworks
- → Energy pricing strategies (e.g., carbon or energy taxes, and reduced energy subsidies)
- → Reducing or removing other subsidies (e.g., agricultural and transport subsidies) that increase greenhouse gas emissions.
- → Tradable emissions permits
- → Voluntary programmes and negotiated agreements with industry
- → Utility demand-side management programmes

- → Regulatory programmes, including minimum energy efficiency standards (e.g., for appliances and fuel economy)
- → Stimulating RD&D to make new technologies available
- → Market pull and demonstration programmes that stimulate the development and application of advanced technologies
- → Renewable energy incentives during market build-up
- → Incentives such as provisions for accelerated depreciation and reduced costs for consumers
- → Education and training; information and advisory measures
- → Options that also support other economic and environmental goals.

16

Global Environmental Concerns

Till now in the previous chapter we describing the likely changes in climate which may occur as a result of human activities and the impact these may have in various parts of the world. But large and potentially devastating changes are likely to be a generation or more away. So why should be concerned? What responsibility, if any, do we have for our planet as a whole and the great variety of other forms of life which inhabit it? And does our scientific knowledge in any way match up with other insights like religious ones, regarding our relationship with our environment? This chapter is divided in two parts: Part one looks into factors that provoke us to take action and Part two is about action needed to be taken.

Why We should have Concerns

(a) Our planet: Al Gore, the Vice-President of the United States, entitled his recent book on the environment *Earth in the Balance*, means that there are balances in the environment which need to be maintained. A small area of a tropical forest possesses an ecosystem which carries some thousands of plant and animal species, each thriving in its own ecological niche in close balance with the others. Balances are also significant for larger regions and for the Earth as a whole. These balances can be highly precarious, especially where human beings are concerned. Of those to point out was Rachel Carson in her book *Silent Spring*, first published in 1962, which mentions the damaging effects of pesticides on the environment. We are an important part of the world ecosystem; as the size and scale of our activities continue to escalate, so can the seriousness of the disturbances we generate to the overall balances of nature. We should recognize these balances, in particular the careful relationship between humans and the world around us. It needs to be a balanced and harmonious peaceful relationship in which each generation of humans should leave the planet in a better state, or at least in as good a state as they found it. The word that is often used for this is sustainability—politicians talk of sustainable development. This principle, and its connection with the harmonious relationship between humans and nature was given prominent place by the United Nations Conference on Environment and Development which held at Rio de Janeiro in June 1992. The first principle in a list of 27 at the Rio Declaration adopted by the Conference is 'Human beings are at the focus of concerns of sustainable development. They are entitled to a healthy and productive life in harmony with nature. Still, despite such statements of principle from a body such as the United Nations, many of the attitudes which we commonly have to the Earth are anyway, neither balanced, harmonious nor sustainable.

(b) The Exploitation of Qualities: Mankind has over many centuries been exploiting the Earth and its resources. It was at the beginning of the Industrial Revolution some two hundred years back that the potential of the Earth's minerals began to be realized. Coal, the result of the decay of primaeval forests and laid down during many millions of years, was the main source of energy for the new industrial developments. Iron ore to make steel was mined in vastly growing quantities. The search for other metals such as zinc, copper and lead was intensified until today many million of tons are mined every year.

Around 1960, oil took over from coal as the dominant world source of energy; oil and gas between them today supply over twice the energy supplied by coal.

Not only that we been exploiting the Earth's mineral resources. The Earth's biological resources have also been cut down on a large scale to make room for agriculture and for the purpose of human habitation. Tropical forests are a particularly valuable resource, important for the maintenance of the climate of tropical areas. They have also been estimated to contain perhaps half of all the Earth's biological species. Yet only about half of the mature tropical forests which were present a few hundred years ago still stand. At the present rate of destruction virtually all will be gone in less than fifty years. Maximum amount of this exploitation has been carried out with little or no thought as to whether this use of natural resources is responsible.

In the early days in the Industrial Revolution it seemed that resources qualities were essentially limitless. Later on, as one source ran out others became available to more than happens its place. Even now, for most minerals new sources are used. But the increase use is such that this situation cannot continue. In many cases known reserves or even likely reserves will begin to run out during the next hundred or few hundred years. All resources have been laid down over many millions if not thousand millions of years. Nature took almost a million years to lay down the amount of fossil fuel that we now burn worldwide every years—and in doing so it seems that we are causing fast change of the Earth's climate.

Such a level of exploitation is clearly not in balance, not harmonious and not sustainable.

(c) Readoption of Primitive Lifestyles: An opposite of this attitude is the suggestion that we all adopt a much more primitive lifestyle and give up a large part of industry and comprehensive farming—that we effectively put the clock back two or three hundred years to before the Industrial Revolution. That sounds quite seductive and some individuals can clearly begin to live that way. But there are two main problems. One is that it is just not practical. The world population is now some six times what it was two hundred years back and about three times that of fifty years back. The world cannot be adequately fed without intensive farming and without latest methods of food distribution. Further, most people in the developed world just would not be ready to be without the technical aids— electricity, central heating, refrigerator, washing machine, television and so on which give the freedom the interest and the recreation which is so much taken for granted. In fact, people in the developing world are also beginning to take advantage of and enjoy these aids to a life of least drudgery and more freedom.

The other problem is that it fails to take account of human creativity. Human scientific and technical development cannot be frozen at any given point in history, insisting that no further ideas can be developed. A proper balance between humans and the environment must leave room of human beings to exercise their creative skills.

Moreover, therefore, a 'back to nature' viewpoint is neither balanced nor sustainable.

(d) The Technology Fix: Another common attitude to the Earth is to invoke the 'technology fix'. As a senior environmental official from the United States said to me some years back, 'We cannot change our lifestyle because of the possibility of climate change, we just need to fix the biosphere.' It was not clean whether what he supposed the technical fixes would turn out to be. The point that he was making is that, in the past, humans have been so effective at developing new technology to solve the problems as they arise, can it not be assumed that this will continue? Concern about the future then turns into finding the 'fixes' as they are needed. On the surface the 'technology fix' route may sound a good way to proceed; it needs effort and no foresight.

It implies that damage can be corrected when it has been created rather than avoided in the first place. But damage already made to the environment by human activities is causing problems now. It is as if in looking after home We decided not to carry out any routine maintenance but 'fixed' the failures as they occurred. For our home that would be a high risk route to go through failure to rewire when necessary could easily lead to a disastrous fire. A similar attitude to the Earth is both arrogant as well as, irresponsible. It fails to recognize the vulnerability of nature to the large change which human activities are now able to generate. Again, this approach is neither balanced nor sustainable.

(e) Responsibility of Future Generations: There is our responsibility to future generations. It is a basic instinct that we want to see our children and our grand children well set up in the world and wish to pass on to them some of our most possessions.

A similar desire would be that they inherit from us an Earth which has been well looked after and which does not present them with more tough problems than those we have had to face. But such an attitude is not universally held. We really do need to face up to the problem now for the sake of the coming and subsequent generations. We have no right to act as if there is no tomorrow. We also have a responsibility to give to those who follow us a pattern for their future based on the idea of sustainable development.

(f) Common Global Concerns: This point of view sees us as having some responsibility, not just for all generations of humanity,

but also for the larger world of all living things. We are, after all, part of that larger whole i.e., world. There is good scientific justification for this. We are becoming more and more aware of our dependence on the rest of nature and of the interdependences which exist between various forms of life, between iiving systems and the physical and chemical environment which surrounds life on the Earth—and indeed between ourselves and the rest of the world. The scientific theory named Gaia after the Greek Earth goddess and publicized particularly by James Lovelock stresses these interdependencies. Lovelock points out that the chemical composition of the Earth's atmosphere is very different from that of our closest planetary neighbours, Mars and Venus. Their atmospheres, apart from some water vapour, are clearly pure carbon dioxide.

The Earth's atmosphere, by contrast, is 78 per cent nitrogen, 21 per cent oxygen and only 0.03 per cent carbon dioxide. This composition is very different from chemical equilibrium arid, so far as the major constituents are concerned, has remained substantially unchanged over many millions of years. This very different state of on the Earth has come about because of the emergence of life. Early in the history of life, plants appeared which photosynthesize, taking in carbon dioxide and learing out oxygen. There followed other living systems which 'breath', taking in oxygen and giving out carbon dioxide. The presence of life this may influences the environment, and living systems in turn adapt to the environment. It is the close match of environment to the necessities of life and its development which seems so remarkable and which Lovelock has emphasized. Here, we will quote one concerned with oxygen in the atmosphere. There is a critical reaction between the oxygen concentration and the frequency of forest fires. Below an oxygen concentration of 15 per cent, fires cannot be started even in dry twigs. At concentration above 25 per cent fires burn absolutely fiercely even in the damp wood of a tropical rain forest. Some species are dependent on fires for their survival; for instance, some conifers need the heat of fire to release their seeds from the seed pods. Above 25 per cent concentration of oxygen there would be no forests; below 15 per cent, the regeneration that fires provide in the world's forests would not be there. The oxygen concentration of 21 per cent is ideal. It is the sort of relation that has driven Lovelock to propose that there is tight coupling between the organisms that make up the world of living systems and their environment. He has therefore suggested a simple model of an imaginary world called Daisyworld (see box) which illustrates the type of feedback mechanisms which can lead to tight coupling. This model is almost similar to the one he has proposed for the biological and chemical history of the Earth during the first 1,000 million years after primitive life first appeared on the Earth some 3,500 million years back. It is true that the real world is, enormously more complex than Daisyworld, which is why the Gaia hypothesis has led to so much debate. Lovelock's leading statement in 1972 of the hypothesis was that 'Life, or the biosphere, regulates or maintains the climate and the atmospheric composition at an optimum for itself.' In his subsequent writings he has introduced the analogy between the Earth and a living organism, introducing a new science which he calls geophysiology. In fact, his latest book is entitled *Gaia, the practical science of planetary medicine.*

It says that an advanced organism such as a human being has many built-in mechanisms for controlling the interactions between various parts of the organism and for self regulation. In a similar way, Lovelock argues, the ecosystems on the Earth are so tightly paired to their physical and chemical environments that the ecosystems and their environment could be regarded as one organism with an integrated 'physiology'. In this sense he believes that the Earth is 'alive'. While Gaia has stimulated much scientific comment it remains a hypothesis. What the debate has done still is to emphasize the interdependencies which connect all living systems to their environment. There we also find hint of a suggestion in the Gaia hypothesis that the Earth's feedbacks and self-regulation are so strong that we humans need not be concerned about the pollution we generate Gaia has enough control to take care of anything we might do. Such a view fails to recognize the effect on the Earth's system of substantial disturbances, particularly the vulnerability of the environment with respect to its suitability for humans. In the words of Lovelock,'Gaia, as I see her, is no doting mother tolerant of misdemeanours, nor is she some fragile and delicate damsel in danger from brutal mankind. She is stern and tough, always keeping the world warm and comfortable for those who obey the rules, but ruthless in her destruction of those who transgress. Her unconscious goal is a planet fit for life. If humans stand in the way of this, we shall be eliminated with as little pity as would be shown by the micro-brain of an intercontinental ballistic nuclear missile in full flight to its target.'

This Gaia is a scientific theory. But some have been quick to see it as a religious idea, supporting ancient religious beliefs. Most of the world's religions have drawn attention to the close relationship between humans and the Earth. The Native American tribes of North America lived close to the Earth. One of their chiefs when asked to dispose off his land expressed his dismay at the idea and said, 'The Earth does not belong to man, man belongs to the Earth. All things are connected like the blood that unites us all.' We also find an ancient Hindu saying, 'The Earth is our mother, and we are all her children.' Modern civilization has taken us away from this feeling of belongingness to the Earth. The Gaia scientific hypothesis can help to bring us back to recognize two things, first the inherent value of all parts of nature and then our dependence, as human beings, on the Earth and on our environment.

What else, the Islamic faith teaches the value of sustainable development, for example, in a saying of the prophet Mohammed: 'He who revives as dead land will be rewarded accordingly, and that which is eaten by birds, insects and animals out of that land will be charity provided by God'. This underlines both our duty to care for the natural environment and our obligation to let all living creatures have their rightful place within it.

While seeing into the themes which emphasize the unity environment, we need not confine ourselves to the Earth. There is a very much larger sphere in which almost similar perspective of unity is becoming apparent. Some astronomers and cosmologists, overwhelmed by the size, scale, complexity, intricacy and precision of the universe, have started to realize that their quest for an understanding of the evolution of the universe right from the 'Big Bang' some fifteen thousand million years ago is not merely a scientific project but a search for meaning. Why else has Stephen Hawking's book *A Brief History of Time*, in selling over six million copies, become one of the bestsellers of our days?

In the course of In the this new search for meaning the perspective has arisen that the universe was made with human in mind—an idea expressed in some formulations of the anthropic principle. Two specific pointers emphasize this. First, we have already seen that the Earth itself is fitted in a remarkable way for advanced forms of life.

Cosmology is disclosing to us that, in order for life on our planet to be possible, the universe itself at the time of the Big Bang and in its early history needed to be 'fine-tuned' to an incredible degree.

Moreover, there is the remarkable fact that human minds, themselves dependent on the whole universe for their existence are able to appreciate and understand to some levels the fundamental mathematical structure of the universe's design.

As Albert Einstein commented. "The most incomprehensible thing about the universe is that comprehensible." In the theory of Gaia, the Earth itself is focal and humans are dispensable; the insights of cosmology suggest that humans have a particular place in whole scheme of things.

(g) Stewardship of Humanity: Association between humans and Earth is often described as one of *stewardship*. We are on the Earth as its stewards. The word implies that we are carrying out our duty as stewards or agents on behalf of someone else—but whom? Some environmentalists see no need to answer the question particularly, others might say we are stewards on behalf of future generations or on behalf of a generalised humanity.

But a religious person would want to be more specific and say that we are stewards on behalf of God.

Generally, it is thought that religious belief is not consistent with a scientific outlook. Scientists are, after all, looking for an explanation of the world in scientific terms which, when they know enough they believe can be complete. For example, scientists are looking for mechanisms to describe the 'fine-tuning' of the universe (these are known as 'Theories of Everything'!) mentioned before. They are also looking for mechanisms to describe the interdependencies between living systems and the environment. If we imagine, scientists are successful in finding the mechanisms for which they are looking will that negate the religious opinion that it is God who is responsible for the design of the universe and who had humans in mind in his creation? Not at all. What scientists are doing is trying to find out how the universe moves, they cannot answer the ultimate questions as to why it is there. In the words of Johannes Kepler, who in the sixteenth century was one of the first of the modern observational astronomers, scientists are 'thinking God's ideas, after him.'

The science we study is God's science; the mechanisms we discover are God's mechanisms. The fact that God may have set up automatic means to accomplish his purpose provides us with an even greater idea of what God is like.

However, all religious people are not so convinced that the Earth belongs to God. Reacting against the materialism of our time, they believe that God is only really interested in what is called the spiritual as against the material part of life. Although their day to day living is dominated by the material, when it comes to the religious self of their lives, they feel the material has little or no part.

This has been advocated time and again that science and religion need to be seen as complementary ways of looking at truth, a point made strongly by Al Gore in *Earth in the Balance* which lucidly discusses present environmental issues such as global warming. He blames much of our lack of understanding of the environment on the modern approach which tends to differentiate scientific study from religious and ethical issues. Science and technology are after pursued with a clinical detachment and without thinking about the moral consequences. The new power derived from scientific knowledge could be used to dominate nature with ethical impunity, he writes. He goes on to describe the modern technocrat as 'this barren spirit, precinct of the disembodied intellect, which knows the style in which things work but not the way they are. However, he also points out that 'there is now a powerful impulse in some fragments of the scientific community to heal the breach' between science and religion. In particular, as we pursue an understanding of the Earth's environment, it is important that scientific studies and technological inventions are not divorced from their ethical and religious context.

(H) Caretakers of the Earth: Supportive picture of stewardship is found in the Judaeo-Christian tradition in the story of creation in the early chapters of the Bible. God's purpose, we are told, in creating people was to care for the rest of creation—the idea of human stewardship of creation is very old one! Adam and Eve were made to live in a garden, the garden of, 'to work it and take care of it'. The animals, birds and other living creatures were brought to Adam in the garden for him to name them. We are given a picture of our first parents as 'gardeners' of the Earth; the Earth as God's garden and us as gardeners. What does our work as 'gardeners' imply?

(a) As we all know garden provides food and water and other materials to sustain life and human industry. It is interesting that the Genesis story not only describes food and water from the garden but also mineral resources. Regarding part of the garden we are told 'the gold of that land is good; aromatic resin and onyx are also present. The Earth provides resources for us humans to use as we need them.

(b) A garden is to be cared as a place of beauty. The trees in the garden of Eden were 'pleasing to the eye'. We are to live in harmony with the remaining creation and to appreciate the value of all parts of creation. Indeed, a garden is a place where care is taken to preserve the multiplicity of species, in particular those who are most vulnerable. Millions of people each year visit gardens which have been especially designed to express the incredible variety and beauty of nature. Gardens are meant to be enjoyed.

(c) Also a garden is a place where humans can be creative. Its resources provide for great potential. The variety of species and landscape can be used to increase the garden's beauty and its productivity. Humans have learnt to generate new plant varieties in abundance and utilise their scientific and technological knowledge coupled with the enormous variety of the Earth's resources to create new probabilities for life and its enjoyment. However, the potential of this creativity is such that increasingly we need to know where it can take us, it has potential for evil as well as for good.

(d) A garden is to be maintained so as to be of benefit to future generations. In this context, I shall always remember Gordon Dobson, a distinguished scientist, who in the 1920s evolved new means for the measurement of ozone in the atmosphere. His home outside Oxford in England possessed a large garden with number of fruit trees.

Now we ask ourselves, how well do we humans match up to the description of ourselves as gardeners caring for the Earth? Not very well, it must be said; we are more frequently exploiters and spoilers than cultivators. Some have placed part of the blame for this on attitudes which they think originate in the early chapters of Genesis, which talk human beings having rule over creation and subduing it.

Those words, however, are not a mandate unchecked exploitation.

(e) Partnership with the Almighty: A number of the principles we have been enunciating are included at least implicitly in the declarations, conventions and resolutions that came out of the United Nations Conference of Environment and Development held in Rio de Janerio in June 1992; indeed they form the background of various statements emanating from the United Nations or from official national sources. We are not short of statements of ideals. What tend to be lacking are the capability and resolve to continue with them. We are only too aware of the strong temptations we experience at both the personal and the national levels to use the world's means and resources to gratify our selfishness and greed. As we realize how formidable is the task of stewardship of the Earth, we may often more often feel that it is beyond the capability of the human race to tackle it adequately.

But an important religious message is that we do not have to carry this responsibility on our own. Our partner is nobody else other than God himself. The Genesis stories contain a beautiful description of this partnership where they talk of God walking in the garden in the cool of the day and humans disobeying him.

Still, that did not put an end to God's purpose for humans or for the Earth. God continually offers a way back to that position of partnership. One of the most known stories in the Old Testament is the story of Joseph, who interpreted the dream of Pharaoh, the ruler of Egypt, in terms of a climate forecast.

There were to be seven years of affluence followed by when, because of drought, there would be poor crops. Pharaoh asked Joseph to arrange the country's resources so that provision for the years of famine could be made during the years of plenty. Joseph witnessed the trying events in his life up to that time as part of God's plan to prepare him for the position of great responsibility which was now thrust upon him. He knew that his intellect to interpret Pharaoh's dream and the ability for his new political and management task could only come from his close association with God.

It is taught in Christianity that this partnership God and humanity reached its climax when in Jesus God became human, as the New Testament discloses, thus demonstrating to the fullest possible extent God's commitment to the material world. When Jesus told people about God, many of his examples came from human interaction with the natural world—sowing seed, looking after sheep, fishing. And in his parable of the talents Jesus stressed the importance of taking responsibility to the greatest possible extent; his harshest words were kept safe for the servant who failed to use wisely the money entrusted to him by his master, but hid it in the ground.

During the course of problems, facing environmental problems, therefore, we are called to exercise stewardship in as thorough a manner as possible, looking to God for the ability to carry it out. For any situation there are definitely some limitations to our knowledge and our ability to control; what we are invited to do is to go into the situation in partnership with God, knowing that he can take care of those things which we are unable to. A clear understanding of the responsibilities and abilities we have been given coupled with trust in God's presence and trustworthiness is the blend that makes stewardship of the Earth an exciting and challenging activity.

Keeping the uncertainties that surround the science of global warming, where does the path of wisdom lie? For example, should action be taken now or should we wait until the uncertainties are less before deciding on the right action to take?

To conclude, a prayer of Reinhold Niebuhr, an American theologian who lived earlier this century, is appropriate in this section, as we face the seemingly impossible demands and challenges of world stewardship: "O God, give us serenity to accept what cannot be changed; courage to change what should be changed; and wisdom to distinguish the one from the other."

Handing the Environmental Disturbances and Uncertainties

In the previous pages of the chapter, we have seen what the factors are which provoke us to make a concerted effort in the direction of global environment. Let us now see what and how we can sustain and stabilize the changes that are taking place. As we have said time and again, for the past several years, scientists have issued ominous warnings about the future of the Earth's climate. Predictions of dramatic global change generating from the continued dumping of industrial by-products into the atmosphere and forest loss of massive scale can no longer be ignored.

Compelling scientific evidence strongly suggests that global climate patterns, previously regarded as reliably stable, could be thrust into a state of turmoil. Emissions of natural and synthetic gases are increasing the heat-trapping limits of the atmosphere through a phenomenon known as the greenhouse effect. The projected impacts of this worldwide climatic disruption dwarf many of the environmental problems of the past and augur political, economic and social hurdles on an enormous scale.

Global warming could have catastrophic cons- equences for the habitability and productivity of the whole planet. The accompanying strain and upheaval on the global scene, in turn, could have serious foreign policy consequences for all countries. Broad scientific agreement exists on the underlying theory of climate change, although the nature and magnitude of expected from greenhouse warming remain in debate. Nonetheless, the range of consequences is sufficiently clear and the magnitude of the resources at stake so high that policy action is required sooner rather than later. Once a crisis is reached, it will be too late to act. The international political and legal system remains ill-equipped to present a solution that will assure the integrity of the Earth's climate. Arresting the impending climate instability will require a concerted international agenda and a reorientation of energy and development priorities in virtually all nations of the world. Heading this agenda for action should be a global multilateral agreement that sets strict, binding standards for level emissions of greenhouse gases.

(a) The Greenhouse Impact

Our activities since the industrial revolution have dramatically altered the composition of global atmosphere. A number of gases, emitted in small but significant amounts, absorb infrared radiation reflected from the bottom of the Earth. As concentrations of these heat-absorbing gases increase, average global temperatures will rise. Emissions of carbon dioxide are the single greatest cause of elevated terrestrial temperatures from the greenhouse effect accounting for about half of the problem.

Concentrations of carbon dioxide in the range of 280 parts per million (ppm), together with water vapor in the atmosphere, set up the preindustrial equilibrium temperature of the planet. Since the middle of the 19th century, atmospheric carbon dioxide levels have gone up by about 25 per cent to approximately 350 ppm and are continuing to rise by about 0.4 per cent per year. Elevated carbon dioxide concentrations result primarily from the intensified burning of fossil fuels like coal, oil and natural gas—which liberates the chemical in varying amounts.

Global forests are vast storehouses, or "sinks," for carbon. Worldwide loss of forest cover, by releasing this vast stockpile of carbon into the atmosphere as carbon dioxide aggravates the greenhouse issue.

Deforestation in Third World countries is particularly severe, with the destruction of tropical forests in countries like Brazil and Indonesia exceeding ten million hectares annually from activities like burning, logging and conversion to agricultural and pasture land. Indeed, the release of carbon dioxide into the atmosphere as a consequence of deforestation amounts to 2,000 million to 10,000 million tons per year. Concentrations of second important greenhouse gas, nitrous oxide, have also been rising, probably because of heavier fossil fuel use, more agricultural activity and other ecological disturbances. Average global atmospheric levels of nitrous oxide are increasing at an annual rate of 0.2 per cent. Both carbon dioxide and nitrous oxide are quite stable compounds; carbon dioxide remains in the upper atmosphere for decades after its release, and nitrous oxide for considerably more than a century. In the absence of major reductions in emissions of these gases their concentrations will continue to grow. One popular group of volatile chemicals known as chlorofluorocarbons (CFCs) is believed to be currently responsible for 15 to 20 per cent of the global warming trend. These synthetic chemicals are brought in use as refrigerants, propellants, solvents and thermal insulators. A related class of bromine-containing chemicals called "halons" is found in fire extinguishing systems. Atmospheric concentrations of CFC-11 and CFC-12 among the most commercially important chlorofluorocarbons, are growing at a rate of more than seven per cent annually as a result of more world production in recent years.

Fig. 16.1. Scientists of the U.S. Department of Agriculture undertake tests to determine the impact of global warming on cotton plants.

Although their concentrations are small relative to that of carbon dioxide, CFCs are up to 10,000 times more potent in absorbing infrared radiation. After having released CFCs and halons reside in the atmosphere for a century or more because of their great chemical stability at low altitudes.

Consequently, an immediate 85 per cent decrease in emissions of CFC-11 and CFC-12 would be necessary merely to stabilize their atmospheric concentrations. With their long atmospheric lifetimes, CFCs and halons eventually go till the upper atmosphere. There, they are the principal culprits in the worldwide loss of the protective stratospheric ozone layer, which shields life on the planet Earth from harmful levels of ultraviolet solar radiation. Methane, the principal component of natural gas, is another significant climate-modifying chemical. It has an atmospheric residence duration of about 11 years. Average global concentrations of methane are increasing by about one per cent per year. Animal husbandry and rice cultivation have been identified as major sources of grown methane emissions; coal mining and landfills are also significant sources, with large potential for growth in the future. Low-level ozone is another greenhouse gas.

Although ozone in the stratosphere is useful, this highly unstable chemical is the leading component of photochemical smog pollution at the Earth's surface.

Developed World and Industrial Emissions

While greenhouse gases are dispersed relatively fast throughout the global atmosphere after release, industrial emissions of these heat-absorbing chemicals are highly concentrated in the third world. In 1985, 23 per cent of total global emissions of more than 20,500 million tons of carbon dioxide produced in the United States. Other major contributors are the Soviet Union (19 per cent), Western Europe (15 per cent), Japan (five per cent) and the People's Repubilc of China (11 per cent). Other developing nations together accounted for only 20 per cent of total industrial carbon dioxide emissions. Emissions of CFCs are even more strongly skewed. In 1980, the United States generated roughly 28 per cent of the global total. Western Europe produced about 30 per cent, industrialized Asian countries 12 per cent and the Eastern bloc countries an estimated 14 per cent. The developing nations accounted for just over two per cent of this amount. (In the December 1990 issue, *SPAN* reported on recently passed amendments for America's Clean Air Act.) An international scientific consensus now supports the assertion that the accumulation in the atmosphere of carbon dioxide, nitrous oxide, CFCs, methane and short-level ozone could have far-reaching effects on the Earth's climate. By as early as the year 2030, the heat-retaining capacity of the atmosphere may have increased by an amount equal to doubling preindustrial concentrations of carbon dioxide. The absolute magnitude of the temperature changes and their will exceed any previously experienced in human history.

(a) The Results: Consequences of a greenhouse-driven climate disruption will be characterized with complete certainty only after significant damage has already occurred. However, among the most dramatic possible effects is an unprecedented rise in sea-level resulting from thermal expansion of the oceans and melting of glaciers and polar ice. Over the past century, the average global sea-level has increased less than 15 centimetres. By comparison, the sea-level will have a total increase of between 30 and 213 centimetres by 2075, depending on the degree of global warming that takes place.

The effect of sea-level rise in the United States is likely to be severe. The anticipated increase in the elevation of the oceans could permanently inundate low-lying coastal plains, accelerate the destruction of shorelines and beaches, increase the salinity of drinking water aquifers and biologically sensitive estuaries, and increase the susceptibility of coastal properties to storm destruction. An increase of one-and-a-half to two metres in sea-level would submerge 30 to 80 per cent of the coastal wetlands in the United States, which are crucial to the growth of commercially important fisheries. Extensive existing coastal development may check the widespread formation of new wetlands.

Even in undeveloped coastal areas, the rapidity of the predicted sea-level hike will mean that existing wetlands would be lost faster than new ones can be created. The increase in elevation of the oceans will also surely affect the approximately 50 per cent of the Earth's population that inhabits coastal regions. A rise in sea level of just one metre could flood an area of the Nile Delta that constitutes 12 to 15 per cent of Egypt's aráble land, produces a similar part of the Egyptian annual Gross National Product (GNP), and is home to a comparable percentage of the country's 51.4 million people.

In Bangladesh, a one-metre rise would inundate 11.5 per cent of the country's land area, displace 9 per cent of the 112.3 million people and threaten 8 per cent of the GNP. The dramatic anticipated growth in global temperature are virtually certain to cause a wide variety of modifications in regional climates. In middle latitudes, summertime temperature growth is expected to exceed the global average by 30 to 50 per cent. Forests could begin to die off as early as the year 2000 if they are unable to adapt to rapidly shifting climatic zones. Regions of agricultural productivity could shift at the expense of the American Midwest, which presently has some of the most fertile soils in the world. Even a moderate warming could decrease wheat and cereal yields by three to 17 per cent.

Computer models forecast continental drying in middle latitudes, which means that parched soils, scorching droughts and massive heat waves, like those that destroyed crops in the American Midwest in the summer of 1988, could become commonplace. Water levels in the Great Lakes could drop by 30 centimetres, intervening with navigation for ocean-going vessels.

Countries with tropical climates could experience especially severe consequences. Semi-arid areas might suffer from even less rainfall; tropical humid climates could become hotter and wetter, with an increase in the frequency and severity of tropical storms.

Floods, which between 1968 and 1988 took lives of more than 80,000 people and affected at least 200 million more, could worsen. Indeed, climate disruption caused be the greenhouse effect may already be evident. Global temperatures in 1988 were at or close to the record for the period of instrumental data, with temperatures somewhat elevated relative to the average for the 30-year period beginning in 1950. And since there is a lag on the order of decades between emissions of greenhouse gases and their impact the level of heat-absorbing chemicals already released into the atmosphere has irrevocably committed the world to an extra warming over the next 50 years, even if the atmosphere's composition were stabilized today. The greenhouse effect, if uncontrolled, is also likely to cause unpredictable disruptions in the balance of power worldwide, exacerbating the risk of war.

Fig. 16.2. In the United States pine tree seedlings, found under controlled greenhouse conditions, will be transplanted in fields where the impact of airborne pollution on them will be monitored.

It is very possible that any region of the world will be a net "winner" from climate change. The very concept of "winning" implies the existence of a stable warmer climate, which will not happen unless the warming trend is halted. Even the limited goal of a steady-state warmer climate will require major policy change. Otherwise, greenhouse gas concentrations and global temperatures will continue to increase indefinitely, nullifying any short-term benefits.

Though in this process, all countries are likely to be losers in the global climate gamble, some countries have more at stake than others. The United States has a specifically large investment in the status quo. Impending climate change means that the productivity of the country's natural resources can no more be taken for granted.

America has one of the most productive agricultural sectors on Earth, producing nearly half of the world's corn and nearly 60 per cent of its soybeans. It is also the world's leading exporter of wheat and corn. On the other hand, the Soviet Union is one of the planet's largest importers of wheat and corn. Climate models suggest that this pattern could change dramatically if the American Midwest became 10 to 20 per cent drier and crop yields were areas. At the same time, Soviet agricultural areas, located considerably farther north, could suffer smaller losses in productivity relative to their American counterparts.

Ill effects of greenhouse warming will also be felt in other parts of the world, potentially fueling turbulent regional conflicts that could disturb the existing global balance of power. Loss of low-lying territory could create refugee problems of an unprecedented scale. Competition over region and natural resources launched by those displaced could create or exacerbate regional strife. Famine by greenhouse-driven crop failures could also create regional clashes that might encourage the major powers to take sides. Such an acceleration in showdowns among the superpowers would shake the world political balance in highly unpredictable ways.

The Ill Effects

The worst effects of a greenhouse-induced climate cataclysm can be averted. And the sooner action is taken, better it will be:

(1) CFCs and halons are by far the easiest component of the greenhouse problem to eliminate. Motivated by concern over the control role these chemicals play in depleting the stratospheric ozone layer, 45 countries and one international organization have signed the Montreal Protocol on Substances which Deplete the Ozone Layer, which took effect at the beginning of 1989 after negotiations sponsored by the UN Environment Program.

(2) Aside from representing a diplomatic milestone for international cooperation on environmental problems, the Montreal Protocol is significant precedent for a multilateral strategy on the more challenging issue of greenhouse warming.

(3) The Montreal Protocol needs an incremental 50 per cent reduction in the consumption of five ozone-depleting CFCs by the end of this century. In July 1989, consumption of these substances was checked at 1986 levels. A reduction of 20 per cent must be achieved beginning in July 1993, and an additional 30 per cent beginning in July 1998.

(4) Every country may implement these requirements as it chooses through recycling, destruction, or abandonment of unnecessary uses of these chemicals. Anyway, the overall strategy is to stimulate the development of alternatives to CFCs by constricting supply. The Montreal Protocol carries groundbreaking trade incentives for broad participation, including a ban on imports of controlled substances from those countries who are not party to the accord. It resolves delicate equity issues by allowing Third World countries a ten-year grace period to make required reductions.

(c) Drawbacks of Montreal Protocol: In spite of the precedential importance of the Montreal Protocol, the agreement is inadequate. Due to loopholes and leakages built into the document, the actual reductions in emissions of substances controlled by the protocol will be only about one-third under even the most optimistic assumptions. Consumption of halons is just leveled off, not reduced.

The agreement explicitly specifies that production—as distinct from consumption of CFCs and halons may really increase by as much as ten per cent over the 1986 level. It is now clear that emissions of CFCs and halons must be virtually eliminated because of the overwhelming risks these chemicals affect climate and stratosipheric ozone. Soon after the Montreal Protocol was signed, a seasonal thinning of 50 per cent of the ozone layer over Antarctica—the ozone "hole"—was conclusively linked to CFCs.

New and widely accepted scientific evidence documents that average global losses in stratospheric ozone of about 3 per cent—two to three times that previously predicted by computer models—have already taken. Even if CFCs and halons are phased out within five to seven years, the long atmospheric lifetimes of these chemicals mean that the environment could take up to a century to recover.

For stabilizing global concentrations of carbon dioxide gas, it will be necessary to cut global emissions of carbon dioxide by at least one-half. Burning fossil fuels releases most of the extra carbon dioxide in the atmosphere. Because no economical technology for removing carbon dioxide from waste-gas streams is now available, reducing back releases of carbon dioxide will require a lower total energy consumption and a shift in energy sources toward low-or non-carbon dioxide emitting technologies. Cuts in fossil fuel use will also ease other environmental problems associated with current patterns of energy use, such as acid rain and local air pollution.

Despite the most optimistic assumptions about economic growth, major reductions in carbon dioxide emissions from industrialized countries can be attained with energy conservation, efficiency technologies and renewable energy sources.

For example, the 1,200 kilowatt hours per year used by a typical frost-free refrigerator can be reduced to only 500 with a state-of-the-art model. Latest technology can light an office building with an expenditure of only 0.55 watts per square metre, as little as one-fifth of today's average. It is now possible to produce motor vehicles that have fuel economies of up to 42 kilometres per litre, two to five times as efficient as those now on the road. Efficiency betterments have meant that the amount of energy used in the United States today is about the same as in 1973 despite a 40 per cent hikes in GNP during the same period.

Application of existing efficiency technologies could reduce US carbon dioxide emissions by 14 to 18 per cent by the end of the century. Reversing deforestation and generating new forested areas will help to offset current levels of carbon dioxide emissions. New forests, in absorbing carbon dioxide from the air during photosynthesis, will help in climate stabilization by serving as supplementary reservoirs for carbon. Aggressive policies to conserve existing forests and create new forested areas will yield other environmental benefits, including erosion checks and the preservation of species whose genetic potential is only now becoming accessible to humankind.

(D) Contribution of Third World: Similar response to the special needs of developing countries is crucial to removing greenhouse threats to the global climate. While developing countries have caused little of the problem to date, as economic development accelerates they may account for the preponderance of greenhouse gas emissions by the middle of the next century. At the same time, these countries, with less resources to adapt to environmental disturbances, stand to suffer disproportionately from a fast climate change.

For example, the productivity of common rice varieties falls off greatly at temperatures just a few degrees more than those prevailing in many rice growing areas. Tapping the tremendous potential for conservation and improved end-use efficiency in the developing nations would contribute to a solution for greenhouse warming while meeting much of the Third World's growing energy needs. However, macro-economic policies in most of developing countries, such as electricity price subsidies, discourage conservation and efficiency improvements.

Firms in Brazil, where electricity prices are subsidized manufacture energy-efficient air conditioners for export but cheap, inefficient models for consumption at home. Investments in efficiency require less capital and less foreign exchange than do comparable amounts of new power supply, contributing to overall economic productivity.

By efficiency and conservation, developing countries could avoid at least $1,400,000 million in power supply expansion rates between now and the year 2008. Efficiency investments represent a major opportunity for donors like the United States and the World Bank to assist developing countries in making energy choices that avoid blunders made earlier in the developed world and reduce risks to the entire planet from the effects of greenhouse warming. The World Bank, which limits an annual energy lending portfolio averaging $3,500 million, is one of the principal donors supporting power generation, projects in the Developing World.

Through measures such as pricing reforms and improvements in the operation of existing power plants and distribution systems, the bank has already made a commitment to enhance conservation and the efficient use of energy. There is anyway, considerably more than that the bank can do. Demand-reduction measures, such as end-use efficiency improvements, which are most of the time, economically as well as environmentally superior to investments in energy supply, have not been consistently considered as alternatives to conventional power production projects by the bank. Demand- reduction options would help developing countries reduce the rate of growth in power generating and greenhouse gas emissions without sacrificing energy required current for economic development.

Forest policy is another area where development assistance can provide benefits to Third World nations while cutting emissions of greenhouse gases. Donor countries historically have devoted little capital to conservation of this crucial resource and have earmarked even less for new forest areas.

Also, developed countries provide the main market for tropical hardwoods, virtually all of which are unsustainably harvested, and firms based in industrialized countries after reap the profits of this trade. Governments of industrialized nations can take a serious look at controlling trade in tropical woods and compensate exporting countries for lost revenues through alternative investments.

The Third World of Debt crisis presents major opportunities for encouraging better forest management in developing countries. As the market value of such debt has came down, a number of private banks have sold debt owed to them by Third World governments to private conservation organizations, which have then moved off the debt in return, for example, for a commitment by the governments concerned to conserve a particular area and to support its maintenance with a stream of payments with local currency. Such "debt. for nature" swaps are already in place in Bolivia, Costa Rica and Ecuador, and more are under negotiation.

(e) The Golden Path of Multilateral Approach: Cooperative policies on the international level to fight greenhouse warming will maximize environmental and foreign policy benefits. While unilateral cuts in releases of greenhouse gases by large emitters will go a long way toward arresting global climate disruption, a multilateral consensus strategy will push the crucial goals of creating incentives for universal participation and establishing an equitable balance of responsibility for solving the problems. Present international mechanisms are an important part of such a strategy.

Indian Scientists studying the greenhouse effect have published hundreds of papers detailing their findings. In 1982, A.P. Mitra, now director-general of the Council of Scientific and Industrial Research, published a monograph on "Human Influences on the Atmospheric Environment." A year later, an Indo-US workshop on ozone was held at the National Physical Laboratory (NPL) in New Delhi.

Among the many current NPL projects is the sutdy of methane, a major climate-modifying gas. In the photo above, scientist Prabhat Kumar Gupta (left) and an assistant test the amount of methane produced in paddy fields in different regions in India under the International Geosphere-Biosphere Program.

A reassessment of the Montreal Protocol, a process that is incorporated in the document itself, is the most expeditious way to eliminate the contributions CFCs and halons make to the global-warming problem. The World Bank's institutional structure also involves mechanisms for member countries to redirect priorities in the critical energy and forest sectors. The remainder of the greenhouse problem could be handled most effectively through a multilateral treaty, with standards bound under international law that would require each country to take prescribed actions to reduce and halt greenhouse warming.

Any multilateral treaty to arrest global climate changes should satisfy several basic requirements.

(a) It must need reductions in releases of greenhouse gases of a magnitude and at a speed sufficient to stabilize the Earth's climate.

The most important gas to control is carbon dioxide, for which global cuts of at least 50 percent are necessary. Participating countries should accomplish these reductions by means of environmentally and economically affluent technologies that do not present unacceptable risks to public health or world security.

The creation of new forested areas might be encouraged by allowing credits against reductions of carbon dioxide emissions that would otherwise be required and by provisions establishing or promoting me forestry programmes. Because the agreement would likely to cover a large number of emission sources, it should mandate strict mechanisms for enforcement through reporting of emissions, on-site audits and internationally controlled remote sensing.

(b) Equal responsibility, the responsibility for making reductions must be distributed equitably. Among the mode that could be applied is relative national wealth as measured by per capita GNP. Another test could be per person emissions of carbon dioxide, with the highest of reductions required of those countries with the maximum emission per unit of populations.

(c) A treaty should also require a commitment from the wealthier countries for more research into non-carbondioxide energy supply technologies and development assistance to help poorer countries meet the requirements forced on them by the agreement. One mechanism for generating the necessary capital is to require countries to contribute to a money in proportion to their carbon dioxide emissions.

Keeping the importance of the resources at risk, it would be nothing short of reckless to continue with business as usual. A failure to respond to the fears of greenhouse warming would amount to an affirmative decision to wager the health and well-being of current and in view coming generations against overwhelming odds.

17

Computer and Scientific Study of Environmental Change

Since environment is a complex phenomena, so, its study require systemic scientific tools not only for today, but also for future predictions. Article of the UN Framework Convention on Climate Change (FCCC) defines the threatened climate system as "the totality of the atmosphere, hydrosphere, biosphere, and geosphere and their interactions". This way of framing the issue notes that the reasons for climate change, such as fossil fuel combustion, deforestation, and rice and cattle agriculture, extend across the face of the planet. They are embedded in core sectors of modern economic systems and affect the routine activities of everyone on the planet.

The global-risk perspective emphasizes that the projected consequences of climate change will implicate virtually all human communities and natural ecosystems. In the beginning of twenty-first century, then, climate change can be put forward as the quintessential global environmental problem.

Historical Evolution of Science in Environment Studies

Yet when the human risks posed by rising atmospheric concentrations of carbon dioxide were first noticed in the late 1950s and early 1960s, they were often understood primarily in local or regional, rather than global, terms. As with other environmental problems, such as earthquakes, urban smog, and drought, the impacts of climate change would, it was thought, affect some places more severely than others. In most places, on this view, people would simply adapt to these changes.

Thus, a 1966 report by the US National Research Council (NRC) expressed complacency about climate change:

"It is perhaps worth nothing that, even in the more extreme estimates of the possible climatic consequences of increased atmospheric CO_2, the calculated temperature changes have been of the order of a few degrees, generally less than five or ten. From glacial-geologic data, it is known with some certainty that North America and Europe have, since the last maximum of the Wisconsin Glaciation, experienced climates that have averaged several degrees warmer than the present. As mentioned earlier, although some of the natural climatic changes have had locally catastrophic effects, they did not stop the steady evolution of civilization."

After the passage of two decades, in its 1983 report *Changing Climate*, the NRC once again stressed that climate change not only could, but for pragmatic purposes should, be defined "flexibly" in local terms:

"Viewed in terms of energy, global pollution, and worldwide environmental damage, the "CO_2 problem" appears intractable. Viewed as a problem of changes in local environmental factors—rainfall, river flow, sea level—the myriad of individual incremental problems take their place among the other stresses to which nations and individuals adapt. It is important to be flexible both in definition of the issue, which is really more climate change than CO_2, and in maintaining a variety of alternative options for response."

Besides all this, by the mid-1980s, most conceptions of climate change painted its risks almost exclusively in global terms. How, and why, did scientific and political discourses about the human risks of climate change turn the emphasis from local to global concerns? To answer this question, this chapter will explore in detail the history of the competing, and contested, representations of climate through which the present day's debate has been structured. One clue comes from an important scientific paradigm shift. Historically, the science of climatology consisted primarily of record keeping and analysis of climate trends at a given location (see Miller, forthcoming). Although a global conception of weather had developed by the early 1900s, climatology continued for decades along this rather separate, particularistic track.

Even in the 1960s and 1970s, the major scientific tools for representing climate remained the long-term statistical databases compiled by climatologists. But in the decade between about 1965 and 1975, the locally oriented climatologists were quickly displaced by a new breed of global modelers.

By the late 1970s, computer-based climate models—more or less identical to the weather models in use since the 1950s, although used differently (see below)—had come to dominate climatological discourse. With this change, the very meaning of *climate* changed from a local to a global understanding. The term climatology gradually fell from favor (although it is still used), replaced by the term *climate science*. This shift reflected the new model-based, globally oriented paradigm.

Present Day State of Affairs

Now, climate models are essential not only for predicting future climates, but also for attributing the causes of climatic change in the recent past. With for out a model of what would have happened *without* anthropogenic (human-caused) environmental change, scientists cannot separate out the effects of rising greenhouse gas concentrations from natural climatic variability. The inherent variability of weather makes it impossible to attribute individual disasters like storms, floods, droughts, or hurricanes to changes in the global climate. Only by coupling statistical analyses to climate modeling exercises have scientists been able to isolate and display the "fingerprint" of global warming in changing weather situation around the world.

Owing to its long-terms, statistical character, even local climate change is difficult to grasp experientially. A few hot summers, an unusual spate of major storms, or even a decade-long drought can be elements of "normal," regional climate variation, instead of signals of long-term climate change. By the same token, *global* climate change cannot be grasped experientially at all. The most commonly cited figure in climate change debates—change in the average world temperature—has no correlate in anyone's actual living conditions.

Thus, while public awareness and understanding of climate change have always depended on the work of the scientific community, they do so ever more today than ever before. Knowledge of climate change, in the contemporary sense of the term, comes only from science; in Bruno Latour's phrase, climate modeling has become an " obligatory passage point" for information of climate change.

Furthermore, knowledge about changes in the global climate system depends on very many sciences, from meteorology to oceanography to ecology. Various theories, models, standards of evidence, and data sets of these various contributors are generally quite, different, not to mention contested. Modern climate science is a multidisciplinary and interdisciplinary field, rather instead of speciality of statistical climatology. The increasingly complex articulation between a science-based, descriptive understanding and normative climate politics—where the global climate is understood as a system in which political intervention could be both important and effective—has generated unprecedented interdisciplinary scientific collaboration and political coordination. These phenomena needs historical explanation. At the same time, they present an opportunity to grapple with the central question of knowledge-power relationships at the interfaces between local, national, and worldly communities. How have scientists tied the wide-ranging strands of their work together? How have their effort linked up with the formation of new transnational scientific and political communities? How have specific representations of climate linked multiple communities of researchers, government officials, and citizens? How have national efforts differed and conflicted, and how have these differences been caped with in the international community? These are the kinds of questions to which a science studies theoretical approach may offer new and different answers.

This chapter focuses on two key "boundary objects" in this enormous and enormously confusing arena: computer models of the atmosphere and global satellite data sets. Boundary objects are things, theories, symbols, or other entities used by multiple communities; even if they may have different meanings and functions for each group, they provide conceptual and pragmatic links that bind the communities together. Computer models and global data sets perform this role for many of the scientific and political groups focused on climate change.

Significance of Computer Models

There are arguably the single most important tool of global climate science. They range in size from simple programmes that can run on a desktop computer to ultracomplicated simulation models of the entire Earth system, which are useful for even the most powerful supercomputers. Much of climate science could not exist without them, since planetary-scale processes cannot be studied by controlled laboratory experiments. Rather, climate science relies on global "experiments" performed on models to provide it with insights into the dynamics of the atmospheric system as a whole.

Satellite data—encompassing many facets of the atmosphere, and a smaller number of characteristics of the Earth's oceans, ice, snow, and land surfaces—are likewise central to contemporary scientific understandings of the entire planet. While many other forms of data are collected on a worldwide basis (from surface stations, radar, weather balloons, ships, and so on), their coverage is far less uniform, less easily standardized, and less easily collected in a single location. The vital size of global data sets makes it impossible to process or understand them in any detail without the aid of computers (Edwards 1999).

In fact, global data sets of the relevant density cannot even be collected without the aid of computerized interpolation models that mediate between raw instrument readings and usable data formats.

I. Environmental Science: Instruments

Here, will begin by describing briefly the scientific concepts on which the models are based and how these models work.

(a) Principles of Atmospheric Science

The principal sources of atmospheric science lie in various branches of physics: theories of the behaviour of gases (pressure, temperature), the radiation absorption and emission characteristics of various gases, and turbulent fluid (gas) flows. The earth is bathed in a constant flood of solar energy, all of which it ultimately reradiates into space. One important aspect of climate, the Earth's temperature, is therefore a matter of what climate scientists call *energy balance*: all the energy that goes into the system must, eventually, come out again. The atmosphere forms a blanket of gases (mainly nitrogen, oxygen, and water vapor) capable of absorbing the holding a great deal of this incoming energy as heat. The oceans, too, absorb and retain heat. They play a major role in the total climate system, "damping" the system's response to change with their enormous heat-retention capacity (far larger than the atmosphere's). In theory, if the earth had no atmosphere its average surface temperature would be near -19°C. Instead, the heat retained in the atmosphere maintains it at the current global average of about 15°C. Due to the influence of solar heating and the earth's rotation, both the atmosphere and the oceans "circulate," carrying heat around the globe in moves of air and water. The general circulation refers to the motion and state of the entire atmosphere (or ocean); it is sometimes (more aptly) termed the global circulation. Ultimately, the circulation conducts heat from the equator, which receives the maximum amount of incoming energy from the sun, to the poles, where more heat is radiated into space than is received. Since weather moves freely around the globe and changes with considerable speed, merely by modeling the general circulation can meteorologists hope to understand the evolution of weather over more than a couple of days. The rotation of the earth on its axis in relation to the sun, atmospheric and oceanic turbulence, and many other factors render circulation patterns highly complex.

In the short term (hours to weeks), such patterns are experienced as weather: rain, dry spells, clouds, hurricanes. Long-term patterns (occurring over months to decades, and beyond) are understood as climate, and include such phenomena as the seasons, with their regular annual changes in temperature and precipitation; prevailing regional climates (deserts, tropics, ice caps, and so forth); multiyear environmental variations (droughts, the El Nino/Southern Oscillation, and so on); and very long-term climate changes such as ice ages.

(b) Climate Models

These are mathematical simulations, based on physical principles, of these long-term atmospheric conditions. Although many discussions focus on the most complicated, supercomputer-based climate models, in fact there is a wide range of complexity, sometimes addressed by scientists as the hierarchy of models.

(1) The simplest, "zero-dimensional" models rely solely on the principle of energy balance. Using measured values for the factors like solar radiation and concentrations of the atmosphere's constituent gases, they compute (for example) a single global average temperature, treating the earth as if it were a point mass. Models this basic may involve merely a few equations and can readily be solved by hand.

(2) One and two-dimensional energy-balance models also exist. Another class of two-dimensional models, called *radiative-convective*, measures the atmosphere's vertical temperature structure. In these models, temperature is computed as a function of latitude and either longitude (a second horizontal dimension) or air pressure (the vertical dimension). Many two-dimensional models are relatively simple-typically, a few hundred to a few thousand lines of computer code-compared to the three-dimensional.

(3) These models known as atmospheric general circulation models (GCMs, or AGCMs to distinguish them from OGCMs, which model the oceanic general circulation).

(4) Contemporary atmospheric GCMs are clearly expressed in some 30,000 to 60,000 lines of FORTRAN code. They represent the atmosphere as a three-dimensional lattice or "grid." Typically, the grid resolution at the surface is 3°-5° latitude by 6°-8° longitude. (This goes roughly into squares or rectangles 300 to 500 km on a side). Eight to twenty layers of varying depth represent the vertical dimension up to a height of 20 km or so, with more surfaces at lower altitudes, where the atmosphere is denser and most weather occurs.

Equations of state computer the effect of various forces (radiation, convective heating, and so on) on the air masses and moisture (clouds and water vapor) within each grid box. Equations of motion compute the direction and fastness of the air's movement into the surrounding grid boxes. AGCMs usually also include representations of certain aspects of the land surface, such as elevation and albedo (reflectance). Moreover, they usually include some representation of the oceans, which may be as simple as a shallow, one-layer "swamp" ocean with regular surface temperature. Today's most sophisticated models dynamically couple AGCMs to full-scale OGCMs of equivalent complexity. In addition, they may also include models of sea ice, snow cover, vegetation, agriculture, and other natural phenomena with important effects on climate; such models are sometimes known as Earth Systems Models (ESMs).

As we all in study of environment can well asume that such models demand enormous computational power. The first GCMs required twenty-four hours of computer time in order to simulate a single day of global circulation. By the mid-1970s, faster computers decreased the time to about twelve hours per simulated year. For a typical climate modeling run of twenty simulated years, a GCM still required as much as 240 hours—ten continuous dyas—of expensive supercomputer time. While computer speeds continue to increase, these long run times have declined little since then. Modelers prefer, instead, to represent more variables, increase resolution, and carry out longer runs.

Weather Forecast and the Computers

Modern weather forecasters also use GCMs. Weather forecasters use the highest possible model resolution, because their purpose is prediction and because their model runs are only a few days. Principally, weather models must resolve relatively small-scale processes, such as the formation and motion of clouds. Grid cells as small as 60 km on a side are common in the best present weather GCMs. They are initialized with observational data, such as temperature, humidity, and wind speed, from a wide range of sources, including surface weather stations, satellites, and radiosondes (weather balloons). The models then measure the likely evolution of this observed initial state over short periods (hours to days).

On the other hand, climate modelers, use *coarse-grid* GCMs that cannot simulate clouds and many other atmospheric processes directly; climate scientists refer to such phenomena as *sub-grid-scale* processes. This necessitates *parameterization,* or representation of small-scale changes by large-scale variables (Hack 1992; Kiehl 1992). In addition, when used for climate research, GCMs generally are not initialized with observational data. Instead, GCMs are autonomous simulations that cause their own "climates," starting—in principle, if not in practice—with only a few empirically drawn inputs such as solar radiation, gas composition of the atmosphere, sea surface temperatures, and orbital precession. These simulated climates must be moved until they stabilize, then compared with observed long-term trends and phenomena in the earth's climate system. This needs multidecade, even millennia-long time series (Manabe and Stouffer 1994,1979,1994; Wigley, Pearman, and Kelly 1992). These characteristics of climate modeling lead to uncertainties and epistemological issues discussed by several authors.

Global Data Networks

The concept of anthropogenic climate change has surprisingly deep historical roots, reaching back over 100 years. In this section, we discuss the background of climate modeling and its role in the emergence of climate change as a political issue.

(a) Initial Approaches: Scientific theories of climate change date back to mid-nineteenth century. In 1824, Jean-Baptistc Joseph Fourier hypothesized that the atmosphere retains heat, keeping the earth's surface temperature far higher than it would be if the earth had no atmosphere if the atmosphere carried no water vapor or carbon dioxide (CO_2). Fourier likened the heating action of the atmosphere to a "hothouse," thus christening what we now call the greenhouse effect.

(1) Well-known Physicist John Tyndall, in Great Britain, first calculated the radiative potential of CO_2 in 1863. His result paved the way for the Swedish scientist Svante Arrhenius, in 1896, to make the very first calculation of the contribution of carbon dioxide to the earth's surface temperature. In 1900, another British scientist, T.C. Chamberlin, published a sweeping theory of climatic change over geological time scales, with CO_2 as the primary mechanism. Chamberlin argued that volcanic eruptions produce CO_2, warming the earth; the weathering of rocks absorbs the gas, accounting for glacial cycles. Chamberlin's opinion that CO_2 was the *determining* factor in global climate change is no longer current. Orbital cycles, water vapor, ocean currents, and other factors are presently believed to be more important. Yet Chamberlin did identify one of the basic mechanisms.

(2) During this year, 1903 Arrhenius went on to calculate that the CO_2 added to the atmosphere by human combustion of fossil fuels might eventually raise the earth's temperature substantially. Indeed, he predicted that if the amount of CO_2 in the atmosphere were to double, the global average temperature would rise somewhere between 1.5° and 4°C. What else, the most sophisticated modern climate models run on supercomputers still predict approximately this same range of probable change. Arrhenius, perhaps since he lived in a highly cold place, thought that such a global warming might be a good thing. But in his time, world consumption of fossil fuels remained low enough that this seemed merely an idle speculation, not a near-term feasibility. Tellingly, Arrhenius also computed the effect of decreasing CO_2

on the atmosphere. He noted that natural factors might also produce such a change.

Apart from the fact that these scientists never thought of climate change as a political concern, in fact concern about anthropogenic climate change long predates the present concept of greenhouse warming. James R. Fleming, Nico Stehr, Hans von Storch, and Moritz Flugel have uncovered numerous historical episodes of attribution of climatic changes to human causes.

For instance, in the Middle Ages climate anomalies were sometimes explained by the church as a divine response to human sin (Stehr, von Storch, and Flügel 1995), while Thomas Jefferson apparently believed that clearing land for agriculture changed the climate of the early United States in favourable ways (Fleming 1998). Similarly, Richard Grove (1997) has argued that some nineteenth-century colonial forest policies gave on a "dessicationist" theory of relations between deforestation and local, regional, and even continental climate change. According to Grove, these policies are the direct ancestors of some modern forest-conservation agendas. Grove also tells that colonial meteorologists in India and Australia developed early theories of global "teleconnections" (long-distance interactions of ocean currents and weather patterns, such as El Nino) by finding coincidence between Indian and Australian droughts.

(3) Approach which perhaps most nearly resembles modern climate politics occurred in the 1890s, when German scientists Edward Brückner and Julius Hann said (separately) that human-induced climatic warming was already occurring in Europe and America as a result of deforestation and other causes. They based their speculations on trends derived from observations, instead of physical theories of the atmosphere. Brückner thought that crop failures, economic crises, and epidemics would result, and argued that countries should undertake vast reforestation programmes to counteract the continuing trend. Prussia, Italy, and France established government reforestation committees as a result, while scientific societies debated the issue in the United States. In the end the issue fizzled, but it became a remarkable precursor to modern climate politics (Stehr and von Storch 2000).

(b) Weather Numerical Models: During the last century, the history of climate politics is intimately linked with the history of numerical models of the atmosphere, initially introduced to forecast weather. By the end of the nineteenth century, meteorology began to build theoretical foundations. By the early 1900s, the Norwegian meteorologist Vilhelm Bjerknes could argue that atmospheric physics had advanced sufficiently to allow weather to be predicted using calculations. He developed a set of seven differential equations, derived from basic physics, whose simultaneous solution would predict the large-scale movements of the atmosphere. Today these are popular as the primitive equations.

Bjerknes proposed a graphical calculus, based on weather maps, for solving the equations. This analog technique made no attempt to treat the problem numerically, a feat far beyond the limits of human or mechanical computers of the day. Although forecasters continued to use and develop his methods until the 1950s, both the absence of faster calculating methods and the dearth of accurate observational data limited their success (Nebeker 1995).

(i) Richardson's "Forecast Factory": In 1922, the English mathematician Lewis Fry Richardson evolved the first Numerical Weather Prediction (NWP) system. His calculating techniques—finite difference solutions of differential equations in a gridded space—were the same ones employed by the first generations of GCM builders. Richardson's method, relying on simplified versions of Bjerknes's equations, reduced the important calculations to a level where manual solution could be contemplated. Still, the task remained fantastically large. His own attempt to calculate weather for a single eight-hour duration took six weeks and ended in failure. Enormous calculation of this model requirements led Richardson to propose a fanciful solution he called the *forecast-factory*. The *"factory"*—really more like a vast orchestral performance—would have filled a large stadium with 64,000 people. Each one, armed with a mechanical calculator, would perform one element of the calculation. A leader, stationed in the center, would coordinate the forecast using coloured signal lights and a telegraph system. Despite all this, even with this impossible apparatus, Richardson thought he would probably be able to calculate weather only about as fast as it actually happens (Richardson 1922). Only in the 1940s, when digital computers made available automatic calculate on an unprecedented scale, did Richardson's technique become practical.

(ii) Functional Predictions: The Princeton mathematician John von Neumann was among the earliest computer pioneers. Engaged in computer simulations of nuclear weapons explosions, he suddenly saw parallels to weather prediction. (Both are nonlinear problems in fluid dynamics). In 1946, von Neumann began to advocate the application of computers to weather prediction (Aspray 1990). As a sincere opponent of Soviet-bloc communism and a key member of the World War II-era national security establishment, von Neumann hoped that weather modeling might lead to weather control. This, he was sure, might be used as a weapon of war. Soviet harvests, for example, might be ruined by a US-induced drought. On this basis, von Neumann sold out- his weather research to military funding agencies.Under grants from the Weather Bureau, the Navy, and the Air Force, he gathered a group of theoretical meteorologists at Princeton's Institute for Advanced Study (IAS). If regional weather prediction proved feasible, von Neumann planned to move on to the extremely ambitious problem of simulating the complete atmosphere. This, in turn, would allow the modeling of climate. Jule Charney, an energetic, visionary young meteorologist, was called to head the new Meteorology Group.

(iii) The Meteorology Project: It ran its first computerized weather forecast on the ENIAC in 1950. Although not identical to Richardson's, the group's model followed his in representing the atmosphere as a grid, calculating changes on a constant time step, and employing finite difference methods to solve differential equations numerically. The 1950 forecasts, covering North America and part of the surrounding ocean, used a two-dimensional grid with 270 points about 700 km away. The time step was three hours. Results, while far from perfect, were good enough to justify more work. Anticipating futures success, Charney and his colleagues convinced the weather Bureau, the Air Force, and the Navy to set up a Joint Numerical Weather Prediction (JNWP) Unit in 1954. In December of that year, an independent attempt at the Royal Swedish Air Force Weather Service became first in the world to use computer models for routine real-time weather forecasting (i.e., with broadcast of forecasts in advance of weather), using a model evolved at the University of Stockholm (Bergthorsson *et al.* 1955 ; University of Stockholm Institute of Meteorology 1954).

Routine computer forecasting began in the United States in mid-1955.

(c) Circulation Model: Till the end of 1970s, the weather models used by forecasters were still regional or continental (vs. hemispherical or global) in scale, and they made no attempt to look ahead further than a few days. Calculations for numerical weather forecasts were confined to what could be accomplished in a couple of hours on then-primitive digital computers. Yet, for theoretical meteorologists, more interested in causal patterns than in real-time forecasting, general circulation modeling quickly became a kind of holy grail. By mid-1955 Norman Phillips had completed a two-layer computer model of the general circulation (Phillips 1956). Despite its primitive nature, Phillips's model is now regarded as the first working GCM. Like other early GCMs, this model employed major simplifying assumptions, modifying the equations to reduce the number of factors and calculations. As computer power grew, the need for simplifying assessments diminished (although as we will see, it has hardly vanished). Between the late 1950s and the early 1960s, a number of separate groups in the United States, England, and Germany started—more or less independently—to build many-leveled, three-dimensional GCMs based on the full Bjerknes/Richardson old equations. The General Circulation Research wing of the US Weather Bureau became of the first laboratory to build a continuing programme in general circulation modeling. It opened in 1955, under the direction of Joseph Smagorinsky. Smagorinsky realised that his charge was to continue with the final step of the von Neumann/Charney computer modeling program; a three-dimensional, global, primitive-equation general circulation model of the climate (Smagorinsky 1983). The lab—renamed the Geophysical Fluid Dynamics Laboratory (GFDL) in 1963—moved to Princeton University in 1968, where it rests.

Starting in the year, 1959, Smagorinsky and his colleagues, especially the Japanese emigre Syukuro Manabe, proceeded to develop a nine-level primitive-equation GCMs, still hemispheric. One more important general circulation modeling groups formed during the 1960s at UCLA, the US National Center for Atmospheric Research, the UK Meteorological Office, and elsewhere.

Before the decade came to an end, general circulation modeling was firmly established as a basic research tool of meteorology and climate science. The European Center for Medium Range Weather Forecasts (ECMWF), founded in 1975, was the first to employ a global (world level) general circulation model in operational weather forecasting, beginning in 1979. Today, most weather forecasting centers around the world get global and regional weather data from the ECMWF and very few other large centers; they may use these data as is, or plug them into their own regional models. GCMs have not replaced simpler models altogether; in fact, many climate model makers play off one and two-dimensional models against GCMs in the course of their research. But GCMs' sophistication and their apparent realism—as the highest-resolution theoretical representations presently available of the general circulation—have won them a possible inordinate prestige. Perhaps ironically, this is somewhat less true in the modeling community than among the "consumers" of model results in politics, the media, NGO sector, and academic communities, such as the one responsible for the book you are presently reading—wording on climate science and climate change.

(d) Data for Numerical Models: While modeling is, of course, one part of the story of meteorology and climate science, the collection and processing of weather data (and its derivative, climate data) is the other. Once meteorology had offered theories of the general circulation, scientists faced the problem of acquiring data commensurate with the models' needs and capabilities. As computers became the tools of choice for this purpose, this task evolved in unprecedented ways that basically transformed the atmospheric sciences. According to Miller and Edwards, international agreements to share weather observations date to the 1878 founding of the International Meteorological Organization (IMO). Long back prior to World War II, standard coding systems had been worked out to facilitate transfer of this information.

In 1951, under the UN, the IMO became the World Meteorological Organization (WMO). Both organizations developed and promoted data distribution systems and standardized observational methods. Computerized weather prediction brought vastly intensified needs for data and for ways to handle those data. Weather models required information about the conditions of the atmosphere from ground level to very high altitudes. Ideally, data would be collected from locations as near as possible to the points on the model three-dimensional grids. But in the 1950s, such data were just unavailable. Observation stations, concentrated in urban regions, provided only very scattered and irregularly spaced coverage of the world's oceans and sparsely populated land areas.

Moreover, the mere acquisition of weather information was only one step toward real-time numerical forecasting. The computer programs were useless without well-structured, reliable data in digital form. Most weather data, at that time, were gathered by analog instruments (e.g., mercury thermometers or barometers). A human instrument reader converted them into numbers (digits) and charted them on maps, interpolating medium values, by eye or with simple calculating aids. The time delays inherent in this analog-digital data conversion were magnified by delays in large distance communication. All of this imposed limitations on the scale of operational weather forecasting and left the global general circulation out of approach of predictive models. In 1954 "gathering, plotting, analyzing and feeding the necessary information for a 24-hour forecast into a computer [took] between 10 and 12 hours," with another hour needed for computation ("Long-Range Weather Forecasts by Computer," 1954).

Well into the 1960s, even in the industrialized world, much weather data was hand-recorded and hand-pro cessed before being entered into computers (Collins 1969). Data distributed in potentially machine-readable type, such as teletype, often arrived in a Babel of different formats, necessitating conversions (World Meteorological Organization 1962). Much of the available data was never used, since the time involved to code it for the computer would have delayed forecasts beyond their short useful lifetimes. Meteorologists had always engaged in "smoothing" data (eliminating anomalous data points). Another common practice was the interpolation of intermediate values from known ones. To feed the grids of computerized weather models, this activity became a central element of meteorological work. By the year 1960s, it was being automated.

The methods did not really change, but their automation required explicit, computer programmable theories of error, anomaly, and interpolation. The effect was at the same time, to render this data "massage" invisible (Filippov 1969). By the early 1960s, atmospheric scientists realized that the core issue of their discipline had been turned on its head by the computer. In the very recent past, through the data networks formed for World War II, they had acquired far more statistics than they could ever hope to use. But now, already, they did not have enough of it—at least not in the right formats (standard, computer processable), from the right places (uniform grid points), and at the right times (on the uniform time steps followed by the models). The computer, which had created the possibility of NWP, now also became a tool for refining, correcting, and shaping data to fit the models' needs.

(e) The Networks: The International Geophysical Year (IGY), a UN-sponsored program of global cooperative experiments to know about the earth's physical systems, including the atmosphere and the water sources like oceans (see Miller, chapter 6, this volume), began in 1957. As it opened, the theory of carbon dioxide-induced global warming was finding renewed scientific attention. Suess had already drawn conclusion that fossil fuel combustion was producing so much carbon that some of it remained in the atmosphere, causing a continual rise in the atmospheric concentration of carbon dioxide (Suess 1953).

Plass created new interest in carbon dioxide as a factor in climate change. The IGY's meteorological component concentrated most of its attention on the global general circulation problem. Three pole-to-pole chains of atmospheric observing stations were established along the meridians 10°E (Europe/Africa), 70°-80°W (of USA), and 140° W (Japan/Australia). Dividing the globe roughly into thirds, these stations coordinated their observations to gather data simultaneously on specially designated "Regular World Days" and "World Meteorological Intervals." An atmospheric rocketry program retrieved information from very high altitudes. Data from all aspects of the IGY were submitted at three World Data Centres, major repositories of climatological information to this day (Comité Spécial de I' Année Géophysique International 1958; Jones 1959).

The attempt of the IGY represent the first global data networks conceived on a scale to match the developing atmospheric models. Nevertheless, even these covered the Southern Hemisphere only sparely. They marked the beginning of a trend toward global programs such as the World Weather Watch (WWW) and the Global Atmospheric Research Program (GARP). WWW, coordinated by the WMO, eventually connected global data collection from satellites, rockets, buoys, radiosondes, and commercial aircraft as well as traditional observing stations. This was necessary, according to one participant, because "currently conventional methods will never be sufficient if the state of the atmosphere over the whole world is to be observed at reasonable cost with the time and space resolution which can be used with advantage in computer-assisted research and forecasting" (Robinson 1967, 410).

GARP's roots stem from a 1961 US proposal for "further cooperative efforts between all nations in weather prediction and eventually in weather control," backed by President John F. Kennedy (Robinson 1967, 409). Among GARP's leading organizers was Joseph Smagorinsky, founder of GFDL and builder of the first primitive equation GCM. With the participation of scientists from the United States, the Soviet Union, and many other countries, GARP eventually sponsored a series of regional and global observations and experiments.

At the height of the Cold War, the IGY and its successors marked a new era of international cooperation in meteorology. Despite the interesting links between climate change concerns, the IGY, and the construction of global digital data networks, the concrete issue of climate change had hardly, any, effect on data networks until the 1970s. Instead, the early impetus came from the desire of both weather forecasters and theoretical meteorologists to achieve better coverage of the globe.

The former were motivated by practical concerns of prediction. But the latter hoped to achieve a grander goal: modeling the detailed dynamics of the global atmosphere. By 1969, the WMO had called for extending the global atmospheric data network to monitor pollutants that might affect the climate, such as CO_2 and particulate aerosols. Anthropogenic climate change began to become a public policy issue within the US government.

However, it was almost two decades before global warming became a serious pubic concern at the level of mass politics. Meanwhile, attempts continued to build models capable of "realistically" representing the global climate, and to construct data sets accurate enough to distinguish "alarms" of long-term climatic change from the "noise" of natural climatic variation. These goals were tightly intertwined. Without global data sets, modelers could neither validate nor parameterize their models. Without the help of computers and satellites, uniformly gridded global data sets could not even be created, much less manipulated.

Without NWP models and GCMs, these data was difficult to be understood. The UN Conference on the Human Environment, held in Stockholm in 1972, approved plans for more comprehensive global data network "with little discussion" (Hart and Victor 1993). During the rest of the 1970s, increasingly sophisticated data collection and processing networks evolved in tandem with GCMs and weather models at NCAR, ECMWF, the US National Meteorological Center, and numerous other locations.

World Environmental Politics for the Models

Concerns of scientists about climate change allowed climate science to ride the 1970s political wave of environmentalism. By no means was this a cynical attempt at self -promotion; for many, it represented true alarm aroused by significant scientific results. Nevertheless, these worries provided practical reasons for accelerating expensive research programmes.

But in the 1970s, the immaturity of climate science and climate models received consensus on anthropogenic global warming impossible.

Climate theorists did not agree on the relative roles of such factors as solar variability, sunspots, and cloud feedbacks in environmental change; global cooling, some argued, was also a possibility (Edwards and Lahsen, forthcoming). Chaotic qualities of the climate system added to the uncertainty over model results. Nevertheless, by the late 1970s climate change had begun to generate an ever-broadening circle of scientific and policy concerns. At the First World Climate Conference in 1979, WMO scientists set up the World Climate Programme to coordinate and develop climate research and climate data. The "nuclear winter" issue of the early 1980s and the Antarctic "ozone hole" discovered in 1986 were the first events to push the general issue of anthropogenic atmospheric change to the level of front-page news (Edwards and Lahsen, forthcoming; Morrisette 1989; Schneider 1989).

Both issues generated an awareness that human actions were capable of causing sudden, potentially catastrophic changes in the atmosphere not just regionally, but on a global scale. The Cold War fizzled to a close, leaving a kind of "apocalypse gap" in popular political consciousness, which was readily filled by global warming issue. As the basis of key scientific results, computer models played substantial—even decisive—roles in the nuclear winter and ozone depletion issues as well as in environmental change. In 1985, at Villach, Austria, an influential climate-science conference recommended policy studies of climate change mitigation techniques, including international treaties. Ozone destruction concerns resulted in a near-comprehensive international ban on chlorofluoro-carbons, completed in 1990 after just five years of negotiation.

In 1988, the WMO and the UN Environment Program appointed the Intergovernmental Panel on Climate Change (IPCC). The group, consisting of experts on climate, ecology and environmental and social impacts from around the world, was asked to work as the scientific adviser for international climate negotiations. In 1990, the organization released its first report, designed as input to the Second World Climate Conference held later that year. The report noted a qualified consensus on two matters.

First, greenhouse gas concentrations were rising rapidly due to human activities.

Second, if this trend continued, global average temperatures were likely to rise somewhere between 1.5° C and 4° C by about 2050 AD.

Amongst all the panels, the IPCC played a crucial role in the 1992 UN Conference on Environment and Development (UNCED). The UNCED created the landmark FCCC. Signed by 165 nations, the Framework Convention entered into force in early 1994. It sets voluntary goals for stabilizing greenhouse gas emissions. More important, the FCCC need, signatories to prepare national greenhouse gas emission inventories and commits them to ongoing negotiations toward an international treaty on climate change (Bodansky 1993).

The IPCC carries on to provide scientific input to the periodic Conferences of Parties to the FCCC. An era of global atmospheric politics had dawned, with computer models at its very core. Associated with the political arrival of the climate change subject was a trend toward ever more comprehensive global models, from two directions. The first, *Earth system* or *Earth systems* models (ESMs), was a direct extension of natural-science attempts to couple oceanic and atmospheric general circulation models. The goal is to couple models of other climate-related systems (land surface, sea ice, and so on) to an OAGCM, eventually capturing all of the prominent elements of the total climate system including anthropogenic effects such as agriculture and artificial greenhouse gas release. In general, sophisticated models of human socioeconomic activities have been last in queue for integration into ESMs which focus most of their effort on natural systems. Most of these models descend from existing GCM efforts.

The second type, integrated assessment models (IAMs), aims to simulate the impacts of climate change on human society, and the costs and usefulness of possible mitigations (Alcamo 1994; Dowlatabadi and Morgan 1993; Hope 1993; Rotmans 1990, 1992). IAMs typically do not incorporate GCMs directly. Instead, they rely either on chosen and aggregated GCM outputs or on much simpler energy-balance climate models. Their purpose is to allow rough, rapid analysis of the possible effects of various politicoeconomic scenarios on environmental change. IAM developers generally spend much more of their energy than climate system modelers do on the social, political, and economic elements of their models, relying for the natural-systems side on outputs from other efforts lying in the natural sciences. IAMs incorporate empirically derived trends, heuristics, and unproven or qualitative theories into their modeling techniques far more freely than do climate and Earth system models. Their objective is comparison of policy scenarios and forecasting of trends, not prediction at statistically significant levels; this is the point of the term *assessment*. Not all IAM outputs are global in scope—for instance, the first IMAGE model focused primarily on the Netherlands (Rotmans 1990). Many IAM builders hope that their models—unlike the hypercomplex, supercomputer based ESMs—will be simple, transparent, and mobile enough that policy-makers, or perhaps their staffers or administrative agencies, can engage with the models directly. If so, they could observe for themselves, on a desktop computer, the differential influences of various politicoeconomic scenarios, such as carbon taxes, population stabilization, or reforestation efforts, on global change.

Table: GENESIS Earth system model and the IMAGE integrated assessment model: A Comparison

S. No.	*(A) GENESIS*	*(B) IMAGE*
1.	Roots:previous NCAR climate models	Roots: Ph.D. thesis
2.	Orientation:natural/physical science	Orientation: policy analysis tool
3.	Based on modernised,high-resolution atmospheric GCM; other models added later	Simple, one- or two-dimensional atmospheric models; modular; formaed as integrated unit
4.	Parameterization:moderate, relatively model-specific	Parameterization: extreme, literature-based
5.	Approach to terrestrial biosphere: potential vegetation, to be modified later by agriculture model	Approach to terrestrial biosphere: actual land use: mosaic of natural and human-altered landscapes
6.	Typical experiments: regional climate change due to CO_2 doubling, paleoclimate scenarios	Typical experiments: impacts of IPCC scenarios on Dutch coastal defenses; emissions
7.	Technology: supercomputers	Technology: PCs
8.	Architecture: partially modular, ,model-specific, but publicly available and user-manipulable within limits	Architecture: highly modular, open,links easily with other models, user-manipulable
9.	Institutional context: Interdis-Ciplinary Climate systems Group, climate and Global Dynamics Division, NCAR, USA	Institutional context: National Institute for Public Health and Environmental Protection (RIVM), Netherlands
10.	Audience/accessibility: climate science community terres-trial ecosystems	Audience/accessibility: climate science community, community, policy-makers, educators
11.	Funding: EPA; NSF	Funding: RIVM, European Economic Community

The idea is to offer policy-makers an effective way to know about a set of *heuristics*—a quasi-intuitive "feel" or rule of thumb based on, yet not fully determined by, data-driven analysis for global change policy options. Table follows compares a first-generation Earth system model i.e., GENESIS with a first-generation integrated assessment model (IMAGE).

Both the terms ESMs and IAMs have become focal points in a relatively new, very broad effort to integrate results and methods from many different sciences. Social, behavioural, economic, and policy sciences are components of this mix, albeit more so in IAMs than in ESMs. Doing this kind of modeling means that each discipline—often extending to members of policy communities, such as regulatory agencies—must ultimately embrace its data and principles in computer code that can "talk" to the model's other modules (i.e., perform "intermodel handoffs"). Thus, IAMs and ESMs are increasing the foci of an emerging epistemic community.

May be yes or no, they are ever used directly by policy-makers, ESMs and IAMs in fact contribute substantially to the basis of global change politics, in the important sense that they act as a central organizing principle for a large, growing, epistemologically coherent community. This community shares the crucial belief that global natural systems may be significantly affected by human activities—a faith to which few would have subscribed three decades ago.

It also, in general, shares the values that such systems are worth preserving and that rational political decision making can be obtained, at least to some degree, which could preserve them. Integrated model building contributes directly to this base of common assumptions, to a scientific macroparadigm that approves computer simulation as a substitute for (infeasible) traditional forms of experimentation, and to a network of individuals, laboratories, and institutions such as the US Global Change Research Program and the IPCC. The models support to create a public space, including shared knowledge, shared values, and access to common tools and data, for consensus building on global change issues. In this very important, totally nonpejorative sense, comprehensive model building—as the core represen- tation of the global atmosphere—is simult -aneously scientific and political.

Issues and Methods for World Level Models

With the fact that climate change became a major public issue in the last decade, an acrimonious debate about the relationship between models and data moved from the scientific arena into the mass media. IPCC "consensus" opinion met severe opposition from a small but vocal "contrarian" group, especially in the United

States. These skeptics raised many objections to models, from poor parameterization of cloud feedbacks to differences between the studied warming to date (about 0.5°C) and model calculations showing a 1°C warming for the same period (white 1990). Recently, GCMs incorporating particulate aerosol effects have aligned more closely with observations; the IPCC's most recent report say that "the balance of evidence suggests a discernible human influence on global climate".

But despite the appearance of scientific consensus and goes toward a binding emissions-limitation treaty at the international level, debate continues into the present, with skeptics arguing that models cannot be trusted without higher levels of observational confirmation. These debates are at the same time scientific, political, and epistemological. They go to the heart of the question of what we know about the world and how we can know it. At the same time, by projecting the extent and impacts of climatic change in the future, and by finding it in data about the past, they set the stage for policy choices.

(a) Problems of Computerisation

GCMs recompute the state of the whole atmosphere every fifteen to thirty simulated minutes. This process is extremely computationally intensive. At each time step, hundreds to thousands of complex calculations must be imposed on each of the tens of thousands of grid boxes. This consumes vast quantities of supercomputer time; a typical state-of-the-art GCM currently requires tens to hundreds of hours for a full-length "run" of twenty to a duration of hundred simulated years. In principle, climate modelers could achieve far better results with high-resolution NWP models. But the number of model calculations increases exponentially with higher resolutions. This generates a computational bottleneck, forcing GCM builders to make trade-offs between a model's resolution and its complexity. "Complexity" here refers to two related things: the number of phenomena simulated, and the state of detail at which they are modeled. Existing models do not directly simulate a vast number of basic atmospheric events.

The most important is the formation of clouds, which form typically on scales of a few kilometers or less. Clouds are believed to play many key roles in climate, such as trapping heat at night or reflecting it back into space during the day. Certainly, these phenomena are notoriously difficult to study empirically, and their role in climate remains controversial. Clouds are not yet perfectly modeled even with NWP techniques. Other phenomena not well seen at GCM resolutions are the activity of the planetary boundary layer (the layer of air nearest the earth's surface) and many factors relating to the land surface, such as its roughness and elevation. Their low resolution is one factor for the high levels of uncertainty surrounding climate models. Techniques for getting the most out of these low-resolution models have improved them, but have also been deeply controversial.

(b) New Issues

A number of major issues in climate modeling stem from the problem of scale described above. All sub-grid-scale processes must be represented parametrically, or parameterized. For example, instead represent cloud formation in terms of convection columns, cloud condensation nuclei, and other direct causes, a GCM typically calculates the amount of cloud cover within a grid box as some job of temperature and humidity. This approach embodies what is known as the closure assumption. This is the postulate that small-scale processes can finally be represented accurately in terms of the large-scale variables available to the models. Parameterization is controversial, and its effects on the activity of models are not entirely encouraging (Shackley *et al*, 1998). For instance, some cloud parameterization schemes in early GCMs resulted in cloud "blinking," an oscillation between the presence and absence of cloud cover in a given grid box at each time step when same variables happened to be just at the critical threshold. Real clouds do not, of course, behave like this. The question is whether and how unrealistic behaviour of this sort in one element of the model influences the quality of influences overall model results.

Another tragedy is that such modeling is too computationally expensive. Instead, absorption is represented in GCMs by coefficients that implicitly integrate all the absorption lines. In an ideal model, the only fixed conditions can be the distribution and altitude of continental surfaces. All other variables, such as sea surface temperature, land surface albedo (reflectance), cloud formation, and so on would be caused internally by the model itself from the lower-level physical properties of air, water, and other basic constituents of the climate system. To say that current GCMs are far from reaching this goal is a vast understatement. Rather, "virtually all physical processes operating in the atmosphere require parameterization" in models. Generating these parameters is therefore the largest share of the modeler's work. Climate modelers do this partly by reviewing the meteorological literature and observational data to try to determine how small-scale processes and large-scale variables might be connected. When they succeed in finding such relations, they call the resulting parameters physically based. Often, however, they do not find direct links to large-scale physical variables. In this common case, modelers discover ad hoc schemes that provide the models with the necessary connections. For example, one method of cloud parameterization represents all the cumulus clouds in a given region as an only "bulk" cloud. Moreover, observed patterns exist that can be mathematically described, but whose physics are not understood. These, too, are represented in the models as parameters.

(c) Exchange Arrangements

Most sophisticated present climate models couple atmospheric general circulation models with general circulation models of the oceans. The latter operate on principles much similar those of atmospheric GCMs. These "coupled" models, known as OAGCMs, must somehow provide for the exchanges or "fluxes" of heat, momentum (wind and surface resistance), and water (precipitation, evaporation) with in the ocean and the atmosphere. Empirical knowledge of these fluxes is not very good, but their values have profound effects on model behaviour. Most OAGCMs include temporary terms, known as flux adjustments, that modify and correct the overall model results to bring them more closely into line with observations. Without them, the models' climates drift out of line with observed values and methods. These adjustments are "non-physical" model terms, in modelers' language, although they are also characterized as "empirically determined" (Houghton *et al.* 1995, 237, 34); they are a significant example of "highly tunable" parameters. Recently the National Center for Atmospheric Research introduced the first OAGCM that does not require flux adjustments. Parameterization and tuning are therefore, scientific art forms whose connection to physical theory and observational data varies widely.

(d) Uniform Code: GCMs as a Common whole

Another significant issue about GCMs concerns their relationships with each other. Because of their complexity and expense, the total number of atmospheric GCMs is not large—probably fewer than fifty worldwide. Many of these models share a common heritage (Edwards 2000). Clearly, one modeling group "borrows" another group's model and modifies it. This avoids unnecessary replication of effort, but is also means that the "new" models may retain trouble shooting elements of those from which they were created. Several modelers told me that substantial segments of the computer code in modern GCMs remain unchanged from the original models of the 1960s. This may be one factor for the fact that some systematic errors in GCMs are common to virtually all extant models.

(e) Modular Focus on Physical Variables

Here, simulation models are typically described as theoretical constructs, deriving their results from equations representing physical laws. In this regard—shared by most modelers—models use basic information about key physical variables only as a starting point (what modelers call initial conditions). However, as the foregoing discussion has shown, the reality of environmental modeling practice is at best an approximation of this goal. Most of the basic physical laws governing atmospheric behaviour are well understood and relatively uncontroversial. Modelers call these the primitive equations. But the big range of spatial and temporal scales involved—from the molecular to the global, from milliseconds to millennia—makes it impossible to build models from these principles alone.

Therefore, the need for measurement i.e. parameterization much of which can be described as the integration of observationally derived approximations or heuristics into the model core. Schneider sometimes refers to these parameters as "semiempirical," an intriguingly vague description that highlights their fuzzy relationship with observational data. For the foreseeable future, all GCMs will carry many of these "semiempirical" values and equations. Thus, we might say that GCMs are data-laden.

They say that the data are "theory-leden". In one sense there is nothing odd about this, since theory in the physical sciences always includes constants (such as the gravitational constant or the sun's energy output) derived from experimental measurements. However, physical-science practice normally attempts to explain large-scale phenomena as an outcome of smaller-scale processes. The "data-ladenness" I describe here points at the inclusion of large-scale, empirical statistical data in models, which necessarily goes against the reductionist imperative of the physical sciences.

(f) Data Corrected through Processing

Data related to environment sets are deeply problematic. Some of the reasons are obvious. Many kinds of measurements, from many different instruments, are necessary to make up a data set that covers the entire world atmosphere in three dimensions and over many years. These measurements are taken under a vast variety of conditions, which differ for reasons that are not only physical (e.g., Antarctic vs. temperate zones), but social and past changes in techniques, instrumentation, and so on over time. Fairly good records of land and sea surface meteorology exist for the last hundred years, but changes over period in instrument quality, location, number, and measurement techniques create many uncertainties. For example, most thermometers are located on land and clustered in urban regions, where "heat island" impact raise local temperatures above the regional average.

Meteorological records at sea tend to be drawn from shipping lanes, ignoring the globe's less traveled areas. For the last several decades, records from the atmosphere above the surface have been driven from increasingly extensive commercial aircraft, radiosonde (weather balloon), and rawinsonde (radar-tracked radiosonde) networks, put these too are concentrated in specific areas. Coverage in the tropics and in the Southern Hemisphere is particularly poor. Heroic efforts continue to purify these data by estimating and correcting for systematic errors (Houghton *et al.* 1996, 133-192). For instance, satellite data are being used to estimate the effects of urban heat island bias on global surface temperature data ; historical sea surface temperatures have been set right for the effects of different kinds of buckets used to draw water samples ; and problems with rawinsonde data are being addressed by comparisons with satellite data and corrections for different sampling errors (Parker). Among the chief tools of this data-filtering process are what we might call intermediate models. These also contain models of instrument behaviour, interpolation techniques (for converting actual observations into gridded data), techniques for automatic rejection of anomalous data points, and many other methods. At present, a number of laboratories are using computer models to produce "reanalyses" that attempt to calibrate, correlate, and smooth data from multiple sources into long-term, internally consistent global climatological data space.

Global Data

Unlike all others, satellite data have the signal advantage of being genuinely global in scope. Weather satellites overfly the entire globe at least twice in a day. This total coverage makes satellite data extremely attractive to climate modelers. "We don't care about a beautiful data set from just one point," one modeler told me. "It's not much use to us. We have one person whose almost full job is taking satellite data sets and putting them into files that it's easy for us to compare our stuff to." Yet satellite data are also faulty. Satellites provide only proxy measurements of temperature; these may be distorted by optical effects. In addition, their lifespans are short (two to five years) and their instruments may drift out of calibration over time. Many scientists, including one responsible for satellite data analysis at a major climate modeling group, told me that the quality of these data was not very good.

One said that their main practical usefulness has been for television weather images. Nevertheless, the satellite data are generally regarded as the most reliable global observational record. Here too, the solution to troubles in these data is a suite of intermediate models. Statistical models filter out "signals" from noise; models of atmospheric structure and chemistry are used to disaggregate radiances seen at the top of the atmosphere into their sources in the various atmospheric layers and chemical constituents below. Moreover, models are used to "grid" the data and to combine them with other data sources. Among the most important data sources are the twice-daily atmospheric analyses of the American National Meteorological Center and the European Centre for Medium-Range Weather Forecasting. These atmospheric analyses "incorporate observational data from both the surface and from satellites into a 4-D data assimilation system that follows a numerical weather prediction model to carry forward information from previous analyses, giving global uniformly gridded data". Thus, the twice-daily time of actual observation is transformed into twenty-four-hour data sets by *computer models*.

Conclusion

We have seen that the model-data relationship in climate science is thus exceptionally complex. Models contain "semiempirical" parameters, or heuristic principles derived from observations. Meanwhile, global data sets are derived from direct observations by modeling. Since the difficulty of scale that create this situation are present in all global dynamic processes, the same could be said of all world-scale models. These facts about data and models have a number of important but hardly noticed consequences for climate change concerns.

(1) It is models, not data, that are global. They make inaccurate, incomplete, inconsistent, poorly calibrated, and temporally brief data *function* as global by correcting, interpolating, completing, and gridding them. The sheer size of world level data sets makes it unlikely that much could be learned from them without the computer models that make them comprehensible. Furthermore, global uniformly gridded data would never have been created in the first place without the models that required data in that form. The dynamics of the earth's atmosphere could not be understood without them.

(2) Formation of knowledge about the past (data) and knowledge about the future (model projections) exhibits a surprising symmetry in the climate change field. Models, often the same ones used for future projections, are needed to produce global data in the first place.

The youth of the climate field means that data sets remain in flux, not only because new data are acquired but because intermediate models keep on to evolve. Yet detecting climatic change in the historical record depends on comparing a present state against a past baseline-which in this case remains a moving target. Since detection requires a long historical record; there is no alternative other than model-based reanalysis. Forecasts of future climate change rely on comparisons with the same (shifting) baseline.

(3) Despite the fact that the historical record were absolutely firm, so that future trends could be projected "directly" from the data, forecasts of climatic change would still necessarily depend on modeling. This is the case because in a highly complex system with multiple feedbacks, there is no a priori reason to suppose that any given historical trend will continue on the same path. In effect, extrapolating clearly from data trends would itself be a model of atmospheric behavior—but one without any basis in physical theory.

Fourth, modeling is necessary to separate human from natural contributions to climate change. For example, major volcanic eruptions, such as those of El Chichon (1982) and Mount Pinatubo (1991), can inject vast quantities of particulate aerosols into the stratosphere, causing cooling near the surface and warming in the stratosphere that can last several years. To understand the human role in global climate change, the effects of these and other natural events must be extracted from the global data. This can only be done through modeling.

(4) Lastly, models offer the only practical way to discern the effects of policy choices about climate change. As a thought experiment, imagine that a strong, wide climate change policy (regulating, say, not only greenhouse gas emissions and energy efficiency, but agriculture, forestry, population, and economic development) were somehow instituted tomorrow and went on for fifty years. At the end of that time, how would we measure its success or failure? The only way to do so would be to compare the historical record with models of what would have happened had the policy never been initiated. This point is important, since it indicates one potential role for models that has rarely been highlighted.

Referring to all these reasons, computer models are, and will remain, the historical, social, and epistemic core of the climate science/policy community. Without them, we would know little if anything about the causes and possible future results of climate change. At least as importantly, from a science-studies viewpoint, the global epistemic community that now surrounds the climate change issue would have resulted in lack of a fundamental organizing principle. This point has sociological and historical ramifications as well as epistemological ones. Climate science communities developed around the practice of computer modeling.

By its nature—resource-intensive "big science"—this practice reduced the number of expert groups and focused them on a common strategy of "parameteri-zation" and model-based experimentation. With the growth of computer power and the extention of political interest in (an funding for) climate science, especially in the last decade, related science began to culster around the models, using them as a common language for scientific integration. Along with this, policy communities came to depend on (and at least in part to trust) models for advice. Thus, global modeling does not merely represent, but in a social and semiotic sense *constructs*, the world atmosphere.

18

Economics of Changing Environment

Threats posed regional effect of environmental change demand a serious assessment of policy making on economics. From an economic viewpoint, the best approach is to apply 'cost-benefit thinking'. The essential trade-off is between doing nothing now and investing in either significant preventive or adaptive measures. The choices involve analysis of incurring costs now against the benefits of reducing vulnerability and future destruction costs.

For any given level of warming, the aim is to minimize the sum of policy costs and costs of adaptation by individuals. Any consequent policy decision will have to address issues of international cooperation and compensation. These considerations may in turn affect the resulting policy choices between 'carbon' taxes marketable permits and regulatory restrictions. A general consensus is taking place in the scientific community that, if present trends in the emissions of greenhouse gases continue, global mean temperatures could go up substantially compared with observed historic changes.

The resulting effects on the distribution of precipitation and climate would have a profound impact on global agriculture and unmanaged ecosystems. Half arid and arid regions particularly may suffer, and any disruptions to global food supplies and trade may severely effect low-income food-deficit nations. If thermal expansion of the oceans leads to substantial sea-level rises, low-lying and coastal regions will be threatened. Once more, low-income countries such as Guyana, Bangladesh and the Maldives will suffer.

Keeping in mind the implications of this scenario for human welfare, current attention is increasingly focusing on the appropriate policy responses to sea-level rises and global warming in general. Yet, in terms of environmental and socioeconomic impacts, the slow changes in mean climate or sea-level may often be apparent as large changes in the risks of extreme events (e.g., droughts and floods). Changes in the earth's climate are more likely to be sudden than gradual, magnifying the possibility of so-called 'natural' disasters whose timing and magnitude will become increasingly unpredictable.

Our Plan and Policy

How should we design policy in the face of uncertain climatic change? This article addresses this important question in terms of an economic approach. We argue for 'cost-benefit thinking' even if we cannot, and may never be able to, assess quantitatively all costs and benefits. The doubts involved include the unknown magnitude of costs and benefits from controlling both the level and cost of change of global warming, and the unknown temporal distribution of costs and benefits.

The theory of decision making under uncertainty gives us some guidance on how risk-averse societies should behave in these contexts. Moreover, controlling climate change requires international action and hence cooperation across nations. Designing incentives for cooperation is of great importance in combatting global environmental damage. These features (a) cost-benefit thinking, (b) appropriate behaviour under uncertainty and (c) incentives to cooperate—define what we call 'thinking economically about climate change'.

Costs and Benefits of Policy

The indefinite impacts arising from global warming can be classified in terms of:

(A) Average regional temperature and rainfall changes;

(B) Average sea-level rise; and

(C) Frequency and severity of weather 'events' (natural disasters).

Impact on agricultural and ecological systems is likely to vary significantly by region, and hence will be difficult to predict, until improved Global Circulation Models (GCMs) more predictive models are developed. Some of the areas currently believed to be particularly susceptible to productivity losses include:

(a) the irrigated semi-arid areas of northern midlatitudes, specifically in the US midwest;

(b) the lowland areas and island countries of the humid tropics in Asia, the Pacific and Caribbean that are suspicious to excessive precipitation, violent storms and flooding;
(c) the arid and semi-arid zones of Africa, south Asia, west Asia and north Africa that are already vulnerable to environmental variability;
(d) rainfed upland and highland regions, partic- ularly those with poor soil conditions;
(e) severe northern latitudes, particularly in terms of livestock raising;
(f) the mid-latitude temperate forests in the northern hemisphere, and probably some tropical forest systems.

Despite all this, some agricultural and ecological systems may actually benefit from a warmer world. For example, many crops, such as rice, wheat, alfalfa, maize, sugar cane and sorghum, may definitely have higher yields. In northern latitudes especially, rising temperatures may allow lengthening of the growing season and expansion of rain-fed arable region. Northern latitude forests, particularly the boreal forests, could also benefit. The variable nature of the impacts and the fact that some nations lose while others initially appear to 'gain' has important' implications for the chances of global cooperation, as is discuss follows. The impacts of a sea-level rise will universally impact on low-lying, island and coastal regions, and the there will be:

(1) More risk of flooding;
(2) More beach and coastal erosion, damage to ports and coastal infrastructure and the wholesale disappearance of some islands and coastal strips;
(3) Salt-water intrusion and greater demand for drainage;
(4) Loss of agricultural land and productivity and changes in agricultural production;
(5) Loss of coastal fisheries and fish homes;
(6) Loss of wetlands.

Possible Policy Options

Given the above impacts, there are three possible policy responses. (a) 'do nothing' now and adapt to the impacts as they go up. (b) implement 'preventive' measures by reducing greenhouse gas emissions. (c) invest in anticipatory 'adaptive' measures today.

The first and second are not mutally exclusive; adaptation and preventive measures can be combined. Doing nothing can also be an optimal strategy if the damage done by inaction (i.e., the costs of doing nothing) is less than the money saved (the benefit of doing nothing). Doing nothing must thus be treated as a legitimate option. In evaluating this option, however, due regard must be had for the nature of the costs incurred. Doing nothing now might incur irreversible costs in the form of forced adaptations to climate warming over the foreseeable future, and the more burden of the risk and uncertainties associated with these future outcomes.

The treatment of irreversibilities is still widely debated. Orthodox discounting ways would register irreversibilities as a perpetual stream of costs, the importance of which declines exponentially with time. Alternative approaches tend to concentrate on avoiding irreversibilities as a constraint on policy choice. These issues are explored later.

The Wayout

As we can see the essential trade-off is between doing nothing now (which obviously involves little current cost but may incur greater future costs in terms of reducing vulnerability and modifying results) and investing heavily in greenhouse gas emission reduction, or in sustainable management of tropical forests, in order to avoid the anticipated future costs.

Thus, a concerted effort to limit the greenhouse effect would involve more relative costs in the present but would avoid the costs incurred by forced adaptation and residual impacts in the future. The discounting issue is clearly important in this regard. However, a concerted effort to reduce emissions now would at least lower the costs of an anticipatory action, such as the building of dikes, water storing and irrigation.

We are only beginning to understand the nature of these policy options and trade-offs; a full assessment of the costs and benefits of every option is not yet possible.

But several points crucial to this analysis are worth highlighting.

(1) There is clearly a waiting cost for doing nothing: The longer we do nothing, the higher will be committed warming and hence the higher will be the future costs of forced adaptation and residual effects. The important questions are how large is this waiting cost and how fast is it growing over time?

(2) There is a high cost attached: To a 'surprise' of an extreme event suddenly taking place. Both the unpredictability surrounding the impacts of the greenhouse effect and their tendency to enhance the risk of extreme events suggest caution about underestimating the probability of a 'surprise' occurring. We will return to these two aspects of cost later. Analysis of policy options will need this and benefits. The costs of investments today in anticipation of future climate change can obviously be monetized. Imposed adaptation in the future, however, involves both monetized costs (e.g., costs of relocating a flooded village) and costs that are more difficult to monetize (e.g., environmental loss, human mortality and morbidity). Fair assessment of the trade-offs among policy options will therefore require a thorough assessment of both monetized and non-monetized costs and benefits.

Important Adaptive Measures

(A) Evolution of a global food security system while northern countries are still able to generate an agricultural surplus at relatively low costs;

(B) Arrangement for additional financial assistance to developing countries to help them establish a self-supporting agricultural infrastructure, appropriate technology and better water management;

(C) The allocation of development funds in Third World countries for growing food production and sustainable agricultural development

(D) A greater international effort to halt desertification; and

(E) More commitment to curbing population growth where it inhibits development.

These Analysis measures would to some extent lessen the more severe impacts of the economic and environmental disruptions accompanying any world level greenhouse effect. They also involve economic costs that would mean the diversion of resources away from other economic activities. On the other side, some of these options, such as the commitment to sustainable agricultural development in the Third World, have long been supported in their own right; the greenhouse effect just adds force to arguments in their favour.

Preventive Measures

These would essentially involve:

(A) Decreasing fossil fuel burning, particularly through the development of non-fossil fuel energy sources and through improvements in energy efficiency;

(B) Decreasing the emissions of trace gases from other anthropogenic sources; developing technological processes to 'scrub', recover and recycle greenhouse gases;

(C) Interrupting or slowing tropical deforestation through alternative development strategies and incentives; and

(D) Enhancing the rate of replanting in deforested areas, encouraging afforestation and improving forest management.

Analysis

To make any major impact on reducing greenhouse gas emissions would mean rapidly instigating these measures by diverting resources from monetary activity, perhaps with some sacrifice in short-term economic growth. This may not necessarily be the case, however, for steps that improve the efficiency of fossil fuel consumption have consequent savings in energy costs. Table sets out the options for containing global warming and comments on the cost-benefit implications. The leading objective is to determine an 'acceptable level of warming, which itself could be based on costs and benefits comparisons. As noted, this comparison will be necessarily judgemental due to the difficulties of monetizing impacts. The alternative is to determine a 'critical load' of warming based on, say, maximum acceptable sea-level increase (plus a safety margin). In addition, the acceptable rate of warming needs to be chosen as nations will not be indifferent to when the acceptable level is reached, not to the path by which it is reached. Each given level of warming corresponds to a requirement to reduce greenhouse gases relative to some initial point, or alternatively, to invest resources in adjustments to a warmer world. Thus, various 'mixes' of preventive and adaptive measures can be employed.

Adaptation will include government-induced measures and 'natural' adaptation, i.e., actions undertaken by individuals in response to warming. These measures will typically involve private costs for those making the adjustments. The overall aim should be to minimize the sum of the policy and private costs for any specific level of warming.

Table 1. Expenditure and Benefits of Containing Global Warming

Levels		*Approach*
1. Determine acceptable level of warming		Use judgemental cost-benefit analysis
	and or	
		Critical load analysis
2. Determine acceptable rate of warming		Use judgemental cost-benefit analysis
3. Determine least-cost mix of prevention, adaptation and aisser *faire*		For any specific level of warm-ming the aim is to minimize the sum of policy costs and costs of adaptation by individuals

Uncertainty and Risk

Evaluating policy options to counter the greenhouse effect is not a simple task. The challenge is how to make decisions in the face of irreversibility, uncertainty and risk over long duration of time. The irreversibility of climatic change arises because past emissions of greenhouse gases ensure that the world is inevitably committed to some coming warming. If atmospheric concentrations of greenhouse gases were stabilized now, the climate would carry on to warm for decades to come as the oceans released heat that they previously absorbed. If present emissions continue, by the year 2030 the world would experience an actual temperature alter of 1.0°-2 -0°C warmer than today, with the ocean lag effect committing us to an eventual increase of 1.5°-3.1°C warmer than today.

Above said difficulties in projecting climate change scenarios accurately and in predicting the resulting impacts in turn add to the risk and uncertainty surrounding the greenhouse effect. Risk concerns broadly quantifiable probabilities, e.g., the likelihood of a drought. Uncertainty relates to contexts in which probabilities are not known. Evidently, there are great uncertainties involved in global warming—scientific uncertainties over the precise atmospheric, geographical and climatic responses, predicting uncertainties in predicting future changes and the scale of their effects, and finally, time-lag uncertainties over the urgency in devising right policies to contain global warming.

Guessing the magnitude of impacts is unaffected by the presence of risk and uncertainty, but translating these magnitudes into decision-criteria is affected. Risk should be treated through expected value approaches, but this is unlikely to be satisfactory if the pay-off is a catastrophic event (e.g., major flooding by sea water). Uncertainty can be handled by decision-theory in which mixes of strategies and pay-offs are addressed according to the degree of risk-aversion.

This can also be reduced through the acquisition of more information, and in some instances improved research techniques, over time. Indeed, the informational approach to uncertainty is frequently used to justify a 'wait and see' answer. But climatic change is irreversible, so that there is likely to be an additional cost associated with waiting to respond before more information is available. By the time we are sufficiently certain of the risks associated with climatic change, we may be already committed to a future temperature growth that increases the probability of the impacts actually occuring.

Therefore, the proper approach is a cost-benefit one. The costs of 'doing nothing' need to be compared to the benefits. The costs are those associated with the additional committed warming because of delayed response. The benefits are the avoided costs of prevention and adaptation. Discounting, if permitted (see next page), will impact the calculation since avoided costs of action occur now, whereas the costs of delay occur in the future. We can assume that society is risk-averse; that is, society prefers gaining a sure income of, say US $ 100 million over an uncertain expected income (i.e., the average income over all future probable states) of the similar amount.

In the case of global warming, the source of the risk is on the supply-side: society is certain of demanding the services of the environment in the future, but the future of changing climate and sea-level rises means that we are uncertain about the state of the environment in the future. Bishop demonstrated that in such conditions of supply-side risk, society would be willing to pay a sum to avoid the future risks of climatic change—an option price (OP), which can be greater than the expected loss of social welfare from all these risks (ESL). This risk the aversion premium is the option value (OV) to society of decreasing the risks associated with climatic change.

Therefore,

$$OP = ESL + OV$$

and (1)

$$OV = OP - ESL > 0$$

The positive option value on the supply-side may show the need for investment in uncertainty-reducing activities. This is clearly the case in the presence of general uncertainty (as opposed to the estimable risks) over the impact of global warming, where the expected value of new information, or quasi-option value, to society must be extremely high.

Nordhaus suggests that the appropriate policy response in the face of uncertainty is to use the 'best guess' and proceed as if the world is certain, while at the same time thinking that the high expected value of new information requires that 'the best investment to ameliorate the CO_2 problem today is possibly expand our CO_2 knowledge'. But in analysing the stream of future benefits and costs and every policy option (and consequent global warming scenario), we can go beyond that. As the impacts of climatic change involve pure public risk, this risk cannot be pooled across individuals in society as one individual's assumption of risk does not reduce the risk borne by others. The policy implication is that a risk premium should be assigned to the assessment of the risks associated with global warming such that when these future environmental risks are costed, these costs attain greater importance in terms of their, current values. In other words, in taking investment and policy decisions today, policymakers should attach greater importance to the future risks associated with environmental change.

An alternative would be to use a lower, risk-adjusted interest rate to discount future costs in terms of their present values. But as indicated in Equation (1), in the presence of supply-side risk, community is already demonstrating its willingness to pay to avoid these future costs, through which the risk aversion premium, or option value can be calculated. Due to the long-term nature of climatic change, the main losers in the case of the greenhouse effect are most likely to be future generations.

Thus, the issue of climatic change also looks at questions of intergenerational equity. Concern over intergenerational fairness, and ultimately 'sustainable' development, may need compensation of future generations for the irreversible loss of natural capital today. In the context of the greenhouse effect, pollution by present generations will harm future generations, at best by imposing risk, and at worst by causing serious adaptation problems. Consequently, the choice is between environmental change with actual compensation of future generations and climatic change without compensation. Moreover, if the compensating investment is not done in the present, compensation is not an option in the future.

Measuring Compensation

How would such compensation be calculated? If we knew the actual damage, Y, associated with climatic change, we could set aside an amount of money, X, today which would grow at some interest rate, r%, to be equal to Y in the relevant future year.

That is,

$Y = X(1+r)^T$

Anyway, as we do not know T or Y, the computation of the required compensation cannot be made. Some writers suggest a proxy in the form of the sum that current generations would be interested to pay to prevent future risks of the damage Y, i.e., the option price embodied in Equation.

(1) Estimating option price may by extremely difficult if, as in the case of climatic change, the future is expected to include low-probability, high-loss events like natural disasters. However, Brookshire *et al* have measured expected damages from earthquake losses in California and individuals, self-insurance through purchasing 'safe' site housing, that suggests an implicit option price. Similar approaches could be extended to the risks associated with climatic change.

Analysis

This discussion suggests that compensation of future generations can take two forms: direct compensation by the current generation in the form of final goods, capital and technology, or indirect, compensation in the form of willingness to pay now to decrease future risks and to accumulate knowledge to reduce general uncertainty. Direct bequests of final goods are problematic, because the preferences of future generations may vary from current preferences.

In terms of capital, there is a strong argument that the minimum criterion for any compensation for the future is that they inherit a total stock of wealth not less than that enjoyed by the current generation. This means that, if some environmental assets are to be depleted as a result of climatic change, they should be compensated for by current generations building up other forms of wealth. Of particular concern would be the excessive depletion of important life-supporting natural capital—tropical forests, coastal zones and biological diversity.

In case, global warming results in an irreversible and non-substitutable loss of capital, then indirect compensation is the best ways of ensuring intergenerational equity. Cost-effective preventive and adaptive measures today, coupled by increased research and knowledge of climatic change, are the most compensatory investments for the future. Moreover, many of the actions might generate other benefits, increasing the benefit-cost ratio of taking action right now. Energy conservation is a conspicuous example— the benefits include energy savings and acid rain reduction.

Possibilities for Greenhouse Agreement

Steps by single countries to combat global warming will be ineffective except through a 'demonstration effect' to other countries. International agreement is necessary and will require to come grips with a major concern: the design of incentives to secure cooperation. There are several causes for thinking that compensatory financing will be necessary as an incentive for the developing world to cooperate. One, greenhouse effect may have its most dramatic impacts on many developing countries. Sea-level increase could be potentially catastrophic for low-lying and deltaic countries such as the Maldives, Guyana and Bangladesh. What else, even the agricultural and ecological impacts are heavily weighted against the developing world (as noted above). Two, developing countries are in no position to afford the measures needed to adapt to and mitigate the effects of climatic change. Thirdly, tropically forested developing countries have a special role to play in conserving forests as carbon 'sinks'.

Above implications for rethinking aid and monetary transfers are therefore formidable. The debate has centred on (a) mechanisms to induce tropically forested countries not to deforest;

(b) the scale of foreign aid required from industrialized countries; and (c), the creation of a 'carbon fund' through which international transfers might be made. All these three approaches reflect the wholy correct idea that the greenhouse effect is the equivalent of a 'game' with a large number of players. In order to obtain a cooperative solution it is necessary to make 'side payments' to induce unwilling partners to enter the game. Unwillingness in this regard may simply reflect an inability to do anything significant because of lack of resources. But it will also unquestionably reflect game strategies by poor nations to acquire the largest sums possible from the developed world in return for forest conservation or for foregoing some of the industrialized sector's technologies.

This game is already being played in the international arena on the Montreal ozone protocol, with China and India particularly looking for big technology transfers and cash compensation.

There is one interesting presumption that a global warming convention must closely follow the Montreal ozone convention. But Montreal may be a poor precursor for a bigger warming convention. For one, the number of key countries involved in the global consumption of CFCs as well as the overall economic costs of decreasing their use is relatively small, thus facilitating the negotiation of a cooperative solution.

Moreover, there is evidence that, prior to the Montreal agreement, some of the more important producers and consumers of CFCs (e.g., the USA, the EC) already willing to take substantial unilateral action. Consequently, the conditions existed for an international agreement on CFCs limitation, but the protocol may have been less important than originally thought for achieving reductions in the global levels of CFCs.

Opposite to this, in the case of the greenhouse effect, the lack of incentive for any one country to take unilateral action, coupled with the limited effect of such unilateral decrease on global emissions, means that full international cooperation is necessary for major gains in global welfare. Unfortunately, the number of nations required to cooperate is large, which reduces the likelihood of agreement. In addition, for each country, the costs relative to the benefits it receives will be more: the additional costs of abating greenhouse gas emissions will rise very steeply as fossil fuels must be substituted for and energy is conserved.

Additional complications are that a world level agreement on reducing greenhouse gases would have to take into account not just the limitations on fossil fuel use but also on global deforestation and other human activities (like agriculture) contributing to emissions of these gases. This will require cooperation by both industrialized and developing countries.

This way, unlike the ozone case, the costs for abating all greenhouse gases will vary significantly across countries and emitting countries, making international compensation necessary, particularly for the developing world. The complexity and scale of the constraints on international action to reduce greenhouse gases are gradually being appreciated.

A Ministerial Conference on Atmospheric Pollution and Climate Change in the Netherlands has called for a two-phase approach. The first phase needs primarily industrialized countries to abate their emission of greenhouse gases so that world levels are reduced by the year 2000 by 30 per cent, relative to 1986. However cut by OECD countries alone are not considered sufficient to deal with the global warming problem.

A second phase, stressing global cooperation on joint international action, is required. The objectives would be to continue reductions in emissions from fossil fuel use in industrialized world, phase out CFCs worldwide and reduce deforestation while stimulating reforestation globally. The establishment of an international funding agency (the 'carbon found' idea) with initial funds of US$ 500 million a year, is considered essential to these objectives.

Remaining behind these movements towards a global warming convention has been the discussion of appropriate policy instruments to gain reductions in greenhouse gas emissions. Part of the problem is that environmental policy as it has been practised to date has been greatly in the 'classical' mould of standard-setting and emissions monitoring. Where charges and subsidies have been employed, they have been mainly used for 'administrative' purposes or to raise revenues rather than as incentives to reduce pollution.

Anyway, the standard setting approach is inadequate for handling the uncertainties of the greenhouse effect. These require a policy regime based on an enforceable upper limit on carbon emissions, imposed by an incentive system that is flexible enough to adapt to changes in that limit as new information becomes available.

Hence greater reliance on variable, or market-based, incentives is asked for. Both the use of 'carbon taxes' and marketable permits may be applicable. A carbon tax on energy would be levied proportionally to the potential carbon content of fuels, therefore providing a direct incentive to all users to reduce their carbon emissions. Even more flexibility may be built in to a marketable permit system: overall emission controls are set and permits to emit carbon up to these limits are allocated to polluters, who in turn are allowed to engage in permit trading. Carbon polluters with great abatement costs might prefer to buy permits, whereas the low abatement cost polluters might prefer to sell.

The overall emission limits could be enhanced by the authorities issuing new permits, or alternatively, reduced by their intervening to 'buy back' permits. As a result, new innovative approaches to economic instruments are needed if the world is serious about the need to reduce significantly its carbon emissions.

To conclude, we can say that the cost-benefit mode of thinking offers a framework for analysing global warming policy issues. This remains right even in the context of both the impossibility of monetizing all costs and benefits and the extreme uncertainty about the timing and scale of effects. The prime task is to determine an acceptable level and rate of warming, which in turn means having a much clearer understanding of the costs of control measures and the loss costs of impacts. The appropriate criterion for determining the policy mix is cost minimization, which must encompass the costs and benefits of late action. Traditional approaches to uncertainty may not be adequate for evaluation of risks. Above all, the analysis suggests a premium on action now instead later. This reflects the results of risk-averse approaches to uncertainty in which outcomes can be catastrophic, and the multiple uses from some policy options such as energy conservation.

At last, global warming can be dealt with only through international agreement. The context is one of game theory, and the stressing need is to design incentive systems for global cooperation. The Montreal protocol on ozone may be an ineffective guide to the prospects for a greenhouse agreement. The most urgent need is to develop appropriate policy instruments and compensatory mechanisms for better results.

19

Conclusion

In the previous chapters, we have gone through the various factors that cause and effect environmental change. We have also seen, how in turn these changes impact the society and humanity and particularly those areas where consequences have become quite visible. Agricultural productivity and thus supply of food items, electrical and mineral energy, and industry and economy are some very significant ones. There is thus, need to sustain and stabilise environmental changes and their impact so that future generations receive a state worth living. This last and concluding chapter presents a summary of effects and suggestions in the context of so discussed environmental change.

Time and again, we start with the observation that environment is forever changing, in many cases, for the reasons that we do not yet understand. Extreme changes are brought about by the variability of sun; by volcanic eruptions—the natural ones and; over exploitation of natural resources for human living—these are man-made. The greatest impact of natural exploitation is global warming. There is considerable evidence that the surface based thermometers, generally located at airports near cities, have been contaminated by "urban heat island" effect, which locally produces warmer temperatures. Climatic records corrected for this effect show maximum temperatures occurring around 1940 rather than in the 1980s.

A difficult situation has arisen with the computer models. Three-dimensional climate models, as has been discussed in detail in the related chapter, run on fast computers, the so-called General Circulation Models (GCMs) have become much more sophisticated but still, do poor job of representing the environment. Their results differ widely, some showing warmth of 1.5° C or less, others of

4.5°C or more. Since these models suffer from the poor spatial resolution about 300 km and an incomplete knowledge of cloud physics, computer modelers cannot depict actual clouds but must, instead, 'parameterise' cloudiness, which accounts for much of widerange of GCM results. The IPCC has taken a remarkable initiative in this regard by trying to explain the discrepancy between observed and calculated temperatures. In its first assessment in 1990, it simply did not lend ears to the satellite data and pronounced the observations and calculations to be broadly consistent. The second and more recent assessment, no longer uses this phrase. Rather, IPCC tries to explain the difference between the observations and theory by introducing the cooling effects of particles derived largely from sulfur pollution produced by burning coal, i.e, anthropogenic sulfate aerosols. Just a year after the publication of IPCC report in 1996, it has become apparent, on the basis of recent computer studies that the discrepancy between the observations and theory cannot be explained by assumed cooling effects of sulfate aerosols. With the science largely unsettled, there is thus, need for urgent further research.

Also, other human effects have been ignored. There are other greenhouse gases, in addition to CO_2 from burning fossil fuels like nitrous oxide from agricultural fertilisers, various holo carbons, methane from oil and gas operations, cattle raising and rice growing. International control efforts focus almost exclusively on CO_2 yet methane has increased more than 100 per cent in the past century. Apart from raising the level of greenhouse gases, an expanding population is changing the ratio between cropland and forests and thereby; the reflecting power of the surface. It is thus, the task of research scientists to decide which of many human influences are important enough to be incorporated into climate models.

The IPCC has determined that maintaining the present atmospheric concentration would require that CO_2 emissions be reduced by well over 60 per cent world wide and kept at that value. Any lesser reduction would only slow down the ongoing increase of CO_2 in the atmosphere. But there is no scientific guidance on how to define and avoid a 'dangerous' level of CO_2, the announced goal of the Global Climate Treaty.

Regarding drastic reductions in energy use, there is considerable concern, particularly in United States senate that imposing energy restrictions will not only raise energy prices, but cause industries to transfer operations to that do not incur these restrictions. US Congress has been assured that the economic loss will not occur or at least will not be too severe. But if it becomes apparent that global warming could produce net benefits rather than net losses, it may be difficult to prepare cost-bénefit analysis to convince the government to go along with restriction an energy use through what amounts to a hidden energy tax.

The Precautionary Principle seems to answer decisively many questions and solve many problems even in the face of scientific uncertainty discussed before. We should act of head-off potential destructive trend. But the principle, in reality does not help much. Its attractiveness masks a simplistic world in which the cost of delaying or blocking the economic and technological change are assigned zero weight. An alternative to the Precautionary Principle is provided by Statistical Decisions Theory with the belief that the world is warming and this warming will be catastrophic and that we can prevent this warming at a reasonable cost. We must estimate the expected consequences—the cost and benefits of each course.

Now we turn to the situation of world's forests and the contribution that they can make to mitigation of environmental problems, particularly of global warming. Action here can easily be taken now and is also commendable for numerous reasons. During the last two decades, the additional needs of the growing population of developing countries and agricultural land and for fuelwood together with the rise in demand of tropical hard wood in developed nations has led to worrying rate of loss of forests in the tropical regions. To control and reverse of ill-effects of the above said facts, a possible at afforestation programme has been presented by IPCC Action programme to illustrate the potential for carbon sequestration.

Reduction in the sources of Methane is also another recommendation. Though it is less important greenhouse gas than carbon dioxide, the stabilising of its atmospheric concentration would contribute a small but significant amount to the overall problem.

In short, in the concluding part of the concluding chapter, we can make the following recommendations for sustainable environment and stabilisation of environmental changes:

(1) The reduction by some countries of carbon dioxide emissions.

(2) The Provisions of the Montreal Protocol (as discussed in previous chapter) regarding the emission of CFCs and CFC substitutes.

(3) A reduction of deforestation and a substantial increase in forestation.

(4) Some easy to do reductions in methane emissions.

(5) An aggressive increase in energy saving and conservation measures.

For the above, the most important thing is how fast we get information. There is likely to be a complex and shifting set of winners and losers. It is important to identify thresholds and discontinuities than may matter for impacts. The economics of hedging strategies need to be demonstrated.

Index